MW00831480

Victor A. Kanke

Encyclopedia of Metascience and Special Philosophy of Science

EurAsian
Scientific Editions Ltd

UDC 001.2:1(030)
LBC 72:87.3(92)
K 19

Victor A. Kanke. Encyclopedia of metascience and special philosophy of science. – Tallinn and Wanchai: EurAsian Scientific Editions Ltd, 2021 – 1187 p.

The formal philosophy of science, its two components, conceptology, and methodology, as well as 21 varieties of special philosophy of science, are considered in a systematic theoretical form. All theories are interpreted within the framework of the main philosophical directions of modernity, in particular, analytical philosophy, hermeneutics, poststructuralism, phenomenology, and critical rationalism. An original theory of intratheoretical and intertheoretical transduction developed. Ethical representations are widely used. Exceptional attention is paid to the transdisciplinary approach, as well as the conceptual development of pluralism in modern science and the fullness of scientific knowledge. The book has no analog in literature. It is intended for researchers, university professors, graduate students, and undergraduates.

Image: Freepik.com

© EurAsian Scientific Editions OÜ, Tallinn, Estonia, ISBN 978-9949-7485-0-1

© EurAsian Scientific Editions Ltd, Wanchai, Hong Kong, ISBN 978-988-14066-1-3

www.eurasian-scientific-editions.org

Table of contents

4

Preface

The rapid development of science is the main achievement of the modern era. It brings the boldest hopes. Armed with science, humanity has become a planetary system. This fact is not only pleasing but also evokes a sense of unrelenting anxiety, especially in the face of growing technological, environmental, economic, political, and other disasters, which everyone knows. There is something wrong with the science. It seems to me that this fact should be analysed, first of all, by scientists. For it is unacceptable to transfer the problems caused by them onto the shoulders of people who are outside of science.

Science has a lot of problems.

Firstly, throughout its history, it has been forced to play an auxiliary role. A very common view is that science is needed mainly to achieve an abundance of material goods. This understanding of the meaning of science opens the gates to a wide range of misunderstanding

Secondly, scientists often focus their efforts primarily on some areas, in particular, physics, computer science, and biology. Such a one-sided concentration of social forces necessarily leads to a disharmony within the system of sciences, which is especially painful for the state of humanitarian knowledge.

Thirdly, the diversity of science is growing. Never before has it been so diverse and devoid of unity.

Fourthly, the possibility of awareness of modern scientific knowledge as a single whole with an integral meaning is being questioned so categorically as never before. It seems that scientists are not able to prevent the destruction of the integrity of science.

Fifthly, and perhaps most importantly, science, steadily increasing its power, has not developed effective ways to control its own development. There is no doubt that any force invented by man must be controlled by him. Unfortunately, with respect to science, this duty remains ounly a good wish.

The list of alarming symptoms of the evolution of modern science can be significantly expanded. However, it is quite enough to understand the need to develop ways to improve the situation under discussion. In my opinion, in this regard, the philosophy of science becomes the decisive factor, which, as the lessons of development of science show, does not condone either giving science only instrumental value or hypertrophy of its parts or moral indifference of knowledge and helplessness in the mastering of its diversity. It is the philosophy of science that gives science its existential pointedness. Ultimately, the most significant challenges facing scientists, are focused on the philosophy of science. It is designed to problematize and enhance the potential of science.

At this point, it is necessary to clarify the difference between philosophy, philosophy of science, special philosophy of science and metascience. Philosophy is usually understood as one of the branches of science. In modern knowledge, the status of any branch of science is determined only in unity with other branches of science. The possibility of such a definition did not appear immediately, but only after the formation of the whole complex of modern sciences was formed, not earlier than the 20th century. This possibility, in particular, was not in those ancient times when philosophy was passing the first phases of its development. In this regard, philosophy stayed in a purely speculative, metaphysical shell. This continued until the philosophy of science was developed. The overwhelming majority of philosophers failed to correctly assess the cardinal change in the situation around the philosophy. They believed that the philosophy of science was part of philosophy. In reality, the philosophy of science replaced philosophy. The need for the latter ceased to be urgent. All those researchers who persisted in their commitment to traditional philosophy continued to pursue metaphysics, unsuccessfully trying to master the achievements of modern science.

So what is the philosophy of science? It expresses similar conceptual and methodological features of all branches of science. This means that it has a formal character. Of course, its development involves the development of provisions relevant to all sciences. Their use leads to special philosophies of science, for example, the philosophy of physics or the philosophy of economics. As we can see, the fate of the formal and special philosophy of science largely depends on an understanding of the status of individual sciences. In this regard, the relevance of metascience is revealed. The fact is that accessing of the philosophy of science to individual sciences requires a preliminary identification of their essential features not by philosophers but by representatives of these sciences themselves. As a result, a whole complex of metascientific disciplines appears, in particular, metamathematics, metabiology, metaeconomics, etc.

As a rule, metascience is identified with a special philosophy of science. However, such identification is untenable. To illustrate this, let us consider the relationship between metamathematics and the philosophy of mathematics. Metamathematics is a theory of conceptual and methodological features of mathematical theories irrelevant to the content of the formal philosophy of science. Metamathematics does not go beyond mathematics. On the contrary, the philosophy of mathematics evaluates the content of mathematics in terms of the achievements of the formal philosophy of science. Thanks to the philosophy of mathematics, mathematics is embedded in the unity of all sciences. The story that I described in relation to mathematics is repeated in basic terms with other sciences. Each time it makes sense to distinguish from each other metascience and the special philosophy of science.

My book is an encyclopedia of, above all, metascience and the special philosophy of science. Of course, it also does not do without considering the formal philosophy of science. In modern science, attention to the formal philosophy of science prevails. To the best of my modest ability, changing this situation, I pay due attention to both metascience and the special philosophy of science. This feature of my research defines the title of the book — "Encyclopedia of Metascience and the Special Philosophy of Science".

In addition to the above, I note the need to discuss the problem of the encyclopedic training of a modern scientist. According to a very common opinion, due to the versatility of modern science, the age of encyclopedists has become a thing of the past. I think this view is deeply flawed. Great encyclopedists were, for example, John von Neumann, who made a significant creative contribution to the development of mathematics, computer science, physics, economics, and George Gamow, known among other things for inventing the concept of the hot universe and decoding the genetic code. Is not cultivated encyclopedic scale in the training of students and schoolchildren studying not one, but many disciplines? In my opinion, encyclopedic awareness is desirable for any scientist. It was this belief that prompted me to create this encyclopedia.

My scientific and pedagogical destiny has developed in such a way that already in the young years I was vigorously engaged in the study of physics, economics, and philosophy. At the age of 40, I learned how to use effectively ideas from one of these three branches of science in the other two. I never used to try to put my interlocutors in an uncomfortable position, but I naturally noticed that their narrow professional orientation often limited their creative possibilities. Many years of work with graduate students contributed to the significant development of my philosophical and interdisciplinary capabilities. With them, each time in separate groups, I discussed the philosophy of mathematics, computer science, physics, chemistry, biology, psychology, technology, and economics. Classes with graduate students have become a wonderful cure for alienation of sciences from philosophy. Over the years, I have been convinced that science without a pronounced special philosophy of science is a form of underdeveloped knowledge, in a word, nonsense. The other thing I came to was that the scientific orientation of both philosophy and formal philosophy of science, in particular, needed substantial development. The quasi-scientific shell of modern philosophy limits its effective use in sciences.

On the other hand, reading the course of formal philosophy of science to graduate students, I became more and more convinced that it was inappropriate to present them truths regardless of the sciences and explain them exclusively by achievements of some selected sciences, for example, physics. There was an urgent need to develop provisions that would be relevant to all individual sciences. In this regard, I have developed a theory of intratheoretical and intertheoretical transduction. I hope that the reader of the encyclopedia will be convinced that the theory of conceptual transduction is a real basis for understanding all existing sciences as a vast ordered whole. This theory forms the methodological framework of the entire encyclopedia. It is summarized in the first chapter. Of course, the theory of conceptual transduction should not be perceived dogmatically. Nevertheless, checking its content in a wide variety of sciences for decades, I do not see a worthy alternative to it.

One more leitmotif of the whole book is the pluralism of the main modern philosophical systems, its interface with the content of various sciences. I sought to avoid two undesirable extremes: both philosophical isolationism, and philosophical indifferentism. In the first case, the material is presented exclusively from the standpoint of one philosophical direction, for example, analytical philosophy, hermeneutics or poststructuralism. In the second case, the author's philosophical position is not clear at all. Such indifference, in the book devoted to special and formal philosophy of science, is obviously unacceptable.

The actual idea of the encyclopedia is to understand ethics as the pinnacle of science. It is not introduced to science from outside but is formed in it in the process of rising to conceptual and existential heights.

I briefly described the main leitmotifs of the encyclopedia. To describe many other ideas, in fact, there is no printed space. I tried to justify the priority of the conceptual development of modern scientific pluralism. To the best of my ability, I tried to destroy the eclectic shell of philosophy and any other branch of science.

When writing this book, I was guided by diverse interests of intellectuals, be it a scientist, a philosopher, a graduate student or an inquisitive reader. The direct addressees of the encyclopedia are researchers, university professors, graduate students, and undergraduates.

Chapter 1. The theory of conceptual transduction

1.1. Concepts of theory and intratheoretical transduction

The book deals with hundreds of theories. We will save a lot of printed space by presenting the conceptology and methodology of science, which operate provisions relevant to all sciences.

The uniqueness of man is that he operates with concepts as constituents of theories. By definition, a theory is a coherent set of concepts. This conclusion I have confirmed by the whole course of the centuries-old development of science. Turning to any theory, the researcher discovers that it consists of variables, laws, and principles. What they call concepts. Of course, objects, since scientists reduce them to concepts, are also concepts. The same applies to people. In mathematics, the principles are the axioms, laws are theorems, and the variables included in the wording of the laws. Physicists implement the principle of least action, biologists the principle of natural selection, economists the principle of maximizing the rate of return on advanced capital. The reader, obviously, is well aware that in all these sciences there are laws. You can recall Newton's laws of physics, Mendel's laws of biology, and the laws of supply and demand from economics.

Continuing the analysis, we turn to the variables, examples of which are the length of the sides of geometric shapes, mass in physics, the price of goods in the economy. As you can see, they do not exist in the form of an arbitrary placer but form certain clots, things (objects and persons). Variables are always

19

characteristics of things, physical bodies, animals, markets, countries, etc. The thing is the totality of variables. The meanings of the variables vary within certain limits. Because of this, it is reasonable to call them variables. Scientists measure any variable in certain units. For example, they measure the electron charge in coulombs, the price of goods in dollars, and the dance girl in beauty points.

If the variable is not to reduce to other variables, it is elementary. For example, mass in many physical theories is an elementary variable. If the variable is composed of other quantities, it is a derived variable. For example, the density of a physical body is a derivative of the mass and volume. Like elementary variables, derived variables are measured. For example, people measure the speed of a car by a speedometer. I also note that all the so-called constants, for example, the speed of light in a vacuum, strictly speaking, are also variable. This is clear insofar as their meanings are constantly being refined.

Let me now turn to the laws. The law is the relationship between variables. A derived variable is also a relationship of variables. However, unlike it, the law is not measured. The law is a special concept. In European cultures, particularly in English, German, French and Italian, the law means something established. Scientists understand the law as the connection of variables established in the process of cognition. Contrary to popular belief, the law does not have to be stable and necessary. Scientists determine exactly what this or that law is.

Principle (from lat. *principle* – the beginning, the source) is such a relationship of variables, which in deductive terms prevails over the laws. This means that scientists from principles derive laws, but not principles from laws. Sometimes the principles just considered major laws. In this case, scientists mistakenly do not emphasize the uniqueness of both principles and laws. Logicians and mathematicians are commendable in this regard. They never define the axioms as the main theorems. To equate principles and laws is unacceptable.

As for the term 'theory', it is of Greek origin. Literally, theory means scrutiny, research, reflection. What exactly is the focus of scientists? Principles, laws, variables, entities (objects and individuals). Scientists use the concepts. With that said, a theory is a conception. The doctrine of concepts is conceptology.

The theory contains principles, laws, and variables. However, what exactly do people with them? They control them and transform them. It was in this regard that the Greeks used the verb *gogi* (Greek. γωγή), production. It means that people produce knowledge. Since XV century Latin synonym of gogi *ducere* (lead, produce) has been widely used. Since scientists manage concepts in various ways, they began to use the appropriate prefixes *de, in, ab, ad* (compare deduction, induction, abduction, and adduction). The four ways of managing the concepts, I shall discuss in detail later. Of course, their development was not instantaneous.

Aristotle's creation of formal logic (theory of syllogisms) and Euclidean's invention of the first axiomatic geometric theory was a significant achievement in the development of the operation of deduction. Both scientists presented deduction in a distinctively vivid form and understood it primarily as a derivation from the axioms of theorems. To shift the triumphal procession of deduction from formal Sciences to experimental disciplines, for example, in physics, was possible far not at once. The status of these disciplines clearly indicated the need for conclusions from experimental variables to laws and principles. This way of management concepts has received the name of induction. It became the visit card of British empiricism from F. Bacon to J.S. Mill. Historically it so happened that rationalists, especially Descartes, Leibniz, Kant, gave preference to deduction and empiricists – to induction. Sometimes this difference of opinion took on sharp forms. The most visionary researchers understood that deduction and induction complement each other. For example, the famous economist A. Marshall noted in 1891 «Induction and deduction are both needed for scientific thought as the left and right foot are both needed for walking. The methods required for this twofold work are not peculiar to economics; they are the common property of all sciences. » [2, 24].

C.S. Peirce opened a new page in the understanding of management concepts of the theory. He had added to deduction and induction abduction.

«Abduction is the process of forming an explanatory hypothesis. This is the only logical operation that introduces a new idea; abduction is the process of forming an explanatory hypothesis. This is the only logical operation that introduces some new ideas; induction only determines values, and deduction only deploys the consequences of a pure hypothesis. Deduction proves that something has to be; induction shows that something actually is; abduction simply assumes that something can be» [3, para 171].

Before C.S. Peirce, scientists usually understood induction as a confirmation or refutation of some of the laws. He emphasized the need to introduce new laws. Peirce understood the hypothesis as the totality of hypothetical laws.

However, why do we have to introduce new laws? Obviously, only to the extent that the results of the experiment contradict the predictions made by using the deduction.

Unfortunately, Peirce did not distinguish between the factualization (experiments, observations, and practices) and the processing of its data. Traditionally, scientists understood induction as the transition from measurement results to laws. There is no reason to refuse such a submission. In this case, it is necessary to determine for example the experiment, because in itself it is not such a transition. The experiment is not processing of measurement results. It performs another function, namely, fixes facts. Its purpose is precisely to make the transition from hypothetical, predicted variables to real ones, to facts. The method of such operation I have called *adduction* [1, 116].

So, starting with the two-tier concept of knowledge (deduction + induction), we moved to the three-tier (deduction + induction + abduction) and finally finished the four-tier (deduction + adduction + induction + abduction). All transitions together deserve the term transduction (from the Latin. *transitus* - transition). Figure 1.1 presents the main contents of intratheoretical transduction in schematic form.

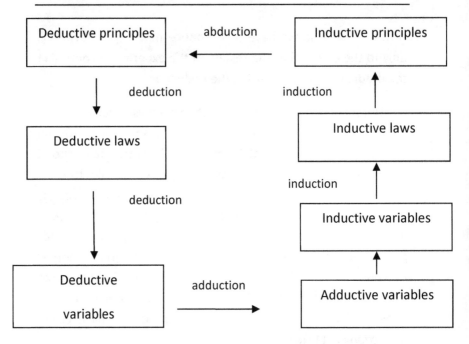

Figure 1.1 Intratheoretical trunsduction

References

1. Kanke, V.A. (2013) Metodologiya nauchnogo poznaniya [The Methodology of Scientific Knowledge]. Moskva: Omega-L. [In Russian].
2. Marshall, A. (2013) [1891] Economic generalizations or laws. In: Principles of Economics. Palgrave Classics in Economics. London: Palgrave Macmillan.
3. Peirce, C.S. (1958) Collected Papers of Charles Sanders Peirce. Hartshorne C., Weiss P., Burks A. (Eds.). Vol. 5. Cambridge MA: Harvard University Press.

1.2. The principle of theoretical representation and expressions of theories

Intratheoretical conceptual transduction, discussed in section 1.1, has a central place in epistemology (from the Greek. ἐπιστήμη – knowledge and λόγος – word). In the existing scientific literature, this fact is often misunderstood. In the end, many dogmas are widespread. Some of them I discuss below.

The principle of theoretical representation (from lat. *repraesentatio* – view).

By it, we understand the position that all the phenomena with which a person deals are in theories. In other words, they are varieties of concepts and cannot be anything else. At first glance, this statement contradicts the status of, for example, physical objects. Nevertheless, as will be shown below, this impression is erroneous.

The representatives of the philosophy of science K. Popper, T. Kuhn, P. Feyerabend, and W. Quine were the closest to understanding the importance of the principle of theoretical representation. K. Popper wrote

> «My point of view is, briefly, that our ordinary language is full of theories: that observation is always observation in the light of theories; that it is only the inductivist prejudice which leads people to think that there could be a phenomenal language, free of theories, and distinguishable from a 'theoretical language'; and lastly, that the theorist is interested in explanation as such, that is to say, in testable explanatory theories: applications and predictions interest him only for

theoretical reasons—because they may be used as tests of theories [3, 37].

Quine took an even sharper position: he «see[s] all objects as theoretical... Even our most primordial objects, bodies, are already theoretical» [6, 20].

As for the modern literature on the philosophy of science, philosophers considered mainly not the principle of theoretical representation, and the position of the theoretical loading of the facts. It is quite common for N.R. Hanson, T. Kuhn, and P. Feyerabend. Hanson is the inventor of the term 'theory-loaded'. «[S]eeing is a 'theory-laden' undertaking» [2, 19]. Kuhn believed that «[S]omething like a paradigm is prerequisite to perception itself. What a man sees depends both upon what he looks at and also upon what his previous visual conceptual experience has taught him to see» [3, 113]. P. Feyerabend argued that «experimental experience arises together with theoretical assumptions, not before it, and... this experience without theory is as incomprehensible as (presumably) the theory without it» [1, 151].

In our opinion, the thesis of the theoretical loading of facts is untenable to the extent that the facts obtained in the course of the experiment are part of the theory. The considered thesis contains a logical circle. It is no coincidence that the authors, writing about the theoretical loading of facts, very vaguely characterize this loading itself. The conception of intratheoretical transduction allows us to understand the essence of the situation. Researchers anticipate the experiment by deduction, which in turn prepare the potential of induction and abduction. In this regard, instead of theoretical relativity, it is legitimate to talk about the deductive relativity of the experiment.

Unable to count the number of authors who believe that objects are independent of the theory. It means, for example, that the Sun exists in itself and does not depend on theoretical human inventions. This argument cannot be called convincing. The lack of clarity arises from the peculiar substitution of the real subject of discussion by the discussion of the topic of dependence. Is there an interdependence between things is determined in theory. The Sun as a physical object really only to a small extent depends on the masses of people. The principle of theoretical representation is not about the relationship of dependence, but about the status of phenomena in which they are available to people. Everything that exists people can perceive only in the form of concepts, the very ones that appear in theories. The idea that there are objects given to us in another, non-theoretical form is illusory. The principle of theoretical representation confronts these illusions. The statement that the Sun has characteristics independent of humans, is true. It is false to say that the Sun is given to us by itself, outside the theory, i.e. no conceptual.

There is a widespread false claim that theory always interprets something. It is mistakenly to assume the existence of something non-conceptual. The principle of theoretical representation just refutes this assumption.

Many researchers because of the following widespread pattern of reasoning do not accept this principle: people invent theories and yet, the existence and certainty of many objects do not respond to these inventions; therefore, objects are not conceptual. This argument misses the mark. Improvement of knowledge does not indicate the non-conceptuality of objects. Before scientists discovered the sunspots, people thought they do not exist. People were wrong. Concepts of people can be wrong; in the process of learning, they improve them. Erroneous concepts correspond to non-existent entities. Through actual theories, people do not form entities, they deny cognitive chimeras.

Transitions between forms of presentation of the theory

We are talking about the fact that people presented the same theory in different forms, in particular, in the object, mental, language, behavioral, activity. The human world consists of concepts, but their varieties differ from each other. Objects and their signs, names and their predicates, emotion and their attributes do not coincide with each other. The Sun as an object, as a word (name) and as a mental image represents three expressions of the same theory. It is not the case that the same person, moving from mental concepts to language and from them to object, uses different theories each time. He remains within the framework of the same theory but moves from one representation to another. We are talking about a kind of conceptual parallelism, in the absence of which hardly anyone could survive in our volatile world. Innovations can happen within any representation. Once established, they affect all other views. Thus, the unexpected thought finds its continuation in the language and then in the object representations, or in behavioral and activity expressions, so popular in the social sciences.

Conceptual transitions unite in a single theoretical whole, not only the concepts but also their expressions. Depending on the specific situation, any expression can come to the fore. In all cases, when there are cyclic transitions, there is no primary, secondary or tertiary. I should note that this fact, as a rule, is misunderstood. This is evidence in particular by the insistence of materialists in the question about the primacy of matter (K. Marx and V. Lenin). By the equating by some idealists bodies with complexes of sensations (J. Berkeley and E. Mach). By the long-term abstention of some analytical philosophers from studying mentality because of their preference given to language (L. Wittgenstein and W. Quine). In all these cases, researchers do not carry out the transition between different expressions of the theory. As a result, they see the origin of a theory or in the matter, or in mentality, or in language.

The mistake of materialists is that they absolutize the object expression of the theory. As a result, human activity realized through consciousness and language does not get its expression. Of course, it is untenable to equate objects with complexes of sensations. These complexes belong to the sphere of mentality. People are not able to reduce mentality to objects or language. Every exciting language is also untenable. Unlawful is, for example, a downplaying the language, which occurs, for example, in the declaration of its secondary nature, that it follow the mentality. In this sense, it is significant that analytical philosophers, who initially talked about mentality in a condescending manner, then again began to study it actively.

W. Quine in 1968 introduced in the philosophy of science the principle of ontological relativity: ontology is defined, firstly, as a specific theory, and secondly, as a way to include antecedent theory to subsequent [5]. The Greek term 'ontologia' means the doctrine of being of objects. In his article, Quine talked extensively about language. In fact, he justified ontological relativity based on language and its volatility. There is a more thorough approach, which proclaims the theoretical relativity not only of objects, but also of language, and mentality, and behavior, and activities, and interactions. This conclusion follows from the principle of theoretical representation. It is quite legitimate and even necessary, along with the object (ontological) relativity to distinguish mental, linguistic, behavioral, activity and interactive relativity.

References

1. Feyerabend, P. (1975) Against Method. London: Verso.
2. Hanson, N.R. (1958) Patterns of Discovery. Cambridge: Cambridge University Press.
3. Kuhn, T.S. (1970) The Structure of Scientific Revolutions. Second ed., enlarged. Chicago: The University of Chicago Press.
4. Popper, K. (1959) The Logic of Scientific Discovery. London and New York: Routledge.
5. Quine, W.V.O. (1968) Ontological Relativity. Journal of Philosophy 65(7), 185–212.
6. Quine, W.V.O. (1981) Theories and Things. Cambridge, MA: Harvard University Press.

1.3. Criticism of the epistemological dogmas and the status of concepts

The dogma of the universal law

K. Popper argued, «Scientific theories are universal statements» [4, 37]. R. Carnap pointed out that when writing the scientific law it is necessary to use the universality quantifier [1, 4]. He did stipulate that this statement is true for all cases of x rather than only to a certain percentage of cases [ibid.]. Nevertheless, this reservation did not affect the logic of his reasoning. As his main opponent, Karl Popper Carnap held to a universal law. The same applies to scientific principles. Many researchers also considered them as universal concepts. However, Carnap and Popper rarely talked about principles.

The concept of conceptual transduction, which has a cyclic character, is incompatible with the concepts of universal principles and laws. Indeed, the process of learning is always limited to the circle of well defined, but not of all possible cases. Consequently, the conclusions do not apply to all phenomena. The new cycle of cognition involves some but not all of the existing phenomena.

Scientists promote the strengthening of dogma about the universal law by an uncritical perception of logical and mathematical records. In the simplest case, the law is written as follows: $f(x_i, y_i) \geq 0$, where i is assigned a series of values from 1 to ∞. Meanwhile, to use the infinity sign there is no reason. The correct reasoning should be following: the cycles of knowledge in a specific kind of attest to the status of n cases; and as to new cases, scientists need to study them in a new cycle of producing knowledge. The law must contain the existence quantifier, i.e. relating to some xi, rather than the universality quantifier.

It seems that the arguments given by us do not correspond to the presence of universal laws in physics. We mean that for decades, many scientists write numerous physical laws, for example, the Schrodinger equation in the same form. The idea of universal laws in physics is deceptive. First, in physics, as in any other science, there are certain cycles of knowledge, which do not give the basis to talk about universal laws. Secondly, in the records of physical laws should appear the reference values of variables obtained from the processing of measurement data, involving the use of certain techniques, such as least squares. In this case, the physical law is never in the strict sense of the word the same for different cases of intratheoretical conceptual transduction. All experimenters are aware of this fact. However, it is less known to theorists who are inclined to universal mathematical records.

Dogmatic understanding of verification and falsification

One mistake leads to another. For example, the dogma of the universal law led to a certain understanding of verification and falsification of laws. As you know, scientists seek to increase scientific knowledge. Hence their critical attitude to deductive laws. Scientists are not able to test universal laws, because of the immensity of their application. K. Popper noticed this circumstance. He therefore rightly criticized the position of R. Carnap and of other logical positivists that with extraordinary perseverance sought to prove the possibility of confirmation of the truth of universal laws.

Popper contrasted falsification to verification: if the data of the experiment contradict universal laws, they are not true. [3, 67]. He rejected verification in favor of falsification. The piquancy of the situation is that, like his opponents, he proceeded from the dogma of the universal law. Refusal of it forces to reconsider ideas of verification and falsification. Researchers are not able to either verify or falsify universal laws. The fact is that it is impossible to check or refute what does not exist. Therefore, Popper was just as wrong as Carnap.

What is the status of verification and falsification in the light of the conception of intratheoretical transduction? The situation is quite simple. Deductive law is already at the stage of induction, confirmed, or disproved. Of course, there may be complex cases that require special effort. Researchers preserve any scientific law only as some approximation to a specific situation, and not as something accurate. Concepts of verification and falsification are necessary; however, their unilateral linking exclusively with the experimental stage is also incorrect.

Dogma of empiricism

Many scientists attach decisive importance in their judgments about the status of theories for the experiment. Neopositivists, in particular, R. Carnap and H. Reichenbach, argued that the construction of the theory begins exclusively with the experiment. In contrast to them, the critical rationalist K. Popper believed that the theories are not the result of experimental data processing and particularly depend on intuitive insights. Nevertheless, he also attached great importance to the experiment. Popper compared the theory with the experiment; he did not recognize induction and abduction at all. The analytic philosopher W. Quine opposed some dogmas of empiricism, but he also based his ideal of the naturalistic theory on experiment.

In our opinion, Carnap, Popper, and Quine made a double mistake. First, they contrasted the experiment with the theory. In fact, the theory they understood only as of the deductive stage of cognition. Secondly, they did not interpret the content of the experiment in its relation to induction and abduction. Sufficiently rigorous reasoning should include all four stages of transduction, the prediction, experiment (factualization), data processing and updating of the original deductive principles. Methods according to which are carried out these stages are deduction, adduction, induction, and abduction. The experiment is not the foundation of scientific knowledge. Stages of intratheoretical transduction succeed each other and together form a stable system. In the cycle of knowledge, each subsequent stage presupposes the previous one. It is not permissible to reduce the intratheoretical transduction to a ratio of only deduction and abduction. The identification of the theory with the deductive stage of cognition brings additional confusion to the philosophy of science.

The dogma of the analytic and synthetic sentences

In the history of the development of the philosophy of science, the distinction between analytical and synthetic propositions occupies a prominent place. The main persons of this distinction were I. Kant, R. Carnap and W. Quine. I. Kant in «Critique of pure reason» called sentences, which do not depend on the experiment a priori proposals". Sentences, depending on the experiment, he called synthetic. Kant's views did not satisfy neopositivists [1, 257f]. They believed that Kant had introduced the false notion of «a priori synthetic sentences». In fact, there is none, the proposal is either analytical or synthetic. Neopositivists considered a priori sentence as analytical. They established a dichotomy between analytic and synthetic sentences. Against this dichotomy was made by W. Quine, who believed that any proposals depends on empirical data, and therefore, to separate analytical proposals from synthetic in principle is impossible [4].

The described discussion does not take into account the status of intratheoretical transduction. Turning to it makes it clear that the proposals can relate to all four stages of transduction. Hence, it is necessary to distinguish between deductive, adductive, inductive and abductive sentences. In addition, scientists should consider sentences in relation to different types of sciences. The propositions of all formal sciences, in particular mathematics and logic, express some similar features of natural and axiological theories. In this capacity, they differ from the proposals of natural and axiological sciences. Kant, Carnap, and Quine did not consider in detail the structure of modern science, in particular, the ratio of proposals of natural, axiological and formal sciences.

On the status of abstractions and idealization

We have to come back to the status of concepts. Section 1.1 dealt with the difference between principles, laws, and variables. Now the task is to characterize the nature of any concept, whether it is a principle, a law or a variable. Those who want to navigate confidently in the jungle of the modern philosophy of science should certainly be knowledgeable about the concepts of abstractions and idealizations. In modern sciences, it is widely believed that all concepts are abstractions. Perhaps the most energetic way this point of view is cultivated in mathematics. Unfortunately, the theory of abstractions rarely becomes the subject of philosophical analysis. Meanwhile, the identification of concepts with abstractions raises many questions.

Most often abstraction is understood as 1) a distraction from the nonessential, 2) isolation due to the distraction of generalized images, 3) which are sensually unknowable and do not have spatial and temporal characteristics. Idealization is a kind of embellishment of reality. If a scientist does not take into account some of the features of the object, then he uses abstraction. If scientists these features modify to some extent, then there is an idealization. If the teacher believes that the student's temper is insignificant, he performs an abstraction operation. If the teacher approves the sameness of pupils forgetting about their differences, then there is an operation of idealization.

Many scientists not without pathos argue that abstraction is a necessary condition of knowledge, through the formation of «secondary images» of reality [2]. A person who thinks sensibly may be surprised: should scientific knowledge deviate sharply from real things? To them who doubt the truth of the theory of abstractions, its supporters immediately remind of the points, lines, and planes, absolutely solid and completely black physical body, ideal-typical images, which are not in reality, but which certainly should be part of a theory. The resistance of the person doubting the theory of abstraction quite often they try to break by references to the profoundness of science.

What is the actual cognitive meaning of abstractions in the framework of intratheoretical transduction? In those cases in which they are relevant, abstractions are always means of simplification. They are a way not to form concepts, but to simplify some of them. Before refusing to consider something as unimportant, you should already have the appropriate concept. Otherwise, it is impossible to determine neither essential nor nonessential. For example, the object under study has features A, B, and C. the researcher has the right not to consider one or even two of these signs. Thus, he makes an abstraction. Perhaps it will be an ineffective cognitive operation. However, that is another question.

Idealization is a known embellishment of reality, which, however, is not arbitrary. Scientists accept idealization only when it ensures the progress of knowledge. At the same time, the researcher assumes the obligation in the future to achieve greater efficiency of the theory, if possible, to abandon abstractions and idealizations, or to weaken their distorting effect on individual stages of intratheoretical transduction. This fact clearly indicates the need for a critical attitude towards the institution of abstractions and idealization. They are not fundamental concepts. In science, a crucial meaning has not of abstractions and idealizations, and the operations of deduction, adduction, induction, and abduction. It is widely believed that the operation of abstraction depends exclusively on experimental data. This is wrong. Abstraction and idealization take place within the boundaries of any stage of conceptual transduction, including within the framework of deduction, induction, and abduction.

Unfortunately, historically it happened that many scientists began to connect the very originality of scientific theory with abstractions and idealizations. They do not allow including in the theory those things on which are performed the operations of abstraction and idealization. Then they say, for example, about the ascent from experiment to theory, or about the formation of theoretical concepts through the manipulation of feelings and thoughts. In fact, from the experiment researchers can move to data processing, but not to theory. As for feelings and thoughts, they are initially conceptual. Their conceptual weight as quite concrete, not impoverished or distorted concepts is not less, but more, than the corresponding indicator at abstractions and idealizations. Note that I consider abstraction and idealization exclusively within the framework of intratheoretical transduction. Outside it, they acquire a new meaning.

The next debatable question of epistemology concerns the question of the correlation of the different stages of conceptual transduction. The question of conformity rules allowing to move from observational data to theoretical terms is often discussed [3, 310-319]. Again, the question is sloppy. Observational data are theoretical terms. Another thing is that they are not deductive variables. Given this observation, it is obvious that there is a need to link concepts relating to the various stages of intratheoretical transduction. It really takes place. There is nothing mysterious in it, although sometimes this docking forces to conduct quite sophisticated cognitive operations.

References

1. Carnap, R. (1966) Philosophical Foundations of Physics. New York, London: Basic Books, Inc.
2. Novoselov, M.M. (2001) Abstraktnyy ob"yek. [Abstract object]. In Novaya filosofskaya entsiklopediya [New philosophical encyclopedia]. In 4 Vol. Moskva: Mysl', Vol. 1, 15-16.
3. Popper, K. (1959) The Logic of Scientific Discovery. London and New York: Routledge.
4. Quine, W.V.O. (1961) [1953] Two dogmas of empiricism. In Quine W.V.O. From a Logical Point of View. Second ed. Cambridge, MA: Harvard University Press, 20–46.

1.4. Intertheoretical transduction

In the previous paragraph, I considered the intratheoretical transduction. Of course, in a certain way are interconnected not only individual concepts, but also theories. Therefore, along with intratheoretical exists also intertheoretical transduction. Its content is subject to further consideration.

A typical situation for all sciences is that an outdated theory T_1 is replaced by a new theory: $T_1 \rightarrow T_2$. How does it happen? The new theory does not appear by chance, but due to the difficulties of the old theory. Of course, it is preceded by clarification of these difficulties, which in the scientific literature are called problems. The word problem denotes what needs to be clarified and overcome, propels the theory forward. The problem is the difficulty, overcoming which is essential for the successful formation of new knowledge.

The problem is a kind of congestion on the path of intratheoretical transduction. It is not possible to carry out a particular stage of the study, for example, deduction. Or the research stages are not coordinated with each other. Predicted variables are not detected in the experiment. Attempts to organize the successful functioning of the theory encounter obstacles that are often manifested in the form of contradictions, aporias (hopeless situations), paradoxes (arguments that seem clear, but, nevertheless, cannot be explained in the existing theory). Systematic work to identify contradictions, aporias, and paradoxes is exactly the problem. Problematization begins with questioning. Are the principles of the theory independent from each other and consistent? Is the selection of measurement results correct? Did the regression analysis lead to errors? Theory, devoid of problems, is only at first glance successful. In fact, it is poorly understood by the researcher. An in-depth understanding of the theory always leads to problems. The stage of cognition considered by us can be schematically represented as follows: $T_1 \rightarrow T(p)_1$, where p is the revealed problems.

Scientists identify problems not for reconciliation with them. Researchers certainly strive to overcome them. Of course, success is not easy, but it certainly happens. The new theory is the result of innovation. The history of science gives a wealth of material in this regard. N.N. Lobachevski discovered the era of non-Euclidean geometries, Einstein came up with special theory of relativity, J.M. Keynes created an impressive version of macroeconomics. The discovery of a new theory is always associated with the development of previously unknown concepts. Lobachevski came up with the assumption that through a point outside a given line it is possible to carry out two parallel to it. Einstein introduced into physics the postulate of the finiteness of the rate of transmission of physical interactions. Keynes showed that people's economic actions are determined by their expectations. Innovation can be schematically depicted as follows: $T(p)_1 \rightarrow T_2$.

Theory T_2 arose as a reaction to the problems of the theory of T_1. However, this reaction is not only on problems but on all content of the theory. Before developing a theory T_2, there was no scale for evaluation (interpretation) of the theory T_1. As soon as the scale appeared, so immediately becomes the relevant interpretation of the theory of T1 from the standpoint of the theory of T2. This interpretation operation can be written as follows: $T_2 \rightarrow T_1\{T_2\}$. For example, we propose to turn again to the history of the development of various sciences. From the positions of the special theory of relativity in classical mechanics, instead of the concept of short-range interaction in physics, the concept of long-range action was cultivated, according to which the rate of transmission of physical interactions can be infinitely large. According to the theory of totalitarian society, this society is the result of the oblivion of the principles of democracy. Etc.

Interpretation allows identifying the extent to which the original theory is amenable to renovation or must be deemed unsuitable for further use. The theory of phlogiston from chemistry is archived in the history of science, but this cannot be said about the theory of atoms of J. Dalton, as well as, for example, the theories of Newton, Darwin, and Smith. Interpretation allows deciding the fate of the original theory. In the former, unmodified form, this theory is misleading. Therefore, it should be replaced by its interpretation. This operation has a pronounced critical character. It is the result of criticism of theory T_1.

The cycle of intratheoretical knowledge includes four methods, namely, deduction, adduction, induction, abduction. As for intertheoretical knowledge, it also implements cycles. His methods are problematization, discovery, interpretation, and ordering of theories. Schematically, the cycle of intertheoretical cognition can be written as follows:

$$T_1 \rightarrow T_1(p_1) \rightarrow T_2 \rightarrow T_1\{T_2\}. \qquad\qquad 1.1$$

In this recording $T_1\{T_2\}$ expresses the relationship between old and new theory. Bundle $T_2 \rightarrow T_1\{T_2\}$ expresses ordering of theories.

As well as a deduction, adduction, induction, and abduction, problematization, discovery, interpretation, and ordering are some forms of conceptual management. In our view, there is every reason for an introduction to the philosophy of science the concept of the cycle of intertheoretical transduction.

So far I sought a systematic presentation of the theory intertheoretical transduction, without being distracted by the discussion of its disputable aspects. Of course, they must also be taken into account.

The dynamics of the theories did not immediately come to the attention of researchers. It began in earnest only in the 1960s. Scientists have paid special attention to concepts philosophers of science of Karl Popper, Imre Lakatos, Thomas Kuhn, and Paul Feyerabend. All of them are representatives of the historical school in the philosophy of science, a key figure which should be recognized, Karl Popper.

Popper himself illustrated the variability of theories by the following scheme [6, 455]:

$$P_1 \rightarrow TT \rightarrow EE \rightarrow P_2. \qquad\qquad 1.2$$

Scientific analysis starts with some problem P1, for which scientists offer a trial theory TT. It may contain errors EE, which must be corrected. To this end, scientists carry out a critical discussion of the content of the theory and its experimental testing. As a result, sooner or later there is a new problem, P2. Relay of problems generates a relay of hypothetical theories. Not every problem leads to a new theory. But, ultimately, any theory is doomed to replace itself with its more substantial scientific rival. Like all other living organisms, people are a Darwinian struggle for their existence. In science, this struggle acts in the form of evolutionary epistemology, theories replace each other. That's the concept of Popper.

Popper's understanding of the dynamics of knowledge raises some doubts. It is hardly legitimate to take the problems beyond the theory. Problems should be within the theory. Like facts, problems do not exist outside, but inside theories. The organic drawback of the Popper concept is that it has no stage of interpretation, $T_2 \rightarrow T_1 \{T_2\}$. In his absence and criticism cannot be presented in a systematic way. Popper liked to talk about problems, but not about the method of problematization. The stage of innovation is also mentioned only in passing. Of course, the full-fledged cycle of intertheoretical transduction was absent in his reasoning.

Lakatos believed that any scientific theory has a solid core, which is surrounded by a protective belt of auxiliary hypotheses [5, 135]. Principles and laws form a solid core. It remains unchanged, and the protective belt is modified until the scientific revolution. But, as we believe, the theory has no center. It does not contain hypotheses that are isolated from principles and laws. As for the correlation of theories, Lakatos was so stingy that we do not even have the opportunity to bring any of his decisive judgment. Assessing the creativity of Lakatos, it should be noted that he's the term 'research program' has gained wide popularity. It is understood that researchers tend, on the one hand, to preserve the theory (negative heuristics) and, on the other hand, to find an alternative to it (positive heuristics). In fact, the terms 'theory' and 'research program' in the interpretation of Lakatos are synonymous. This fact was misunderstood both by himself and by his many followers. There is no reason to replace intertheoretical relationships with the relevance of research programs. As for the idea of negative and positive heuristics, it does not explain much. There are researchers who are either conservative or progressive. But it's just their subjective attitudes, which does not clarify the nature of intertheoretical transduction.

P. Feyerabend and T. Kuhn are the authors of the thesis about the incommensurability of theories, which they vigorously promoted since 1962 [2; 4]. The main idea of Kuhn and Feyerabend was to underline the fundamental differences of the concepts of all theories. They considered that this fact was not taken into account in the concept of cumulative knowledge, according to which knowledge is continuously increased, excluding any revolution.

True whether the thesis of Kuhn-Feyerabend? In our opinion, it is true. Theories differ from each other, primarily by their principles, the meaning of which is translated into other theoretical concepts, including laws and variables. Why this thesis is so often met with hostility? The fact that many researchers have mistakenly assumed that Kuhn and Feyerabend deny the possibility of a comparison of theories [6, 4]. In reality, they did not deny the possibility of comparing theories. The theories are incommensurable, but they are proportionate. [3]

The key issue is the careful introduction of the thesis Kuhn-Feyerabend in the context of the cycle of intertheoretical transduction. Kuhn and Feyerabend did not own this conception. It is not surprising that they have not been able to contribute decisively to its development. According to Feyerabend, since the theories are incommensurable, each one is good in its own way. But this assertion is patently incorrect, as evidenced by the previously conducted analysis of the cycle of intertheoretical transduction. The interpretation of $T_2 \to T_1\{T_2\}$ is consistent, but not $T_1 \to T_2\{T_1\}$.

For completeness, we mention N. Bohr's the correspondence ptinciple. An outstanding physicist, trying to understand the origins of quantum mechanics, thought a lot about its relationship with classical mechanics. In this regard, he came up with the correspondence ptinciple. «The correspondence ptinciple, – said Bohr – expresses the tendency to utilize in the systematic of the quanta theory every feature of the classical theories in a rational transcription appropriate to the fundamental contrast between the postulates and the classical theories" [1, 849]. In a generalized form, the correspondence ptinciple is that the new theory must take into account all the achievements of its predecessor. At first glance, this requirement is quite legitimate. But according to closer examination, it does not have clear content. Indeed, look again to the cycle of intertheoretical transduction. A new theory arises on the basis of the old one. This just means that the achievements of the partially outdated theory are taken into account. However, it should also be borne in mind that in the cycle of intertheoretical transduction, the new, not the old theory, is crucial. The correlation between the two theories is expressed by an interpretation of $T_2 \rightarrow T_1\{T_2\}$. Wanting to express the correlation of theories, in the end, we have to rely on the principle of the relevance of mature knowledge. A more developed theory is the key to interpreting the content of a less developed theory. This epistemological principle is extremely relevant. To my great surprise, over the years I have not been able to identify its author.

References

1. Bohr, N. (1925) Atomic theory and mechanics. Nature, Supplement 116 (2927), 845–852.
2. Feyerabend, P. (1962) Explanation, reduction and empiricism. In Feigl, H., Maxwell G. (Eds.). Scientific Explanation, Space and Time. Minneapolis: University of Minneapolis Press, 28-97.
3. Hoyningen-Huene, P., Oberheim, E. Incommensurability of scientific theories. Stanford encyclopedia of philosophy. Available at: https://plato.stanford.edu/archives/fall2018/entries/incommensurability/

4. Kuhn, T. (1979) [1962] The Structure of Scientific Revolutions. Chicago: University of Chicago Press.
5. Lakatos, I. (1978) Falsification and the methodology of scientific research programs. In J. Worrall, J., and Currie, G. (Eds.). The Methodology of Scientific Research Programs: Philosophical Papers. Cambridge: Cambridge University Press, 8–101.
6. Popper, K.R. (1979) Epistemology without a knowing subject. In Popper, K.R. Objective Knowledge. An Evolutionary Approach. Oxford, Clarendon Press, 1979, 106-152.

1.5. The league-theories, their relation and calculation

Consider three cycles of intertheoretical knowledge:

$$T_1 \rightarrow T_1(p_1) \rightarrow T_2 \rightarrow T_1\{T_2\}; \qquad\qquad 1.3$$

$$T_2 \rightarrow T_2(p_2) \rightarrow T_3 \rightarrow T_2\{T_3\}; \qquad\qquad 1.4$$

$$T_3 \rightarrow T_3(p_3) \rightarrow T_4 \rightarrow T_3\{T_4\}. \qquad\qquad 1.5$$

It is easy to see that each new cycle of knowledge puts forward a new theory that dominates its predecessor. Ultimately, it turns out a number of theories, the basis and the top of which is the most developed theory. In the case of three cycles of knowledge, it is the theory T_4.

If desired, you can isolate the historical relay of theories. It acts as a problematic set of theories: $\qquad T_1 \rightarrow T_2 \rightarrow T_3 \rightarrow T_4.$

The organic drawback of this series of theories is that it does not express the process of updating the content of partially outdated theories. This disadvantage is absent in a critical-interpretative set of theories 1.7. $T_4 \Rightarrow T_3\{T_4\} \Rightarrow T_2\{T_4\} \Rightarrow T_1\{T_4\}$.   1.7

Somewhat unexpectedly it turns out that the four discussed theories form an organic whole, which we propose to call league-theory. The original theories, namely T_1, T_2, and T_3, are part of the league-theory not in their original, and in the corrected form. Their problems have been overcome. Not overcome are the problems of the most developed theory, T_4. But it's a matter of the future.

In the record of a number of problem theories, the arrow $\rightarrow$ indicates the need to overcome some problems. Bearing in mind the difference, on the one hand, of a number of problem theories and on the other hand, the series of transduction theories, I decided to use an arrow $\Rightarrow$ when recording the latter. It refers to the process of interpretation.

Of current importance is the question of the need to operate league-theories. It seems reasonable to limit knowledge to only the most advanced theories. All other theories can be abandoned. There is no need, for example, to refer to classical Newton's mechanics, which by its potential is clearly inferior to the relativistic Einstein's mechanics. Why not reduce all underdeveloped theories to the most advanced concepts?

I have conducted experiments with students. And it turned out the following curious circumstance. With the limitation of the league-theory only by its most developed concept, the trainees constantly reproduced the conceptual content of supposedly already overcome theories. Without turning to league-theories, knowledge lost its problematic nature. I had to spend enormous efforts, teaching students to carry out problematization. League-theories do not arise by chance, they are not only ways of development but also of the preservation of knowledge. The greater the number of conceptions the researcher is able to include in the relevant league-theory, the more relevant is his knowledge.

Of course, only concepts that share some common criteria can be included in the same league-theory. Biological concepts, for example, cannot be included in the physical or economic league-theory. Equally unsuccessful will be an attempt to include Freudian concepts in psychological behavioral league-theories. Moreover, even in the analysis of related theories, arise non-obvious bundles.

Suppose that we consider a set of interpretations of quantum mechanics. And here the discrepancies are revealed. Thus, the Copenhagen interpretation differs from the ensemble one, and from the multi-world one. For each interpretation will have to build their league-theory. However, even under this condition, the researcher maybe not satisfied with the degree of thoroughness of the analysis. In this case, it is advisable to continue the stratification of the league-theory, for example, the Copenhagen interpretation, taking into account, in particular, that some authors focus on the nature of quantum measurements (N. Bohr, W. Heisenberg), others on the account of consciousness of the researcher (J. von Neumann, E. Wigner).

Something similar takes place in all sciences. Not to be unfounded, here is another example, this time from pedagogy. It is possible to distinguish a number of theories of different orientation [3, 224-227]. In some of them, the central

importance is given to the personality of the child, in others –
activities, in the third – ethics, etc. Theories of activity
orientation developed, in particular, such outstanding teachers
as I. Pestalozzi, M. Montessori, J. Dewey, G. Kerschensteiner, A.
S. Makarenko, J. Piaget, L.S. Vygotsky. All these concepts are
valid to include in the same league-theory. More careful
analysis forces to distinguish, for example, the theory of labor
orientation (I. Pestalozzi, G. Kershensteiner, A.S. Makarenko)
and the concentration of activity-psychological orientation (J.
Piaget, L.S. Vygotsky). It is also possible to isolate the theory of J.
Dewey, who, unlike other teachers listed above, adhered to the
principles of pragmatic philosophy. However, one should not
think that he would be left alone in theoretical terms. In the US,
and in other countries, Dewey had numerous supporters who
did not agree with him in everything.

In all sciences, there is a similar situation. The set of
theories is not accepted as their arbitrary scattering, they are
ordered in a certain way. So, physicists talk about Maxwell-
Einstein-Dirac electrodynamics, and economists talk about the
Smith-Ricardo-Marx theory of labor value. There are varieties of
league-theories. However, it is appropriate for one significant
explanation. At the head of league-theories as explained above
are the most developed theories. From this point of view, the
above league-theories should be called in the following way:
electrodynamics of Dirac-Einstein-Maxwell and the theory of
Marx-Ricardo-Smith. In historical terms, of course, Maxwell's
theory preceded Einstein's concept, which, in turn, was
developed earlier than Dirac's theory. But in terms of content,
of course, more recent theories are relevant. Of course, no
league-theory is once and for all finished. Prior to the famous
electrodynamic innovations of the Nobel Prize winners in
physics Feynman, Tomonaga and Schwinger, relating to the late

1940s. it was reasonable to start the name of the electrodynamic league-theory named Dirac. But later, wanting to express the relevance of quantum electrodynamics, it is necessary to include the names of new authors in the name of the league-theory, in particular, Feynman.

In all sciences, scientists operate with the league-theories. They are, if necessary, divided into smaller components. But to reach the theories that would not be included in any league-theory fails. Ultimately, each researcher structures a set of theories in his own way. The degree of stratification of league-theories is determined by the purpose of the study, it cannot be set arbitrarily.

Unfortunately, many researchers have a poor grasp of the concept of league-theory. They operate exclusively with separate theories. The links between them, if they were taken into account, are far from adequate. Another common error is that the history of science is not always seen with the use of the concept of league-theory. Meanwhile, it is it who is of key importance. The researcher should always be guided by the principle of the relevance of mature knowledge, giving the greatest importance to the most developed theories in the composition of league-theory [2, 14-15].

Since there are league-theories, it is reasonable to raise the question of their relationship. In its presence, there is no doubt. Suffice it to recall the theories whose names include the mention of two sciences, for example, such as physical chemistry, biophysics, political economy, pedagogical psychology. The presence of theories with hybrid names clearly indicates its relationship to the league-theories relating to various sciences. My experience in understanding this connection is associated with the distinction of acceptor and donor league-theories.

Consider, for example, the ratio of physical and biological theories within biophysics. Biophysics is considered as a biological discipline. This means that the biological theory is an acceptor conception, which is forced to perceive the achievements of the adjacent theory of physical content. To put it more simply, it is permissible to say that in this case, biology is primary and physics is secondary. Physical league-theory has donor character. This is the cognitive situation from the standpoint of a biologist. It is significantly different if similar phenomena are studied from the standpoint of physics. A professional physicist is primarily interested in the physical status of the phenomena that he considers. If they are not isolated from biological processes, he has to take into account their biological relativity. For a physicist, the primary science is not biology, but physics. Therefore, in this cognitive situation, physical league-theory has an acceptor (basic) nature. Thus, the acceptor or, alternatively, the donor status of league-theory depends on the position of the researcher, from his conceptual frame of reference.

Considering the various league-theories, first of all, it should be noted their fundamental difference from each other. All attempts to reduce one league-theory to another invariably ended in failure. Biological and technological league-theories cannot be reduced to physical league-theories, sociological league-theories cannot be reduced to biological ones, and pedagogy cannot be transferred to the rails of psychology.

Many years reflecting on the status of the relationship between the acceptor and donor league-theory, I came to the conclusion that, for their characteristics, it is reasonable to use the notion of symbol. In this case we take into account the context of the semiotics of C.S. Peirce. He used three types of signs namely icons, symptoms, and symbols. He characterized relations of concepts with each other by means of symbols only, but not icons and symptoms. «The objects of the understanding, considered as representations, are symbols, that is, signs which are at least potentially general. But the rules of logic hold good of any symbols, of those which are written or spoken as well as those which are thought. They have no immediate application to likeness [icons] or indices, because no arguments can be constructed of these alone, but do apply to all symbols. »[4, 56] Thus, the connection of concepts of various league-theories is symbolization. What is its specificity? That the concepts of donor league-theory are considered as symbols of concepts of acceptor league-theory. Political scientists are interested in economic phenomena only to the extent that political processes depend on them. The economist pays attention to political processes only if they influence economic phenomena in a certain way. Donor league-theories do not cancel the status and identity of the acceptor league-theories but constitute their context, some restriction. In this sense, they are symbolic.

The presence of the donor league-theories compels us to consider their status in the implementation of intertheoretical transduction. I write in this context, the cycle of intertheoretical transduction, denoting the donor league-theory by letter d:

$$T_1[d_1] \Rightarrow T_1[d_1](p_1) \Rightarrow T_2[d_2] \Rightarrow T_1[d_1]\{T_2[d_2]\}; \quad 1.8$$

In all four members of the interdisciplinary transduction, a theory is considered not in itself, but in relation to its donor companion, which is the theory d_1 for the theory T_1, and for the theory of T_2 – theory d_2. It is possible that the new donor theory helped to overcome the difficulties of the original concept. Let me illustrate this fact with the following example.

In the classical Newton's gravitation theory physicists use Euclidean geometry. In the relativistic theory of gravitation, Einstein used non-Euclidean Riemannian geometry. Some difficulties of the classical theory of gravitation could be overcome not without the help of Riemann geometry. The link of the classical theory of gravitation and a relativistic theory of gravitation forms the physical league-theory. Another link, namely, Euclidean geometry – Riemann geometry, forms a geometric league-theory, which in relation to physics has a donor character. This example shows that not just individual theories but the league-theories correlate with each other.

Successively cycles of inter league-theoretical transduction lead to the formation of the corresponding league-theory. Compare the results respectively of intertheoretical and inter league-theoretical transduction:

$$T_4 \Rightarrow T_3\{T_4\} \Rightarrow T_2\{T_4\} \Rightarrow T_1\{T_4\}; \qquad\qquad 1.9$$

$$T_4[d_4] \Rightarrow T_3[d_3]\{T_4[d_4]\} \Rightarrow T_2[d_2]\{T_4[d_4]\} \Rightarrow T_1[d_1]\{T_4[d_4]\}.$$

In both cases, transduction leads to the formation of league-theories. But it is essential to note that a separate league-theory is a degenerate case of acceptor-donor league-theory. The world of science is the world of acceptor-donor league-theories. This conclusion can be reinterpreted as follows: in the world, there is nothing but acceptor-donor league-theories. Everything that really exists, including objects and persons, is a representation of the acceptor-donor league-theories.

At this point, it is reasonable to recall the often mentioned in the scientific literature interdisciplinary connections. Unfortunately, the authors considering these relationships do not provide a clear definition of discipline. My analysis shows that if you want to define the concept of discipline, it should be reduced to the concept of league-theory. But most authors do not know the concept of league-theory. As a result, the concept of discipline and the concept of interdisciplinary connections are uncertain and, therefore, not properly understood. The same applies to the concepts of mathematical and computer modeling.

Mathematical modeling is a special case of inter league-theoretical transduction. It is not that a mathematical copy of the object under study is being built. The correspondence between concepts, including objects of acceptor and donor theory, is established. This operation, as explained above, is a symbolization. If desired, this symbolization can be called modeling. If you do not use the concept of symbolization, the content of the modeling process is something in the highest degree mysterious.

Let me summarize the review of the concept of transduction. There are only two types of transduction, intratheoretical and intertheoretical. Below we indicate their methods.

Intratheoretical transduction = deduction + adduction + induction + abduction.

Intertheoretical transduction = problematization + discovering + interpretation + ordering.

In the XX century, researchers met with a difficult phenomenon to comprehend. There are a lot of theories, but what to do with them, scientists who are usually not familiar with the concept of league-theory, don't know. As a result, eclecticism flourishes almost everywhere in science. The antidote against it is the theory of conceptual transduction. It is highly relevant that in this context it is possible to use not only qualitative representations but also quantitative evaluations. In this regard, eclecticism is finally overcome.

Table 1.1 gives an idea of a typical scientific situation

Table 1.1. Ranking of theories

№	League-theories and local ratings of theories	Rank weights of League-theories
1	**(10)** $A_n \Rightarrow$ **(8)** $A_{n-1}\{A_n\} \Rightarrow$ **(7)** $A_{n-2}\{A_n\}$ $\Rightarrow$, ..., $\Rightarrow$ **(2)** $A_1\{A_n\}$	[10]
2	**(10)** $B_m \Rightarrow$ **(9)** $B_{m-1}\{B_m\} \Rightarrow$ **(6)** $B_{m-2}\{B_m\}$ $\Rightarrow$, ..., $\Rightarrow$ **(3)** $B_1\{B_m\}$	[6]
3	**(10)** $C_k \Rightarrow$ **(7)** $C_{k-1}\{C_k\} \Rightarrow$ **(5)** $C_{k-2}\{C_k\}$ $\Rightarrow$, ..., $\Rightarrow$ **(1)** $C_1\{C_{nk}\}$	[4]

In table 1.1, three league-theories, A, B, and C, whose number of members is equal to n, m, and k, are written. There are also given in parentheses my estimates of the theories, the meaning of which is explained below.

In the league-theory, each subsequent conception is less relevant than the previous one. This fact was clarified in the process of consideration of the nature of intertheoretical transduction. But previously, the degree of superiority of one theory over another was not determined. However, it is well known from the theory of decision-making that if there are differences between some phenomena, they can always be measured, i.e. represented in numerical form. Measured not only the signs of physical phenomena but also values, sometimes quite bizarre, for example, artistry of dancers on ice.

It follows from the above that there can always give estimates of individual theories within the framework of the league-theory. In table 1.1, they are given in parentheses. It is reasonable to consider these estimates as local ratings of theories. It means that they are determined by the place of the theory within the league-theory. Here, perhaps, is appropriate some example.

Suppose that we consider physical theories: quantum field theory $\Rightarrow$ quantum mechanics $\Rightarrow$ relativistic mechanics $\Rightarrow$ classical mechanics. After the discovery of the Higgs boson, the prestige of quantum field theory was strengthened. Estimating it, for example, on the 10-point system, it is reasonable to expose to it the highest assessment because there is no best theory (the best theory is always exposed to the highest assessment). But if the quantum field theory is rated 10 points, then what estimates deserve less developed theory. A connoisseur of the history of physics knows that the conceptual distance between different theories is not the same. Scientific revolutions took place during the transitions to relativistic mechanics, quantum mechanics, and quantum field theory. The extremely radical restructuring was associated with the invention of quantum mechanics, in particular, due to the development of the concept of the wave function. Relativistic mechanics differs from classical mechanics to a lesser extent than quantum mechanics from relativistic mechanics. This means that the distance between quantum mechanics and relativistic mechanics is greater than the distance between relativistic and classical mechanics. It is unacceptable, for example, to award three considered physical theories with 6, 4 and 1 points, respectively. Indeed, in this case, the conceptual distance from quantum mechanics to relativistic mechanics is not more as required by the actual state of things, but less than the distance from relativistic to classical mechanics

Until now, only the location of theories within the boundaries of individual league-theories has been considered. But it is also necessary to take into account the difference between the league-theories, which by definition form a hierarchy. In the case I am considering, there are only three league-theories. But their number can be much more than three. Once again, the rule is that differences can always be measured. League-theories differ from each other by their criteria. Therefore, they should be assigned, as expressed in decision theory, some rank weights. They are indicated in the third column   of Table 1.1 in square brackets. Again, perhaps some example is appropriate. Let us turn to management in this regard [1].

Here it is necessary to distinguish, in particular, the theory of strategic management, growth of organizations, human relations to producers, orientation to consumers, knowledge, and ethics. Each researcher ranks them in one way or another. In other words, he prefers this or that league-theory. For example, one of the founders of scientific management P. Drucker clearly speaks on behalf of strategic management and theories of knowledge. Not less famous researcher M. Porter prefers strategic management to an even greater extent than P. Drucker, but he's condescending about ethical theories. H.

Mintzberg speaks on behalf of the theory of organizations. So, in the case of the league-theories, you can set how one theory is more relevant than another. This is done by dimensionless quantities. The maximum rank weight is given to the acceptor league-theory. The rank weight of the donor league-theories must be less than ranking weight of acceptor league-theory.

The third step of the definition of the integral rating of a theory is the multiplication of the local rating and corresponding ranking weight that league-theory, the composition of which theory enters. The final formula is as follows:

Integral rating of theory = Local rating of theory $\times$
Ranking weight of league-theory.

Now all theories can be written in a hierarchical order corresponding to the values of their ratings.

A simple method of rating theories is described above. It was important for me to determine the possibility of such a definition. There is no doubt that different conceptions from the arsenal of the theory of decision-making can be used in calculating the rating of theories.

Of course, quantifying the relevance of theories is extremely important. In working with graduate students, I have repeatedly seen their extreme degree of surprise due to the fact that, according to the relevant calculations, the highest ratings were awarded not to the theory of their idols, but of other authors.

At first glance, it may seem that the ranking of theories and league-theories cannot avoid subjective arbitrary estimates. But this impression is deceptive. The results of the research will put everything in its place. That researcher who will unreasonably persist in the estimates containing an element of arbitrariness will inevitably lose the competition with the more conceptually substantial opponents. The history of science allows citing numerous examples in this regard. The same researcher can be either a winner or a loser in intellectual competition. Famous A. Einstein surpassed everyone in understanding the conceptual nature of relativistic mechanics. But his persistent criticism of the probabilistic description used in the quantum mechanics turned out to be a flawed action.

References

1. Kanke, V.A. (2010) Filosofiya menedzhmenta [Philosophy of Management]. Moskva: Knorus. [In Russian].
2. Kanke, V.A. (2007) Filosofiya uchebnika [Philosophy of the Textbook]. Moskva: Universitetskaya kniga. [In Russian].
3. Kanke, V.A. (2011). Filosofiya pedagogiki [Philosophy of Pedagogy]. Moskva: [without publisher]. [In Russian].
4. Peirce, C.S. (1984) The Writings of Charles S. Peirce: A Chronological Edition. Vol. 2.   Moore, E.C., et al (Eds.) Bloomington I.N: Indiana University Press.

1.6. Science and the problem of demarcation

This book is devoted primarily to science. But in this case, I cannot avoid discussing its correlation with nonscience. This problem question is known as the demarcation problem. How and where exactly should the line be drawn between science and nonscience?

Many authors have discussed the problem of demarcation. It occupied a particularly prominent place in the works of critical rationalist K. Popper. Contrary to statements of neopositivists, in particular, R. Carnap and H. Reichenbach, the criterion of science is not verification of the theory, but its falsification. «In so far as a scientific statement speaks about reality, it must be falsifiable: and in so far as it is not falsifiable, it does not speak about reality. » [4, 316]

If we reject K. Popper's excessive claims to the only true position, it becomes obvious that the problem of demarcation is interpreted differently by representatives of various philosophical and scientific directions. In fact, neopositivists and critical rationalists come from different understandings of intratheoretical transduction. Neopositivists focus on experiment and induction, while critical rationalists focus on deduction and falsification. Accordingly, the problem of demarcation is interpreted differently. But, of course, the two installations in question are not the only ones. In this connection, the survey article of the Swedish researcher S.O. Hansson [2] as a representative of analytical philosophy is of considerable interest.

He considers five ways of interpretation of the demarcation criteria: neopositivist, critical-rationalist, neopragmatic, as well as through criteria based on an understanding of scientific progress and epistemological norms and, finally, a multicriteria approach. The proposed strategy for the interpretation of the problem of demarcation, of course, deserves attention.

The neopositivist and critical-rationalist approaches were mentioned earlier. Neopragmatic approach Hansson covers, referring to the works of one of the classics of the philosophy of science, American T. Kuhn, who believed that the main criterion of science is to overcome puzzles.

Many authors, including M. Bunge [1] and G.A. Reisch [5] believe that knowledge is unscientific if it cannot be consistently incorporated into the existing network of developing sciences.

The sociologist R. Merton considered epistemological norms, namely, the universalism of scientists, their communicative community, impartiality and organized skepticism as criteria of scientific research [3]. Hansson rightly points out that this approach, due to its lack of specificity, did not have a significant impact on the discussion about the nature of science.

Another approach to characterizing the nature of science is that several criteria are specified. Hansson does not give a list of criteria. But he gives a list of seven deviations from the scientific, their antonyms can be considered as criteria of science. The list includes: 1) belief in the indisputable authority of some outstanding scientists, 2) the failure from repeating actual experiments, 3) broad appeal to not representative examples, 4) the rejection of theory testing, 5) ignoring information contrary to theory, 6) the presence in the theory of tricks that complicate its refutation, 7) the lack of continuity in the explanation. S. O. Hansson concludes his article with the conclusion that science is a systematic search for new knowledge, the reliability of which does not depend on the individuals, and at the same time open to everyone to check them.

This definition can hardly be considered clear. What is the systematic search for knowledge, authenticity, verification, and rediscovery? Hansson failed to address this issue with a definite answer. Our position is fundamentally different. We believe that the desired response is possible, but only when referring to intra- and intertheoretical transduction. Always when a researcher describes the phenomenon of meaningful science, he uses the concepts of the composition of intratheoretical and intertheoretical transduction. Neopositivist and critical rationalists, focusing respectively on verification and falsification, in fact, used some of the ideas about intratheoretical transduction. Puzzles that attracted the attention of T. Kuhn, are similar to the problems of theories. The authors, referring to scientific progress in determining science, in fact, refer to the area in which intertheoretical transduction is crucial. Thus, scientists determining the nature of science should turn directly to the conceptual transduction. Otherwise, statements of unclear content cannot be avoided.

Science is true knowledge, fixed through the league-theories. If knowledge cannot be incorporated into them than it is unscientific. If you want to give a more detailed description of science you should use the concepts of intratheoretical and intertheoretical transduction.

Appeal to the conception of intertheoretical transduction also clarifies the question of the beginning of science. Is it correct to assume that logic started with Aristotle, mathematics with Euclid, physics with Newton, chemistry with Dalton, biology with Darwin, economics with Smith, sociology with Durkheim, etc.? Is it right to take the predecessors of these researchers beyond the limits of science? In our view, the answers to these questions should be negative. Here is the corresponding argumentation.

A number of theories included in the league-theory can be extended from our days to the most ancient times. By definition, all theories that have passed the crucible of scientific criticism should be recognized as scientific. Let us explain this by the example of economics. It is widely believed that scientific economics began with A. Smith, the founder of the labor theory of value. But before Smith were mercantilists (T. Mann, J. Stewart) and the physiocracy (F. Quesnay, M. Turgot). They were not wrong in everything, therefore, their theories are amenable to scientific interpretation. So, the exclusion of mercantilism and physiocracy from science is untenable. Nevertheless, the countdown of the era of scientific economics from A. Smith also has a certain meaning. He developed the theory which was for the fate of the scientific economic much more important than, for example, mercantilism.

As a rule, the beginning of science is associated with those researchers who came up with the theory of high relevance. They are considered the creators of scientific revolutions. Of course, an exhaustive scientific analysis is achieved only when the whole range of theories available to researchers is considered. From this point of view, the countdown of the beginning of science from the first scientific revolution is not correct. It is wrong, for example, to assume that the true scientific physics began with Newton. The one who notes scientific merits, for example, of Galilei and Aristotle as physicists are right. But at the same time, he has to specify that Newton, having created classical mechanics, acted as a scientific reformer.

In conclusion of the paragraph, I note the unfounded accusations of scientists in scientism, namely, in ignoring the achievements of nonscientific knowledge. The fact is that nonscientific knowledge has no real achievements. The task of the scientist is to carefully separate any knowledge, the separation of the grains of truth from the chaff of delusions. Being a stickler for the truth, of course, he can't assume fallacy as intellectual achievements. The moral ethos of the scientist does not allow him to be arrogant to the bearer of any, including non-scientific knowledge. Showing him respect, scholar, however, qualify non-scientific knowledge adequately its contents. Opponents of scientists refuse a thorough analysis of the theories that guide them. Since these theories usually contain both scientific and nonscientific knowledge, but no distinction is made between them, then there is indivisible confusion.

References

1. Bunge, M. (1982) Demarcating science from pseudoscience //Fundamenta Scientiae 3(3-4), 369–388.
2. Hansson, S.O. (2012) Science and pseudo-science. The Stanford Encyclopedia of Philosophy. Available at: http://plato.stanford.edu/archives/win2012/entries/pseud o-science/
3. Merton, R.K. (1942) Science and technology in a democratic order. Journal of Legal and Political Sociology 1(1-2), 115-126.
4. Popper, K. (1959) The Logic of Scientific Discovery. London and New York: Routledge.
5. Reisch, G.A. (1998) Pluralism, logical empiricism, and the problem of pseudoscience. Philosophy of Science 65(2), 333-348.

1.7. Fields and types of sciences

Knowledge is a tapestry, woven from the league-theories. But, of course, not all of them are located at an equal conceptual distance from each other. Researchers have to take into account the structure of knowledge, highlighting, in particular, the branches (or fields) of science, discipline, and sub-discipline. Three considered levels of science, as a rule, are indicated by a six-digit code.

This classification of levels of science was adopted by the United Nations Educational, scientific and cultural organization [2] and the Organization for economic cooperation and development [1]. In both cases, an attempt is made to present in a clear form the hierarchy of parts of science. This hierarchy can be considered in two directions: bottom-up (from theories to branches of science) or top-down. In the two documents under consideration, the hierarchy of scientific formations is considered from top to bottom. There are three upper levels of science. But the lower levels of science remain unknown. There is no doubt, however, that the three-level classification of science under consideration does not reach the fundamental level of science, which is a set of league-theories. As a result, the entire nomenclature is deprived of its real foundation. The right path of analysis should start from below, not from above. The whole history of science shows that the attempt to dispense with the investigation of the foundation of the phenomena leads to conceptual superficiality

The branch of science is an extensive set of league-theories, which have a certain conceptual similarity. It is recognized, for example, in relation to physics. There are well-known reasons to believe that the principle of least action is fundamental for all physical league-theories. According to its content, all physical league-theories use the concepts of energy, momentum, length, and duration. Another example. Economics is recognized as a branch of science. Again, this recognition is valid only to the extent that there are some principles that are typical for all league-theories enrolled in this branch of science. With regard to economic league-theories, one of their principles is to maximize the rate of return on advanced capital.

Thus, there are grounds to consider the concept of the branch of science legitimate. Unfortunately, anybody and never conducted a complete inventory of the totality of league-theories. In this regard, the statements about the branches of science are marked with a seal of obscurity. It is not surprising that even the number of branches of science is unknown. With a certain degree of confidence, wl can say that there are about two dozen fields of science.

According to popular classifications, branches of science consist of disciplines and subdisciplines. Here is a good example. Physicists distinguish between electroweak, strong and gravitational interactions. It is reasonable to correlate some discipline to each type of interaction. Varieties of disciplines are, for example, topology in mathematics, genetics in biology, the doctrine of mass society in sociology, and energetics in technology. Disciplines are divided into separate subdisciplines. For example, nuclear energy is a technological subdiscipline in the energy sector as a discipline.

Note also that quite often groups of branches of science are combined into types of sciences. For example, according to the document of the Organization for economic development and cooperation, six types of sciences should be distinguished, namely, 1) natural, 2) engineering and technological, 3) medical and health, 4) agricultural, 5) social and 6) humanitarian sciences [3, 12]. In my view, three branches of science, namely technology (engineering and technological sciences), medicine (medical and health sciences) and agrology (agricultural sciences) are considered mistakenly to be types of science in this classification. It is also very controversial to enroll in the number of natural sciences mathematics and computer science. They are formal sciences. As for the distinction between natural and social sciences, it is quite relevant.

According to my research, the most relevant classification of types of branches of science is the one shown in table 1.2.

Table 1.2. Types and fields of science

Types of fields of science	Subtypes of fields of science	Fields of science
Natural sciences	–	Physics
		Chemistry
		Geology (all sciences about the Earth)
		Biology
Axiological sciences	Basic axiological sciences	Technology (all technical and engineering sciencies)
		Agrology (all agricultural sciences)
		Medicine
		Economics
		Sociology
	Auxiliary axiological sciences	Psychology
		Pedagogy
		Political science

		Jurisprudence
		Ethics
	Integrated axiological science	History
	Offset axiological science	Art
General formal sciences	—	Linguistics
		Logic
		Mathematics
		Computer sciences
		Philosophy

Natural sciences deal with natural phenomena, principles, laws, and variables that people are unable to abolish. That is why these sciences are considered natural.

Fundamentally different is the nature of axiological sciences (from the Greek αξία – value). All their concepts are values invented not by nature, but by people. In table 1.2 indicated 12 of the axiological fields of science. Three of them, namely, technology, agrology, and medicine, despite their fundamental difference from the natural sciences, however, retain very close ties with them. For example, technology is connected with physics much more closely than, for example, any of the social sciences. Accordingly, there are no other axiological branches of science, which would be so closely related to biology, as agrology and medicine.

The distinction between basic and auxiliary axiological sciences is of extremely urgent importance in understanding the nature of science. Basic sciences are autonomous, they arose as independent conceptual units. In contrast, auxiliary sciences are not primary, but secondary. The condition for their formation and development are basic sciences. By virtue of the scientific division of labor, certain aspects of the basic sciences are studied in auxiliary sciences. These aspects are justice in ethics, permitted actions in jurisprudence, power relations in political science, individual characteristics of people in psychology and ensuring the growth of people's competence in pedagogy. All of these aspects are inherent in the basic axiological sciences. They do not exist autonomously from them. A common scientific mistake is that auxiliary axiological sciences are considered basic.

History as an axiological science has a special status. In relation to the past, it unites the achievements of all sciences.

As for the art, it stands out for its focus on fiction, which is invented. This means that the difference between art and social sciences is quite sharp. However, this difference should not be exaggerated. Art retains close continuity with all axiological sciences, but it is shifted from the real to the realm of fiction.

Let me now turn to the formal sciences, i.e. to linguistics, logic, mathematics, informatics, and philosophy. Their concepts express the similarity of all branches of science, but not their fundamental differences. In this sense, they are not substantive, but formal sciences. Linguistics is very different from logic, mathematics, and informatics. It is not characterized by a system of calculus. But in this case, another circumstance is crucial. Like its formal sisters, linguistics does not delve into the specific content of others, in particular, natural and axiological sciences.

Finally, the status of philosophy should be considered. The Greek φιλοσοφία literally means the love of wisdom. This wisdom is that philosophy distinguishes similar conceptual and methodological features of the most developed theories. It gives them new impulses of development and thus creates knowledge relevant to all other sciences. Philosophy is a formal science. As such, it operates on the concepts and conceptions that are part of the intratheoretical and intertheoretical transduction. If this circumstance is not understood, then philosophy acquires a quasi-scientific character. Unfortunately, a significant part of modern philosophy really has only a quasi-scientific meaning.

References

1. Organization for economic cooperation and development. (2007) Revised field of science and technology (fos) classification in the frascati manual. Available at: https://www.oecd.org/science/inno/38235147.pdf/
2. United Nations Educational, Scientific and Cultural Organization. (1988) Proposed International Standard Nomenclature for Fields of Science and Technology. Paris: UNESCO. Available at: http://unesdoc.unesco.org/images/0008/000829/082946E B.pdf/

1.8. The truth

Science accepts not any, but only true knowledge; false knowledge is not accepted in science. But what is the truth? Reflecting on this question, the philosophers developed three conceptions of truth, correspondence, coherent, and pragmatic. The most ancient of these is the correspondence conception of the truth of Plato and Aristotle, according to which the sentence is true if the statement in it corresponds to the actual state of things [1, sec. 1]. But what does it mean - to correspond to the actual state of things? This complex issue is still the subject of heated discussions. Only at first glance does the correspondence conception of truth seems credible.

The coherent conception of truth is a modification of the correspondence conception. It was invented in connection with the language revolution that occurred in philosophy in the early XX century. According to the coherent conception of truth, a sentence is considered true if it is consistent with other propositions of the theory. As noted by O. Neurath, it is possible to compare some parts of the language with others, but it is unacceptable to proceed from the pre-language position, asserting the independence of reality [3, 396]. Any sentence must match the language in which the objects are described. As a rule, proponents of a coherent concept of truth recognize that ultimately sentences must be factual.

The pragmatic conception of truth was brought to life by the development of pragmatism in the United States. It was a favorite topic of reflection of W. James, who considered the truth as a kind of good. Ideas "become true only to the extent that they allow us to be in coordination with other parts of our experience" [2, 34]. A pragmatic conception of truth is difficult to reconcile with a correspondence conception. Indeed, in accordance with the latter, it is necessary to reproduce correctly, what is, for example, the structure of the solar system. Its structure does not depend on our life experience. Even among Americans, the conception of pragmatic truth was not supported by all philosophers and, especially, scientists. Many of them recognize only correspondence, but not pragmatic truth. Nevertheless, it is among the Americans who are most supporters of the pragmatic conception of truth.

The three conceptions of truth considered to have one common drawback – the definition of truth is considered independently of the conceptual structure of science. Meanwhile, it is obvious that any conception, the conception of truth in this sense cannot be the exception, should be introduced only in the context of science. In this regard, it is immediately discovered that science does have a mechanism for the separation of knowledge, through which its progress is ensured. This mechanism is intratheoretical and intertheoretical transduction. Ultimately, the truth is recognized only to the knowledge that is certified by league-theories. The rest of the knowledge is defined as false. On the truth and falsity of knowledge is possible to judge only on the basis of the cycles of knowledge. The principles and laws of the theory are recognized as true if, as a result of a full cycle of intratheoretical transduction, there is no need to revise them. Theory T_1 is true if the result of intertheoretical transduction gives no need to replace it by the theory $T_1\{T_2\}$.

Quite unexpectedly there is the situation with the most developed theory T_n. About its truth or falsity can be judged only on the basis of the theory T_{n+1}. Therefore, strictly speaking, the truth of the theory T_n is in question until this theory becomes the initial step in the new cycle of intertheoretical transduction.

At first glance, it seems inconsistent, on the one hand, to emphasize the priority of the most developed theory, and, on the other hand, to refuse to recognize the truth of it. Upon closer inspection, it turns out that we are talking about the imaginary contradiction. All true knowledge is not final. It can be revised. Given this circumstance, it is said that the truth is not absolute, but relative. It can be judged only on the basis of really conducted cycles of knowledge. But then it turns out the ambiguous nature of the most developed theory. So, true knowledge is produced in the process of conceptual transduction. This transduction is the key to understanding true and false knowledge.

Researchers who do not know the conception of transduction inevitably give definitions that seem obvious to them, but in reality are false. The corresponding failure happened, for example, even with K. Popper, a rather refined philosopher of science. He argued «Assuming that the truth-content and the falsity-content of two theories t_1 and t_2 are comparable, we can say that t_2 is more closely similar to the truth, or corresponds better to the facts, than t_1, if and only if either: (a) the truth-content but not the falsity-content of t_2 exceeds that of t_1, or (b) the falsity-content of t_1, but not its truth-content, exceeds that of t_2» [4, 233]. In the light of conceptual transduction, Popper's statements are false.

Popper was referring to a deductive statement. Contrary to his statement, it cannot in principle correspond to the facts, i.e. in his interpretation of empirical variables. A deduction is not directly related to empirical variables. A comparison of deductive statements with empirical can be carried out only by induction, and abduction. Popper also repeated the typical mistake of many other researchers who, ignoring the stage of induction and abduction, seek to compare directly the deduction with the experiment and represent this relationship as their correspondence to one another. Since this direct comparison is not possible, then the correspondent and coherent conceptions of truth are false.

Contrary to Popper it is impossible to get close to the truth. The growth of knowledge, about which he rightly talked so enthusiastically, is a process of development, but not of drawing closer to the truth. Truth is true knowledge. It is clear that it cannot draw close to itself. There is knowledge more and less developed, but there is no true knowledge more and less close to the truth. To verify this, it is enough to refer to the content of the league-theory. All the theories included in it are under the aegis of the most developed theory. In this sense, they are all true, and to the same extent.

Above the correspondence and coherent conceptions of truth have been criticized. A critic is also relevant to the pragmatic conception of truth but on other grounds. Pragmatists, in fact, turned to axiological sciences. Consequently, they should have taken into account their very structure, and not speak on behalf of the universal concept of truth. But they didn't make it.

Every theory goes through the stages of intertheoretical transduction. In this regard, the concept of truth cannot be denied. The type of truth depends on the type of science. Once again, I emphasize the main idea of this paragraph: the conceptions of truth should be considered not in isolation from the network of scientific knowledge, and in its composition.

Interestingly, representatives of various sciences like to speak on behalf of the truth. But there are many prestigious scientific journals, in which there is not even one article devoted directly to the conception of truth.

References

1. David, M. (2016) The correspondence theory of truth. The Stanford Encyclopedia of Philosophy. Available at: https://plato.stanford.edu/archives/fall2016/entries/truth-correspondence/
2. James, W. (1975) Pragmatism: A New Name for Some Old Ways of Thinking. Cambridge MA: Harvard University Press.
3. Neurath, O. (1931) Soziologie im Physikalismus. Erkenntnis 2(5/6), 393–431. [In German].
4. Popper, K. (1963). Conjectures and Refutations: The Growth of Scientific Knowledge, London: Routledge.

1.9. Methods of scientific knowledge

Theories have many expressions. One of them is the methodological representation of theories, in which the emphasis is on methods. The method is a word of Greek origin, literally, it means to follow something along a paved road. In the scientific context, the method means some way of carrying out scientific knowledge. Accordingly, the methodology is the doctrine of these methods. From the previous discussion, the reader knows the methods of intratheoretical and intertheoretical transduction. This deduction, adduction, induction, abduction, problematization (of old theory), discovery (of new theories), interpretation (of partially outdated theories via new), ordering (theories in league-theories).

The deductive method in the existing scientific literature is called differently. It is often called axiomatic, as well as hypothetical-deductive and deductive nomological. I am talking about different accentuations, thanks to which either axioms or hypothetical nature of laws or laws themselves are placed in the center of understanding. Deduction can be done in many ways. In this regard, it is particularly common to distinguish between direct and indirect evidence.

The adductive method is commonly known as the experimental method. It involves a lot of intricacies. The phenomena under study should be presented in such a way that they are not distorted by side circumstances. Considerable attention is paid to instruments and their calibration. The principle of relativity to the means of observation is taken into account. The experiment is put in such a way that, on the one hand, there is continuity with deduction, and, on the other hand, everything would be prepared for induction.

The inductive method provides the processing of experimental variables and the formation of the corresponding, namely, inductive laws and principles. The achievements of mathematical statistics, in particular, correlation and regression, are widely used. In pursuing the principles, which generally are the extremals of the utmost importance has functional analysis.

The inductive method also allows you to find out the causes of the phenomena. What is happening is always determined by some active factors. They are called causes. Examples of causes are, for example, potential energy in physical phenomena and the motives of people, according to which they perform certain actions.

The abductive method is intended to ensure the updating of the principles of the theory, to ensure their completeness, consistency, and independence from each other. As in the case of other intratheoretical methods, various search strategies are used, in particular, the relevant historical experience is taken into account.

In the composition of intratheoretical transduction, scientists often use the techniques of approximations, abstractions, idealizations. This time I am not talking about full-fledged methods, but about techniques designed to ensure the success of the transduction.

When thinking about intratheoretical transduction often used the concepts of structure, function, elements, and systems. Consider some set of interrelated concepts: $a_1 \rightarrow a_2 \rightarrow a_3 \rightarrow a_4 \rightarrow a_5 \rightarrow$. Together, they form a structure. Each a_i is a conceptual atom, i.e. element. Correspondence a_i for a_{i+1} is called a function of a_i. If the independence of each a_i is recognized, then there is conceptual atomism. If the nature of each a_i is determined by its place in the structure, then there is structuralism.

A system is a whole composed of conceptual atoms, functions, and structures. There is no whole inside the system, it always manifests itself outside the system. The described conceptual connections are often presented in the form of methods, in particular, atomic, structural, structural-functional or system. All of them, in my opinion, lack conceptual content, because the nature of the concepts themselves is not given, in particular, the principles, laws, and variables do not stand out. This circumstance gives me a reason to consider the atomic, structural, structural-functional and system method not as the main methods of knowledge, but as auxiliary ones. The same applies to analysis and synthesis.

The analysis is that the whole is broken into its parts. In the process of synthesis, these parts are reunited with each other.

Analysis and synthesis involve a thorough understanding of the league-theories. The scientist is not able to carry out the analysis first, and only then the conceptual transduction. In the process of implementation of conceptual transduction, it is constantly accompanied by analysis and synthesis. For example, the experiment involves the measurement of variables. This is a kind of analysis. In the process of induction, variables are combined into inductive laws. There is some process of synthesis. On the other hand, induction allows determining the average values of variables and deviations from them. It's analysis. Thus, analysis and synthesis are the methods of cognition accompanying all the methods of conceptual transduction.

Turn to intertheoretical methods. Problematization is the essence of the problem method. It consists of the purposeful search of "weak" places, i.e. problems of the theory breaking its harmony. Usually, problems are fixed in the form of conflicting opinions, antinomies, aporias, and paradoxes.

The discovery method is to overcome problems. For this, it is necessary to harmonize all the components of the theory, including all its stages. In the process of innovation, new variables, laws, and principles are introduced. This is done not on a whim, not intuitively, and in full accordance with the understanding of the nature of theories and league-theories. The scientist understands that to overcome the problems he needs to make changes in the conceptual apparatus of the theory. He is searching for these changes quite purposefully. The history of the discovery of relativistic mechanics is very revealing in this respect.

For a quarter of a century, physicists could not explain the independence of the speed of light in a vacuum from the speed of its source. The meaning of Einstein's discovery was that he correctly interpreted the structure of the physical theory. The stated independence is not an ordinary empirical fact, which should be explained by the laws of physics. It is the physical principle of close-range interaction for electromagnetic phenomena.

K. Popper believed that each discovery contains «an irrational element» [2, 8]. The discovery is made by intuition, which does not need discursive sequential thinking. This view cannot be reconciled with the status of conceptual transduction. The scientist always goes on the roads of conceptual transduction, and this is impossible without discursive thinking.

It's time to turn to the interpretive method. Its meaning consists in the critical evaluation of partially outdated knowledge. The scientist is not able to treat him indifferently. He refuses false knowledge without regret but includes true knowledge in league-theory.

The ordering method is necessary to express the unity of theories. Without this method, it is impossible to understand the integrity of scientific knowledge.

So, a brief outline of the methodology of scientific knowledge is presented. For help, I refer the reader to one of my books. [1] Add to the above that the content of not only this paragraph but the whole chapter will be developed in further texts. The first chapter of the encyclopedia is just its plot, conflict points of which will be discussed and clarified throughout the book under critical fire of conceptual guns of various sciences.

References

1. Kanke, V.A. (2013) Metodologiya nauchnogo poznaniya [The Methodology of Scientific Knowledge]. Moskva: Omega-L, 2013. [In Russian].
2. Popper, K. (1959) The Logic of Scientific Discovery. London and New York: Routledge.

Chapter 2. The nature of philosophy

2.1. Theory of forms by Plato and Aristotle

Philosophy for 26 centuries of its development has accumulated a huge amount of material. We are interested in it mainly in connection with the fate of science. This means that when we consider the teachings of different authors, we will pay primary attention to the knowledge that relates to the philosophy of science. In this regard, it is reasonable to pass the roads of the history of philosophy. This approach will allow us to bypass the most coveted spots of philosophy.

My choice forces me to turn to the initial stages of the development of philosophy. It is always difficult to give them an exhaustive description. Much of what will bloom only later is presented here in an undeveloped form. It is difficult to understand its actual content. Of course, at the same time, there is something to rely on, namely, the lessons of the already established history of philosophy. For centuries, there was a separation of conceptual achievements of philosophers, sifting seeds from the chaff. It is necessary to address, first, to two geniuses of antiquity Plato and Aristotle. They lived almost 2.5 thousand years ago, and their innovations do not cease to be passed on the relay of human achievements. It is Plato and Aristotle reasonably often called the founders of Western civilization.

From a scientific point of view, the most interesting concepts and methods, which Plato and Aristotle used in their theories, are the concepts of form and of the inductive method. Repeated attempts have been made to present the theory of forms in a systematic way. [1-4] The main thing is that «Platonic Forms are universals; Aristotelian forms are particulars; where

81

there can be at most one Platonic Form corresponding to a given predicate, there may be several Aristotelian forms; and many Aristotelian forms, though no Platonic ones are sensible, perishable, and changeable». [2, 23]

The concept of the form to the greatest extent in keeping with the work of Plato. Of course, in his position, it was difficult to determine the terminology. What eventually led to the doctrine of forms, he called both forms, and eidos, and ideas, and paradigms (samples), and a kind, and essence, and a thing in itself. With the development of his work, it became increasingly clear that Plato from different sides represents the same thing, namely, some beginning that forms a certain class of things. Examples of forms are good, beauty, truth, justice, and humanity. Philosophical tradition cemented this beginning the name 'form'. Platonic forms exist on their own, that is, they are transcendental things. People can reason about them. Things of a certain class represent the same form, but with varying degrees of perfection.

Our brief review of Plato's work shows that his main interest is focused on the search for the general and the transition from it to the single. From the standpoint of conceptual transduction, the search for a general, i.e. principles, is provided by abduction. Moreover, the transition from general to single is carried out by means of deduction. Plato only in vague outlines possessed these methods. He also did not know the concepts of law and variables. However, based on the ideas of Plato, his student Aristotle was able to achieve amazing success.

He was dissatisfied with the conception of Plato's forms because it does not explain the nature of actual things. Aristotle makes a decisive step: the essence of things is not general, but specific. The genus is secondary; it does not exist by itself and is by its nature completely determined by the form.

The scientific search for Plato and Aristotle is impossible to understand without explaining it from modern positions. In my opinion, the essence of the matter is as follows. A thing is a collection of attributes. A particular feature P_i exists in many instances, namely, P_1, P_2, P_3, ..., P_n. The concept of the Platonic form captures the general quality of all the attributes, the P, but ignores their quantitative differences. Plato has P, but not P_i. Aristotle corrects this flaw in the concept of Plato. Thus, the theories of Plato and Aristotle should be combined.

In fact, both Plato and Aristotle talk about the signs of things. At the same time, they are trying to highlight the essence that is opposed to matter. Modern authors see the fundamental difference between things from each other in principles and laws. They cannot be reduced to signs. Plato and Aristotle tried to distinguish this difference based on signs. In this respect, of course, they could not succeed. The same applies to matter. Plato and Aristotle were not able to give a clear idea of its nature. Theories of the forms of Plato and Aristotle are primarily the theory of things and their signs, but not of laws and principles.

Having decided on the conceptual content of form theories, their methods should also be highlighted. In fact, the interest of Plato and Aristotle was focused on two transitions, first, from individual things to the class of things and, secondly, from the class of things to their individual representatives. According to Aristotle, the first transition is realized through the inductive method and the second through the deductive method. In «Posterior Analytics», he defines his position regarding the inductive method. [3]

> So from perception there comes memory, as we say, and from repeated memories of the same thing [there comes] experience (ἐμπειρία); for many memories constitute a single experience. And from experience, or rather from the whole universal which has come to rest in the soul, the one apart from the many, that which is one and the same in all these things, [comes] a principle of craft or understanding [i. e. νοῦς] — of craft if it concerns coming-to-be, of understanding if it concerns what is. (B19, 100a3–9)

It should be remembered, assessing this statement of Aristotle, that he did not know the true principles of scientific theories. In discussing the principles, Aristotle had in mind the genus of things in contrast to their kind. As for the deductive method, it allows moving from the conception of the genus of things to their species differences through syllogisms. Typical is the following reasoning: "All x have the attribute P, therefore, the individual x also has this attribute." Thus, the methodological content of the theory of forms of Aristotle is reduced to the methods of induction and deduction

In the theory of Plato's forms, a reference to intuition is added to these two methods. Platonic forms, unlike the Aristotelian forms, are not perceived sensually, an intellectual intuitive leap leads to them. Judgments relating to all things cannot be obtained simply by inductive means. However, science does not need universal attributes just as it does not need universal laws. In this regard, there is no need for intuition.

Thus, my conclusion is as follows. In the theories of forms, Plato and Aristotle presented the conceptual transduction of signs of things through methods of deduction and induction. This is an underdeveloped theory. It is remarkable, however, that it is the prototype of more mature forms of conceptual transduction.

In my opinion, paying tribute to Aristotle, undoubtedly ingeniously gifted philosopher, it is necessary, nevertheless, to treat his creativity critically. Like Plato, Aristotle did not possess the concepts of principle and law. It was their trouble, not their fault. After all, at this time, natural and axiological disciplines have not yet reached the stage of scientific maturity. It is in our days, the careful student, referring to science, unwittingly forced to operate with principles and laws. At the time of the ancient geniuses of philosophy, they were not known. Plato and Aristotle had no choice but to cultivate the scientific virgin soil. They coped with this task brilliantly. Indeed, Plato and Aristotle created the main prerequisites for the future development of science as the most mature knowledge. Thus, the doctrine of Plato's forms and the theory of Aristotle's forms a very actual approach to conceptual transduction.

References

1. Ainsworth, T. (2016) Form vs. Matter. The Stanford Encyclopedia of Philosophy. Available at: https://plato.stanford.edu/archives/spr2016/entries/form-matter/
2. Fine, G. (1983) Plato and Aristotle on Form and Substance. Proceedings of the Cambridge Philological Society 209, 23-47
3. Gasser-Wingate, M. (2016) Aristotle on induction and first principles. Philosophers' Imprint 16(4), 1-20.
4. Silverman, A. (2014) Plato's middle period metaphysics and epistemology. The Stanford Encyclopedia of Philosophy. Available at:

https://plato.stanford.edu/archives/fall2014/entries/plato-metaphysics/

2.2. The opposition of rationalism and empiricism

Methods of modern science are part of the intratheoretical and intertheoretical transduction. Their content is revealed in the study of the nature of scientific theories. In their absence, judgments about the methods of science are largely undetermined. Let me explain this by reference to the status of induction. It can be confidently judged only under certain conditions. First, there must be appropriate scientific theories, such as physics and economics. Secondly, you cannot do without mathematical statistics. Thirdly, we need the logic of predicates, in the absence of which judgments about the features of objects will be extremely controversial. Let me now pay attention to the timing of the appearance of quite mature theories.

Scientific physics in its modern sense emerged only in the late XVII century; the scientific economy in the late eighteenth century, mathematical statistics and the logic of predicates – in the late XIX century. In this regard, it is obvious that until the beginning of the XX century nobody, including philosophers, have not been able to talk over the induction with the desired level of thoroughness. This means that, considering the historical and philosophical material, you should always take into account its limitations, determined primarily by the current state of scientific knowledge. The confrontation between rationalism and empiricism that we are interested in arose early, in the age of insufficient development of science. As a rule, this was due to an ambiguous interpretation of the ratio of general and particular.

This opposition is already visible in the works of Aristotle. Even he did not manage to present the nature of the general in a distinct form. With this difficulty had to face and medieval thinkers who tried to understand the nature of universals, for example, concepts such as redness, goodness, man.

Realists (from Latin realis – real), in particular, Anselm of Canterbury, Albert the Great and Thomas Aquinas insisted on the validity of the general. The nominalists (from the Latin nomine– name), including J. Roscelin and W. Ockham, denying the reality of universals, believed that there are only things. Both considered universals as convenient verbal forms. Conceptualists (from Latin conceptus – concept) sought to find a middle way between realism and nominalism. According to P. Abelard (XII century) concepts express the result of generalization in the mind of similar properties of things. The notions do not exist in nature, nevertheless, they have important theoretical significance. Realists, nominalists and conceptualists built their judgments for the most part regardless of the content of scientific disciplines, in particular, mathematics and logics.

A modern researcher is reasoning in a fundamentally different manner. He links the status of the general with laws and principles, as well as with the nature of mathematics and logic. Rationalists R. Descartes, G. Leibniz, and I. Kant believed that from the general could be deduced through deduction the particular. However, what is the nature of the general and how does it get at the disposal of a person? Of course, Descartes, Leibniz, and Kant in the scientific sense surpassed medieval thinkers many times. For them, the general is the axioms of mathematics (Descartes), principles of logic (Leibniz), and principles of philosophy (Kant). Nevertheless, how do these principles fall at the disposal of man? To answer this question researcher should refer to the abduction. However, this operation is unknown to all three philosophers. Two of them, namely Descartes and Leibniz, argued that clear ideas are innate to man: because man has a reason, he has clear ideas. Kant left the question under discussion unanswered.

Did the scientists really manage to deduce from principle the single? Only in the first approximation. Indeed, the experiment is often clearly contrary to the predicted variables. This fact was already understood by Frances Bacon: «The syllogism consists of propositions, propositions consist of words, words are symbols of notions. Therefore if the notions themselves (which is the root of the matter) are confused and overhastily abstracted from the facts, there can be no firmness in the superstructure. Our only hope therefore lies in a true induction» [1, 49] According to this logic, scientists should proceed from experimental data. This is the setting of all representatives of empiricism, in particular, F. Bacon, J. Locke, J. Berkeley, and D. Hume. However, they also meet with insurmountable difficulty.

They should have deduced laws and principles from the experimental data. How to do it through induction? Bacon outlined his program in «New Organon», but failed to implement it. Induction boils down to clarify the facts that either confirm a certain conclusion or refute it. A full induction as a method of inductive approvals of the laws and principles he did not have. Bacon is partly at odds with genuinely scientific concepts. He continued to use the Aristotelian notion of form.

John Locke breathed new life into Bacon's project. Innate human ideas do not exist. There are simple ideas; complex ideas made up of simple ones (such as the perception of things, for example, apples); relations obtained by the comparison of ideas, for example, the concept of brother fixes the kinship of some males; and finally, ideas become common because they are abstracted from those qualities that are not typical for all individuals. « ...Nature in the Production of Things, makes several of them alike: there is nothing more obvious, especially in the Races of Animals, and all Things propagated by Seed. But yet, I think, we may say, the sorting of them under Names, is the Workmanship of the Understanding, taking occasion from the similitude it observes amongst them, to make abstract general Ideas, and set them up in the mind, with Names annexed to them, as Patterns, or Forms, (for in that sense the word Form has a very proper signification,) to which, as particular Things existing are found to agree, so they come to be of that Species, have that Denomination, or are put into that Classis. » [4, 276] The idea of 'man' covers all people of the human race, but it does not mean their sameness. Thus, the general is deduced at the expense of operation of abstraction.

Alas, this argument caused a sharp objection from the main opponent Locke G. Leibniz. The real definition, which shows the possibility of the phenomenon to be determined in all the richness of its properties, no matter how many they are, cannot be abstract. Real definitions are essential, they are not the result of abstractions. We know necessary truths only by the natural light of general principles like axioms of mathematics, «and not at all by the experiences of the senses». [3, 189]

Surprisingly, empiricists, ultimately, recognized the well-known failure of their project. D. Hume notes that it is unacceptable to consider cases about which we have no empirical experience similar to those already studied [2, 89]. In other words, the general cannot be deduced. Hume's position initiated Kant's activity: since the general is not deducible, it should be recognized as the principles of cognition as a pre-experimental, a priori knowledge. If people did not possess it, it would be impossible to have experimental, i.e. a posteriori knowledge. Unfortunately, Kant clearly overestimates the merits of his theory. Like all other rationalists, he cannot bridge the gap between general (read: principles and laws) and particular (read: experimental variables). In fact, two stages of intratheoretical transduction, namely, induction and abduction do not fall within the field of view of Kant.

Thus, the programs of rationalism and empiricism met with insurmountable difficulties. Both parties cannot understand in any way that their programs complement each other. They should not be opposed to each other but be combined into a cycle of intratheoretical transduction.

References

1. Bacon, F. (2011) The works of Frances Bacon. Vol. 4. Translation of the Philosophical Works 1. Ed. by Spedding, J., Ellis, R.L., and Heath, D.D. Cambridge; Cambridge University Press. 2011.
2. Hume, D. (1975) Enquiries Concerning Human Understanding and Concerning the Principles of Morals. Oxford: Clarendon Press.
3. Leibniz, G.V. (1989) Philosophical Essays. Transl. by Ariew, R. and Garber, D. Indianapolis: Hackett.
4. Locke, J. (1876) An Essay Concerning Human Understanding. Philadelphia: Kai and Troutman.

2.3. Dialectics of G. Hegel

Philosophers, by definition, create philosophical theories. These theories contain certain concepts, which, of course, differ from the concepts of other sciences. This raises two natural questions. First, what is the connection of philosophical concepts with the concepts of other sciences? Secondly, what is the connection of philosophical concepts with each other? In this regard, the grandiose project was implemented by the germen philosopher Georg Wilhelm Friedrich Hegel (1770-1831). Let me formulate the main provisions of his project.

First, Hegel was convinced that it was philosophy, and only it, that could rationally represent the absolute as something that does not depend on anything. In essence, he offers the metaphysics of the absolute. [1] Philosophy consists of three parts, the science of logic, the philosophy of nature and the philosophy of spirit. Its original abstract foundation is the science of logic. «It is only through a profounder acquaintance with other sciences that Logic discovers itself to be subjective thought as not a mere abstract Universal, but as a Universal which comprises in itself the full wealth of Particulars». [3, 58] It follows, in particular, that philosophy, as a universal doctrine, contains science along with religion and art. Philosophy dominates science.

Secondly, everything that exists is ideal. «The proposition that the finite is ideal [ideell] constitutes idealism. The idealism of philosophy consists in nothing else than in recognizing that the finite has no veritable being. Every philosophy is essentially an idealism or at least has idealism for its principle, and the only question then is how far this principle is actually carried out. » [2, 154-155] The concept of an idea is of paramount importance to Hegel. He significantly reinterprets the content of ideas.

It is a mistake to imagine that the objects which form the content of our mental ideas come first and that our subjective agency then supervenes, and by the aforesaid operation of abstraction, and by colligating the points possessed in common by the objects, frames concepts of them. Rather the concept is the genuine first; and things are what they are through the action of the concept, immanent in them, and revealing itself in them. [4,163]

Thirdly, philosophy as a doctrine of the absolute needs an absolute method, it is dialectics with its long history, which content Hegel interpreted in a new way. «This movement is the Absolute Method of knowledge and at the same time the immanent soul of the Content of knowledge. It is, I maintain, along this path of self-construction alone that Philosophy can become objective and demonstrated science» [3, 28]. Dialectics always acts as a transition of fundamental categories into their opposite. [2]

Fourth, ideas are connected with each other through dialectical transitions: thesis - antithesis - synthesis. Hegel never used the terms himself, however, in his works there are numerous triples of categories that correspond to the triad under consideration. Such, for example, being – nothingness – becoming and quality – quantity – measure.

Fifth, in the framework of dialectics, Hegel pays special attention to the relation between the abstract and the concrete. Inconsistent thinking, in particular, one that comes exclusively from the demands of practice is always abstract in the negative sense of the word. [5] Abstract knowledge is relevant if it reaches the concrete as a diverse unity. Adherents of Marxism often view Hegel's methodology as an ascent from the abstract to the concrete. [6] In my opinion, Hegel ends the methodological ascent not on the concrete, but the absolute. Again, there is a triad: the abstract - the concrete - the absolute.

In his main work, «Encyclopedia of philosophical Sciences» (1817), Hegel successively considered: 1) the science of logic (the doctrine of being, essence, and concept); 2) the philosophy of nature (mechanics, physics, organic physics (that is, biology)); 3) philosophy of spirit: subjective spirit, that is, personality; objective spirit (family, civil society, state); absolute spirit (art, religion, philosophy). Hegel interpreted the whole world as a transition of categories from one dialectical contradiction to another. However, he believed that the logic of the world coincides with its history. Interestingly, the ultimate link in the movement of ideas is philosophy itself. The movement of categories begins and ends with philosophy. The circle is closed. The world is developing in a circle.

Which of the provisions of Hegel stood the test of time? Only one provision, namely that the whole world is a set of ideas. This is correct if scientists understand ideas as the concepts of the most advanced scientific theories. Today, Hegel's position must be reproduced on behalf of the principle of theoretical representation (see par. 1. 2): all objects are initially conceptual. Of course, if by ideas we mean exclusively mental and linguistic phenomena, then the considered position of Hegel is incorrect. The materialists, in particular, K. Marx, criticizing Hegel for his idealism, attributed to him their own understanding of ideas, interpreting them as mental formations.

Let me now turn to the position of the universal nature of philosophy, as well as its dominance over science. For example, some sciences are considered and the task is to find their similar features. It is possible. For example, the provision that any science considers certain laws is a formal provision. However, it is impossible to deduce features of these laws from it. Hegel clearly had this in mind, talking about the universality of philosophy. However, whatever he meant, the philosophy does not contain science and not dominant over it. On behalf of philosophy, it is possible to identify some similar aspects of the sciences. Philosophy can act as a formal science, but not as a universal science in the sense of Hegel.

How are concepts interrelated with each other? Inside the theory by means of operations of deduction, adduction, induction, and abduction. To verify this, it is enough to turn to any scientific theory. At the same time, the scientific connection is formed by well-defined concepts, namely, principles, laws, and variables. Hegel postulates another connection, namely: A → not-A → B (integration A and not-A). All categories are divided into triplets of concepts. Individual concepts are connected by means of two negations, simply negation (A → not-A) and negation of the negation (not-A → B). Examples: essence – phenomenon - reality; subjective concept - objective concept - idea. Are there really such transitions in scientific theories? The answer to this question is negative. Hegel's imagination is not supported by scientific data. Of course, following Hegel, a scientist may try not to take into account the relevance of experimental data. In this case, it will not be possible to find the connection between philosophy and science. Thus, there are no dialectical contradictions in scientific theories. The attempt to identify the connection between concepts without reference to the concepts of principle, law, and a variable is doomed to failure.

The researcher should always keep in mind that philosophy should measure its concepts, which are often called categories, with the concepts of science. It is unacceptable to enter a category regardless of the content of the sciences. A critical attitude to philosophy is necessary. Many categories, which at first glance seem obvious in their content, turn out to be simply untenable on closer examination. This category is, for example, the category of nothing, with which Hegel begins to build his system of categories. There is no category of nothing in any theory. It is impossible to determine the nature of nothing. Moreover, it is impossible to turn nothing into something. Another example. It is apparent that if A leads to B, then A is the cause and B the consequence. Let us turn, for example, to physics and economics. It is immediately clear that the philosophical definition of cause and consequence cannot be applied directly in physics and economics. Trying in physics to clarify the content of the category of the cause will have to turn to the concepts of action, strength, energy, and many others. Accordingly, in economics it will be necessary to refer to the concepts of utility, purpose, mutual influence of people. Unfortunately, Hegel did not take into account the correlation between philosophical categories and concepts of science. He simply imposed on the sciences philosophical categories of his own invention.

Hegel's dialectical method did not revolutionize the methodology of science. It is impossible to find a convincing example of the use of dialectics by any of the outstanding scientists From Hegel's project to the true philosophy of science is very far away.

Of particular note is the popularity of Hegel's dialectics. It is often enthusiastically accepted by philosophers far from science as a kind of revelation. Marx and Engels, the founders of dialectical materialism, did not escape this fate. They wanted to clarify the nature of science genuinely. Nevertheless, they failed to recognize the speculative character of the Hegelian dialectic.

References

1. Beiser, F.C. (2006) Hegel and the problem of metaphysics. In The Cambridge Companion to Hegel. Ed. by Beiser, F.C. Cambridge: Cambridge University Press, 1-24.
2. Forster, M. (2006) Hegel's dialectical methods. In The Cambridge Companion to Hegel. Ed. by Beiser, F.C. Cambridge: Cambridge University Press, 130-170.
3. Hegel, G.W.F (1969) Hegel's Science of Logic. Transl. by A.V. Miller, London: George Allen and Unwin.
4. Hegel, G.W.F. (1873) The Logic of Hegel translated from the Encyclopedia of the Philosophical Sciences. Transl. by W. Wallace. Oxford: Oxford University Press.
5. Hegel, G.W.F. (1977) Who thinks abstractly? In Hegel: Texts and Commentary. Transl. by W. Kaufmann. Notre Dame: University of Notre Dame Press, 117–118.
6. Ilyenkov, E. (1982) Dialectics of the Abstract and the Concrete in Marx's 'Capital'. Transl. by S. Kuzyakov. Moscow: Progress Publishers.

2.4. Three positivistic trends

Formal philosophy, the main object of our consideration in this chapter, has acquired developed forms for the first time in positivism. Its founder was Auguste Comte, author of the six-volume «Course of positive philosophy» (1820-1842). He set himself the task of overcoming the metaphysical era of the last three centuries. He saw the sin of metaphysics in the postulation of the transcendent, the traces of which are not found in strict science. According to Comte's the development of society takes place in accordance with the law of three stages. «The law is this: that each of our leading conceptions – each branch of our knowledge – passes successively through three different theoretical conditions: the Theological, or fictitious; the Metaphysical, or abstract; and the Scientific, or positive. » [5, 1] None of the scientists and politicians before Comte did not raise the banner of science so high. Saying their global aspirations in the elucidation of the meaning of scientific knowledge, Comte faced complex issues, many of which have remained without the answer.

In my opinion, John Stuart Mill adequately expressed the main content of Comte's philosophy of science:

> We have no knowledge of anything but Phaenomena; and our knowledge of phaenomena is relative, not absolute. We know not the essence, nor the real mode of production, of any fact, but only its relations to other facts in the way of succession or of similitude. These relations are constant; that is, always the same in the same circumstances. The constant resemblances which link phaenomena together, and the constant sequences which unite them as antecedent and

consequent, are termed their laws. The laws of
phaenomena are all we know respecting them.
Their essential nature, and their ultimate causes,
either efficient or final, are unknown and
inscrutable to us. [9, 5]

Vincent Guillin notes that Comte took into account the role
of hypotheses and abstractions and did not deny the need for
causal explanations. [6] Abstraction acts as the allocation of the
essential. Without abstractions, the concept of law cannot be
developed. The hypothesis must be based on laws. The
structure of science, according to the Comte, is as follows: the
studied objects - experiment - facts - abstraction - empirical
laws - a hypothesis

The second representative of the so-called first, i.e. the
classical positivism was John Stuart Mill (see par. 16.9). Unlike
Comte, he paid considerable attention not only to induction but
also to the deduction. However, like the Comte, he believed
that the foundation of knowledge is experiment and induction.
Thus, both of them in epistemology are supporters of inductive
fundamentalism. Mill's work was relevant for the development
of positivism, primarily because he paid paramount attention to
the method of induction. «The business of Inductive Logic is to
provide rules and models (such as the Syllogism and its rules
are for ratiocination) to which if inductive arguments conform,
those arguments are conclusive, and not otherwise. » [8, 533]
Mill identified five rules for finding the causes of phenomena.
He founded the actual direction of the development of
scientific knowledge, focused on the comprehensive
development of causal relationships. Mill rejected a priori ideas
and intuitions as false reference points of knowledge. [4, 1]

In the late nineteenth century, Richard Avenarius and Ernst
Mach became famous as prominent positivists. They are

considered representatives of the second positivism, or empirical criticism. Especially significant were the views of Mach, not only a philosopher but also an outstanding physicist. He was convinced that the empirical experience of cognition should be thoroughly analyzed and cleared of all metaphysical impurities. At the same time, all its positive content will be revealed and preserved, and only various kinds of misconceptions deserve to be a refutation. In the shortest exposition, the Mach theory is based on the following three principles

- The source of all forms of human cognition is what is given to man directly, and these are sensations.
- The World and I are one; their separation from each other is untenable
- Any metaphysical teaching regarding the extrasensory reality is not scientific.

Mach's innovation consisted primarily of analyzing the ultimate foundations of scientific knowledge, i.e. the sensations. Comte and Mill did not address the issue of how sensations can be used to adequately judge objects. They often talk about objects in such a way that they supposedly exist independently of consciousness. Meanwhile, it should be explained how people develop the concept of an object. Trying not to fall into the trap of the metaphysics of objects, Mach comes to the following extraordinary conclusion:

> Bodies do not produce sensations, but complexes of elements (complexes of sensations) make up bodies. If, to the physicist, bodies appear the real, abiding existences, whilst the "elements" are regarded merely as their evanescent, transitory appearance, the physicist forgets, in the

assumption of such a view, that all bodies are but thought-symbols for complexes of elements (complexes of sensations). Here, too, the elements in question form the real, immediate, and ultimate foundation, which it is the task of physiologico-physical research to investigate. By the recognition of this fact, many points of physiology and physics assume more distinct and more economical forms, and many spurious problems are disposed of.

For us, therefore, the world does not consist of mysterious entities, which by their interaction with another, equally mysterious entity, the ego, produce sensations, which alone are accessible. For us, colors, sounds, spaces, times, ... are provisionally the ultimate elements, whose given connexion it is our business to investigate. [7, 29]

Mach's reasoning has been criticized several times. However, Manuel Bächtold holds a fundamentally different position. «While the new experiments in microphysics refute indeed his scientific arguments against the atomic hypothesis, his epistemological arguments are unaffected. In this regard, Mach's epistemological approach remains relevant for today's discussion on the status of the notion of atom. » [1, 1] In my opinion, it should be recognized that Mach epistemology contradicts scientific ontology. Real dogs bite people, not installations sensations. It should be noted that the mistake of Mach is not devoid of known grounds. The world of objects is conceptually arranged in the same way as the world of subjective mental forms. The opposition of two conceptual frameworks is untenable. They belong to different representations of the theory that Mach did not take into account. Nevertheless, they are conceptually equivalent to each other. This last circumstance Mach, in fact, took into account in his theory of the identity of the phenomenal world and the existence of objects. Thus, he understood the conceptual structure of science as follows: the original world of sensations – new facts-sensations – empirical laws – simplified laws – possible sensations.

The immediate heirs of Mach's positivism were the philosophers of the new generation M. Schlick, R. Carnap and H. Reichenbach. All of them belong to the so-called third positivism. It is also called neopositivism or logical positivism. Until 1922, the prominent philosophers who founded the Vienna circle in that year were members of the Mach society. From him, they took the installation on the central position in the science the experiment and induction, which allow finding the expression of the laws. The source of the other two epistemological preferences, namely, of the emphasis on the phenomenon of language and its subsequent logical analysis, was received from the founders of analytical philosophy B. Russell and L. Wittgenstein. In 1929, the Manifesto of the Vienna circle was published [3]. It focused on six points.

1. Science must be freed from all metaphysics.
2. The scientific method in its strict understanding is the same for all sciences
3. The experiment is the foundation of science.
4. Based on the experimental data, through induction determine the scientific laws.
5. The central position in science should be given not to mental phenomena, but to language.
6. Language to avoid metaphysical errors requires thorough analysis by means of symbolic logic

Rudolf Carnap became the informal leader of logical positivists. He was a gifted logician. Following G. Frege and B. Russell, he began to implement a program of logicism. The key to the philosophy of science, he believed the logical clarification of all statements, including those relating to the characteristic of induction. Carnap develops inductive and modal logic in which the concept of probability is widely used. It should be noted that Carnap and Reichenbach were well aware that in the XX century all sciences were transferred to probabilistic rails. Consequently, the logic must be translated to the same basis. No sooner said than done. If the concept of probability is relevant in all sciences, then so should be in the philosophy of science.

Let us assume that some empirical law is established. Is it permissible to attach to it universal importance? Carnap, of course, was well aware that the universal law is a hypothetical concept. Nevertheless, this statement he did not want to be limited. Carnap believed that the more evidence, that is, experimental data in favor of the hypothesis h, the greater the probability of its truth p(h) [2, 32]. Thus, about laws, you should talk using the concept of probability. Carnap noted that it is never possible to achieve full verification of the law. «In fact, we should not talk about "verification" at all – if by this word we mean a definitive establishment of truth – but only about confirmation ». [2, 21]

Unfortunately, we have to note that R. Carnap, a fierce critic of speculative philosophy, himself made a metaphysical error. He introduced the notion of the truth of the theory as a probabilistic measure. However, what exactly is the truth of the theory, he did not explain. Nevertheless, one cannot speculate about the probability of what is not properly defined.

Besides Carnap reinterpreted the operation of induction. It consists of establishing of inductive laws and principles. He did not pay much attention to this conclusion, replacing it with the question of the degree of confirmation of the theory.

Carnap is considered the main representative of neopositivism. However, he established himself for real only as a leading specialist exclusively in logic. With his theoretical background, it is difficult to expect the creation of a comprehensive philosophy of science.

Unlike Carnap H. Reichenbach was an outstanding physicist. His analysis of the philosophy of physics, especially the special and general theory of relativity, proved to be extremely fruitful [10]. Reichenbach showed that the development of the philosophy of science is impossible without a thorough clarification of the conceptual structure of the science that has become the subject of analysis.

Unfortunately, to repeat the success of Reichenbach none of the neopositivists failed. Especially clumsily, they handled the social sciences. In the end, it turned out that neo-positivists could not avoid a number of absolutization, known, in particular, under the names of logicism, physicalism and empirical fundamentalism. Finally, they were quite helpless in understanding intertheoretical relations. With all these shortcomings, neopositivists demonstrated a previously unprecedented level of development of the philosophy of science. Neopositivism, in general, has become a significant milestone in the history of the philosophy of science.

References

1. Bächtold, M. (2010) Saving Mach's view on atoms. Journal for General Philosophy of Science, 41(1), 1-19.
2. Carnap R. (1966) Philosophical Foundations of Physics. New York, London: Basic Books.
3. Carnap, R., Hahn, H., and Neurath, O. (1973) [1929]. The scientific conception of the world: the vienna circle. In Empiricism and Sociology. Ed. by M. Neurath and R.S. Cohen. Dordrecht: Reidel, 298-318.
4. Cobb, A. D. (2016) Mill's philosophy of science. A Companion to Mill. Ed. by C. Mckleod and D.E. Miller. MA: Blackwell, 234–249.
5. Comte, A. (1853) The Positive Philosophy of Auguste Comte. Transl. by H. Martineau. London: J. Chapman. Vol. 1.
6. Guillin, V. (2016) Aspects of scientific explanation in Auguste Comte. Revue européenne des sciences sociales [European Journal of Social Sciences] 54(2), 17-41.
7. Mach, E. (1996) [1886] The Analysis of Sensations. London: Routledge and Thoemmes Press.
8. Mill, J.S. (1882) A System of Logic, Ratiocinative and Inductive, Being a Connected View of the Principles of Evidence, and the Methods of Scientific Investigation. Eighth Edition. New York: Harper and Brothers.
9. Mill, J.S. (2005) [1865] Auguste Comte and Positivism. [EBook #16833]. Available at: http://library.umac.mo/ebooks/b21819853.pdf
10. Reichenbach, H. (1958) [1928] The Philosophy of Space and Time. English trans. by M. Reichenbach and J. Freund. New York: Dover Publications.

2.5. Critical rationalism of Karl Popper

Critical realism is an influential philosophical trend. Its exemplary content is contained in the books of the founder of this trend, Karl Popper. He became widely known as an implacable critic of positivism. Let me present in the list form the main provisions of Popper's theory.

1. Knowledge of the world is carried out in the form of scientific theories: "Theories are nets cast to catch what we call 'the world': to rationalize, to explain, and to master it. We endeavor to make the mesh ever finer and finer. "[1, 37-38].

2. «The central problem of epistemology has always been and still is the problem of the growth of knowledge. » [1, XIX]

3. «The method I have in mind is that of stating one's problem clearly and of examining its various proposed solutions critically. » [1, XIX].

4. «Scientific theories are universal statements. » [1, 37]

5. Due to the variability of scientific theories, they are not verifiable. Nevertheless, theories can be falsified. Falsifiability is the main sign of the scientific nature of the theory. [1, 18]

6. The method of induction is untenable because the transition from singular to universal statements is impossible in principle. [1, 4-7]

7. Scientific discoveries are made thanks to creative intuition. [1, 8]

8. The nature of science is expressed by the deductive method. According to it, there is a scientific explanation. [1, 9f]

Let me introduce the theory of Popper in the schematic view: intuition – the hypothetical universal laws – deduction – predicted facts – experiment – empirical facts – falsification (the facts refute the hypothesis) – intuition – a new hypothesis. Of course Popper's theory deserves critical consideration.

The argument about the insolvency of experimental facts as the basis of science

According to Popper, the facts are theoretically loaded, because they are explained by universal laws. The one, who, based on the facts, deduces the laws, makes a mistake of the logical circle. Popper did not take into account the recurrence of concepts. The facts are predicted by the deductive laws; the laws are justified by induction and abduction. Popper, legitimate refuting fundamentalism of facts, himself absolutized laws. This is also a form of fundamentalism. The absolutizing of one or more scientific concepts leads to some form of scientific fundamentalism.

The argument about the impossibility of inductive derivation of universal hypothetical laws

This argument is formulated carelessly. The universal laws cannot be inferred neither by induction nor by abduction. Nevertheless, it should be borne in mind that the very idea of them, shared by Popper, is inappropriate. The negation of the derivation of inductive laws contradicts the data of science. Popper's denial of induction as a scientific method is his gross epistemological error. His argument was that it was impossible to derive universal laws by induction. Consequently, it is scientifically ineffective. However, as already noted, the true purpose of induction is to derive not universal but inductive laws and principles. Scientific laws are not universal, they can only be correlated with those phenomena that have already been studied.

The argument about the intuitive comprehension of the hypothetical universal laws

The appeal of rationalists to intuition is somewhat fun. Popper, denying the legitimacy of induction and abduction, but trying to say something about the origin of the laws, turns to intuition. Popper shares the trouble of all representatives of rationalism, namely, their inability to explain the origin of the foundations of the theory. In our view, the situation is as follows. At the induction stage, inductive laws and principles are derived. They are then usually adjusted through some abstraction and idealization operations and used as deductive principles and laws. In doing so, researchers implement the continuity of scientific knowledge. There is nothing intuitive about the operation in question. There is no need to refer to the phenomenon of intuition if scientists in the process of abduction introduce some innovations. The fact is that they are introduced purposefully, namely, to give the theory more consistency and efficiency. Thus, the researchers at all stages of intratheoretical transduction implement some of the mechanisms of conceptual transitions. Intuition is an instant action, which, at least in the case under consideration, is excluded.

The argument on the impossibility of verification of universal laws and the need for their falsification

As already mentioned, the concept of a universal law is untenable. The question of verification and falsification should be raised in relation to deductive laws and principles. The correct formulation of the question shows the relevance of both concepts, verification, and falsification. If deductive predictions are confirmed by experiment and induction, then there is verification. Otherwise, there is a falsification. Verification and falsification should be considered part of a cycle of intratheoretical transduction. It can be shown that in this context, it is necessary to use the potential of intertheoretical transduction.

The argument of falsifiability as a criterion of scientific theory

Scientific theories differ from their non-scientific relatives by conceptual elaboration. The scientific test is not limited to falsifiability.

The argument for ensuring the growth of scientific knowledge and the rejection of obsolete theories

Popper quite rightly focused his attention on the phenomenon of the growth of scientific knowledge and the need for criticism of theories. However, we note that he did not consider this phenomenon in the composition of full-fledged intertheoretical transduction (see par. 1.6).

The argument about the need to highlight the problems and their critical discussion

It is legitimate. However, it is also necessary to explain how problems should stand out. In this respect, Popper was quite laconic. Nevertheless, Popper managed on behalf of critical rationalism to present the actual version of the philosophy of science. Unfortunately, he failed to incorporate achievements of neopositivism into his theory. In the end, he only exacerbated, rather than overcome, the confrontation between rationalism and empiricism. It should be noted his polemical gift. As a result, Popper managed to present neopositivism in a rather unsightly form. In the camp of neo-positivists, there was no person who could adequately respond to his criticism.

It should also be noted that the philosophical potential of a researcher is largely determined by his competence in certain branches of science. Popper often turned to the socio-political philosophy [2]. However, he rarely considered the conceptual device of the social sciences. His analysis of the problems of quantum mechanics [3] was also not recognized as exemplary.

As a final conclusion, I will take the liberty of asserting that Popper, denying induction and abduction, substantially distorted the nature of intratheoretical transduction. At the same time, his ideas about the growth of scientific knowledge significantly contributed to the development of the theory of intertheoretical transduction.

References

1. Popper, K.R. (1959) The Logic of Scientific Discovery. London and New York: Routledge.
2. Popper, K.R. (1945) The Open Society and Its Enemies. Vol. I. The Spell of Plato. London: Routledge.
3. Popper, K.R. (1982) Quantum Theory and the Schism in Physics. London: Hutchinson.

2.6. Analytical philosophy of science: W. Quine

Modern philosophy of science is represented by many thousands of books. Most of the authors are representatives of analytical philosophy. Unfortunately, it is rare to express an analytical version of the philosophy of science in a holistic form. Perhaps, the most distinctly it is presented by American Willard van Orman Quine. It is believed that the quintessence of the analytical philosophy of science was also expressed by neopositivists. It is not so. Outstanding neopositivists came from Europe; they have never been able to express the American pragmatic tradition adequately. In this regard, the construction of Quine is of particular interest. To begin with, I list the main provisions of Quine's philosophy of science.

1. The principle of naturalism. «Philosophically I am bound to Dewey by the naturalism that dominated his last three decades. With Dewey I hold that knowledge, mind, and meaning are part of the same world that they have to do with, and that they are to be studied in the same empirical spirit that animates natural science. There is no place for a prior philosophy. » [4, 26]

2. The principle of behaviorism. The indisputable grounds of philosophizing are a) selective behavior of people in different situations, b) language as an intersubjective social system of signs, and c) excitation of sensory receptors of a person [4, 26-27; 4, 75].

3. The principle of ontological relativity: ontology determined by the theory [4, 59].

4. The inscrutability of reference [4, 30-34].

5. The conception of translation indeterminacy: there might be different ways of translating a language which is equally correct; there is no reality regarding which a particular translation can be considered correct [2, ch. 2].

6. Duhem-Quine's thesis: since the hypothesis of h is part of a larger whole and is therefore always associated with additional assumptions of A, then h can be preserved by compensating modifications in the rest of the theory [1, 42-43].

7. Refutation of analytical proposals [1, 20].

The principle of naturalism, in my opinion, deserves approval. Philosophy must grow inside the science, not to prescribing it the contents. The same view was held by the teacher of Quine R. Carnap. Quine qualified this view as naturalism. In our opinion, a review of the state of modern science shows that in all theories conceptual transduction is made. Quine makes emphasis on empirical data; he is close to the representatives of empiricism.

The principle of behaviorism is highly questionable. Speaking on his behalf, Quine clearly did not take into account the lessons of the use of the behavioral doctrine in various sciences, particularly in psychology and economics. From Quine, we could expect refined the wording of the maxim of pragmatism, but that did not happen. As a behaviorist, he denied the inner world of man, limited to indicating only the excitation of sensory receptors.

The principle of ontological relativity seems quite natural. What exactly exists is determined only based on theory. Something similar long before Quine claimed I. Kant.

Quite unusual is the thesis about the indeterminacy of translation. Quine notes that the theory is not testified by reality. If the theory were a description of reality, then it could be argued that it was accurate or inaccurate. Since the theory itself testifies to reality, there is no unshakable basis for translation. In the first approximation, Quine, of course, is right. However, it does not take into account the different status of theories. Any translation should be guided by the most developed theory. The translation may be more or less relevant. Quine does not agree with this statement. In my opinion, the history of science indicates that the theories being compared in the cycles of conceptual transduction are never completely equivalent.

Extremely great importance attaches Quine to the integrity of separate theory and any scientific knowledge. The founders of analytical philosophy B. Russell and L. Wittgenstein adhered to the concept of logical atomism: separate proposals correspond to atomic facts. Quine contrasts logical holism to logical atomism: the nature of the facts is not evidenced by separate sentences, and the theory of the whole, in the end, science as a whole.

A reference would be possible if the facts could be presented in separate sentences and the knowledge would be unchanged. Nevertheless, there is neither the first nor the second. Therefore, the reference is not possible.

The hypothesis should also be evaluated from the standpoint of the whole, not as an atomic conception. If desired, the hypothesis can be saved at the expense of some modifications of other parts of the theory. The distinction between analytical (non-empirical) and synthetic (empirical) sentences, recognized in neopositivism, is untenable because again the integrity of scientific knowledge is not taken into account. Analytical and synthetic sentences are understood as atomic phenomena. In reality, they represent the same whole.

Quine seeks to take into account in his conclusions both the variability of knowledge and its integrity. Such a program of development of the philosophy of science is commendable. But unfortunately for Quine, he implements the specified program only in the most general terms without discussing the nature of the different theories and of intertheoretical relations. In this regard, it seems to me that the theory of conceptual transduction compares favorably with the holism of Quine. This theory takes into account the variability of knowledge and its integrity in much more detail than does Quine and, especially important, through a network of conceptual transitions. In light of the theory of conceptual transduction, some of Quine's conclusions seem largely unfounded.

Reference is possible. When physicists discover new elementary particles, they carry out a reference. There is no reason to claim that particles do not exist because they can be judged only based on all scientific knowledge. About them really should be judged 'wide', only in this case, their nature would get comprehensive coverage. This fact does not force to deny the existence of these particles, but only clarifies their nature.

There are as many types of scientific proposals as there are branches of science. From this point of view, it is clear that at least three types of sentences should be distinguished, namely, the proposals of natural, axiological and formal sciences. An attempt to reduce these proposals to the analytic and synthetic sentences is untenable. Quine's main idea was to substantiate the involvement of formal branches of science, primarily mathematics and logic, in the experiments. This line of thought deserves attention. Are the sentences of the formal sciences involved in the experiments? Peculiar, not like the proposals of natural and axiological sciences. Formal sciences summarize the proposals of all four stages of intratheoretical transduction, predictions, factualization, data processing, updating the initial deductive principles. Formal science proposals are formal, but not synthetic or analytic. They bear the seal of deductive, adductive, inductive and adductive propositions

Let me now consider the fate of the hypotheses. Contrary to Quine not every hypothesis can be preserved by modifying other parts of the theory. The fact is that hypothesis and theory are one and the same thing. The hypothesis does not have any environment. Intratheoretical transduction cannot be arbitrary; it develops according to the rules of deduction, adduction, induction, and abduction. In this regard, hypotheses take on certain involuntary content. Here is example from physics. In relativistic mechanics, it was believed that interactions could be transmitted at an infinitely high speed. This hypothesis had to be abandoned, it could not be compensated.

Quine summed up the peculiar results of his work in the book From Stimulus to Science. [5] The basic idea of this book seems to be doubtful. The fact is that there is nothing that precedes science. Developed science is preceded by less developed. If it is claimed that something precedes any science at all, then it is impossible to give any clear description of its nature. Ontological relativity precludes any factors supposedly previous theories. This circumstance passed by the attention of Mach, Carnap, and Quine. On the way to science, Mach proceeded from sensations, Carnap from elementary experiences, Quine from global stimuli. In my opinion, Quine was somewhat uncritical about his behaviorist attitudes.

Thus, W. Quine developed a kind of analytical philosophy of science, focusing on the variability and integrity of knowledge. However, his conclusions are sometimes lacking solidity and detail.

References

1. Quine, W.V.O. (1951) Two dogmas of empiricism. Philosophical Review 60, 20-43.
2. Quine, W.V.O. (1960) Word and Object. Cambridge, MA: MIT. Press.
3. Quine, W.V.O. (1969) Epistemology naturalized. In Ontological Relativity and Other Essays by W.V. Quine. New York: Columbia University Press, 69-91.
4. Quine, W.V.O. (1969) Ontological relativity. In Ontological Relativity and Other Essays by W.V. Quine. New York: Columbia University Press, 26-68.

5. Quine, W.V.O. (1995) From Stimulus to Science. Cambridge, MA: Harvard University Press.

2.7. Trends in the development of analytical philosophy

Analytical philosophy, the same age as the XX century, is connected with science much closer ties than any other philosophical direction, in particular, phenomenology and hermeneutics. However, there is no reason to believe that the union of analytical philosophy and science consists exclusively of achievements. They are, but the ups are replaced by falls. Interest in the philosophy of science, of course, involves a detailed acquaintance with the potential of analytical philosophy. Does it keep its vitality? The extent to which the fate of analytic philosophy allows us to judge the prospects of the philosophy of science in general? In connection with these issues, consider the main milestones in the development of analytical philosophy. Science, language and pragmatism are the three cornerstones of analytical philosophy. In this regard, we consider three trends in the development of analytical philosophy. Let us start with the scientific, which resulted in three quite clearly distinguishable stages.

The first stage of the scientific trend in the development of analytical philosophy was the logicism of G. Frege and B. Russell, supplemented by the logical and philosophical project of early L. Wittgenstein [6]. Frege and Russell were first-class logicians and mathematicians. Their main efforts were focused on the creation of mathematical logic and the reduction of mathematics to it. Unlike them, Wittgenstein was not strong in the sciences, but he had the talent of an integrator of philosophical ideas. He managed to present the project of early analytical philosophy in a holistic form. Its core was logical atomism: the language describes the facts, and each sentence corresponds to quite certain facts. Language represents all the advantages of the theory. The mentality can be excluded. Wittgenstein summarized his review as follows. «The right method of philosophy would be this. To say nothing except what can be said, i.e. the propositions of natural science, i.e. something that has nothing to do with philosophy: and then always, when someone else wished to say something metaphysical, to demonstrate to him that he had given no meaning to certain signs in his propositions. This method would be unsatisfying to the other—he would not have the feeling that we were teaching him philosophy—but it would be the only strictly correct method. » [6, 189] This quote should hardly be regarded as any consistent description of the scientific method. The first philosopher-analysts are not able to give detailed characteristics of scientific theory and the correlation of its methods, in particular, deduction and induction. The first stage of development of analytical philosophy mainly refers to the first three decades of the XX century.

The second stage in the development of the scientific trend of analytical philosophy was the neo-positivism of M. Schlick, R. Carnap, and H. Reichenbach. It began in the 1920s and was very popular until the 1960s; neopositivists extended the influence of analytic philosophy, primarily on the physics. Neopositivists paid considerable attention to the method of induction (see par. 2.5), as well as deduction [6]. However, they experienced significant difficulties in characterizing the nature of scientific theories.

The third stage in the development of the scientific trend of analytical philosophy was the logical holism of W. Quine, considered in the previous paragraph. As an integrator of philosophical ideas, W. Quine was equal to Wittgenstein. Unfortunately, it is difficult to name at least one more equally talented integrator among philosophers-analysts. In this regard, let us recall T. Kuhn, the author of one of the analytical concepts of scientific revolutions [4]. His name is extremely popular among American philosophers. However, he failed to create a holistic conception of analytical philosophy.

Let me now turn to the linguistic trend in the development of analytical philosophy. In the first decades of the development of analytical philosophy, primary attention was paid to logical and mathematical languages. Later there were researchers who turned to the study of ordinary language. Significant studies have been carried out by J. Moore, L. Wittgenstein, J.L. Austin, P. Strawson, M. Dummett, and J. Searle. We are talking about one more stage in the development of analytical philosophy; let us call it the fourth. Its actuality was the highest in 1950-1965. Especially significant was the theory of speech acts of J.L. Austin, according to which every sentence has illocutionary and perlocutionary force, in accordance with which it may be more or less successful [1].

It is significant that almost all representatives of the theory of language consciously turned to the potential of American pragmatism. They are not always quoting his classics, C. S. Peirce, W. James, and J. Dewey, nonetheless, they are under their influence. As a result, European authors easily recognized in the representatives of the philosophy of ordinary language, if not explicit, then hidden pragmatists. Unfortunately, the representatives of the theory of ordinary language do not consider itself bound to use scientific data. This led to a significant weakening of the orientation of analytical philosophy to science. Its alliance with science was not strengthened, but rather weakened.

It is time to turn to the pragmatic trend in the development of analytical philosophy. As you know, the classics of American pragmatism are C.S. Peirce, W. James, and J. Dewey. A thorough understanding of the maxims of pragmatism involves an appeal to the axiological sciences with their valuable content. However, strictly speaking, none of the classics of pragmatism managed to dispose of this potential. Peirce was a first-class logician, but logic is not an axiological science. James was an expert only one science, psychology, but in his years, it was in its infancy. J. Dewey was drawn to pedagogy and political science. Nevertheless, their scientific status left much to be desired. He was unable to create a consistent philosophy of pedagogy and philosophy of political science. Without a philosophy of axiological sciences, it is impossible to reveal the true potential of pragmatism. In this regard, it is not surprising that pragmatism, for all its exemplary significance for English-speaking authors, was largely superseded by behaviorism, which does not recognize value issues. Behaviorists were, in particular, L. Wittgenstein and W. Quine. Nowadays, in American science, behaviorism is universally supplanted by pragmatism. Nevertheless, it is difficult to find a work in which pragmatism is represented in all its scientific significance. Why? Because the union of analytical philosophy with axiological sciences leaves much to be desired.

It is very difficult to realize interdisciplinary connections of philosophy with various branches of science. The age-old development of analytical philosophy shows that its representatives have significantly deviated from this union to the side. For analytic philosophy, the anti-scientific syndrome is characteristic to a much lesser extent than, for example, for hermeneutics and poststructuralism. Partial refusal of the union with science could not pass without a trace for analytical philosophy. Where it happened, eclecticism and metaphysics flourished.

According to A. Preston, analytical philosophy, since 1960, entered the stage of its eclectic development [5]. However, he does not explain the reason for this development. Michael Beaney concluded that throughout more than a century of history, analytical philosophy has demonstrated the unity of style and method. The style of analytical philosophy consisted in an emphasis on argumentation, clarity, and rigor. The method was understood, first of all, as a logical analysis of the language. The long-term continuity in the development of unity of method and style quite precisely represents the nature of analytical philosophy. [2, 20] It is difficult to disagree with this conclusion. Nevertheless, I would like to draw the attention of readers to another traditional feature of analytical philosophy. In my view, analytical philosophy has demonstrated remarkable examples of its unity with science. However, the focus on the philosophe of science coexists in it with the antiscientific syndrome. With the dominance of the latter analytical philosophy cannot avoid the eclecticism. However, this way of evolution can be avoided. In this case, it is necessary to develop a broad program of research philosophe of science, taking into account the achievements of analytical philosophy.

References

1. Austin, J.L. (1962) How to Do Things with Words. Oxford: Oxford University Press.
2. Beaney, M.A. (2013) What is analytic philosophy? In Beaney, M. (Ed.) The Oxford Handbook of the History of Analytic Philosophy. Oxford: Oxford University Press, 3-29.

3. Hempel, C.G. (1965) Aspects of Scientific Explanation and other Essays in the Philosophy of Science. New York: Free Press.

4. Kuhn, T. (1962) Structure of scientific revolutions. Chicago: University of Chicago Press.

5. Preston, A. (2020) Analytic philosophy. Internet Encyclopedia of Philosophy. Available at: https://www.iep.utm.edu/analytic/

6. Wittgenstein, L. (1922) Tratatus Logico-Philosophicus. Transl. by C.K.Ogden. London: Routledge and Kegan Paul, 153-189.

2.8. The main trend of modern German philosophy: Husserl – Heidegger – Gadamer

In the previous paragraph, the main trends in the development of analytical philosophy were considered. Its main competitor is continental philosophy, primarily modern German and French philosophy. Within the framework of this book, it is not possible to examine in detail the main vicissitudes of the development of continental philosophy. However, it would be wrong to leave it unattended. I decided to present its main ideas in two sections, on German and French philosophy, respectively.

Edmund Husserl (1859-1938) - the founder of a special philosophical direction, phenomenology (from Greek φαινόμενο «that which appears» and λόγος «study»). He was dissatisfied with the state of affairs in both philosophy and science. Nowhere take fully into account the world-life (in German – Lebenswelt). According to Husserl, philosophy, and science, in any case, cannot tolerate even the slightest dose of decreasing the life world of people. It is in this regard that he developed the main provisions of the phenomenological method [7]. According to Husserl's idea, the phenomenological method provides science with a solid foundation. Science is not separated from a man but acts as his most vital work. If the essence of science appears, in particular, because of the falsely understood processes of abstractions, idealizations, and mechanizations, then the crisis of humankind develops [6, 5-6, 48f]. The basic idea of Husserl consisted in the fact that abstractions and idealizations need to be an organic result of the synthesis of experiences. It is necessary to explain how theoretical concepts are developed. Husserl had to explain the ascent of man on the steps of the most refined conceptual formations. In this regard, he gave priority to a number of concepts.

Phenomenological reduction consists in the fact that consciousness is chosen as the only source of genuine philosophizing. Everything else, in particular, the objects and original theories accepted without justification, should be put in brackets. This is the meaning of the reception of epoché. In ancient Greek philosophy, epoché was understood as refraining from judgment. Husserl proposes to refrain from making judgments until the relevant philosophical work is carried out. Otherwise not to avoid unclear statements.

Eidetic reduction consists in reducing the facts to complexes of perceptions. Without this, it is impossible to clarify the nature of elementary concepts.

Intentionality is the orientation of consciousness for the subject of study, so it is the consciousness of something. In all acts of phenomenological work, the chosen object of consciousness remains the same. The task is to clarify its meaning. The idea of intentionality was introduced into philosophy by Husserl's teacher F. Brentano. However, unlike his student, he never associated it with the stages of phenomenological work [8]. Strictly speaking, in contrast to Brentano, Husserl used the concept of phenomenological intentionality. Intentionality permeates the whole process of phenomenological work, which Husserl called noesis. The result of noesis is noema, the meaning of the object to be learned. The philosophical tradition is to identify noema with the object itself. But Husserl's noema is not the object itself, and it's meaning. Noema is achieved only after a number of noetic acts. What they represent — that is the question. Husserl's approach involves a wide range of experiences, ending with an intuitive discretion of the concepts.

Phenomenological variation is necessary to avoid the inclusion in the eidos of those fortuities with which the studied object is associated. To present the subject in the fullest possible form, try to take into account the entire history of its perceptions, connect the imagination and even fantasy. Variation acts as a synthesis of experiences. Eidetic intuition is possible only after its preparation by acts of variation.

Life-world is another important concept of Husserl's phenomenology. He relies on it in his final work [6]. This time Husserl sought to outline for his philosophy the broadest possible perspective. There are trivial versions of the life-world. In this case, it is understood as the world of human experiences, not meaningful in accordance with the phenomenological method. Husserl's life-world is the meaning of all human activity, including everyday life and science.

The truth acts as a complete correspondence of the thought with the data. People achieve this correspondence by intuitive acts.

Husserl thought the phenomenological method is a universal scientific method of cognition. He himself tried to implement it in relation to mathematics, but without much success.

Proponents of the phenomenological method particularly appreciate two of its features. First, a special emphasis on the mentality, which because of the language revolution in the philosophy of the XX century fell out of favor with many researchers. Secondly, the desire to ensure the purity of scientific research by avoiding any theoretical prerequisites. However, is it possible in the cognitive process really completely distracted from theories? A positive answer to this question contradicts the principle of a theoretical representation of any statement and any form of mentality. In my opinion, phenomenologists, considering the beginning of philosophizing not as theories, but experiences make a serious methodological error.

Let me now turn to the phenomenological interpretation of the process of generating concepts. Do concepts arise from a synthesis of experiences? The meaning of what is happening in the mind is the conceptual transduction. It is the meaning of both mentality and language. However, this very meaning in the field of consciousness really acts as a synthesis of mental acts. Of course, these acts themselves should not be understood simply, i.e. only as perceptions of some objects. They include all the concepts of the theory as far as they are presented in a mental form. In the case of ignoring these forms, science appears to be largely lifeless. Such science should be avoided. It in full accordance with the warning Husserl can really lead to harmful consequences for people.

The main drawback of the phenomenological project is that it is not possible to find an alternative to methods of intratheoretical transduction. Without them, all the arguments about science are largely devalued. Thus, the phenomenological method is not without its weaknesses. The opposite view is that «phenomenology as a holistic approach ... rightfully defends the role of subjectivity in the constitution of objectivity and recognizes the inherent limitations of all forms of naturalism, objectivism and scientism. » [9, 72]

Martin Heidegger (1889-1976) was Husserl's assistant, he succeeded him in the post of head of the Department of philosophy in 1926. Husserl was not sent to not honorable retirement. The new German authorities punished Husserl for his Jewish origins. In the last years of his life, he spent, in fact, in philosophical exile. Heidegger, who had ten-month affair with Nazis as rector of the University of Freiburg, did not show due to compassion to his teacher. Regardless of this fact, he was an original thinker.

Heidegger shared Husserl's belief that philosophy should deal with the fullness of the human world. He even declared himself a supporter of the phenomenological method but interpreted it significantly differently than Husserl. «Phenomenology of being-there is *hermeneutics*—in the original meaning of the word, according to which it designates the work of interpretation. » [5, 44]

Let us present his project [3-5] in the most laconic expression. Genuine philosophizing Heidegger is metaphysics of existence.

- Being born, the human is just a presence somewhere and in some time, Being-there. It is time for him to be-in-the-world.
- In this regard, the question of existence becomes a priority.

- Being is ex-istentia. Ex means that the human has left the previous state. Ex-istence is the exit (ex) of a person from himself to meet other people, as well as things.
- People assert their existence not through consciousness, but through language. «But man is not only a living creature who possesses language along with other capacities. Rather, language is the house of Being in which man ek-sists by dwelling, in that he belongs to the truth of Being, guarding it. ». [4, 213]
- Things in their being either open towards each other or, conversely, avoid contacts. In the first case, there is truth, in the second – mystery.
- Existence is provided by questioning; acting, people ask questions and get answers to them.
- A person has preserved his authenticity thanks to creativity, poiesis. [compare 3, 34].
- Existence is the answer in the present to the call of the future.
- Existence is the realization of time ending with the death of the man. It is precisely the meaning of life, from which people are not given to evade.

As you can see, Heidegger reduces thought, and with it the consciousness of man as a whole, to existence and language. Everything that is attributed to man, namely the various definitions of consciousness, such as feelings and experiences, ultimately, should be explained as his response to being. Husserl carried out phenomenological reduction; Heidegger replaced it with existential reduction. Heidegger seems to be a very mysterious philosopher precisely because he rethought the content of all the philosophical categories, so familiar to modern man.

Two aspects are particularly characteristic of Heidegger's metaphysics. This is, firstly, the hoisting in the place of the mentality of the language. In English-speaking philosophy of this revolution was carried out by B. Russell, J. Moore and especially L. Wittgenstein. In German philosophy a similar feat, and on a fundamentally new basis, made Heidegger. Secondly, being itself acts as speech acts of questioning and answers to them. Heidegger linking human nature with speech acts was an innovator. In the English-speaking world, theory of speech acts will be developed only in the 1930s (L. Wittgenstein) and the 1950s (J.L. Austin).

It is time for a critical assessment of Heidegger's attempts to debunk science and contrast it with fundamental ontology. He, singling out three ways of understanding the world - the ancient Greek episteme, medieval doctrine, and modern science – strongly preferred the first of them. Science is rejected insofar as it explores objects instead of the truth of being. «Science is one way, and indeed one decisive way, in which all that is presents itself to us. » [3,156]. «Scientific representation, for its part, can never decide whether nature, through its objectness, does not rather withdraw itself than bring to appearance the hidden fullness of its coming to presence. Science cannot even ask this question, for, as theory, it has already undertaken to deal with the area circumscribed by objectness. » [3, 174]

As a metaphysicist Heidegger failed to understand the essence of science. He does not have a friendly criticism of science. He denies science, but without good reason. Heidegger said very little about science where much more should have been said. It should be particularly noted that he overlooked the conceptual nature of scientific knowledge. Above all, he appreciated the power of not scientific concepts, but accurate, mainly of poetic words. Nevertheless, the essence of science is not in defining everything as objectness, as Heidegger believed, but in its conceptual nature. By the way, the power of a poetic word should also be conceptually understood.

In the context of our work, it is essential that Heidegger's views may well be incorporated into the content of science. A connoisseur of his philosophy will certainly pay special attention to the language of science. Of course, there is no need to substitute mentality with language. Essential is another circumstance: the language is not secondary to the mentality and objects. There is always some form of conceptual vitality in it. Secondly, the scientific language does not have to be presented as a mono text. Giving to language a question-answer form may well be both interesting and informative. Heidegger overlooked the conceptual merits of science. However, there is some reason for his criticism of science. Understanding of science is often realized in forms that are inadequate to its actual content. Therefore, the understanding of science deserves critical consideration

Despite the sharp criticism of modern science by Heidegger, he is usually referred to as an outstanding philosopher of the XX century. The fact is that the manner of philosophizing of Heidegger is close to many thinkers, educated by the classical works of philosophers, which were far from science and were dreaming of the development of a universal theory suitable for understanding literally all sides of reality. Secondly, undoubtedly, Heidegger was able to express some problematic aspects of human life, the difficulties associated with their understanding, the establishment of harmony with nature, with the scientific and technical progress. Third, he acted as an innovator in understanding the importance of language, its unique features, and rare potential. Fourth, and perhaps most importantly, Heidegger appeared in his works in the image of the uncompromising innovator

Like Husserl M. Heidegger failed to find an alternative to scientific methods. This is the main failure of both phenomenological and ontological project. Heidegger carried philosophy away from phenomenology to the field of hermeneutics. His student Hans-Georg Gadamer (1900-2002) completed this business.

Hermeneutics is an influential philosophical direction. A significant milestone in its development of steel research V. Dilthey. He believed that the natural sciences are guided by the processes of explanation and the humanities by the processes of understanding. To achieve understanding, we must sympathize with people, to take into account the history of their changes and to consider the relationship of the whole (of culture) and its parts (of consciousness). Largely based on the research of F. Schleiermacher, Dilthey believed that each person can understand the interlocutor better than he understands himself.

Dilthey's views [1] can be represented as follows.
- Everything that exists needs to be understood, not just the consciousness of the individual.
- Each event that is part of the whole is unique.
- The basis of understanding should be categories of experience.
- We understand another person because he is similar to us.
- Understanding the other person contains two things, interpretation, and feeling.
- Understanding is the experience with another person.
- In understanding, the hermeneutic circle is realized: the whole is understood based on its elements and the elements – based overall.

- The whole is life, which is formed through the experience of people and their communication. The spiritual life of an individual is only a part of the life of society as a whole.
- The categories used in the Humanities (significance, value, ideal, purpose) are the categories of life.
- Humanities are not dealing with causal relationships, however, we understand them.

Gadamer reinterpreted hermeneutics from the standpoint of the doctrine of being. Moreover, he did it so talented that he considered the creator of the new hermeneutics. Gadamer published his main book "Truth and Method" in 1960. The year of its publication was 1960. Gadamer's teaching has no name of its own. I propose to consider the theory of Dilthey as the hermeneutics of consciousness and the conception of Gadamer as the hermeneutics of being.

Unlike Dilthey, Gadamer does not fit hermeneutics into the context of science. Not science is the key to understanding hermeneutics, but hermeneutics is a condition for a correct understanding of science. «The hermeneutic consciousness, which must be awakened and kept awake, recognizes that in the age of science philosophy's claim of superiority has something chimerical and unreal about it. But though the will of man is more than ever intensifying its criticism of what has gone before to the point of becoming a Utopian or eschatological consciousness, the hermeneutic consciousness seeks to confront that will with something of the truth of remembrance: with what is still and ever again». [2, XXXIV]

The hermeneutics of being also deserves to be presented in a sequential manner.

Hermeneutic process of reflection is initiated by a person in a particular dialogical situation with which to cope.

- In this regard, implementing a dialectic of questions and answers. The most obvious way it is presented in the communication of people. The question is asked in a way that partly anticipates the answer.
- The real miracle is that there is a language in which things are spoken. Scientifically, this should be understood as follows. For example, physical objects do not speak, but their understanding is realized through language.
- Participants in the conversation are consistently expanding the horizon of their understanding.
- Any portion of the meaning obtained in the dialogue must be used in action. Understanding is always practical.
- Understanding is collected and condensed in words. The word is not just a sign, but anticipation and comprehension of the whole, the unity of man and the situation.
- The hermeneutic circle consists of the mutual definability of the part and the whole. The concept of purpose is not applicable to the whole, and therefore the hermeneutic it is a game, dialectics, uniting the participants of the dialogue.
- In dialogue, people reach consensus with each other.
- Who understand the whole, had learned the truth. Truth is the consent, proportionality, and harmony of a person with the whole to which he belongs.

Thus, we have two hermeneutic theories, Dilthey's and Gadamer's. However, how to evaluate their advantages and disadvantages? First, they should be considered from the perspective of conceptual transduction. Secondly, it is advisable to compare hermeneutic methods with the actual content of the sciences. It is possible that the hermeneutists did not consider it properly.

The significant drawback of both hermeneutic methods is the lack of a sufficiently clear understanding of the concepts of science, in particular, the descriptions of natural sciences and axiological values. In addition, Dilthey contrasts the two mentioned types of sciences. Gadamer believes that the hermeneutic principle is actual both for humanitarians, and representatives of natural science. In my view, there is no reason to distinguish between explanation and understanding. It is the same thing. It is correct to assert that the explanation in natural science is carried out by means of descriptions, and in axiological sciences based on value concepts.

The main drawback of the considered theories is the almost complete disregard for the methods of conceptual transduction. All attempts to find an alternative to them are ultimately unsuccessful.

According to the hermeneutists of being, the explanation is made in language, not in the mentality that they characterize in a condescending manner. Nevertheless, the mentality of man has been successfully studied in all sciences.

Despite their shortcomings, both hermeneutic methods should be recognized as relevant to the cause of scientific knowledge. It is necessary to take into account that the knowledge is carried out not only in the mind but also in the language, which acquires its reality in the dialogue game. Any theory is a constantly modified result of the dialogue of members of a scientific community.

Not all sciences use hermeneutic methods equally well. They are especially often used in psychology, pedagogy, law, sociology, i.e. in all those sciences in which communities of people implementing certain concepts are studied. In these sciences, the object of study is the dialogue of people.

It's time to take stock. I came across quite influential philosophical schools, namely, Husserl's phenomenology, Heidegger's fundamental ontology, Dilthey's hermeneutics of consciousness, and Gadamer's hermeneutics of being. All of them are similar in that their contacts with modern science are quite unproductive. All four authors seek to find an alternative acceptable to science. Ultimately, their metaphysical optimism is not justified. Its basis is the belief that science does not have to be recognized as the quintessence of modern civilization. This is a very substantial error, which will no doubt continue to stimulate the construction of metaphysical systems. Alas, man is weak he is not able to abandon metaphysics

References

1. Dilthey, W. (1989) Introduction to the Human Sciences: An Attempt to Lay a Foundation for the Study of Society and History. Detroit: Wayne State University Press.
2. Gadamer, H.-G. (1989) Truth and Method. Second, Revised Edition. Translation revised by J. Weinsheimer and D.G. Mar. London and New York: Continuum.
3. Heidegger, M. (1977) The Question Concerning Technology, and Other Essays. Translated and with an Introduction by W. Lovitt. New York and London: Garland Publishing, INC.
4. Heidegger, M. (1977) Letter on humanism. Basic Writings. Ed. by D.F. Krell. New York: Harper and Row.
5. Heidegger, M. (2008). Being and Time. Translate by J. Macquarrie and E. Robinson. New York: Harper and Row.

6. Husserl, E. (1970) The Crisis of European Sciences and Transcendental Phenomenology. Transl. by D. Carr. Evanston: Northwestern University Press.

7. Husserl, E. (1982) [1913] Ideas Pertaining to a Pure Phenomenology and to a Phenomenological Philosophy – First Book: General Introduction to a Pure Phenomenology. Transl. by F. Kersten. The Hague: Nijhoff.

8. Landgrebe, L (1963) Der Weg der Phänomenologie: Das Problem einer ursprünglichen Erfahrung. [The Path of Phenomenology: the Problem of an Original Experience]. Gütersloher: Verlagshaus Gerd Mohn. [In German].

9. Moran, D. (2018) What is the phenomenological approach? Revisiting intentional explication. Phenomenology and Mind 15, 72-90.

2.9. The main trend of modern French philosophy: Foucault – Derrida - Lyotard

I pass to the consideration of methodological developments of the French philosophers of the second half of the XX century. All of them were committed within the framework of a philosophical movement, usually qualified as poststructuralism. All poststructuralists share an interest not in structures, but in discourse. I will consider the three most famous projects of group discourse methodology. Let me start with the method of Michel Foucault (1926-1984). Foucault often called his special interest in the history archaeological. To genuine archaeology, this method is in a very indirect relationship. Its core is problematization in the historical field of various discourses.

Foucault believed that any field of knowledge, both scientific and non-scientific, functions only in the form of a group discourse with relevant historical roots. He implements a triad:

genealogy-criticism - problematization. Genealogy studies the formation of discursive practices. Criticism analyzes the processes of thinning, rearrangement and unification of discourses. Nevertheless, decisive philosophical action is problematization in the historical field. Problematization «is the ensemble of discursive and nondiscursive practices that make something enter into the play of true and false and constitute it as an object of thought (whether in the form of moral reflection, scientific knowledge, political analysis, etc). » [1, 18].

As for knowledge, it is built on the discursive thresholds of positivity – discursive formation was formed and began to transform; of epistemology– there are schemes of knowledge that are criticized and tested; of science – developed criteria of argument; of formalization – there are defined axioms and formal rules of discourse. [2, 186-187]

Let me imagine Foucault's philosophy as some systematic process. The first three provisions are principles.

- Always consider the discursive history of the issue.
- Thin out discourses; exclude from them the unacceptable to you.
- Constantly search for problems in all discourses.
- Give the discourse the character of a major historical event.
- Study the process of the emergence of various kinds of exceptions in the discourse (not all can be said, one is true, and the other is false, etc.).
- Focus not on the opposition of the true to the false, but on the historical transformations of discourse.
- Please note that the discourse is based on anonymous rules. It involves thousands of people. Not the authors produce discourse; they themselves act as the stages of dilution of discourse, its nodes.

- Discourse is not continuous; it is a set of discrete practices that intersect each other.
- Search not a core practice, and define the field of its possibilities.
- Study series, not unity; originality, not regularity; conditions for the possibility of events, not their meaning; discontinuity, not continuity; chance, not a necessity; freedom, not dependence; transformation of scattering, not fixed signs and structures; discursive games, not prohibitions.

Foucault proposed to re-evaluate science, based not on ideas and monologue, but on dispositions of pluralistic discourse. There are various thresholds of knowledge, they, once formed, harden, and then dissipate. If discourses are not problematized, they turn into dogmas. According to Foucault, the traditional image of science is outdated; it does not take into account the numerous metamorphoses that occur in discursive scientific practices. Foucault himself tried to demonstrate the effectiveness of his methodology by analyzing the history of the formation of sexual relations, medicine, psychology, law. The success of his attempts was relative, but there is no doubt that in the light of his philosophy, the traditional image of science with its emphasis on authors and ideas has lost a significant share of its appeal. Foucault, firstly, filled the historical method with new content, and secondly, gave it additional weight. Much of what was previously thought to be obvious and only right in science, as it turned out, has its own history. Like everything else in the world, scientific concepts are generated, changed, deformed, and replaced by new formations.

In the context of this book, it is important to note that with all Foucault's attention to the phenomenon of knowledge, he does not directly address the philosophy of science. He is not interested in a specific analysis of the well-established disciplines. His work does not reveal the content philosophy of medicine. However, he not without pleasure considers some questions of the formation of the medicine. Nevertheless, he does not consider it necessary to refer to the principle of the relevance of mature knowledge. He believes that it is enough to problematize historical material regardless of modern sciences. In our opinion, he is wrong. Indeed, with this approach, the concepts he creates are not included in the modern science. Foucault, in fact, does not consistently use any of the methods of conceptual transduction.

Jacques Derrida (1930-2004), the inventor of deconstruction, occupies an exceptionally prominent place in modern French philosophy. What radically new proposed by this author? According to Derrida, linguistic semiotic innovations of philosophers were not properly comprehended. The mobility of language erodes the seemingly stable dispositions of things, concepts and signs. Remain alone traces, or grams. Not accidentally, general ledger Derrida appears under the name "On grammatology" [4]. The trail indicates something. It shows not about the things, concepts and signs, and the distinctions and paradoxes. The difference of signs is noticed by all. Less attention is paid to the process of producing differences, traces.

Producing various traces, the author of the text cannot stop. The introduction of one distinction entails the following. This means that the interpretation is an aporetic one. Derrida has always worked with aporias (puzzlements), so his grams are traces of aporias. His goal is not the rejection of the paradoxes and not in overcoming them and giving them certain mobility.

The specified mobility is reported to the language by the interpreter. Deconstruction does not tolerate any finally recorded oppositions, centers, the only correct interpretations. Derrida is not satisfied with either the formula of traditional philosophy 'only this', or the formula of duality 'and this and that'. He implements the provision 'and this and that; and not this and not that' [5, 89], according to which deconstruction is carried out. It can be stated that deconstruction acts as the apotheosis of uncertainty.

After all that said about the philosophy of Derrida, it is reasonable to raise the question of the rules and techniques of deconstruction. If there are, they form a deconstructive method. Derrida himself refused the honor of being the inventor of a particular method. He avoided the imposition of the philosophy of any standards. Philosophizing is a creative process, a game. Texts are different, they are not compatible with methods. It seems to me that Derrida cannot do without tricks. He refuses method insofar as its content is traditional, not deconstructive. It is not necessary to interpret the method as a set of unshakable rules and techniques. The method also takes place when the rules vary from one text to another. Analysis of Derrida's work shows that he does not philosophize in an arbitrary manner and certainly adheres to some of the canons. We have the right to consider their combination as a deconstructive method.

According to my observations, Derrida, philosophizing, often used, in particular, such techniques [3-6,].

1. Binary oppositions (speech/letter, answer/silence, etc.) are formulated.

2. They are given the character of aporias.

3. Attempts are made to transform these aporias.

4. Morphological word analysis is carried out, in connection with which dictionary entries, translations of terms from one language to another are widely used.

5. Any rule or concept is given a reflexive character, *A* turns into a *non-A*.

6. The requirement of universal substitution is put forward: any other is any other.

7. The text is examined on his distinction from himself.

8. The text is given a conflict character.

9. Special attention is paid to marginal aspects of the text, not to explicit hierarchies, but to deviations from them.

10. There is a constant search for what is not explicitly mentioned in the text, it is apparently absent, but should be taken into account.

These ten techniques, as well as some others that are not considered by my allow you to carry out deconstruction.

Various estimates are made about Derrida's deconstructive method. It irritates many representatives of analytical philosophy. They are well aware of many of the aporia and paradoxes of science, for example, the aporia of movement of Zeno and the paradoxes of set theory. All the paradoxes need to be overcome. A specialist in logic, mathematics, or physics will never argue that one paradox needs to be replaced by another. From the point of view of the philosopher-analyst, Derrida violates the most important scientific commandment: overcome and do not multiply the paradoxes. Unlike analyst

Derrida brings every paradox to its maximum pointed shape, i.e. transforms it into an aporia.

Unfortunately, Derrida was not able to extend the project of his philosophy to science. In his own work, Derrida has not gone beyond metaphysics. If he turned to one of the sciences and showed that it is more effective not to overcome aporias, and to multiply them, it is necessary to believe he would have gained considerable authority from scientists. Derrida took the position of a critical outsider in relation to science. Genuine scientific aporias did not come to his attention.

Jean-François Lyotard (1924-1998) was another outstanding French philosopher of the 20th century. He became famous for his work «The postmodern condition» (1979). [8] He is often considered the founder of philosophical postmodernism. Lyotard's working hypothesis was that the status of knowledge changes as it enters the postmodern era, i.e. of the information society.

According to Lyotard, any knowledge is a language game in which denotative (something fixing), performativity (which are the execution of any action) and prescriptive (prescribing actions to the recipient of information) statements are correlated in a certain way.

Scientific knowledge, Lyotard believed, isolates denotative statements from performativity and prescriptive ones. The misadventure of science is that performative and prescriptive statements remain outside its competence, their legitimacy cannot be proved by scientific means. The one-sidedness of the scientific era has found its solution in the paralogy, which deviate from science In place of scientific knowledge came the diverse agonistic language games. «That is what the postmodern world is all about. Most people have lost the nostalgia for the lost narrative. It in no way follows that they are reduced to barbarity. What saves them from it is their knowledge that legitimation can only spring from their own linguistic practice and communicational interaction. » [8, 41].

After «The Postmodern Condition», Lyotard decided to present his theory in the most adequate form in another book, «The differend» (1983). Differend is «a case of conflict, between (at least) two parties, that cannot be equitably resolved for lack of a rule of judgment applicable to both arguments. One side's legitimacy does not imply the other's lack of legitimacy. » [7, xi] Differend is an insurmountable disagreement. People operate with phrases that do not relate to the referent, but to the situation, which is formed by the interrelation of phrases. Phrases can be joined to each other by different rules that form the respective regimes (narratives, descriptions, commands, questioning, explanations, beliefs) and their genres (scientific, psychoanalytic, pragmatic, ethical, dialectical, etc.). According to Lyotard, there is no reason to prefer one genre to another. When this fact is recorded then there is differend. Differend never exist in the singular, therefore, the great stories, including science, in principle, untenable.

Lyotard radically rethought the traditional rational western philosophical paradigm. All its basic concepts are replaced with some alternatives. In place of concepts are phrases, logical rules are replaced with modes of realization of language games, objects dissolve in situations, semantics is absorbed by pragmatics, truth by effectiveness, commensurability of the theories by their incommensurability, values by differend.

Let me note the weak points of Lyotard's philosophizing about the sciences, their present, and the future. First, he mistakenly believes that pragmatic knowledge is not available to science. In fact, for example, all social and technical sciences are pragmatic. Moreover, they use the concept of truth, which Lyotard wrongfully excluded from the field of pragmatic knowledge. In the axiological sciences, effective knowledge is recognized as true.

Secondly, another weakness of the position Lyotard is the absolutizing of the incommensurability. He is irritated by the search for unity in science, as well as in any other knowledge. Nevertheless, the absolutizing of incommensurability is as absurd as the absolutizing of commensurability. People are guided by certain theories. The degree of their incommensurability or comparability is revealed not by philosophical rhetoric, but by concrete scientific analysis. Lyotard does not implement this analysis.

Thus, Lyotard's philosophy lacks a sophisticated theoretical conceptualization. He regarded cognition as a situational act in which the sender and the addressee are involved. If each of them stubbornly stands on its own, a productive dialogue between them is not possible. However, contrary to Lyotard theorist is not obliged to limit himself exclusively to situational acts. Scientists are improving theories and their relationship with each other. In this connection, the unity of theory certainly makes itself felt.

Thus, all poststructuralists concentrate on the production of not identity, but the diversity of human life. In this regard, they are in a hurry to provide some kind of alternative to scientific knowledge. These alternatives include, in particular, the archeology of Foucault, the deconstruction of Derrida, and the differend of Lyotard. All three authors carefully avoid comparing their theories with the achievements of science. In this regard, it is not surprising that their conclusions lack thoroughness. It is not achieved without the use of scientific methods. For all the controversy of poststructuralism, it sets a well-known framework for understanding the differences that accompany various areas of human activity, including science. These differences need special study. In this regard, it is reasonable not to lose sight of poststructuralism.

References

1. Foucault, M. (1984) Interview with François Edwal, «Le Souci de la vérité». [«The Concern for Truth»] Magazine littéraire 207, 18-24. [In French].
2. Foucault, M. (1972) The Archeology of Knowledge and the Discourse on Language. Transl. from the French by A.M.S. Smith. New York: Pantheon Books.
3. Derrida, J. (1985) Letter to a Japanese friend. In Derrida and Difference. Ed. by D. Wood and R. Bernasconi. Evanston, IL : Northwestern University Press.
4. Derrida, J. (1974) Of Grammatology. Transl. by G. Spivak, Baltimore: The Johns Hopkins University Press.
5. Derrida, J. (1995) On the Name. Ed. by T. Dutoit. Stanford: Stanford University Press.
6. Derrida, J. (1981) Positions. Transl. by A. Bass. Chicago: University of Chicago Press.
7. Lyotard, J.-F. (1988) The Differend: Phrases in Dispute. Transl. by G.V.D. Abbeele. Minneapolis, MN: University of Minnesota Press.
8. Lyotard, J.-F. (1984) The Postmodern Condition: A Report on Knowledge. Transl. by G. Bennington and B. Massum. Foreword by F. Jameson. Minneapolis: University of Minnesota Press.

2.10. Philosophy of science, philosophy and metaphysics

The history of the development of philosophical theories, including those considered in the previous sections, makes a strange impression. Their authors are outstanding thinkers, who, of course, were at one time in the know about the latest scientific discoveries. However, their final conclusions very often prove to be incompatible with scientific evidence. I have to reveal the origins of this non-matching of philosophy and science. In my opinion, it is the result of insufficient attention to the correlation of philosophy, philosophy of science and metaphysics. As repeatedly noted earlier, the philosophy of science deals with the conceptual and methodological nature of scientific theories. Metaphysics is "[t] he philosophical discipline which contains the most fundamental concepts and principles." [7, 588] A natural question arises about the need to develop metaphysics in addition to the philosophy of science. Are not "the most fundamental concepts and principles" part of scientific theories?

The vast majority of philosophers believe that metaphysics has autonomy, it cannot be reduced to the philosophy of science. At the same time, the authors of philosophical theoretical systems from Plato and Aristotle to Gadamer and Derrida believe that they consider nothing less than "the most fundamental concepts and principles". This means that the vast majority of theories developed by philosophers are related to metaphysics. As a rule, proponents of metaphysics tend to use their achievements for the development of science. In this regard, they speak of the need to recognize the autonomy of the metaphysics of science. Stephen Mumford and Matthew Tugby define the nature of the metaphysics of science as follows.

> The metaphysical study of the aspects of reality,
> such as kindhood, lawhood, causal power, and
> causation, which impose order on the world and
> make our scientific disciplines possible (that is,
> disciplines which are able to provide predictions –
> often novel – and offer explanations for new facts
> and anomalies within their given domain), and also
> the study of the metaphysical relationship
> between the various scientific disciplines. [4, 14]

Thus, four philosophical disciplines should be involved in the field of analysis. Metaphysics of science is added to philosophy, philosophy of science and metaphysics. Of course, one must not forget science itself. In my opinion, an attempt to clarify the relationship between philosophical disciplines involves, first of all, an appeal to the nature of science. Philosophy is a derivative of science. Understanding this circumstance excludes the distinction, on the one hand, of philosophy, and, on the other hand, of the philosophy of science. It is extremely important to understand that the derivative nature of the philosophy of science lifts it above the sciences. As a result, it seems that the philosophy of science is not guided by the same methods as basic sciences. In particular, adduction as an experimental method is not characteristic of it. This erroneous opinion does not take into account that when considering the nature of the philosophy of science, one should definitely return to its origins. All methods of basic sciences in a hidden state are also present in the philosophy of science.

Let me now turn to those general principles that supposedly primarily lead to metaphysics. As it turns out in the philosophy of science, the principles are inherent in any basic, i.e. natural and axiological science. For example, physics is guided by the principle of least action, and economics by the principle of maximizing profits. These principles are different; they cannot be generalized. This circumstance indicates that it is impossible to go over to some principles that rise above the principles of basic sciences. Any affirmation of general principles that cannot be reduced to the principles of the basic sciences turns out to be a form of escape from reality. In my opinion, it is metaphysics that is traditionally understood as a discipline autonomous from science and philosophy of science. Adhering to reality philosophically it is impossible to go beyond the philosophy of science. Let me clarify what has been said with a concrete example.

A search is underway for answers to seemingly primordially metaphysical questions. What is the nature of time? Why is it one-dimensional? Can time be multidimensional? Is the time inherent in physical and social processes one the same? All these questions remain unanswered until the researcher addresses the nature of the basic sciences. From physics, in particular, from quantum field theory, the researcher learns what the nature of physical time is. From molecular biology, he learns the nature of biological time.

It should be noted that in his scientific search, the scientist often poses questions that cannot be answered. There are different questions. In some cases, their content can be included in the chain of conceptual transduction. In this case, they receive quite definite answers. If the content of the question cannot be included in the chains of conceptual transduction, then the answer to it is also impossible. The degree of validity of the questions varies within certain limits. The Higgs boson hypothesis expressed in 1964 was confirmed only in 2013. Scientists exclude unfounded questions from their activities. However, it is they who make up the content of metaphysics. Thus, only sciences are valid, including the philosophy of science, but not philosophy and metaphysics. Philosophy appeared here along with metaphysics insofar as it shares its fate.

Supporters of metaphysics, as a rule, try to substantiate the actuality of metaphysics and metaphysics of science by the history of the development of philosophical knowledge. [2-7] They say, an attempt by Rudolf Carnap [1] to refute metaphysics failed. Allegedly, criticism of logical positivism with its emphasis on empirical research has led to the rehabilitation of metaphysics. According to Julia F. Göhner and Markus Schrenk, «Science and Metaphysics of Science have different but complementary approaches to reality: the scientist's work in this respect is predominantly empirical and consists in finding instantiations – describing particular causal interactions, listing things which are disposed in certain ways, pinning down particular laws of nature, and so on—while the metaphysician's focus is on understanding and clarifying general concepts or the corresponding phenomena (like *causation*, *disposition*, and *law of nature*). » [3, sec 3] Cláudia Ribeiro believes «what is considered as reliable by empirical evidence and the very nature of that evidence, as well as the questions and answers that science deems acceptable, depends on metaphysical assumptions. Science's empirical content cannot simply be separated from its theoretical and metaphysical content. » [5, 2]

Contrary to the above quotations, modern scientific knowledge in no way comes down to its empirical content. In cycles of intratheoretical transduction, empirical content is included in the content of the theory. This circumstance was misunderstood by logical positivists. Correction of their error did not rehabilitate metaphysics. Moreover, it just showed the insolvency of metaphysics. Metaphysics as a complex of unfounded questions is unproductive. It is outside of science and philosophy of science.

The foregoing is directly related to the status of those philosophical trends that were discussed in the previous sections of this chapter. All of them belong to the field of philosophy, i.e. to such prototypes of the philosophy of science, which are saturated with numerous metaphysical connotations. There are fewer of them in analytical than in continental philosophy. Nevertheless, analytical philosophy is also marked by a distinct seal of metaphysics. The actual conclusion follows from this. In order to understand the true content of philosophical systems, one should compare it with the achievements of the philosophy of science. The metaphysical content of philosophical trends should not be increased, but significantly reduced.

Another pressing issue is the pluralism of philosophical systems. How to deal with it? It is advisable to consider each question from the standpoint of the most relevant philosophical directions for it, not forgetting to critically treat their metaphysical content. The pluralism mentioned above is overcome by a critical analysis of the achievements and shortcomings of philosophical trends. This technique will be repeatedly used in the subsequent text of the book

References

1. Carnap, R. (1959) [1931] The elimination of metaphysics through logical analysis. English translation by A. Pap. In Ayer, A. (Ed.). Logical Positivism. Glencoe IL: The Free Press, 60-81.

2. Fios, F. (2016) Critics to metaphysics by modern philosophers: a discourse on human beings in reality. Humaniora 7(1), 108-115.

3. Göhner, J.F, and Schrenk, M. (2020) Metaphysics of philosophy. Internet Encyclopedia of Philosophy. Available at: https://www.iep.utm.edu/met-scie/

4. Mumford, S. and Tugby, M. (2013) What is the metaphysics of science? Metaphysics and Science. Ed. by S. Mumford and M. Tugby. Oxford: Oxford University Press, 3–26

5. Ribeiro, C. (2015) Unjustified criticism of metaphysics. Revue de la société de philosophie des sciences 2(1), 3-13

6. Schrenk, M. (2017) Metaphysics of Science: A Systematic and Historical Introduction. London: Routledge.

7. Simons, P. and Cameron, R.P. (2009) A short glossary of metaphysics. The Routledge Companion to Metaphysics. Ed. by R.L. Poidevin, P. Simons, A. McGonigal, and R.P. Cameron. London and New York: Routledge, 221-224.

Chapter 3. The nature of linguistics

3.1. Linguistics and philosophy of linguistics

Traditionally, it is believed that linguistics is a branch of science, the subject of which is an ordinary language, for example, English, Russian or Chinese. [4, 199; 8] In light of the theory of conceptual transduction, this interpretation is not correct. The fact is that the linguistic representation of the theory with all its specificity conceptually coincides, in particular, with the mental and object representation. This means that in principle it is impossible to distinguish the conceptual content of the language and, for example, mentality. Branches of science never deal with just one representation of the theory. Otherwise, the number of branches of science would be uncountable.

To understand the nature of linguistics, first, it is necessary to take into account its formal status.   Like philosophy, logic, and mathematics, linguistics is necessary for all branches of science, because it expresses some similar features. As has been noted before, such branches of science are formal. Secondly, since linguistics is a formal branch of science, it is reasonable to compare it with other formal branches of science. It is obvious that linguistics focuses on such concepts that express exactly its specificity. Linguistics operates with parts of speech (nouns, verbs, adjectives, adverbs, prepositions, unions, etc.), with sentence members (subjects, predicates, additions, etc.), with parts of words (roots, prefixes, suffixes, endings), and with sentences and their combinations. To put it not exactly, but briefly, we can say that the main concepts of linguistics are morphemes (the smallest grammatical units in a language) and syntagmas (the elementary consistent segments within a text)

The basic laws of linguistics are expressed in grammar. The main ones of them It is accepted to assume as principles. These are, for example, suggestions about the order of words in a sentence, that the singular subject should be a singular predicate, that the sentence should express a complete thought. Considering the principles of formal sciences, it should always be borne in mind that they express similar features of natural and axiological sciences. This circumstance is not evident. However, it is very important in understanding the status of the principles of formal branches of science. Their true status is most evident when they are integrated into interdisciplinary relations. Suppose that the economic situation is considered. In this case, the principle of maximizing the rate of return on advanced capital becomes crucial. This means that the principles of linguistics are painted in the colors of the mentioned economic principle.

Thus, the essence of linguistics consists of its special conceptual character, which is morphic and syntagmatic. For linguistics in the degree not less than for the other sciences is characterized by the mental, the object and behavioral performance.

Of particular note is the scientific nature of linguistics. The most important milestone in its formation were the works of ancient Indian grammatist Panini (V century BC). In the following centuries, his efforts were picked up by many other authors. As a result, the scientific status of linguistics was strengthened. It should be noted that the fate of logic and mathematics is largely connected with linguistics. Their success did not overshadow the scientific status of linguistics, but only contributed to the identification of its specificity. Linguistics is also closely related to philosophy.

There is no universally recognized system of classification of linguistic sciences. Often distinguish between general, special, and applied linguistics. General linguistics includes phonetics, phonology, grammar, lexicology, stylistics, syntactic, semantics, and pragmatics. Special linguistics studies individual languages and language groups, their genesis and development. Applied linguistics deals with the interdisciplinary relations of linguistics.

Linguistics like other branches of science has a philosophical companion. It is the philosophy of linguistics, the object of which is this or that linguistic theory. Since a substantial object of linguistics is language, then often the philosophy of linguistics is equated to the philosophy of language. This adequation contains the danger of forgetting the conceptual apparatus of linguistic theories, which, of course, is undesirable. With this observation in mind, let us briefly consider the history of the philosophy of linguistics.

For Plato, the name imitates the essence of the object. Christian theologians believed that the ability of language is given to man by God. J. Locke considered words as signs of objects and their mental images. In the first half of XIX century, the philosophy of language was productively developed by the German philosopher and linguist W. von Humboldt [12]. The language he understood, as the source and the result of the spiritual activity of the people. «Language embraces the whole genus more than anything else in humans. » [12, 427] Much later, in the middle of the XX century, M. Heidegger expressed the idea of language actuality. «Language is the house of Being. In its home man dwells» [5, 217].

A new milestone in the understanding of the language was discovered by F. de Saussure, founder of structural linguistics [3]. He considered language a social system of signs, having a certain structure. Saussure's approach was concretized by N. Chomsky [2], who carefully analyzed the syntactic rules of the language.

Within the framework of analytical philosophy, two directions in the analysis of language were implemented. One of them was the close coordination of language and logic. In this regard, G. Frege, B. Russell, S. Kripke, and R. Montague succeeded in particular. The second direction was expressed in special attention to the pragmatics of natural language. L. Wittgenstein said, «the meaning of a word is its use in the language». [13, sect. 43]J. Austin and J. Searle developed the theory of illocutionary and perlocutionary speech acts [1; 9].

German philosophers also turned to semiotics and pragmatics. For K. Apel and Y. Habermas language is a transcendental condition of philosophy and science.

The theme of language has become central for all poststructuralists. M. Foucault focused his attention on the practice of discourses. J. Derrida has made a priority of deconstruction of texts. J. Kristeva developed the concept of intertextuality. [6, 66] Following J.-F. Lyotard the poststructuralists began to study the agonistics of language games.

Significant works in the field of philosophy of linguistics realized Russian researchers, in particular, N. S. Troubetzkoy, the inventor of linguistic structuralism [11], A.F. Losev, who developed a symbolic interpretation of the nature of language [7], as well as Y.S. Stepanov, who considered the relationship of linguistic syntactic, semantics and pragmatics [10]. Thus, philosophers have given the subject of language extraordinary sharpness. They greatly contributed to the development of linguistic theories. Nevertheless, philosophers did not take into account the nature of these theories enough. In addition, as already noted, it is incorrectly to absolutize language, forgetting that there is also a world of mentality and, finally, of material objects. Language is just one, far from the only representation of theory.

References

1. Austin, J.L. (2005) [1962] How to Do Things With Words. Second ed. Cambridge, Massachusetts: Harvard University Press.
2. Chomsky, N. (1975) The Logical Structure of Linguistic Theory. New York and London: Plenum Press.
3. De Saussure, F. (2006) Writings in General Linguistics. Transl. by C. Sanders and M. Pires. New York: Oxford University Press.
4. Halliday, M.A.K. (2003) On Language and Linguistics. Ed. by J.J. Webster. London and New York: Continuum.
5. Heidegger, M. (1978) Letter on humanism. In Krell, D.F. (Ed.). Basic Writings. London: Routledge, 213-265.
6. Kristeva, J. (1980) Desire in Language: A Semiotic Approach to Literature and Art. Ed. by L.S. Roudiez. Transl. by T. Gora *et al.* New York: Columbia University Press.
7. Losev, A.F. (1990) Filosofiya imeni. [Philosophy of the name]. Moskva: MGU, 1990. [In Russian].
8. Sapir, E. (1929) The status of linguistics as a science. *Language 5(4), 207-214.*
9. Searle, J. (1969) Speech Acts. Cambridge: Cambridge University Press.
10. Stepanov, Y.S., Yazyk i metod. K sovremennoy filosofii yazyka. [Language and method. To the modern philosophy

of language. Moskva: Yazyki russkoy kul'tury, 1998. [In Russian].

11. Trubetskoy, N.S., Osnovy fonologii. [Fundamentals of phonology]. Moskva; Prosveshcheniye, 1960. [In Russian].

12. Von Humboldt, W. (1839) Über die Kawi-Sprache auf der Insel Java. [About the Kawi language on the island of Java.] Berlin: F. Dümmler. [In German].

13. Wittgenstein, L. (1963) Philosophical Investigations. Transl. by G.E.M. Anscombe. Oxford: Basil Blackwell.

3.2. The nature of scientific and non-scientific languages

Many authors seek to give a concise description of the nature of language. Vladimir V. Bibikhin believes language is - "primary, the most natural and public representation of the world" [1, 505]. He explains that is talking about a symbolic language, i.e. language, which operates with signs. According to Vladimir N. Kostyuk, "language is a system of signs possessing, either directly or in mutual communication with each other with values different from those characters. Language is a system of easily perceived signs that can have complex meanings. This is a characteristic feature of the language, due to which language can be: 1) a means of expression, 2) a means of communication, 3) part of social organization and culture; 4) an implicit "image of the world" [2, 507].

As a rule, language is understood only as a system of signs. In all its definitions, language is considered relative to what it represents. In this case, the language is indeed a system of signs. However, in a similar position mentality also is a system of signs. However, it should also be borne in mind that language can be considered on its own. In this capacity, it is no longer a system of signs. Language does not necessarily have to be perceived as a secondary system to the primary system, which is most often considered a set of objects.

In my view, the definition of language should be extracted from science. This means that it is necessary to be guided by the principle of theoretical representation. The definition of language should fix it place in theory. In this case, it is easy to notice that language is characteristic of any theory. Moreover, invariably it is nothing but the communication level of theory. It is significant that neither the mentality nor a set of objects does not have a communication function. Of particular note is that language, as is commonly believed, is not merely a means of communication. He is this communication itself, in possibility or reality. Mentality closed in the skull of people, is alien to communication; it does not have a common value for people. Another thing is language – it embodies the communication of people.

Any theory, and at all levels, is a management concept. Consequently, the language is the management of concepts, but of course, in a specific shell, in particular, of speech or writing. Language is a system of concepts presented in such a form that is accessible to all people. The two most important forms of language representation are speech and writing.

It is extremely important to understand that language is one of the representations of the theory. It certainly correlates in a known way to the other two basic forms of the theory, namely, mentality and objectiveness. In relation to them, language is neither a primary nor a secondary phenomenon. Depending on the specific situation, the language may be in the first or second place. If, for example, language is an expression of mentality, it is secondary to it. If mentality acts as the internalization of language, it is secondary to it.

So far, I have attributed the phenomenon of language to all theories. However, it is clear that in linguistics language is in a special position. Indeed, it is not by chance that linguistics is often characterized as a science of language. In linguistics, the language representation of the theory is absolutized. This is done in order to pay special attention to the language.

Linguistics is relevant to all sciences. It occurs due to the isolation abstraction, the morphe-syntagmatic content of science is separated from it. This is done, however, with the obligation, after a certain period of the autonomous development of the language, to return it to the theories.

Thus, language is one of the representations of the theory, it is communication level, implemented in the form of speech and writing. If desired, you can specify the forms of speech and writing, such as words, sentences, and texts.

Looking at the sciences, of course, we have to distinguish the languages used in them from all other languages. This distinction makes it difficult to understand the exceptional diversity of non-scientific languages. A language always acts as a certain organized set of phonemes, morphemes, and lexemes. This alone clearly demonstrates the theoretical nature of the language. The language sphere in the process of its development was divided into numerous components, each of which has a theoretical character. There is no language beyond theories. What is the status of the theory; such is the status of its language, as well as mentality, objectness, and activity. Language, regardless of its degree of development, is one of the types of conceptual life of people. Thus, the nature of language is determined by the content of the theory. This means that the language is theoretically relative. This leads to another conclusion, namely, just as science is the key to understanding non-science, so scientific languages provide access to an adequate understanding of all other languages.

As already noted, any scientific language is an integral part of the relevant scientific theory, whether it is a mathematical, physical or economic concept. Languages of all Sciences are specific, from logic to law, as well as linguistics. By the way, the language of linguistics is a special scientific language, different in its content from the language, for example, psychology.

In any scientific language, it is easy to find parts of speech and writing representing variables, objects, and their features, mental images, names and predicates, actions, laws and, finally, principles. The management of these linguistic concepts is carried out through intratheoretical and intertheoretical conceptual transduction. Those who have learned scientific theory have also understood the nature of the corresponding scientific language.

It should be noted that the scientific language is not limited to a short line of terms. Not only multi-volume scientific works, but also scientific articles contain many language concepts. However, not all of them get a proper understanding.

Non-scientific languages, obviously, are arranged in comparison with their scientific relatives less presentable, for the most part, they should be referred to common sense, which is sufficient for many, but not all, purposes. Common sense is not able to present in a refined form all the solidity of the scientific language, but in a certain way, it is its pre-leak. Any language, including children, can be built into the series of theories, within which it receives its most comprehensive explanation. What exactly children say and understand will be explained by linguists, teachers, and psychologists, guided by developed scientific languages.

The possibility of a scientific explanation of undeveloped languages does not contradict either the short chains of arguments used by common sense or the abundance of terms. Ultimately, common sense, as well as scientific reason, uses the methods of conceptual transduction. If the child tells the mother:" I want to eat", it is guided by a principle.

The biggest difficulty in understanding non-scientific languages is that they, in particular, everyday languages, are not a well-ordered whole, but a whimsical conglomerate of theories of local significance, which, being initiated by people in various specific situations, unstable, they often arise as spontaneously as they disappear. The same person, even if his education is of dubious nature, speculate on political, economic, philosophical and many other topics, each time constructing new theories from the thesaurus available to him. N. Chomsky, as is known, attracted the attention of scientists to the formulation of sentences. However, the sentence does not make sense outside of theories. The essence of linguistic activity is the formation of theories. In addition, this activity assumes management of the corresponding concepts, each of which gets sense not differently, as in some context.

When you transfer terms from one language to another, their meaning must be appropriately transformed. This fact was well understood by the founders of analytic philosophy G. Frege and B. Russell. They, being adherents of logicism, tried to develop uniform, namely, a logical framework for various, including natural, languages. This ambitious program could not be successful. The language of logic is not universal. The language of physics, biology or sociology cannot be reduced to the language of logic.

The non-universality of the language of logic was realized by those researchers who turned, without fear of shouts from logicians, to the study of ordinary language. This, in particular, late L. Wittgenstein, J.L. Austin, J. Searle, P. Strawson. L. Wittgenstein laid the foundations of pragmatic linguistics. Austin and Searle developed the concept of speech acts, which can be equally successfully applied in the understanding of both scientific and non-scientific languages. A very original position in the dispute about the relevance of studying ordinary language took P. Strawson. He suggested returning to descriptive metaphysics [3]. In his efforts, it is not difficult to consider the desire to create a universal theory of language on behalf of metaphysics. In this regard, he rejected both pragmatic linguistics and the principle of maturity of actual knowledge, according to which scientific language is the key to non-scientific language. In our view, the prosecution of P. Strawson in the lack of proper selectivity in its theory of language is quite legitimate.

The question of selectivity in the space of languages seems to be difficult to overcome in the understanding of everyday languages. The number of words in the most developed languages varies in different estimates from 200,000 to 1,000,000. However, already 10,000 words is considered a very solid vocabulary of a person with an average education. Five hundred words is enough for everyday life. It seems that the words of everyday language because of their abundance cannot be comprehended according to the criteria of scientific theories. In our view, this view is erroneous, largely due to the lack of evaluation of the institute of science. When understanding everyday language, it is necessary to learn at least several important circumstances.

First, the core of any everyday language is made up of the most frequently used (attractor) words, which inevitably arise in the communication of people with each other. The mechanism of their appearance is synergetic. Secondly, it is necessary to take into account that both scientific and everyday languages are formed by means of speech and text acts. In other words, big is made up of small. Any language acts as a multiplication of speech and text acts. Each such act is a realization of conceptual transduction: it is conceived, implemented, its results are evaluated in order to implement a new act from a new position. Third, a successful linguistic activity does not exclude its improvement. Fourth, there is no reason to believe that this improvement is not able to reach the level of scientific knowledge. Fifth, it is necessary to take into account that a person constantly switches from one conceptual framework to another. This pluralism of theoretical frameworks gets its maximum development in science.

Thus, scientific and non-scientific languages are not separated by a chasm; they are interconnected with each other. Scientific languages are the key to understanding non-scientific languages. In this regard, it is difficult to overestimate the importance of linguistics.

References

1. Bibikhin, V.V. (2001) Yazyk [Language]. In Novaya filosofskaya entsiklopediya, v 4 t. [New Philosophical Encyclopedia, in 4 volumes]. Moskva: Mysl', Vol. 4, 505–507. [In Rusian].

2. Kostyuk, V.N. (2001) Yazyk [Language]. In Novaya filosofskaya entsiklopediya, v 4 t. [New Philosophical Encyclopedia, in 4 volumes]. Moskva: Mysl', Vol. 4, 507–510. [In Rusian].
3. Strawson, P.F. (1959) Individuals. London: Methuen.

3.3. On semiotics, externalism, essentialism and emergentism

When considering the nature of linguistics often turn to semiotics. Semiotics – science of signs, classics of which are C.S. Peirce and F. de Saussure. Since the times of Aristotle and the stoics, the concept of the sign has attracted the attention of many researchers. In this regard, Leibniz expressed quite clearly: «all human reasoning uses certain signs or characters. » [3, vol. VII, 204] C.S. Peirce by his own testimony from 12-13 years sought to create the first science that would open access to all other Sciences [8, 85-86]. According to C.S. Peirce, this science is semiotics. Noting the innovation of C.S. Peirce, it should be borne in mind his close attention to the concept of 'relation'. It is not by chance that he became the creator of the logic of relations. It seems that the underlining of the primacy of relationship is what caused C.S. Peirce to semiotics. A sign is always some kind of relation. There is a whole heap of so-called obvious sign definitions. All of them are built according to the scheme of medieval scholastics; "Aliquid stat pro aliquo": something stands instead of another. If A stands for or represents, carries information about B, it is the sign of B; B is the value (denotation, designator, object, referent or extensional) of A.

C. S. Peirce, like Hegel, sought to express the stage of thinking in the strictest form. In this regard, he used the concepts of, secondness and thirdnees. [7, paragraphs 545-558] Firstness is quality of feeling, for example ideas. Secondness is reaction, relation, for example facts. Thirdnees is representation, mediation, for example laws and principles. Firstness is reference to abstractions, to grammar. Secondness is reference to relations, to logic. Thirdnees is reference to interpretation, to pure rhetoric.

After the death of C. S. Peirce, Charles Morris popularized the system of Peirce's categories very successfully. He called grammar – syntactic, logic – semantics, and rhetoric – pragmatics. The process of functioning of signs he called semiosis. Syntactic, semantics and pragmatics are studied by the ratio of signs to one another, to their objects and to the interpreters [5].

The trinity of semiotics is not as obvious an action as it seems at first glance. Indeed, let us consider it from the standpoint of conceptual transduction. Initially, the theory stands as something undifferentiated in its representation. It is this idea that they try to understand by means of syntactic. Nevertheless, the trouble is that it is considered something very poor conceptually. In fact, on the contrary, it embodies all the richness of the theory.

Having singled out mental, language and object representations of the theory it is possible to consider that each of them testifies to two others. This circumstance determines the semantics understood as the correspondence of language to objects.

How is pragmatics achieved? By stating the concepts of axiological sciences as values. In this case, we are not talking about any representation of the theory. In addition, pragmatics in any form is not typical for the natural sciences. In addition, it should be borne in mind that pragmatics should not be understood in the context of American pragmatism, on behalf of which Peirce and Morris spoke. Thus, the idea of unity of syntactic, semantics and pragmatics is extremely doubtful. It is, in fact, not consistent with the status of modern science.

Special attention should also be paid to the symbol as central concept of the semiotics of C. S. Peirce. For him, the symbol is a concept. Unlike many other authors, especially art critics, he does not oppose the symbol to the concept. Taking into account their position, let us turn to the work of T.S. Todorov. He analyzed various theories of symbolism. Summarizing his efforts, it can be stated that the symbol is an indirect, generalized meaning (including a law or rule), represented by the wealth of the special, particular [12]. The piquancy of the situation is that any concept expresses the richness of the special. In our opinion, the widespread campaign of symbolists against concepts is meaningless. Concepts should not be replaced by symbols.

The trouble with semiotics is that it does not properly take into account the nature of scientific theories. That is why the semiotic image of linguistics is not entirely satisfactory. The same applies to the characterization of language through the concepts of externalism, essentialism, and emergentism.

Externalism, essentialism, and emergentism are three research programs popular in the American philosophy of linguistics. In the volume review of three authors [9], they are given Central attention. It seems that they express the quintessence of the philosophy of linguistics. In our view, this opinion should be questioned. Let me turn to essentialism.

Its origins lead to Plato and Aristotle. Aristotle considered things as the unity of matter and form (essence). Translated into Latin, Augustine of Hippo called essence by essentia. The term "essentialism" was introduced into the philosophy by P. Duhem in 1916 [10, 591]. In literal reading, it means philosophy, which declares the essence as its central concept. Essence manifests itself in phenomena. In the philosophy of the twentieth century, essentialism was criticized heavily, especially on the part of existentialists K. Jaspers and J.-P. Sartre. On the place of the essence, they put existence. It is significant that analytical philosophers led by B. Russell also opposed essentialism. The language they correlated with facts, not with essence. The essence was also rejected by American behaviorists and pragmatists. Even surprising that some American linguists revive essentialism, calling its father Chomsky [9].

Noam Chomsky is a mentalist, who appreciates the deduction process but not an essentialist. He rejects the mystique of the mental sphere. It is not right to consider everyone who insists on the relevance of mentality is an essentialist. Strictly speaking, an essentialist is only one who incorporates the concept of essence into deduction itself. Generative linguistics Chomsky has no concept of essence.

As for externalism, it correlates with internalism. One of the first explications of internal and external relations gave J. Moore in 1919 [4]. The controversial position was to prioritize either things over relations (internalism) or relations over things (externalism). Classics of early analytical philosophy B. Russell and L. Wittgenstein as founders of logical atomism became defenders of ontological internalism. Unlike externalists, they, especially L. Wittgenstein, regarded language as an autonomous entity, independent of consciousness. The same position is typical for L. Bloomfield, the founder of descriptive linguistics. He is an internalist in ontological terms, but an externalist in the epistemological sense. The language he, as a rule, considered as an autonomous entity.

It is time to turn to emergentism. This branch of linguistics receives a variety of interpretations [11]. According To W. O'Grady's explanation, the program of emergentism in linguistics consists of explaining the origin of language based on psychophysiological and social components [6]. There is a widespread belief that the opposite of emergentism is reductionism. Suppose that we consider things, which belong to three levels, A, B and C, and the average of them is level B. If B is reduced to A, then there is reductionism. If it sublimates to C, then there is emergentism. If the emphasis is on autonomy B, it is legitimate to talk about autopoiesis.

Programs of both reductionism and emergentism face hardly surmountable difficulties. Indeed, the phenomena of different types are different theories. There is a certain connection between the theories, but each of them, keeping its own independence, is not reducible to the other. For example, biological theory cannot be reduced to physics or sociology. The same applies to linguistics, which in principle is not reducible to any other branch of science.

Without resorting to reductionism and emergentism, one can consider various representations of linguistics itself, in particular, mental, object, activity, and language. Within the framework of linguistics, language is present in two qualities, namely, first, as an object of study, and secondly, as a phenomenon that opposes objects. All representations of a linguistic theory are interconnected, but they appear within the same concept. Conceptually, they do not differ from each other. There are certain transitions between the representations of linguistic theory, but they do not have a reductionist or emergent character.

Therefore, we believe that the concepts of essentialism, externalism and emergentism testify to unsteady philosophical positions of their authors and supporters. Epistemologically they are clearly weaker than the theory of conceptual transduction.

References

1. Gettier, E. (1963) Is justified true belief knowledge? Analysis 23(6), 121-123.
2. Kornblith, H. (Ed.). (2001) Epistemology: Internalism and Externalism. Malden, MA: Blackwell.
3. Leibnitz, G.W. (1875–1890) Die Philosophischen Schriften von Gottfried Wilhelm Leibniz. Ed. by C.I. Gerhardt. Berlin: Weidman. [In German].
4. Moore, G.E. (1993) External and internal relations. In Moore, G.E. Selected Writings. London: Routledge, 106–133.
5. Morris, Ch.W. (1938) Foundations of the theory of signs. International encyclopedia of unified science, vol. 1, no. 2. Chicago: The University of Chicago Press.
6. O'Grady, W. (2008) Emergentism. In Hogan P. (Ed.). The Cambridge Encyclopedia of the Language Science. Cambridge: Cambridge University Press, 274–276.
7. Peirce, C. S. (1960) Collected Papers of Charles Sanders Peirce. Ed. by C. Hartshorne and P. Weiss. Principles of philosophy and Elements of logic (Vol. 1). Cambredge, MA: Harvard University Press.
8. Peirce, C. S. (1977) Semiotics and Significs. Ed. by C. Hardwick. Bloomington I.N.: Indiana University Press.
9. Scholz, B.C., Pelletier, F.J., and Pullum, G.K. (2016) Philosophy of linguistics. The Stanford Encyclopedia of Philosophy. Available at:

https://plato.stanford.edu/archives/win2016/entries/ling uistics/

10. Schwemmer, O. (2005) Essentialismus [Essentialism]. In Mittelstraß, J. (Ed.). Enzyklopädie Philosophie und Wissenschaftstheorie [Encyclopaedia of Philosophy and Philosophy of Science]. Stuttgart, Weimer: J.B. Metzler, vol. 1, 591–592. [In German].

11. Stephan, A. (1999) Emergenz: von der Unvorhersagbarkeit zur Selbstorganisation [Emergence: from unpredictability to self-organization]. Dresden, München: Dresden University Press. [In German].

12. Todorov, T. (1982) Theories of the Symbol. Transl. by C. Porter. Ithaca: Cornell University Press.

3.4. The linguistic turn in philosophy, discourse and games

Man is guided by various representations of theories. Each of them, including the language, attracts special attention. In many cases, it is advisable to refer to the linguistic representation of the theory. Awareness of this circumstance led to the so-called linguistic turn in philosophy. The linguistic turn in recognition of the priority of language over mentality [13]. Until the XX century, the language was considered an expression of consciousness. The mentality of is primary - language is secondary. Difficulties, with which philosophers met, brought them to the idea to prefer the language to mentality. The linguistic turn was embodied in both analytical philosophy and hermeneutics. Gottlob Frege and Bertrand Russell saw in a clear formulation of the language of mathematics and logic a way to overcome the paradoxes characteristic of them. Ludwig Wittgenstein stated, "All philosophy is a «critique of language" [17, 19]. Language has the same form as facts. The most complete description is a set of true elementary sentences. This is Russell-Wittgenstein's program of linguistic atomism.

Gustav Bergmann introduced the concept of linguistic turn into the philosophy of linguistics. In an article first published in 1952, he noted, "recently, there has been a linguistic turn in philosophy. At least, this is true in the main and by general agreement corresponds to what happened in the field of philosophical activity in the English-speaking countries for one two generations" [4, 106].

The linguistic turn was connected with the great hopes of philosophers who, rejecting the transcendental oriented schematics of Kant passed to a fundamentally new philosophical paradigm. In fact, it was about the linguistic relativity of ontology. All knowledge of the objects was recognized as being contained in the language. It was at this point that a hardly noticeable mistake was made. Knowledge about objects is not in language but in theory. Language, like objects themselves, is a representation of theory. In fact, the theory was replaced by language. This is a serious scientific mistake.

In continental philosophy, the linguistic trend was most clearly presented by Martin Heidegger, the founder of fundamental ontology, who relied on the hermeneutic tradition. The language «has its roots in the existential constitution of Dasein's disclosedness. The existential-ontological foundation of language is discourse or talk. » [10, 203] Heidegger believed that his understanding of language would allow him to represent the fullness of life without arbitrariness that is characteristic of the subjective world.

Representatives of first French structuralism and then poststructuralism did not remain aloof from the linguistic turn.

The structuralists, in particular, Roland Barthes, emphasized the semantic dimension of semiotics. [3] The poststructuralists, in particular, Jean-François Lyotard abandoned this dimension in favor of pragmatics. In this regard, they in contrast to reality brought to the fore the concept of language games. Again, preference was given not to mentality, but to language. Participants of the games should influence each other. It is possible in the language, but not in mentality.

Thus, in the first third of the XX century in the most relevant philosophical systems mentality was firmly pushed into the shadows of the language. A precedent was created that could not pass without a trace for linguistics. It is known for a restructuring of linguistics became inevitable. Moreover, it really happened, and professional philosophers, in particular, L. Wittgenstein, M. Heidegger, J. Austin, N. Chomsky, and J. Searle took an active part in it.

In the most distinct form, the special significance of the language is manifested in the dialogue. Dialogue and discourse are forms of implementation of language activities, the participants of which are two or more people. "Dialogue "is a word of Greek, and" discourse" is of Latin origin. Both of them mean conversation through words. Nowadays, in the scientific and other literature discourse is increasingly understood as a developed form of dialogue, taking into account the specific contexts of speech, and the laws of its construction. According to many linguists, the dialogue dominates the monologue. In this regard, M. M. Bakhtin noted, "I hear voices and dialogical relations between them in everything" [2, 372]. Language, not consciousness is dialogical. [2, 366].

Dialogue has since ancient times attracted the attention of philosophers. Widely known dialectical dialogues of Socrates, so masterfully presented in the works of Plato, the medieval scholastic dialogue described by Pierre Abelard, philosophy of dialogue of Martin Buber [1; 5]. Great difficulties began when trying to express the natural features of the dialogue. It is significant that until the second half of the XX century, logicians successfully mastered only a monologue, but not a dialogue. In the future, their successes in the logical development of the dialogue were relative.

As for the concept of "discourse", its boom began in the 1960s. Poststructuralists, abandoning the concept of "structure", replaced it with the concept of "discourse" [7], which in their interpretation allowed not only to pay tribute to the originality of each person but also to present it in the context of language practice. Hermeneutists preferred the concept of "discourse" because of another reason: they survived fascism, it was necessary to find a critical theory that does not allow its revival. This objective is consistent with not any, but only simultaneously critical and mature dialogue, uniting people in their opposition to every totalitarianism. Such a dialogue they called discourse.

Turning to the concept of discourse, philosophers had to determine their attitude to the sciences, including linguistics. It is not without surprise that the authors of the linguistic turn in philosophy treated linguistics rather aloof. They obviously wanted to do without it. Their attitude towards other Sciences was also quite strange. Poststructuralists openly avoided science. Foucault replaced the scientific approach with the archaeological one, the core of which was the immersion of knowledge in the historical context. Although he did not need history as a science. Science itself was one of the thresholds of knowledge, and not the most interesting. Lyotard turned to science even to a lesser extent than Foucault did. He was a thorough connoisseur of only one discipline, namely, aesthetics, which perceived by him, not as a science.

Critical hermeneutists, whose iconic figure is J. Habermas, as inventors of discursive ethics seek to take into account the achievements of logic, sociology and political science. But it never comes to a detailed analysis of their laws. They understand discourse as the reasoned acceptance and rejection of certain arguments. However, the mechanism of this argumentation does not get a bright expression.

Of course, the concept of discourse attracted the attention of not only philosophers but also professional linguists. An early reference to the topic of discourse is the work of Z. Harris [9]. Only in the 1970-s discourse has gained numerous supporters [7; 11; 12; 14; 15; 19]. Let me give below typical arguments of linguists about discourse.

R.-A. de Beaugrande and W.U. Dressler distinguish seven features and three rules of textuality and discursiveness, respectively [6, 3]. These are the following features: 1) the connectedness of the parts of the proposal, 2) the consistency of the proposals, 3) their intentionality, i.e. deliberately and consciously transmitted meaning, 4) acceptability for listeners, 5) informativity, 6) situational conceptuality, 7) intertextuality, i.e., roll call with other texts. The three rules are efficiency, effectiveness, and adequacy.

According to T. van Dijk, the main content of the discourse is expressed by its macrostructure, which is built according to the rules of reducing irrelevant information, generalizations and combining propositions into a single whole [16, 42]. In the framework of the general organizational principles are implemented, in particular, strategies such as: summarizing, giving examples, attracting the attention of the listener, concessions, repetition, contrast, soften, shift, evasion, avoidance of some the wordings [16, 294-300].

In my opinion, the researchers of discursive analysis have achieved great success; in particular, the allocation of discourses styles and genres is relevant. However, both philosophers and linguists do not sufficiently describe in detail the conceptual side of discourse, which acts as conceptual transduction. Without reference to its questions, the understanding of the patterns of discourse is superficial. The content of styles and genres of discourse, various winning strategies depends on some fundamental conceptual dynamics. The conceptual basis of any discourse is seen in the following.

First, each participant of the discourse implements conceptual transduction in his own way. Secondly, as a listener, he considers the conceptual constructions of his interlocutor as symbols of his own discourse. This just means that he really understands the interlocutor. In other words, each participant of the discourse makes a translation from one language to another. This circumstance determines the unity of participants of the discourses. Thirdly, another important condition for the continuation of the discourse is that each of its participants pursues certain goals. If it turns out that the interlocutor does not contribute to their achievement, the discourse is doomed to decay. Fourthly, no participant in the discourse is able to lose his or her own originality. Fifth, this means, that there is a wide range of consensus and disagreements. They accompany each other. Hermeneutists, as a rule, tend to produce consensus, and poststructuralists – disagreements. In fact, they actualize one side of the discourse, ignoring the other. In the sixth, the correct assessment of discourse involves the use of the principle of the relevance of the most developed, i.e. scientific, knowledge.

Contrary to poststructuralists, the diversity of types of discourse does not negate the relevance of the institute of science. Another thing is that science itself needs pluralization. Contrary to hermeneutists, their philosophy does not provide the very possibility of discourse. That is why the estranged attitude of hermeneutists to sciences is untenable. Linguists have another problem. They are lacking metaanalysis. In our view, therefore, they do not pay enough attention to intratheoretical conceptual transduction, as well as intertheoretical and interdisciplinary relations.

The most complex discourses are language games. A language game is a concept of late L. Wittgenstein, who tried to express the creative nature of language communications that do not obey the established rules. Looking at the games on the board, in the cards, with the ball, L. Wittgenstein emphasized that many common features of language games are preserved, some disappear, and others appear. There is some similarity between the language games, which Wittgenstein called family resemblance [18, para 67].

L. Wittgenstein with his outstanding logical preparation had obvious difficulties in understanding of mechanisms of functioning of various ordinary languages. He saw a way out of the predicament in the concepts of 'language game' and 'family resemblance'. L. Wittgenstein's innovation was met by professional linguists not without some confusion. Why pay so much attention to deviations from traditional forms of discourse?

In my opinion, the main question of L. Wittgenstein "How exactly does the language work?" remained unanswered of linguists. Of course, L. Wittgenstein's statement that language is a game is also not an answer to this question. What exactly is a game as language creativity? What is this strange family resemblance? The correct answer to these questions seems to be as follows.

In science, any linguistic act is part of some theory, where the deduction is replaced sequentially by adduction, induction, and abduction. A separate act of cognition contains four stages. A linguistic act may be degenerate, but its nature remains the same, namely, four-act. According to the example of L. Wittgenstein, the master orders his student "Brick". Whether is a sentence composed of one word, the transduction act? Yes, it is. It makes sense only insofar as the master and the student set a goal: to build this wall. Initially, they recognized the need for some chain of command. The master orders - the disciple carries out. The order itself is a deductive act. Execution is an experimental phase of transduction, its efficiency is determined in induction, which receives a final evaluation through the abduction. If the student gave the master is not the brick that he needed, he will have to try again. Thus, the meaning of the sentence "Brick" cannot be defined without reference to the four stages of conceptual transduction. A linguistic act is a conceptual transduction performed by linguistic means.

What about the creative content of language games? The essence of the matter is that deduction, adduction, induction, and abduction are carried out in many ways. For example, a mathematical deductive theorem may be proved constructively or non-constructively, by pointing to the example or without it. The experiment (adduction) is also carried out in different ways. Induction and abduction are also performed in various ways. In our opinion, if L. Wittgenstein would turn to various forms of implementation of the conceptual transduction, the thesis of the game form of language activity would have acquired a specific meaning.

From the philosophical point of view, the phenomenon of family resemblance is also explained. This is the case insofar as the variations occur within the framework of the same theory. Language games are a kind of linguistic acts. The creative content of language games does not go beyond conceptual transduction. Of course, it should be remembered that as creative creatures people are free to set the rules for a wide variety of language games.

References

1. Abelard, P.A. (1979) Dialogue of a Philosopher with a Jew and a Christian. Toronto: The Pontifical Institute of Mediaeval Studies Publications.
2. Bakhtin, M.M. (1979) Estetika slovesnogo tvorchestva [Aesthetics of verbal creativity]. Moskva: Iskusstvo. [In Russian].
3. Barthes, R. (1975) An introduction to the structural analysis of narrative. Transl. by L. Duisit. New Literary History 6(2), 237-272.
4. Bergmann, G. (1954) Two types of linguistic philosophy. In Bergmann G. The Metaphysics of Logical Positivism. New York: Longmans Green, 106–131.
5. Buber, M. (1996) The Letters of Martin Buber: A Life of Dialogue. Ed. by N.N. Glatzer and P. Mendes-Flohr. Transl. by R. and C. Winston and H. Zohn. Syracuse, New York: Syracuse University Press.

6. De Beaugrande, R-A. und Dressler W.U. (1981) Einführung in die Textlinguistik [Introduction to Text Linguistics]. Tübingen: Niemeyer. [In German].

7. Foucault, M. (1972) The Archeology of Knowledge and the Discourse on Language. Translated from the French by A.M.S. Smith. New York: Pantheon Books.

8. Habermas, J. (1995) Vorstudien und Ergänzungen zur Theorie des kommunikativen Handelns [Preliminary Studies and Supplements to the Theory of Communicative Action]. Frankfurt am Main: Suhrkamp. [In German].

9. Harris, Z. (1952) Discourse analysis. Language 28(1), 1-30.

10. Heidegger, M. (1962) Being and Time. Transl. by J. Macquarrie and E. Robinson. Oxford UK and Cambridge USA: Blackwell.

11. Hintikka, J. (1973) Logic, Language-Games and Information: Kantian Themes in the Philosophy of Logic. Oxford: Clarendon Press.

12. Johnstone, B. (2002) Discourse Analysis. Oxford: Blackwell.

13. Rorty, R. (Ed.). (1967) The Linguistic Turn: Recent Essays in Philosophical Method. Chicago and London: The University of Chicago Press.

14. Toolan, M.J. (Ed.). (2002) Critical Discourse Analysis. Critical Concepts in Linguistics. New York: Routledge.

15. Van Dijk, T. A. (2007) Discourse Studies. 5 Vol. London: Sage.

16. Van Dijk, T.A. (1989) Yazyk, poznaniye, kommunikatsiya [Language, Knowledge, Communication]. Moskva: Progress. [In Russian].

17. Wittgenstein, L. (1981) Tractatus Logico-Philosophicus, (London: Routledge & Kegan Paul, 1981), 4.0031, 19

18. Wittgenstein, L. (2009) Philosophical Investigations. Fourth edition. Ed. and transl. by P.M.S. Hacker and J. Schulte. Oxford: Wiley-Blackwell.

19. Wodak. R., Meyer, M. (Eds.). (2009) Methods of Critical Discourse Analysis. London: Sage, 2009.
20. Wooffitt, R. (2005) Conversation Analysis and Discourse Analysis. A Comparative and Critical Introduction. London: Sage.

3.5. From structural to generative linguistics

Within any science stand out researchers who have played an outstanding role as its founders. It is from the works of such researchers the era of science is growing. There is good reason to consider Swiss scholar Ferdinand de Saussure the founder of modern scientific linguistics. He developed a theory with an emphasis on the concepts of sign and structure.

It is significant that de Saussure distanced himself from orthodoxy empiricism: «Far from it being the object that antedates the viewpoint, it would seem that it is the viewpoint that creates the object; besides, nothing tells us in advance that one way of considering the fact in question takes precedence over the others or is in any way superior to them. » [6, 8] Two ways are, first, the belief that the object is primary and the theory is secondary; second, the position that the theory is primary and the object is secondary. De Saussure believes that both of these positions are consistent. In our opinion, the correct point of view is that the object has already been given in theory. No two parties between which it is necessary to do one or the other choice.

Selecting as the core concept of linguistics, a linguistic sign de Saussure in accordance with the contents of semiotics could hardly do without syntactic, semantics and pragmatics. All these three components are indeed contained in his theory.

However, his attitude to syntactic and pragmatics is more transparent than his attitude to semantics. However, the semantic point of view is also not alien to de Saussure. It is manifested in the fact of the unity of ideas and sounds.

> A linguistic system is a series of differences of sound combined with a series of differences of ideas; but the pairing of a certain number of acoustical signs with as many cuts made from the mass of thought engenders a system of values; and this system serves as the effective link between the phonic and psychological elements within each sign. Although both the signified and the signifier are purely differential and negative when considered separately, their combination is a positive fact; it is even the sole type of facts that language has, for maintaining the parallelism between the two classes of differences is the distinctive function of the linguistic institution. [6, 120-121]

In the development of syntactic, de Saussure speaks as a devout structuralist. He implements a structural approach rather than an atomic one. The whole (structure) defines its parts. «[L]anguage has neither ideas nor sounds that existed before the linguistic system, but only conceptual and phonic, differences that have issued from the system». [6,120] Logical atomists, for example, B. Russell and L. Wittgenstein, build a structure from atoms. Atomism and structuralism are two different approaches that can hardly be avoided. One way or another, the structuralist also needs to somehow link parts of the system into a single whole.

De Saussure also paid considerable attention to the social nature of the language. Language is «a product of the collective mind of linguistic groups. » [6, 5] The reference to the collective includes pragmatics in the analysis. Pragmatics dominates over syntactic. How pragmatics is related to the institution of concepts is not explained.

De Saussure also drew attention to the distinction between synchrony and diachrony. Synchrony means simultaneous and static, diachrony means changing in time and evolutionary. Unfortunately, de Saussure correlated diachrony mainly with phonetics. It is difficult to accept this decision for an obvious reason: all language has some kind of transitional form.

According to our observations, linguists, as a rule, find it difficult to distinguish the methods of linguistics. In our opinion, these are already known to the reader methods of conceptual transduction. This fact becomes obvious if we turn to the real situations in which the concepts of linguistics are used. They acquire flesh and blood in real life, not in isolation from it.

Structural linguistics of de Saussure, of course, had significant shortcomings. In my opinion, he did not explain the great mystery of linguistics, namely, the ability of a language to represent the whole world through its conceptual means, primarily the concepts of the subject and predicate. Another weakness of de Saussure's concept is the identification of a system of concepts with a system of signs. A sign to a certain extent is always secondary. Language, as noted earlier, is not necessarily secondary. I think de Saussure has rather successfully managed to represent the problem fields of linguistics. It should also be noted that Roman Jacobson and Claud Lévi-Strauss made a significant contribution to the development of structural linguistics.

Descriptive linguistics is understood as a research program for the development of structural linguistics through the inductive method and the allocation of regularities of certain features of speech. It was developed by Leonard Bloomfield [1].

Zellig Harris also made a significant contribution to its development [7]. Descriptive linguistics bears continuity with the structural linguistics of F. de Saussure, but methodologically it differs significantly from it.

The founders of descriptive linguistics paid special attention to its methodological content. In this regard, they tried to be very careful and clear. First, they decidedly took an anti-mentalist position. It is necessary to study directly linguistic forms, without reducing them to the formations, which are outside language. This requirement can be called a positivistic. Secondly, they adhered to the principles of American behaviorism of B. Skinner, spreading them to the nature of the language. Language is the behavior of people mediated by their speech. Thirdly, descriptivists were adherents of empiricism and the inductive method. They were distrustful of the method of postulates. Descriptivists believed that the postulates do not grasp the variety of experimental language situations, under the pressure of which they have to change constantly. A reliable scientific basis has only distributional relationships of the characteristics of the studied speech. If they are set, then any additional postulates are no longer needed. Deduction follows induction; it is not primary, but secondary. Fourth, the descriptivists were distrustful of the institution of concepts, preferring to operate on the idea of stimuli and reactions. All their work bears the stamp of anti-conceptualism, which complements their anti-mentalism and anti-pragmatism.

The attitude of descriptive linguists to descriptions deserves attention. At first glance, the description is their main concept. It is no accident that we are talking about descriptive not any other linguistics. However, the description can be understood in different ways. If the researcher proceeds from the conceptual analysis, he does not start with the description. It is in the depth of his theory and appears only after the transition to the ontological representation. In this case, each description is by its nature a conceptual formation. Unfortunately, descriptive linguists acted in a fundamentally different manner.

The beginning of their research is not conceptual analysis but a distributive one. Distribution, as a set of all contexts in which some element occurs, is an ostensibly obvious fixed feature of the language, which is given the status of the criterion of compatibility of its units, in particular, backgrounds (individual sounds) and morphs (minimal sequence of phonemes with some value). The analysis procedure used is that the very existence of distributions is recorded, then go from atoms to some structural formations, the highest level of which, as a rule, is the sentence. Linguistic laws are understood as invariants of repetitive distributions. The meanings of words and sentences are recognized. Distributions and their invariants are crucial. In the American philosophy of linguistics, the followers of the program distributivism is called externalists. Obviously, this refers to their detachment from the mentality and pragmatic action. All distributive linguistics bears the stamp of distrust of the theory. This form of linguistic conceptions did not be a long leader in linguistics. It was forced to give way to generative linguistics of Noam Chomsky.

N. Chomsky managed to develop a linguistic direction with an emphasis on syntactics [2-5]. He noted the many difficulties encountered in structural linguistics, especially in the case of understanding the nature of syntax. Its main drawback is that it does not reveal the mechanisms of the construction of sentences, the number of which in each natural language is much larger than the number of phonemes and morphemes.

This led to the conclusion that in structural linguistics the phenomenon of language does not get a proper understanding.

Scientific maturity Chomsky fell for the period when in American science were very strong positions of empiricism and behaviorism.   Both of them were criticized by Chomsky. Behaviorists refused to analyze mentality, relying exclusively on the empirical study of human behavior. This approach did not suit Chomsky. He noticed that natural languages are successfully assimilated by children in the first years of their development. Chomsky believed that this phenomenon has to be expected that they have an innate competence for language, enclosed in the mentality. In this case, we cannot avoid the conclusion that this deep competence is responsible for syntactics. Mentality determines the actual features of the language.

Naturally, Chomsky should have also decided on the process of building proposals. This time to the place was the logical training of Chomsky, received by him at the University. Logicians, as we know, are great masters of the axiomatic method and, accordingly, deductive transitions. Based on axioms and inference rules, they then construct sentences with logical content. The main idea of Chomsky's point is that with the help of a finite set of linguistic concepts, in particular nouns and verbs, as well as grammatical rules on their combination, people can create an unlimited number of sentences. As a follower of logicism [5], he believed that the logical form expresses the true nature of language. In its original form, it refers to syntactics. That is why syntactics prevails in his linguistic theory.

In the second half of XX century, N. Chomsky became perhaps the most authoritative linguist of our time. Of course, his work was not only praised but also criticized. In this regard, he tried to make his theory as presentable as possible. An important milestone on this path was the development of a minimum program of the framework of generative linguistics [2]. The decisive innovation is that linguistic competence does not realize all its possibilities, but only those that are organically consistent with the goals pursued by the individual. It is easy to see that Chomsky explicitly tried not to focus exclusively on syntactics and organically include semantics and pragmatics in he's theory. They define the context and therefore the boundaries of theory. It is significant, in principle, N. Chomsky does not abandon his main idea of the primacy of syntactics over semantics and pragmatics. In the absence of due attention to the semantics of N. Chomsky was justly accused by J. Searle [8].

In my opinion, the main drawback of the theories of de Saussure, Bloomfield and Chomsky is that they did not pay due attention to the formal status of linguistics. Through her concepts, she highlights the similarities of all other sciences. Strictly speaking, the main focus of de Saussure and Chomsky was not on syntactics, but on the type of conceptual transduction that is characteristic of linguistics as a formal science. I think that this circumstance passed by their attention. Otherwise, they would turn to forms of representation of linguistics.

References

1. Bloomfield, L. (1933) Language. New York: Henry Holt.
2. Chomsky, N. (1955) The Minimalist Program. Cambridge, Massachusetts: MIT Press.
3. Chomsky, N. (1957) Syntactic Structures. The Hague: Mouton.

4. Chomsky, N. (1965) Aspects of the Theory of Syntax. Cambridge: The MIT Press.
5. Chomsky, N. (1975) The Logical Structure of Linguistic Theory. New York and London: Plenum Press.
6. De Saussure, F. (1959) Course in General Linguistics. Ed. by C. Bally and A. Sechehaye. Translated from the French by W. Baskin. New York: Philosophical Library.
7. Harris, Z.C. (1951) Method in Structural Linguistics. Chicago: University of Chicago Press.
8. Searle, J.R. (1972) Chomsky's revolution in linguistics. New York Review of Books 18(12), 16-24.

3.6. Pragmatic and functional linguistics

Pragmatic linguistics is a linguistic research program with a focus on pragmatics. It gives linguistics a humanistic dimension, one way or another, always associated with a certain motivation of the interlocutors as participants of the dialogue. The emergence of pragmatics as a linguistic discipline was greatly facilitated by the philosophers, especially Ludwig Wittgenstein and John Austin. As is known, Wittgenstein formulated the famous definition that the meaning of the word is its use [13, para 43]. Austin developed the concept of the illocutionary speech act, which uses the words expressing a request, order, wish, etc. [2] After Austin, it became very clear that linguistics could not do without the theory of speech acts. However, how can we move from the statement of linguistic relevance of speech acts to their theoretical understanding? The most difficult question on which, in our opinion, the unambiguous answer to the present day is not found.

Wittgenstein associated pragmatics with the meaning of the word. However, the meaning of the word is a component of semantics, not pragmatics. It should also be borne in mind that the speech act is implemented as a proposal, not as a word. Wittgenstein saw the deep layer of speech in the customs and habits according to which words are used. In the same direction was going the idea of J. Searle, who developing views of Austin, claimed, a commission of the illocutive act belongs to those forms of behavior, which are realized by rules [12, 211]. The theory should fix the rules of speech acts. We will have to come back to this thesis after additional arguments.

There is no sufficient clarity regarding the origins of pragmatics in the works of professional linguists. In our opinion, the approach to pragmatics can be seen in the concept of significance, used by F. de Saussure. Unfortunately, this concept was given exclusively syntactic significance.

An interesting approach to understanding speech acts was demonstrated by the logicians R. Montague, D. Lewis, and D. Scott. Their decisive thought is the need for a clear understanding of semantics and pragmatics. Comprehension of the speech act is considered possible only when specifying the so-called coordinates of the indices (the term Montague), or reference points (the term Scott). In this regard, Lewis proclaimed the most voluminous list coordinates of indices: 1) possible world, 2) time, 3) place, 4) the speaker, 5) a set of persons, 6) the set of concrete things, capable of being pointed at, 7) the speech segment, 8) an infinite sequence of things [11, 176].

Pragmatics is usually associated with so-called performativity statements or performatives. As explained by J. Austin, performatives unlike constatives are not true or false, but happy (successful) or unhappy (unsuccessful) [2, 59]. Successful or unsuccessful can be, for example, promises, orders, and requests. The proposal «Ivan promised to give Peter a camera» is a constative, it is true if Ivan really promised to give Peter a camera, and otherwise, it is false. The sentence «I promise to give you, Peter, a camera» is a performative. It will be successful only if I really give Peter a camera.

At first glance, it seems that performative statements are so different from each other that it is impossible to bring them under the 'common denominator'. This opinion is disputed. Speech is a kind of production, a form of performing tasks that have arisen in the process of overcoming problems. Consequently, the adjectives successful/unsuccessful and true/untrue signal the fulfillment/non-fulfillment of the tasks solved by the means of performative sentences, respectively.

Performative conditions are determined by the coordinates of the reference points. Nevertheless, what is their meaning? Performative always pursues certain goals, the motivation of which is determined by some values. The isolation of these concepts allows reaching the theoretical level of pragmatic linguistics. What promises, asks or orders someone is determined by his values. The performative will be successful only when the harmony of their values and corresponding goals is realized in the cooperation of the dialogue participants.

Ultimately, the conceptual apex of rules and standards of behavior are values. The meaning of these values is defined outside of linguistics. In its framework, we can only imply their existence. The pragmatic explanation is value-oriented. A person does not speak and does not write if he has no purpose. The goals themselves do not arise spontaneously, but because of the concretization of some basic principles. To achieve this specification people have to pass through all four stages of the conceptual transduction, namely, deduction, adduction, induction, and abduction. Supporters of pragmatic linguistics do not pay due attention to this fact. This is a consequence of the lack of understanding of the conceptual transduction

In my opinion, it's time to turn to functional linguistics. The research program for the development of linguistics with an emphasis on the concept of "function" is called functional linguistics. It, in particular, in the works of the representatives of Prague (R. Jacobson, N. Troubetzkoy) and Danish (L. Hjelmslev, V. Brøndal) linguistic school, has grown based on structuralism F. de Saussure. In view of this circumstance, it seems that functional linguistics should be considered immediately after structural linguistics. I decided to preface the discussion of functional linguistics by the analysis of pragmatic linguistics. The fact is that all functionalists, without exception, deviate significantly from structuralism, seeking to ensure the pragmatic completeness of linguistics. The peculiarity of their position is that they do it by the concept of function, which is not held in high esteem by pragmatists who prefer the concepts of value and purpose. For a pragmatist, a function without purpose is untenable. The obligations assumed by functionalists is much more modest. They do not include references to the original pragmatic principles or to the final objectives of the next cycle of knowledge. For functionalists, language is nothing more than an instrument for achieving a goal that is outside the language [10, 49; 7, 7].

One of the founders of functional linguistics Roman Jacobson identified six factors of communication (content, addressee, message, recipient, contact, code) and, accordingly, six functions (referential, emotive, poetic, conative, factual, and meta-linguistic) [9, 66-71]. The number of functions to be updated varies from one author to another, and the corresponding list is not finite but is always open to new ad hoc innovations. This is a disadvantage rather than an advantage. Any theoretical system contains a finite number of variables rather than an infinite number. If this number is not limited in any way, then it is natural to raise the question of the failure of the theory.

Functional linguistics as the direction includes a large number of theories [3], in particular, structural functionalism of Prague school, functional discourse grammar of S.C. Dik, the systemic grammar of M. Halliday, role-playing and referentially grammar of R. van Valine, the lexical functional grammar of J. Bresnan and R. Kaplan. All these authors one way or another evaluate the correlation of structure and function. There are different opinions on this subject from the very moderate position of S.C. Dik [4] to the distinct radicalism of T. Givon, who sharper than others insisting on the primacy of the function over the structure [8]. The biggest problem of functional linguistics is to find a balance between linguistic form and communicative function. Trying to develop a conceptual framework for understanding this problem, often resort to the distinction of descriptive and explanatory theory. M.S. Dreyer's article is very indicative in this respect [6]. Being critical of functional linguistics, he denies that it alone is an explanatory theory in linguistics. His sympathies are on the side of the basic linguistic theory, whose supporters, adhering to the conservative line, borrow from new theories achievement, but no flaws. [5, 6] It is understood that traditional linguistics can be continuously improved by the ways of structural linguistics while maintaining its main advantage, namely, the explanation of all phenomena by the concepts of linguistics itself.

It is time to consider the problems of functional linguistics from a philosophical point of view. This linguistics theory has found the greatest development in the works of American authors. Considering their innovations, it should be borne in mind that in the process of its scientific maturation, functional linguistics certainly fall into the field of attraction of two traditions, logicism and pragmatism. American linguists tend to seek a middle ground between them, but it turns out to be elusive. Those researchers who gravitate to logicism extol structuralism and generative grammar. Their opponents are more attracted to the pragmatic pole. They are moving towards the theory of speech acts. Functionalists avoid such a radical setup. Their pragmatism is quite moderate, but it is sufficient to cause a critical attitude on the part of logicians.

In my opinion, the common problem of all functional linguists is a misunderstanding of the essence of the scientific method, which for all its variations is the same for all sciences. This method, if we limit ourselves to the consideration of endogenous aspects of linguistic theory, are the methods of conceptual transduction: deduction, adduction, induction, and abduction. Consider, for example, the stage of deduction. It is differently understood by the generalists, structuralists and functionalists. The generalist begins with linguistic axioms; he is like N. Chomsky a constructivist. Structuralist focuses on the structure understood as the invariant unit. The functionalist, whose image we associate, first of all, with R. Jacobson, is most interested not in the original principles and not the whole, the very existence of which he recognizes reluctantly, but the importance of linguistic elements within the entire social whole. Thus, generalists, structuralists and functionalists in their understanding of linguistic deduction place accents differently. Perhaps some of the differences between them would be smoothed out if they took into account their interest in the same phenomenon, namely, linguistic deduction.

The second aspect concerns the commitment of functionalists to pragmatics, which is in fact denied by generalists. They believe that all the achievements of pragmatics can be incorporated directly into the syntactics. Syntactics is primary, pragmatics is secondary. Functionalists wrap up this attitude, putting pragmatics in the first place. In our opinion, both disputing parties are mistaken. The fact that they do not consider essentially the nature of different types of scientific theories.

In axiological theory, syntax unites values, it is an axiological event. However, these values themselves are signs of people doing certain things. Therefore, the essence of the matter is not limited to mere syntactic; we will also have to turn to ontology. Supporters of the basic linguistic theory do not consider this fact. The main trouble of generalists, structuralists, and functionalists is that they strive to develop a general theory without entering into the essence of languages belonging to different disciplines, the nature of which without reference to the philosophy of science does not get an adequate expression.

References

1. Anstey, M. P. and Mackenzie, J.L. (2005) Crucial Readings in Functional Grammar. Berlin, New York: Mouton de Gruyter.
2. Austin, J.L. (1962) How to Do Things With Words. Oxford: The Clarendon Press.
3. Bybee, J.L. (1992) A functionalist approach to grammar and its evolution. Evolution of Communication 2(2), 249-278.
4. Dik, S.C. (1997) The Theory of Functional Grammar. Berlin, New York: Mouton de Gruyter.
5. Dixon, R.M.W. (1997) The Rise and Fall of Languages. Cambridge: Cambridge University Press.

6. Dryer, M.S. (2006) Descriptive theories, explanatory theories, and basic linguistic theory. In Catching Language: Issues in Grammar Writing. Ed. by F.Ameka, A. Dench, and N. Evans. Berlin: Mouton de Gruyter, 2006, pp. 207–234.
7. Foley, W.A. and van Valin R.D.J. (1984) Functional Syntax and Universal Grammar. Cambridge: Cambridge University Press.
8. Givon, T. (1984) Syntax: A Functional-Typological Introduction. Volume 1. Amsterdam: John Benjamins.
9. Jakobson, R. (1987) Linguistics and poetics. In Jakobson, R. Language in Literature. Ed. by K. Pomorska and S. Rudy. Cambridge, Massachusetts; London: The Balknap Press of Harvard University Press, 62–94.
10. Jakobson, R. (1990) Current issues of general linguistics. In Jakobson, R. On Language. London and Cambridge, Massachusetts: Harvard University Press, 49-55.
11. Lewis, D. (1972) General semantics. In Semantics of Natural Language. Synthese Library (Monographs on Epistemology, Logic, Methodology, Philosophy of Science, Sociology of Science and of Knowledge, and on the Mathematical Methods of Social and Behavioral Sciences). Vol. 40. Ed. by D. Davidson and G. Harman. Dordrecht: Springer, 169-218.
12. Searle, J. (1965) What is a speech act? In Philosophy in America. Ed. by M. Black. London: Allen and Unwin, 221-239
13. Wittgenstein, L. (1963) Philosophical Investigations. Transl. by G.E.M. Anscombe. Oxford: Basil Blackwell.

3.7. Cognitive linguistics and linguistic league-theory

Cognitive linguistics is understood as a branch of linguistics, which is characterized by an emphasis on the representation of human conceptual activity by the language. It acquired distinct forms in the 1970s [5; 9; 10], and then received further impressive development in the works of many researchers. There were the classics of this direction, among which the most frequently called names C. Fillmore, J. Lakoff, and R. Langacker. The characteristic of cognitive linguistics, which was presented in a number of reviews [2; 4] is quite exhaustive. In the following text, I am guided by these reviews.

According to three authors [2], the two main obligations of cognitive linguistics enthusiasts are, first, the desire to create a general theory of language, and secondly, to take into account the achievements of the whole complex of sciences, which are called cognitive, in particular, of psychology, neurophysiology, computer science. Both commitments are welcome. Linguists, of course, need to combine all linguistic knowledge. Without the creation of a general theory of linguistics, this goal cannot be achieved. The desire of linguists to be transdisciplinary is also commendable. The conceptual exchange between sciences overcomes their self-isolation. This fully applies to linguistics.

The same authors believe that the main achievements of cognitive linguistics was the development of an integral view of language and thought, a new appeal to the experiment, eliminating abstract speculation, emphasis on conceptual aspects, combining structural and functional issues. It is difficult not to agree with these conclusions, but with one significant clarification. The emphasis on the conceptual content of the language was crucial. Linguistic theory is obviously a set of concepts. However, which ones?

Cognitivists have literally rebelled against categorization based on predicate calculus. In this case, the categories denoting some classes of things ("bird"," furniture") are clearly separated from each other. Each separate category denotes the class of things that have only their inherent characteristics. Cognitive scientists believe that the concept of predicates is acceptable only if it is combined with the idea of the presence of innate abilities of people represented in image schemes [5], prototypes [11], idealized cognitive models, mental spaces [3], metaphors [1], and metonyms [8].

Let me give a sample of the statements of J. Lakoff, a prominent representative of cognitive linguistics [7, 12-13].

Family resemblance: members of a category can be related, but they do not share a common property that defines a category.

Centrality. There may be more or less successful examples of this category among the members of the category.

Polysemy as categorization. The related meanings of the words form categories and enter into a relationship of family resemblance.

Generativity as a prototype phenomenon. This applies to categories that are defined by a generator element (a special member of a subcategory) and rules (or general principles such as similarity). In such cases, the generator element receives the status of a central category.

Membership gradience. At least some categories do not have clear boundaries and belonging to him is not absolute, and gradual.

Centrality gradience. The degree of centrality of members of a category (or subcategory) that clearly lie within its boundaries may vary.

Conceptual embodiment. Properties of some categories are a reflection of the essence of human biological abilities and experience of its functioning in the material and social environment. This thesis contradicts the idea that concepts exist independently of the bodily organization of thinking beings and regardless of their experience.

Functional embodiment. Some concepts are not realized intellectually at all, they are used automatically, unconsciously and without noticeable efforts, being perceived simply as part of normal human activity. The concepts used in this way have a different, more important, psychological status compared to those concepts that are necessarily understood.

Basic-level categorization. Categories are not just organized in hierarchies – from more general to more specific – but are organized in such a way that cognitively more basic categories are centered in the middle of a hierarchy from general to particular. The generalization goes up from the base level, and the specification goes down.

Basic-level primacy. The categories of the basic level from the epistemological and functional point of view are priority in relation to the following factors: perception of gestalts, the formation of images, motor skills, organization of knowledge, ease of cognitive processes (learning, recognition, memorization, etc.) and verbalization of language expressions.

Reference-point, or "metonymic," reasoning. A part of a category (member or subcategory) in some thought processes might replace the whole category.

Lakoff specifically emphasizes that the inherent mental procedure of categorization is essentially based on human experience and understanding – of the features of perception, motor activity, and culture, on the one hand, and the properties of metaphor, metonymy, and mental imagery – on the other. Human thinking depends crucially on the same factors. It should not be characterized simply in terms of manipulating abstract symbols. Of course, it is possible to artificially isolate certain aspects of human thinking and model them with formal systems of abstract symbols – this is justified to the extent that some parts of the process of human categorization correspond to classical theory. However, we are interested not just in artificially isolating part of the human ability to categorize, but also in the whole ability. As we will see, those aspects of categorization that correspond to the classical theory represent particular cases of the theory of cognitive models, the theory that allows us to also describe experimental and figurative aspects of thinking.

Turning to a critical assessment of cognitive linguistics, I note that conceptually, in my opinion, it really does not know its equal in the field of linguistics. Nevertheless, cognitive linguistics is not without its weaknesses. The fact is that its supporters, not opposing the institute of science, nevertheless, represent it in a truncated form. They connect the institute of science mainly with the manipulation of abstract objects. In this case, it is alien to emotions, culture and unusual mental images. It does not take into account that the interpretation of science as manipulation of abstractions is outdated. Scientific knowledge grows through conceptual transduction cycles, each of which, if it is composed rightly, takes into account all the features, including emotional and cultural, of specific situations. In my opinion, representatives of cognitive linguistics do not pay due attention to the essence of the scientific method.

Judging by the above texts J. Lakoff, the epistemological priority of the basic level is formed mainly by the concepts of everyday language. If this were true, the whole institution of modern science would have to be radically revised, in particular, the principle of relevance of mature knowledge would have to be replaced by the principle of priority of everyday knowledge. However, there are no sufficient grounds for such a pseudo-revolutionary step. Indeed, the growth of scientific knowledge eliminates the dictates of everyday categories. They are not the limits of this growth, first. Second, the basic categories do not cancel the essence of the scientific method, i.e., conceptual transduction, intertheoretical and inter-disciplinary crossings. Representatives of cognitive psychology to a certain extent take into account these transitions, considering, in particular, the ratio of mental spaces. Nevertheless, conceptually transduction does not get the proper expression. Thus, considering the question of the conceptualization of linguistics, representatives of cognitive linguistics deviated from scientific knowledge in the direction of everyday ideas. With this trend, it is impossible to achieve the heights of the philosophy of linguistics.

In previous sections, the most influential linguistic directions of modernity are considered. Of course, their list could be continued. Nevertheless, it is quite presentable to express the state of modern linguistics as a science. In this regard, it should be noted that structural (Ts), descriptive (Td), generative (Tg), functional (Tf), pragmatic (Tp) and cognitive (Tc) linguistics, are not separated from each other by impassable moats. They form an upward line of development of linguistics. With this in mind, the innovative (3.1) and interpretative (3.2) series of linguistic directions can be represented in the following form.

$$T_s \rightarrow T_d \rightarrow T_g \rightarrow T_f \rightarrow T_p \rightarrow T_c \qquad\qquad 3.1$$

$$T_c \Rightarrow T_p\{T_c\} \Rightarrow T_f\{T_c\} \Rightarrow T_g\{T_c\} \Rightarrow T_d\{T_c\} \Rightarrow T_s\{T_c\} 3.2$$

In innovation series 3.1, each successive direction is at least in one respect superior to its problematic predecessor. Descriptivists introduced the empirical method more clearly than structuralists did. Generativists strengthened the deductive line, which was not clearly expressed in the theories of structuralists and descriptivists. Functionalists connected to linguistics pragmatics. However, their axiological line, compared to what the pragmatists have proposed, was rather poor.

Finally, cognitivists have surpassed everyone, including pragmatists, in their commitment to thinking.

Referred achievements of linguistic theories allow you to convert an innovative series 3.1 to league-theory 3.2. Each subsequent linguistic direction is rethought from the standpoint of more developed schools, culminating in cognitive linguistics. This or that direction is not rejected but corrected. Its achievements remain in force, and the defects, which were specified in the final paragraphs of the corresponding sections, are corrected or eliminated.

Of course, linguists who are not familiar with the concept of league-theory do not use its epistemological potential to the proper extent. Criticism of a partially outdated linguistic direction often takes too sharp forms. In their self-affirmation, some authors seek to replace the entire league-theory with their own invention. They do not understand that the conceptual potential of a league-theory far exceeds that of any single theory.

Finally, a concluding remark. In my opinion, league-theory 3.2 should begin with a linguistic direction with pronounced scientific and philosophical content. Unfortunately, I do not see any possibility to associate this direction with the name of any authoritative linguist or philosopher.

References

1. Evans, V. (2004) The Structure of Time. Language, Meaning and Temporal Cognition, Amsterdam: John Benjamins.
2. Evans, V., Bergen B., and Zinken J. (2007) The cognitive linguistics enterprise: an overview. In The Cognitive Linguistics Reader. Ed. by V. Evans, B. Bergen, and J. Zinken. London: Equinox, 2–36.

3. Fauconnier, G. (1994) Mental Spaces. Cambridge: Cambridge University Press.

4. Fauconnier, G. (1999) Methods and Generalizations. In Cognitive Linguistics: Foundations, Scope and Methodology. Ed. by T. Janssen and G. Redeker. Berlin: Mouton de Gruyter, 95–128.

5. Fillmore, C. (1975) An alternative to checklist theories of meaning. Proceedings of the First Annual Meeting of the Berkeley Linguistics Society. Berkeley, CA: Berkeley Linguistics Society, 123–131.

6. Johnson, M. (1987) The Body in the Mind. The Bodily Basis of Meaning, Imagination, and Reason. Chicago: University of Chicago Press.

7. Lakoff, G. (1987) Women, Fire, and Dangerous Things. What Categories Reveal about the Mind. Chicago and London: The Chicago University Press.

8. Lakoff, G. and Johnson M. (1980) Metaphors We Live By. Chicago: University of Chicago Press.

9. Lakoff, G. and Thompson H. (1975) Introduction to cognitive grammar. Proceedings of the 1st Annual Meeting of the Berkeley Linguistics Society. Berkeley, CA: Berkeley Linguistics Society, 295–313.

10. Rosch, E. (1975) Cognitive representations of semantic categories. Journal of Experimental Psychology: General, 104(3), 192–233.

11. Rosch, E. (1977) Human categorization. In Studies in Crosslinguistic Psychology. Ed. by N. Warren. London: Academic Press, 1–49.

Chapter 4. The nature of logic

4.1. Specifics of logic, mathematics and computer science. Philosophy of logic

In the previous chapters, the conceptual content of two formal branches of science was considered, namely, first of philosophy, and then of linguistics. It is time to turn to the three other formal branches of science, logic, mathematics and computer science. These three branches of science are conceptually much closer to each other than philosophy and linguistics. Therefore, it is reasonable at this stage of the analysis to consider them together with each other.

Modern authors interpret logic most often as valid inference in its most general form [8]. Of course, logic has its own characteristics, but the investigators do not take into account to an appropriate extent the features that are inherent in other branches of science, for example, physics or Economics, as well as mathematics. Mathematics is the theory of quantities (numbers), structures, spatial relations and changes [18]. Logic does not undertake to consider the many features that are characteristic of topics that are organic to mathematics. Mathematics, in turn, does not have to consider the features of computer science, which are usually associated with the need to ensure the automation of algorithmic calculations [5]. Worthy of attention is the position of A. Tarski, who argued that logic is the name of the discipline, which analyzes the meaning of concepts common to all Sciences, and establishes General laws governing them [15, XI]. However, this definition is true not only for logic, but also for philosophy, linguistics, and mathematics and computer science. It is important to take into account the gradation of the General (formal).

To characterize the specifics of logic, the concept of logical form, developed for the first time by B. Russell, is of actual importance. In 1914, he noted that «... some kind of knowledge of logical forms, through with most people it is not explicit, is involved in all understanding of discourse. It is the business of philosophical logic to extract this knowledge from its concrete integuments, and to render it explicit and pure». [13, 53] He believed that logic is interested only in the forms (schemes) of the reasoning recorded by means of logical variables and constants, and not their content. For example, the modus ponens rule «P implies Q and P are both asserted to be true, so therefore Q must be true» is a logical form. If instead of P and Q substitute the terms of non-logical sciences, there is no logical form. For example, the statement that all metals are current conductors, copper is metal, hence copper conducts current, is not a logical form.

According to B. Russell logical form is extracted from the content, therefore, it is an abstraction. There is a complex question about the relationship of logical form and content. This question is often understood as the ratio of semantics and syntax, respectively. The logical form is understood as the embodiment of syntactics. However, syntactics can be understood in two ways, either as separated from semantics, or as its embodiment. Most modern authors prefer not to take the syntax away from semantics. In this case, the logical form acts as a syntactic version of semantics. Significant in this regard, the position of D. Davidson: «What should we ask of an adequate account of the logical form of a sentence? Above all, I would say, such an account must lead us to see the semantic character of the sentence – its truth or falsity – as owed to how it is composed, by a finite number of applications of some of a finite number of devices that suffice for the language as a whole. To see a sentence in this light is to see it in the light of theory for its language, a theory that gives the form of every sentence in that language. A way to provide such a theory is by recursively characterizing a truth predicate, along the lines suggested by Tarski». [4, 94] As already noted, A. Tarski believed that logic deals with the general. Researchers have traditionally correlated the general with the specific, not with the content. So, in what conceptual context should be understood logical form, of a) content and form, b) syntactic and semantics, or c) the specific and the general?

I prefer to answer this question on behalf of the theory of conceptual transduction. Based on its content, there is no possibility to give a consistent interpretation to metaphysical categories of content and form. The theory of conceptual transduction operates with the concepts of principles, laws, and variables, but not content and form.

According to the theory of conceptual transduction, the consequential conception of syntactics, semantics, and pragmatics cannot be developed either. By the way, in this place, it is appropriate to note that, interpreting the nature of the logical form in the context of the relation of syntactics and semantics, the vast majority of authors forget to pay due attention to pragmatics. According to the principle of theoretical representation, syntactics and semantics should be understood as form of representations of conceptual transduction. In this regard, we can consider the object, mental and language representation. Nevertheless, none of them, including the object representation, can be called semantics, according to which the lack of correspondence between the object and, for example, language representation is possible. In the theory of conceptual transduction, such discrepancy is denied. It is also impossible to imagine a clear idea of syntactics based on conceptual transduction. It itself acts as management of concepts, a sequence of shifts between them, but it is not syntactics with its relatively poor content by definition. Conceptual transduction, unlike syntactics, contains all the richness of scientific theory.

The general and special also do not appear in the composition of the conceptual transduction. However, addressing those leads to actual conclusions. Contrary to A. Tarski, I believe that formal theories do not deal with general, but with certain classes of equivalent relations, which are, for example, relations of isomorphism, equal power, and similarity. In logic, the equivalent relations are reflexive, symmetric and transitive. The logical form is a representation of some classes of equivalent relations characteristic of certain theories, in particular, natural and axiological ones. Here is a typical example of the formation of a logic form. If from two statements A and B get a new statement, "A is equivalent to B" and express it by means of logical variables, then there is a logical form. If a new statement is formulated by means of mathematical variables, then there is a mathematical form. Respectively, if the statement is formulated by means of computer science, then there is a form characteristic of computer science. Thus, the formal is equivalent, not syntactical or general. It is not opposed to content.

With the development of modern science, the number of logical, mathematical and information theories is constantly increasing. It is not surprising that researchers who in one way or another seek to streamline these theories are faced with enormous difficulties. In this regard, almost everyone's attention was drawn to the program of reducing mathematics to logic, known as logicism, the two main inspirers of which

Were G. Frege and B. Russell. Neither they nor their followers managed to implement the program of logicism [16]. In our opinion, supporters of logicism, absolutizing achievements of logic, do not take into account properly the different status of natural, axiological and formal theories.

The foundation of science is formed by natural and axiological theories. Formal theories have a superstructure character in relation to them. They express equivalence of theories, which exists initially, and is not a product of formal sciences. In this regard, it is obvious that no concepts of fundamental sciences can be reduced to the concepts of formal theories. This fact in no way detracts from the relevance of the achievements of formal theories. Nevertheless, the world is arranged as it is arranged. Formal sciences grow as superstructures on the foundations of natural and axiological theories. The basis of science is not reduced to its superstructure. It is possible to understand the content of formal sciences only by finding out their connection with natural and axiological theories. It is necessary to take into account the mechanism of the formation of logical, mathematical and computer forms.

After considering the nature of the formal sciences, it is reasonable to turn to the philosophy of logic, which is usually identified with metalogic. Metalogic is a science, the subject of which is logic as a branch of science [1; 3; 6; 7; 9; 12; 14; 17]. Over 23 centuries of its development, logic has become a system of extremely extensive knowledge, saturated with numerous problematic aspects of conceptual properties. They need special and systematic scientific research. Otherwise, on the way of development of logic congestions occurs.

Fortunately, in the logical community, the need for metalogic was realized along with the emergence of basic logic. The fact is that logicians, as a rule, were not ordinary philosophers. In this capacity, they could not pass by the philosophy of logic. Philosophical and logical trends adorned by such names as Aristotle, W. Leibniz, B. Russell, R. Carnap, W. Quine, and J. Hintikka. On the other hand, the problems of logic were vigorously considered by such researchers, who were not engaged in philosophy. They were characterized by the separation of the metalogic from the philosophy of logic. In this regard, there is another series of names: D. Hilbert, L. Brouwer, A. Church, S. Kleene, and E. Mendelson. Particularly closely related to the intensification of metalogical research was D. Hilbert, who in the 1920s put forward a program of development of formalism.

Perhaps it should be considered that metalogic, on the one hand, and the philosophy of logic, on the other hand, are not identical to each other. The philosophy of logic is, strictly speaking, metalogic and also interdisciplinary relation of logic with the philosophy of science, namely, the use of philosophy achievements to understand the nature of logic.

Thus, the term "philosophy of logic" is polysemous [2, vii-viii]. It is intended to express the unity of philosophy and logic. Four basic his meaning is the next. First, philosophical logic is understood as categorical analysis, examples of which are transcendental philosophy of I. Kant, dialectical logic of G. Hegel, phenomenological logic of E. Husserl, hermeneutic logic of G. Misch. Strictly speaking, these systems do not refer to logic, but to philosophy. They should be grouped under the heading "philosophical and categorical analysis". Secondly, the philosophical logic is understood as logical systems, which involve concepts that seem to be far from the requests of formal sciences [17, 1]. In this regard, philosophical logic includes, for example, deontic, epistemic, temporal logic. Third, philosophical logic includes all symbolic logic because of its philosophical content. Fourth, under philosophical logic understand the philosophy of logic [1; 10].

References

1. Bocharov, V.A. (2001) Metalogika [Metalogic], In Novaya filosofskaya entsiklopediya [New Philosophical Encyclopedia], Moskva: Mysl', vol. 2, 538–540.
2. Burgess, J.P. (2009) Philosophical Logic. Princeton, NJ: Princeton University Press.
3. Church, A. (1996) Introduction to Mathematical Logic. Princeton, NJ: Princeton University Press.
4. Davidson, D. (1984) On Saying That. In Inquiries into Truth and Interpretation. New York: Clarendon Press.
5. Denning, P.J. (2000) Computer science: the discipline. Encyclopedia of Computer Science. Ed. by A. Ralston and D. Hemmendinger. New York: Wiley.
6. Fisher, J. (2008) On the Philosophy of Logic. Belmont: Thomson, Wadsworth.
7. Gensler, H.J. (2001) Introduction to Logic. London: Routledge.
8. Hofweber, T. (2018) Logic and Ontology. The Stanford Encyclopedia of Philosophy. Available at: https://plato.stanford.edu/archives/sum2018/entries/logic-ontology/.
9. Hunter, G. (1971) Metalogic: An Introduction to the Metatheory of Standard First-Order Logic. Berkeley, Los Angeles: University of California Press.

10. Jacquette, D. (2007) Philosophy of Logic. Amsterdam: Elsevier.
11. Karpenko, A.S. (2001) Filosofskaya logika [Philosophical logic] In Novaya filosofskaya entsiklopediya [New philosophical encyclopedia]. Moskva, Mysl', vol. 4, 246–247.
12. Mendelson E. (1997) Introduction to Mathematical Logic. Fourth Edition. London: Chapman and Hall.
13. Russell, B. (1993) Our Knowledge of the External World: as a Field for Scientific Method in Philosophy. New York: Routledge.
14. Sainsbury, M. (2001) Logical Forms: An Introduction to Philosophical Logic. Second Edition. Oxford: Blackwell.
15. Tarski, A. (1994) Introduction to Logic and to the Methodology of Deductive Sciences. Mineola, New York: Dover Publications.
16. Tennant, N. (2017) Logicism and neologicism. The Stanford Encyclopedia of Philosophy. Available at: https://plato.stanford.edu/archives/win2017/entries/logicism/
17. Wolfram, S. (1989) Philosophical Logic: An Introduction. London, Routledge, 1989.
18. Ziegler, G.M., Loos, A. (2017) «What is Mathematics?» and why we should ask, where one should experience and learn that, and how to teach it. In: Kaiser, G. (Ed.) Proceedings of the 13th International Congress on Mathematical Education. ICME-13 Monographs. Cham: Springer, 63-77.

4.2. Formal theory and its criteria

Formal theory is a conception represented by 1) the alphabet of symbols and expressions composed of them, 2) axioms (initial concepts in logical inference), 3) formulas (relations between variables), 4) rules of inference, fixing the relationship between axioms and formulas, as well as between formulas [3]. A formula is a theorem if it is the link of logical inference. If either axioms or inference rules are not specified, the formal system is degenerate. The most important criteria of the formal system are consistency, completeness, and independence of axioms, solvability, and categoricity. None of these criteria is absolute. The meaning of each of them is interpreted by analyzing the content of the formal system. Usually, the formal system is considered a system of calculus. Just such theories are considered in this chapter.

The process of formalization is designed to enhance the perfection of the formal system. The formal system is usually not fully formalized. However, certainly, the task is to complete its formalization. Successes achieved through the formalization of the theory are considered significant achievements. It is indicative, for example, the formalization of logical semantics in the result of the pioneering works of A. Tarski.

Let me turn directly to the criteria of formal theory.

The theory is consistent if there is no contradiction in it. A contradiction is two statements, one of which is a negation of the other.

A theory is complete if it is a consistent set of statements and no extension of it is consistent.

The independence of axioms takes the place if none of them is deducible from the other axioms in accordance with the rules of inference adopted in this theory.

The system of axioms is called categorical if it uniquely defines only one system of objects up to isomorphism, i.e. all interpretations, or models, of this system are isomorphic to each other.

A theorem is considered solvable within the framework of this theory if there is a proof of its truth.

The validity of using the criteria of logical theory should not be taken on faith; it certainly needs to be justified. Criteria for formal theory, as a rule, are specified and complemented with new concepts.

It makes sense to divide predicate logic theorems into two classes, 'positive' (or unlimited) and 'negative' (or restrictive). Most often among the 'positive' theorems of predicate logic are the following.

For the logic of predicates, there is an independence of a certain set of axioms (theorem J. McKinsey).

The classical first-order predicate calculus is semantically consistent, i.e. each of its formulas is universally valid.

Predicate calculus is syntactically consistent, i.e. there is no such formula A that is provable both A and non-A.

K. Gödel's the completeness theorem says that if a formula is logically valid then there is a finite deduction of the formula.

Along with the 'positive', there are also a number of restrictive theorems of the first-order logic of predicates.

Under some rather weak conditions imposed on the theory of T, the property of being a true formula of the theory of T is inexpressible in T (theorem of A. Tarski).

Gödel's second incompleteness theorem asserts that if formal arithmetic is consistent, then it does not derive some formula that substantively states the consistency of this arithmetic.

Another restrictive formula states that the predicate calculus is not syntactically complete, i.e. it can be attached as a new axiom some non-provable formula so that the resulting system will be syntactically consistent.

Further. The logic of predicates is not categorical (the Löwenheim-Skolem theorem), that is, its models can be non-isomorphic.

A. Church's theorem: there is no algorithm allowing for an arbitrary formula of predicate logic to decide whether it is provable in this theory.

The presence of both restrictive and non-restrictive theorems of predicate logic sharply complicates the question of assessing its status. At first glance, it seems that restrictive theorems are 'bad' and non-restrictive 'good'. This opinion is superficial. First, we are not at all able to properly assess the status of the logic of predicates, which is devoid of restrictive theorems. Secondly, restrictive theorems are not without obvious advantages. So, in applied logic, the incompleteness of the syntax of first-order logic is often used: non-logical postulates that do not violate the syntactic consistency of the theory are added to logical axioms. The presence of incompleteness of the syntax of logic provides a field of possibilities for the transition from pure logic to applied logic.

The main advantage of the theorems of logic, both non-restrictive and restrictive, is that they describe the status of a logical theory, as it is productive in science and, in actuality, in the whole of human culture. We must, the other is not given, fully realize the status and possibilities of the logical theory. In this regard, worthy of mention is the question of the so-called logical paradoxes, among which, perhaps, the most famous is the paradox (antinomy) of the liar «I lie». The sentence «I lie» is true if and only if its approver is lying.

A. Tarski has shown that the antinomies of the type of the antinomy of the liar are typical for semantically closed languages. The way out of the paradoxical logical situation is always associated with the detection of a non-critically accepted one or another false premise. Her criticism eliminates logical paradoxes and makes the logical language more effective. It is extremely important to understand what exactly a logical paradox is.

The history of the logic of predicates of the first order, as well as of all other logical theories, indicates that the criteria for logic cannot be given arbitrarily. This is the first. Secondly, these criteria should be constantly improved.

References

1. Kleene, S.C. (2002) Mathematical logic. Mineola: Dover Publications.
2. Mendelson, E. (1997) Introduction to Mathematical Logic. Fourth Edition. London: Chapman and Hall.

4.3. Logical ontology. Descriptions and rigid designators

By logical ontology is meant the doctrine of logical objects. Logic, like all other sciences, deals with certain things. From this point of view, the existence of logical objects can hardly be questioned. Recognition of their existence at the same time is a recognition of logical ontology. Nevertheless, researchers who refer to ontological issues on behalf of logic face significant difficulties [3]. In this regard, a very sharp position was occupied by R. Carnap. All questions of the ontological order he considered to be not theoretical, but practical [1]. As a result, it was impossible to make the transition from theory, including logical theory, to ontology. Logicians in one respect agreed with R. Carnap, namely, due to his criticism, they began to reject metaphysical reasoning about reality. Nevertheless, his alienation of the theory from ontology was not accepted. Objects began to be discussed on behalf of the theory. As W. Quine argued, «it is within science itself, and not in some prior philosophy, that reality is to be identified and described». [5, 21]. He did not doubt the possibility of a transition from logic, in particular, the logic of predicates of the first order, to judgments about reality. Critics of the position of W. Quine noted that logical systems could be used for various purposes, for example, to describe our beliefs. Therefore, there is no reason to state in a straightforward manner the correlation between syntactics and ontology [2]. From myself, I add that W. Quine too hastily moved from logical systems to reasoning about any objects, in particular, physical ones. One must assume, logic itself can only testify to logical, and not to any other objects. In our opinion, the question of the nature of logical objects is largely clarified by involving not only logic but also natural and axiological sciences in the field of analysis.

First, we note that in any science different representations are used, including object, mental and language. All of them testify to the reality that this or that science represents. From this point of view, there is no reason to doubt the existence of a logical ontology. It is, of course, unique, but it does exist.

Unfortunately, in logic, the ratio of its various representations is not often considered. Before the language turn that happened in philosophy and science in the 20th century, logic was mainly viewed from the mental point of view. Then the logic began to be interpreted as a predominantly language enterprise. In both the first and second cases, ontology as a doctrine of objects was not attributed to the core of logic.

The situation in natural science was fundamentally different. Here, contrary to the situation in logic, primary attention was paid to ontology. In axiological sciences, ontology again does not meet favorable attention. Moreover, completely in vain, their entities are people with values concepts. Due to the situation in science, exemplary logic is usually associated with physics. If we now turn our eyes to logic, then at first glance there are no objects in it that are defined as well as in physics. This impression is deceptive. There are objects of logic, but they are different from physical objects. In my opinion, on the right path are those authors who connect logical ontology with isomorphic structures. A. Tarski believed that the concept is logical if it is invariant with respect to any possible, one-to-one transformations of the world into itself [8, 149]. Hence, it follows that logic deals with classes of isomorphic structures, they must be defined as logical objectness.

Another extremely important step in the development of logical ontology is to take into account the pluralism of philosophical systems. Vladimir Smirnov noted in this connection «areas with qualitatively different nature of objects require different logics in their reasoning about them». [7, 289] If logic was a universal discipline, i.e. it would not take into account the uniqueness of the objects, then doubts in the logical ontology would be more justified. However, this uniqueness is taken into account in logic, albeit in an original way.

Any logical theory that is successfully used in interdisciplinary research deals with the same objects as substantive sciences. Logical ontology in the absence of ontology of natural and axiological sciences could hardly have taken place. If the logical theory is untenable in interdisciplinary studies, then its objects are imaginary in the sense that they are not fixed in experiments. By definition, objects must necessarily be studied experimentally. Directly in the logic, such a study is impossible. Logic is attached to experiments through its participation in interdisciplinary connections.

In the ontological sense, the logic of predicates, including the quantifiers of existence and universality used in it, is of exceptional importance. Predicates correlate with the characteristics of objects, quantifiers are necessary for the formulation of principles and laws.

While the relevance of the logical ontology should not be underestimated, it must not be absolutized. In accordance with the objectives of research, it can acquire a priority. However, the same is true of other, in particular language and mental representations of logical theory.

A prominent place in the development of logical ontology is occupied by a long-term discussion about the relationship between descriptions and rigid designators. Descriptions and rigid designators are logical means used to present objects. The theory of descriptions was developed by B. Russell (1905) [6]. He showed convincingly that all proposals for the existence of certain objects should be closely linked with their meaning of truth. This rule is not for the sentence «X is», because it is not clear how it is possible to prove its truth or falsity. The actual proposal «X is P». It is true if the subject X really has the feature of P. Otherwise, it is false. Comparison of the sentences «X is» and «X is P» shows that the word 'is' is not a feature, but only a logical link. In determining the subjects, their features must necessarily be given. This is precisely the basic position of the B. Russell's conception of descriptions. Russell was a realist; he recognized the existence of things as such.

The concept of descriptions was repeatedly criticized, which culminated in the works of Saul Kripke [6]. His innovation was to introduce into the logic of the concepts of rigid designators, in particular, proper names. By definition, a rigid designator refers to the same object in all possible worlds. According to Kripke, in the conception of descriptions, the name always occurs in the chosen possible worlds and its content changes in the transition from one interpretation to another. As a result, the identity of the object to itself is lost from view. 'Water' and H_2O are identical in all possible worlds. The same applies to proper names. Rigid designators are introduced in two stages. First, the name of the object is called, and then it is transferred from one person to another in a communicative society. This is the causal theory of reference S. Kripke.

In my opinion, Kripke dangerously spreads in different directions the theoretical nature of objects and their name due to pragmatic circumstances. He affirms the identity of the object in all possible worlds. However, he does not consider the proof of this position. It is not enough just to explain the identity of objects with pragmatic circumstances. Let me try to clarify the question under consideration

Suppose that the same name a_i occurs in three different theories: T_1, T_2, T_3. All attempts to express the unity of these theories fail. They show that $a1$, $a2$, and a_3 are not identical to each other in any respect, therefore, for the sake of avoiding nonsense, three different names should be used for their name, for example, m, n, l. The situation develops in a fundamentally different way in the case when theories can actually be ordered, for example, by combining them into the same series: $T_3 \rightarrow T_2 \{T_3\} \rightarrow T_1 \{T_3\}$. In accordance with its content, three names form the series: $a_3 \rightarrow a_2\{a_3\} \rightarrow a_1\{a_3\}$. Now there is reason to consider the three names to be similar, which is expressed by the symbol a_i. Nevertheless, and this is extremely important, they are not identical to each other. Consequently, contrary to S. Kripke, names and objects cannot be identical in different possible worlds, about which we have the opportunity to judge only based on theories. The theory T_3 absorbed the achievements of its predecessors. In this case, objects are judged based on this theory.

Thus, it seems to me, S. Kripke failed to refute the theory of descriptions. However, of course, it must be correctly understood. First, it should be borne in mind that naming is the prerogative of not only descriptive but also formal and axiological theories. Secondly, when interpreting the name, one should take into account the dynamics of intertheoretical relations.

Let me explain what has been said above by a simple example. The parents of the great Greek philosopher Aristotle have called him the Greek name, and not Russian, English or Chinese. They were guided by their ideas, i.e. some theory, without suspecting that he will become the founder of the doctrine of forms and formal logic, the teacher of Alexander the Great and the skillful physician. To thoroughly judge of Aristotle as a historical person, you will have to organize knowledge from philosophy, logic, pedagogy, medicine. In these fields, he showed himself in different ways. It is not right to believe that he remained himself. Aristotle improved, developed, and sometimes, and degraded. Applied to it, the name Aristotle is an abridged record of the totality of its definitions.

References

1. Carnap, R. (1950) Empiricism, semantics, and ontology. Revue Internationale de Philosophy 4(1), 20–40.
2. Gottlieb, D. (1980) Ontological Economy: Substitutional Quantification and Mathematics. Oxford: Oxford University Press.
3. Hofweber, T. (2018) Logic and ontology. The Stanford Encyclopedia of Philosophy. Available at: https://plato.stanford.edu/archives/sum2018/entries/logic-ontology/
4. Kripke, S. (1980) Naming and Necessity. Cambridge, Massachusetts: Harvard University Press.
5. Quine, W.V.O. (1981) Theories and Things. Cambridge, MA: Harvard University Press.
6. Russell, B. (1905) On Denoting. *Mind* 14(56), 479–493.
7. Smirnov, V.A. (2001) Yavlyayetsya li klassicheskaya formal'naya logika universal'noy? [Is classical formal logic universal?]. In Logiko-filosofskiye trudy V.A. Smirnova [Logical and philosophical works of VA. Smirnov]. Moskva: Editorial URSS, 287–289.
8. Tarski, A. (1986) What are logical notions? History and Philosophy of Logic 7(2), 143-154.

4.4. Logical consequence and argumentation

Logic is a formal science. This means that not all the features of reality, but only some of them, find expression in its framework. Otherwise, logic itself would not be a formal science. If modeling is used, in which the logic acts as a donor science, then it is absorbed by the acceptor science. Only if the logic is examined in itself, its specificity makes itself felt. Along with such concepts as axioms, formulas, theorems, and variables, the concept of logical consequence becomes crucial. In this case, we are talking about logical transition from premises to conclusions [14]. Naturally, the question arises about the legitimacy of such a transition and the definition of its validity. The legality of logical consequence follows from the centuries-old experience of humankind. It is impossible to imagine science without conceptual following. The connections between the concepts need expression, and this requires conceptual transitions. Alternative is not visible to them. The situation with the validity of the logical consequence looks more variable. The same scientific experience shows that logical adherence can be accompanied by logical errors, which should be avoided. What are the criteria for the logical consequence, and how to ensure their implementation?

Analyzing the nature of the logical consequence, M. McKeon considers two strategies [10]. According to one of them, the logical consequence is characterized based on the theory of models. With another strategy, the logical consequence is considered exclusively within the framework of deduction. The deductive approach is considered classical. The model approach was developed by A. Tarski [16].

According to Tarski's argument, the logical consequence must be necessary, formal and a priori. The first criterion, obviously, is connected with the validity of the reference to the concept of logical consequence. Two other criteria express directly the nature of logic, its cardinal difference from natural and axiological, sciences. The model approach involves addressing the concept of semantic truth. X is a logical consequence of K if and only if an interpretation of the non-logical terms of the language is impossible, for which K is true and X is false.

Within the deductive interpretation, X is a logical consequence of K if and only if X is derivable from K and no logical errors occur. In this case, there is no need to refer to the concepts of the model and the logical semantic truth.

J. Beall, G. Restall, and G. Sagi considering the status of logical sequence, mark the discussed problem field in their own way. [2] First, they correlate logical consequence with deductive and inductive inference. As is known, inductive inference has a probabilistic character. In this case, the logical consequence acquires the same character. Secondly, J. Beall and G. Restall consider the difference between a purely formal consequence and a material one, in which, as is known, not only necessary but also conditioned connections can be taken into account [1]. Thirdly, the logical consequence is considered from the standpoint of model theory and proof theory. Fourthly, when revealing the nature of the phenomenon of logical consequence, attention is drawn to variations in the number of premises and conclusions. The authors in question come to the conclusion about many ways of determining the logical consequence. The orthodox view is that logical consequence should implement one scenario. This is the point of view of logical monism. Contextualists agree with monists that logical consequence is carried out in a unique way. They propose to take into account the relevant context, i.e. the status of a particular logical theory. Beall and Restall take a pluralistic position: the concept of logical consequence can be implemented in more than one way [1].

In our opinion, the concept of logical consequence can in fact be defined in many ways. Each logical theory has its own kind of logical consequence. Of course, one should take into account the uniqueness of logic. Logical adherence is not based on the obligation always to distinguish between the stages of intratheoretical and intertheoretical transduction. The achievements of logic are relevant for the understanding not only deduction but also adduction, induction, and abduction, in the form in which they are characteristic of natural and axiological theories. This means that it is wrong to consider logical adherence necessarily as a deduction.

The logical consequence is the basis of logical argumentation. Arguments are the logical premises used by the subject to justify the truth of the conclusion relevant to the addressee. The justification starting with the arguments is called argumentation. In the absence of the addressee, an individual or a group of people, the argumentation cannot take place. If, for example, the author of the textbook takes into account the peculiarities of the readers of his book, he argues, otherwise there is only an explanation. It is possible that, for all their truth, the explanations will remain unclaimed by readers. Argumentation also may not reach the goal, in which case it is false. As we see, the argumentation includes a certain axiological position. If the sender of the message relies on the concept of logical truth, then he carries out a logical proof. The true logical argument is always proof. This is different from rhetorical reasoning, the purpose of which is to justify the relevance of the conclusion without decisive support for the concept of logical truth. Logical reasoning is a form of persuasion.

Logicians, when considering argumentation, tend to emphasize the difference between deductive and inductive argumentation [10], to which arguments by analogy are often added. We also use the idea of conductive arguments, in which the premises are not connected with each other by a certain logical connection, but to some extent support the conclusion [7].

In our opinion, all the problems pertaining to the argumentation are substantially clarified by reliance on the theory of conceptual transduction. In this case, it is necessary to distinguish intratheoretical and intertheoretical arguments. Intratheoretical arguments are made up of deductive, adductive, inductive and adductive arguments. Any type of argument can be used to persuade the addressee in accepting some conclusions relevant to him. For example, if they rely on the results of experiments, then there is an adductive argument. Intertheoretical arguments refer to problematization, discoveries, interpretations, and ordering of theories.

As for the conductive arguments, at first glance, they seem to be independent of each other. Their connection is sure to be revealed in an analysis that is more detailed. McKeon gives an example of conductive reasoning. Since the evening sky is clear and according to forecasts, the probability of rain is only 30%, then, apparently, tomorrow it will not be [2, sec. 3]. Meteorologists, obviously, will be able to explain why, with a clear evening sky, they predict a low probability of rain. Rhetorical arguments, they, it is likely, leave aside.

Reasoning by analogy is also amenable to refinement. Scientists are never confined to merely stating analogies. They will certainly find out the legitimacy of their same explanation. Then it turns out that, like conductive arguments, and arguments about similarity, ultimately, reduce to statements that are consistent with intratheoretical and intertheoretical transduction.

So, above, with reference to the conceptual transduction, the area of argumentation is outlined in relation to the sciences. In line with this approach, it is now necessary to take into account the uniqueness of logic. As for intertheoretical transduction, all its components, from problematization to ordering of theories, are relevant to logic to the same extent as for all other sciences. The peculiarity of logic is most clearly manifested in the field of intratheoretical transduction. It becomes obvious that logic does not repeat the methods of intratheoretical transduction, but giving them a logical form, generalizes them.

If the argumentation is carried out within the boundaries of logic, then it is sufficient to refer to its concepts. If the argumentation goes beyond its boundaries, then the significance of logic manifests itself through the active use of its achievements in interdisciplinary research. According to V.N. Bryushinkin, the generalized system model of argumentation realizes various connections of logical, rhetorical and cognitive approaches, each of which can be both basic and auxiliary [3]. My position is different; I believe that the most complete interpretation of the argumentation involves the use of a wide range of interdisciplinary relations. All the rest should be transferred to scientific tracks. If this is not done, then the argumentation remains outside the boundaries of the sciences, and this is always associated with certain undesirable consequences. The role of logic in argumentation reaches its peak value if statements related to natural and axiological sciences are formalized based on conceptions of logical theories.

I have repeatedly noted above that logical consequence should be considered in the context of conceptual transduction. It should be noted that the question of the correlation between logic and intratheoretical transduction, despite its relevance, is considered extremely rare. Meanwhile, it is able to shed additional light on the nature of logic.

One of the operations of intratheoretical transduction, namely, deduction, in logic is obviously lucky. To it devoted a huge number of works; moreover, logical deduction is considered an example of logical consequence. If the deduction operation is considered in non-logical sciences, then, as a rule, it is identified with logical deduction.

As for the operation of induction, the very possibility of its logical development was repeatedly questioned, but, ultimately, it took place. There is an inductive logic with all its differences from deductive logic. V.N. Finn states that «induction as a cognitive procedure leading to a generalization as a result of the discovery of the similarity of the observed objects in modern logic can be formalized by various means, forming the corresponding variants of inductive logic» [6].

Thus, there is not only deductive but also inductive logic. It is reasonable to raise the question of the relevance of also the adductive and abductive logic. However, the situation with them looks very problematic. Let us first turn to abductive logic.

In the case of abduction, we are talking about achieving the best explanation by the best theory [9]. Around the possibility of logical formalization of the conclusion to the best explanation arose an acute discussion [4]. Just as skeptics deny the possibility of formalizing inductive inference, many authors postulate the impossibility of a logical representation of abduction. In contrast, many logicians are looking for ways to develop abductive logic. Numerous proposals have been developed on this score [4]. As a rule, a list of competing theories is first formulated, and then a strategy of choosing the best from them is outlined. In our opinion, in this connection, the game semantics of J. Hintikka has good prospects [8; 1]. We state that to date the situation with the creation of abductive logic seems quite encouraging. Let us now turn to adductive logic.

Many neopositivists, including R. Carnap, isolated logic from the empirical sciences. Logic deals, they say, with analytical proposals, the truth of which does not need an empirical justification. Logic is necessary for comprehending experimental data, but it is independent of them.

W. Quine, denying the existence of analytic sentences, but not synthetic [12], clearly brought the last closer to the empirical sciences. Empirical research is important to logic, but it remained unclear exactly how. A more definite position was taken by H. Reichenbach [13] and H. Putnam [11]. They were greatly impressed by the difference between the logic of quantum mechanics and classical logic. In view of this circumstance, they insisted on linking empiricism with logic. Quantum mechanical experiments testify for quantum logic.

The position of H. Putnam seemed contradictory to M. Dummett [5]. He believed that the position of H. Putnam is guided by his realistic attitudes. The researcher, who is guided by antirealistic attitudes, would reason in a fundamentally different way. In our opinion, Dummett's criticism does not reach its goal. The realistic position is quite compatible with the scientific one. It is quite legitimate to use ontological ideas, and in this case, one cannot avoid realism.

In all cases of interdisciplinary relations, one side of which is logic, priority should be given to a completely definite logic, three-valued - in the case of quantum mechanics, deontological - in dealing with the ethics of the debt, paraconsistent - in interpreting the discussions. This circumstance will not allow isolating logic from empirical studies.

The involvement of logic in the empirical sciences is manifested in the fact that when formalizing deduction, adduction, induction, and abduction, it is advisable to resort to logic. The successes of the logic show that there are no such arguments that could not be formalized. Then the hour of logic comes. Experiment planning refers to adduction. As is known, at the same time, the potential of mathematics and computer science is widely used. Immediately, as it is obvious, it cannot do without logic.

Thus, in interdisciplinary studies, logic treats in formal terms all four operations of intratheoretical transduction. From this point of view, it is not legitimate to regard logic as an exclusively deductive science.

References

1. Beall, J., Restall, G. (2000) Logical pluralism. Australasian Journal of Philosophy 78(4), 457-493.
2. Beall, Jc., Restall, G., and Sagi, G. (2019) Logical consequence. The Stanford Encyclopedia of Philosophy. Available at:https://plato.stanford.edu/archives/spr2019/entries/logical-consequence/
3. Bryushinkin, V.N. (2005) Obobshchennaya sistemnaya model' argumentatsii [Generalized system model of

argumentation]. In Argumentatsiya i interpretatsiya. Issledovaniya po logike, argumentatsii i istorii filosofii [Argumentation and Interpretation. Studies on the Logic, Argumentation and History of Philosophy]. Kaliningrad, Rossiyskiy gosudarstvennyy universitet imeni I. Kanta, 11–17.

4. Douven, I. (2017) Abduction. The Stanford Encyclopedia of Philosophy. Avaiable at: https://plato.stanford.edu/archives/sum2017/entries/abduction/>.

5. Dummett, M. (1976) Is logic empirical. In Lewis, H.D. (Ed.). Contemporary British Philosophy. 4th series. London: Allen and Unwin, 45-68.

6. Finn, V.N. (2001) Induktivnaya logika [Inductive logic]. In Novaya filosofskaya entsiklopediya [New Philosophical Encyclopedia, 4 vols.]. Moskva, Mysl', vol. 2, 117-118. [In Russian].

7. Govier, T.A. (2010) Practical Study of Argument. Seventh Edition. Belmont, CA: Wadsworth.

8. Hintikka, J. (1999) Inquiry as Inquiry: Logic of Scientific Discovery. Dordrecht: Kluwer.

9. Lipton, P. (2001) Inference to the Best Explanation. London: Routledge.

10. McKeon, M. (2020) Logical consequence. Internet Encyclopedia of Philosophy. Available at: www.iep.utm.edu/argument/

11. Putnam, H. (1968) Is logic empirical? In Cohen R.S., Wartofsky, M.W. (Eds.). Boston Studies in the Philosophy of Science. Vol. 5. Dordrecht: D. Reidel, 1968, pp. 216–241.

12. Quine, W.V. (1951) Two dogmas of empiricism. The Philosophical Review 60(1), 20-43.

13. Reichenbach, H. (1944) The Philosophical Foundations of Quantum Mechanics, Berkeley: University of California Press.
14. Sidorenko, E.A. (1983) Logicheskoye sledovaniye i uslovnyye vyskazyvaniya [Logical consequence and conditional statements]. Moskva: Nauka. [In Russian].
15. Sidorenko, E.A. (2000) Relevantnaya logika [Relevant logic]. Moskva, Institut filosofii Rossiyskoy akademii nauk. [In Russian].
16. Tarski, A. (1983) On the concept of logical consequence. In Tarski, A. Logic, Semantics, Metamathematics. Second Edition. Indianapolis: Hackett Publishing, 409-420.
17. Vasyukov, V.L. (2003) Nauchnoye otkrytiye i kontekst abduktsii [Scientific Discovery and the Context of Abduction]. Filosofiya nauki. Vyp. 9 [Philosophy of Science. Iss. 9]. Moskva, Institut filosofii Rossiyskoy akademii nauk, 180–203. [In Russian].

4.5. Logical truth, tautologies and paradoxes

As you know, the concept of truth is necessary for rejecting false concepts. No science including logic can do without it. However, with regard to it, the difficulty lies in the fact that it is necessary to formalize the whole concept of truth [4]. This task was partially solved by A. Tarski, who managed to develop the original concept of semantic truth (1935) [10].

Tarski distinguished the object language and metalanguage. In the object language, they talk about objects. In metalanguage, they talk about the object language. Tarski's example reads:

Sentence «Snow is white» is true if and only if *snow is white*.

The right-hand side of the definition of truth indicates a sentence, which in the left-hand side stands in quotation marks. The definition of truth refers to the metalanguage because it is much richer than the object sentence. In a generalized form, the definition of truth can be represented by the following scheme:

«P» is true if, and only if, P.

Tarski's definition of truth satisfies the requirement of the coherence conception of truth insofar as it relates to the sphere of language. However, it does not fully agree with this conception, because the position of the correspondence between «P» and the state of affairs that found expression in it is preserved. In this regard, the definition of Tarski's truth resembles the correspondence theory of truth.

The definition of Tarski contains another important innovation, namely, it uses the concept of feasibility. He noticed that the relationship between the name of the object sentence and the sentence itself satisfies the requirement of implementation, which in the generalized form assumes the use of a propositional function. Suppose that the propositional function "x is greater than 3" is considered. It is true in the case of substitution instead of the free variable x, the corresponding numbers, for example, if instead of number x is placed number five. In logic often free variables are replaced by the names of objects. A. Tarski in his theory did not focus on the concept of correspondence but on the concept of feasibility.

Along with the semantic concept of truth, logicians also use the concept of syntactic truth. In this case, the thought does not go beyond the logical consequence. A concept or a sentence is true if it is part of a logical consequence.

An in-depth understanding of the problem of truth in logic was facilitated by the creation of many-valued logic, in which more than two truth-values are allowed. The first formal multivalued, namely, three-valued logic was created in 1920 by the Polish logician J. Łukasiewicz [6]. Like the state of affairs in classical logic and in many-valued logic, the principle of extensionality is observed: the truth-value of a complex statement is uniquely determined by the truth-values of its constituent utterances. On a wide range of issues, many-valued logic is an extension of classical logic. The relevance of many-valued logic is manifested in the case of logical modeling. For example, it is relevant to artificial intelligence systems.

A widely held view is that there are no criteria of truth. This position does not take into account that the dynamics of knowledge consists in the transition to increasingly perfect theories. True is considered only those conceptual formations that are organically combined with the content of the most developed theories. This statement is relevant for logic to a degree not less than for any other science.

In my opinion, the nature of logical truth in many respects does not receive an adequate expression insofar as the growth of knowledge is not taken into account. For the question of the nature of logical truth, the process of improving logical theories is crucial. All concepts of the most developed logical theories, including all their representations, in particular, object and language, are true. The decisive role in determining the nature of logical truth is not a semantic approach, but a consideration of the status of the most developed conceptions in the composition of league-theories. It is in this context that the status of the metalanguage should also be determined. It is not appropriate to compare the metalanguage with the object language. In this case, the language of the theory is divided into several components, one of which is called the metalanguage. However, conceptually these components are equally significant. The true metalanguage is characteristic only of the most developed theory. The language of this theory is a metalanguage insofar as this theory is the key to understanding the language of a less developed theory.

Discussion of logical truth in many ways allows a better understanding of the nature of tautologies and analytical proposals. Tautologies are always true expressions. They are true in a semantic sense, regardless of the objects in question. For example, the law of the excluded third, according to which it is true that A, or not-A, is often considered a tautology. The identification of true theorems with tautologies (L. Wittgenstein, A. Ayer, and C. Hempel) is not welcomed by all the logicians. J. Hintikka categorically stated that the logical conclusion is not tautological [5, 217]. Not without reason, he argues that in the process of productive logical reasoning increases the measure of logical information. Tautologies do not boil down to a repetition of what was previously known.

As logic developed, it became increasingly obvious that it was not a collection of absolute truths. This circumstance is particularly clear when using logic in interdisciplinary studies. Not every logical theory is relevant to every subject area. The illusion of the tautological content of logic is largely supported by the existence of a so-called general logic, which by definition seems to know no exceptions. However, it should be taken into account that the general logic in itself has only a nominal value. It must certainly be considered in the context of the abundance of the logical sciences. In this case, its imaginary universality is immediately dissipated.

Tautology is a semantic concept that should be clearly distinguished from the theorem as a syntactic concept. If the theorem is given a semantic representation, then it can be transformed into a tautology. However, this rule is not always fulfilled. In addition, it should be borne in mind that the derivation of theorems cannot be reduced to the repetition of trivial operations. In the notion of tautology, it is meant that the same thing is repeated repeatedly.

In classical logic, the negation of tautology is a contradiction. On the other hand, the rejection of the contradiction leads to a tautology.

In traditional philosophical terminology, tautologies are analytic sentences. An analytical proposal is a sentence, the truth of which is determined solely by the meanings of the terms included in it. The truth of the synthetic proposal depends on the experimental data. Since logic experiments are not carried out, the impression is created that all logical propositions are analytic. This belief was criticized by W. Quine [9]. The method of its proof was reduced to the consideration of a nontrivial content of synonyms, the difference of which cannot be achieved by purely logical means. Therefore, logic, in fact, does not cope with synonyms, which contradicts the existing logical practices. Such a method of proof can hardly be welcomed, for it is not carried out in the context of advanced scientific theories. W. Quine really raised an urgent issue. Nevertheless, as it seems to me, it becomes clear only when the correlation of logic, on the one hand, and natural and axiological sciences, on the other hand, is taken into account. In the dispute of W. Quine and R. Carnap, who insisted on the relevance of the analytical proposals [2, 257f], this circumstance was not taken into account.

Logic, of course, differs from other branches of science. Therefore, there are all bases to distinguish between logical and non-logical sentences. The relationship between them is revealed in the process of using logic in interdisciplinary research. In this case, logical proposals are considered as symbols of non-logical proposals. Thus, the dichotomy of logical/non-logical sentences is relevant. Converting it into a dichotomy of analytical/synthetic sentences is inconsistent. Thus, the skepticism of W. Quine concerning the status of analytical proposals and their opposition to synthetic proposals are fully consistent. However, translating, in fact, analytical proposals into a category of synthetic ones, he ignored the difference between logic and natural and axiological sciences. This is a mistake.

The involvement of logic in interdisciplinary research shows that there is no universal science and, consequently, there are no tautologies. The above-mentioned law of the excluded third is not true in all theories.

In logic, as in any other science, one must be guided by the criterion of truth. Any deviation from it is blamed and recognized as a logical mistake [cf. 2]. It can be deliberate and used in argumentation. However, even in this case, there is a logical error insofar as the subject distorts the original conceptual content of logic.

The problem of logical errors has been repeatedly addressed by outstanding philosophers. Already Aristotle in his work "On the sophistical refutations" [3] considered 13 types of logical errors. With the greatest care, logical errors were studied by medieval scholastics. Logical errors were considered in the works of F. Bacon, A. Schopenhauer, J. S. Mill, and W. Quine. In the article by B. Dowden [3] 209 names of logical errors are given, this fact testifies to the thoroughness with which the problematic of logical errors are analyzed. Obviously, this is done not accidentally, but in connection with the need to ensure the truth of logic. Like any other scientific discipline, logic is not built in an arbitrary order, but in accordance with the orientation of conceptual transitions. The lack of proper scientific thoroughness inevitably leads to logical errors.

Numerous attempts have been made to create a detailed classification of errors. There are formal and informal, deductive and inductive, linguistic and material, i.e. not depending on the language, errors. It is possible to correlate errors with parts of the evidence, their bases, theses, and forms of reasoning. In this connection, the main error (Latin error fundamental) is the replacement of the true ground by a false one [11]. Ultimately, it turns out that logical errors are correlated with logical theories, all their components, and with intertheoretical relations.

Logical paradoxes should be distinguished from logical errors. In Greek, the paradox means a strange (unexpected) opinion. It is strange because the conceptual harmony of science is called into question. As for the nature of paradoxes, different points of view are expressed. Some authors believe that the paradox is certainly a delusion. The paradox of logic is a reasoning or a statement in which, using means that do not appear (apparently) beyond the bounds of logic, and the assumptions that seem to be acceptable, come to an obviously unacceptable result. In view of the fact that paradoxes reveal the hidden conceptual contradictions and translate them into direct and open, they, according to the laws of creative thinking, help with the development of new ideas and concepts [3]. Another point of view is that paradox is not always an error.

Considering the problems of paradoxes [8], W. Quine distinguished reliable (truly expressed) and unreliable (falsely expressed) paradoxes. In addition, paradoxes of the third type, intractable paradoxes, exist. They are logically contradictory judgments that are obtained using the correct ways of reasoning. Such, for example, is an antinomy, which is a contradiction between conclusions, usually two, recognized as equally true. We note immediately that along with the antinomies, the aporias are also distinguished; judgments, the contradictions of which cannot be overcome by any means.

Strictly speaking, in science, aporias are not recognized. Statements whose inconsistency is settled forever, are rejected in science. Therefore, aporias are subjected to careful analysis; as a result, they are overcome. A striking example in this regard is the aporia of the movement of Zeno of Elea, in particular, that the fast-footed Achilles is not in a position to catch up with a slow tortoise. At the transition to the concepts of quantum mechanics, Zeno's aporias are overcome.

The theme of paradoxes has an exceptional significance for the development of science, especially logic. The fact is that they in the most vivid form highlight the conceptual refinement of theories and, as a rule, the need to create new theories. Indicative in this sense is the fate of the Russell-Zermelo paradox about the set of all sets that are not elements of themselves. Under the impression of this paradox, not being able to overcome it, Frege abandoned his studies of philosophy by the theory of sets. It took years of hard research before the pioneers of the paradox succeeded in overcoming it in 1908. Each of them made non-trivial discoveries: Russell created a theory of types, and Zermelo developed the axiomatic theory of sets.

Modern logic has learned to work with paradoxes more effectively than their predecessors do. However, the successes achieved, as before, suggest the need for very persistent research [3; 7].

Reference

1. Cantini, A. and Bruni, R. (2017) Paradoxes and contemporary logic. The Stanford Encyclopedia of Philosophy. Available at: https://plato.stanford.edu/archives/fall2017/entries/parad oxes-contemporary-logic/
2. Carnap, R. (1966) Philosophical Foundations of Physics. New York, London: Basic Books, Inc.
3. Dowden B. Fallacies. Internet Encyclopedia of Philosophy. Available at: www.iep.utm.edu/fallacy/
4. Gómez-Torrente, M. (2019) Logical truth. The Stanford Encyclopedia of Philosophy. Available at: https://plato.stanford.edu/archives/spr2019/entries/logical -truth/
5. Hintikka, J. (1980) Logiko-epistemologicheskiye issledovaniya [Logical-epistemological studies]. Moskva: Progress. [In Russian].
6. Łukasiewicz, J. (1957) Aristotle's syllogistic from the standpoint of modern formal logic. Second edition of XVII 209. Oxford: Clarendon Press.
7. Nepeyvoda, N.N. (2000) Prikladnaya logika [Applied logic]. Nowosibirsk: NGU.
8. Quine, W.V. (1966) The Ways of Paradox and Other Essays. New York: Random House.
9. Quine, W.V. (1951) Two dogmas of empiricism. The Philosophical Review 60(1), 20–43.

10. Tarski, A. 1983 [1933]. The concept of truth in the languages of the deductive sciences. In Tarski A. Logic, Semantics, Metamathematics: Papers from 1923 to 1938. Second Edition. Ed. by J. Corcoran. Indianapolis: Hackett Publishing Company, 152-278.

11. Uemov, A.I. (1958) Logicheskiye oshibki. Kak oni meshayut pravil'no myslit' [Logical errors. How do they prevent you from thinking correctly?]. Moskva: GIPL. [In Russian].

4.6. Development of non-classical logics and pluralism in logic

In the XX century, numerous logical theories were created, radically different from classical logic. Classical logic is usually associated with the names of Aristotle and G. Frege. Aristotle stood at its origins, and Frege gave it an exemplary embodiment [4]. Classical logic means a set of logical theories that satisfy five requirements, namely, 1) the law of the excluded third, 2) the law of consistency, 3) the monotonicity of the logical sequence, 4) the commutativity of conjunctions (the terms of conjunctions can change places, and the truth value of the conjunction remains unchanged), 5) de Morgan's laws: pairs of dual logical operators are connected by logical negation in accordance with de Morgan's rules [9]. If one or more of the above requirements are violated, then there is a non-classical logic, examples of which are, for example, intuitionistic, multi-valued and paraconsistent logic.

All inventors of non-classical logic have some general features: they abandon certain ideals of logical classics. The pioneers of non-classical logic are the Dutchman L. Brouwer, the Russian N. Vasiliev, and the Polish J. Łukasiewicz. Revolutionary logical ideas were formulated by them in 1907-

1910. Brouwer, Vasiliev, and Łukasiewicz are the founders of the intuitionist, paraconsistent and multivalued logic. In fairness, we note that of the three authors only Łukasiewicz, who created in 1920 a variant of the three-valued logic, managed to bring his creative ideas to a refined logical form. The system of axioms for intuitionistic logic was invented by A. Heyting in 1930. Developed paraconsistent logics began to appear only after 1948 (the works of S. Jaskowski, N. da Costa and others). They are especially relevant for the history of the development of non-classical logics.

Since the time of Aristotle, the basic principle of logic was the principle of consistency. It is essentially modified in the logic of N.A. Vasiliev [1]. In paraconsistent logics, tolerance for logical contradictions is associated with the productivity of such a logical sequence relationship, which is not excessive, i.e. for any formulas, A and B, A and non-A do not define an arbitrary formula B [2, 198]. In the logical system, an arbitrary formula should not be output. A logical system should not be trivial. In classical logic, contradictory trivial systems were rightly rejected, but non-trivial theories were unreasonably denied. In other words, the consistency principle must take into account the conditions of non-triviality. Logical chaos is rejected not only in classical but also in paraconsistent logic. In our opinion, the development of paraconsistent logics has revealed the necessity of positioning the principle of impermissibility of contradictions. This principle refers to the sphere of the methodology of logic. He admits certain contradictions in the composition of logic, but only those whose permissibility is stipulated with all possible logical rigor.

One of the undoubted merits of paraconsistent logic is its ability to take into account the dynamics of knowledge. As you know, the growth of scientific knowledge is carried out as a relay of theories, not without contradictions. In classical logic, these theories are considered false. They were pushed out of science. Paraconsistent logics open the path of a formalized description of non-trivial theories. Of course, this does not negate the need to compare the merits of different theories. The meaning of the paraconsistent logic is to realize the true place of contradictions in the logical theory.

An important class of paraconsistent logics is the relevant logics. Relevance is usually understood as the correspondence between statements that are parts of the logical consequence. In classical logic, the connection of these parts was not sufficiently taken into account.

The future of paraconsistent logic causes numerous arguments. [7]

Let me, after a brief excursion into the field of non-classical logic considers in more systematic form the problematic aspects of logical pluralism.

Surprisingly, the logicians, relentlessly multiplying the number of non-classical logics, relate to classical logic rather tolerantly, without putting the cardinal question of the necessity of choosing either a logical monism according to which only one logic is true, namely classical, either logical pluralism with its thesis about the existence many true logics. Only at the beginning of the 21st century did researchers appear who firmly took the position of logical pluralism. This trend culminated in the monograph of J. Beall and G. Restall [2]. The positions of logical monism also have their protectors [6]. H. Field assumes logical pluralism, but in an extremely moderate form, believing that he only modifies logical monism; meaning for example that there are systems in which the same theorems receive different interpretations [3].

In a review article, G. Russell considered ways to substantiate the logical pluralism [6], following Beall and Restall he attaches paramount importance to the pluralistic interpretation of the logical consequence. According to the thesis of the general validity of the Tarski argument, it is consistent only when in case$_x$ from true premises the true conclusions follow. Logical pluralists do not deny this thesis, believing, however, that he receives various interpretations in accordance with the understanding of "cases$_x$." It can be about different situations, and about the various methods of interpretation used by them. The ambiguity of the concept "case$_x$" leads to many types of logical consequence as the most essential feature of any logical theory. This is the basis of the variety of logical pluralism, most common among logicians. In accordance with this, various arguments can be proposed in favor of this pluralism [6].

First, it is an argument about the appearance of logical theory, which is correct in all respects. The very appearance of the theory testifies in its favor. There is no reason to reject it. Secondly, the emergence of a new theory is acceptable from a moral standpoint. As R. Carnap once noted, logicians should be tolerant of new theories, however, without forgetting to make sure of their relevance. Thirdly, we should not absolutize the concept "in all cases"; in fact, a logical theory can relate only to some cases from a larger aggregate. Fourthly, an answer is possible that is connected with the many interpretations of meanings. Fifth, the argument for choosing the best logical sequence. This choice is possible only if there are at least several theories.

These arguments do not exhaust the support of logical pluralism. For example, Russell considers logical pluralism in the context of 1) various interpretations of logical constants, 2) different objects of logical implication, 3) different models, and 4) different epistemological norms [8].

In my opinion, logical pluralism has taken place, all the arguments put forward against it are refuted quite easily [8]. It took place insofar as, in fact, is a statement of the existence of various logics that are not reducible to each other. They passed the fire of verification not only directly in logic but also in the numerous interdisciplinary relations. In my opinion, the argumentation both in favor of logical pluralism and against it is not entirely consistent. As a rule, both opponents of logical pluralism and its supporters tend to start from some general position, for example, the postulate of the uniqueness of logical truth, which is introduced regardless of the theories themselves. Our position is those logical theories are the basis of logical pluralism. Based on their content, you can formulate some general provisions. There is no need to justify the existence of logical pluralism by its compatibility with certain general provisions. They have a secondary character. In accordance with the principle of theoretical relativity, the meaning of all logical concepts, from axioms and theorems to variables, is determined by the content of logical theories.

Logical pluralism has taken place. It is not enough to just state this fact. In its horizons, it is necessary to revise the whole content of logic. In our opinion, in this connection, it is necessary to distinguish certain logical league-theories.

References

1. Bazhanov, V.A. (1990) The fate of one forgotten idea: N.A. Vasiliev and his imaginary logic. Studies in Soviet Thought 39(4), 333-344.
2. Beall J., Restall G. (2006) Logical Pluralism. Oxford, Oxford University Press.
3. Field, H. (2009) Pluralism in logic. The Review of Symbolic Logic 2(2), 342-359.
4. Frege, G. (1879) Begriffsschrift, eine der arithmetischen nachgebildete Formelsprache des reinen Denkens [Conceptual writing, one of the arithmetic modeled formula language of pure thinking]. Halle, Nebert. [In German].
5. Karpenko, A.S. (2002) Atomic and molecular paraconsistent logics. Logique et Analyse 45(177-178), 31-35.
6. Priest, G. (2006) Doubt Truth to be a Liar. Oxford, Oxford University Press.
7. Priest, G., Tanaka, K., and Weber, Z. (2018) Paraconsistent logic. The Stanford Encyclopedia of Philosophy. Available at:
    https://plato.stanford.edu/archives/sum2018/entries/logic-paraconsistent/
8. Russell G. (2019) Logical pluralism. The Stanford Encyclopedia of Philosophy. Available at: https://plato.stanford.edu/archives/sum2019/entries/logical-pluralism/
9. Shapiro, S. and Kouri Kissel, T. (2018) Classical logic. The Stanford Encyclopedia of Philosophy. Available at: https://plato.stanford.edu/archives/spr2018/entries/logic-classical/

4.7. The future of logic

In the final section of the chapter, it is advisable, to sum up, some results. The beginning of logical science is rightfully associated with Aristotle. He was able to effectively dispose of the principles of identity, consistency and the excluded third. For 22 centuries, until the middle of the XIX century, Aristotle's logic was an unsurpassed pattern. That is why it was given the title of scientific logic. However, of course, she was not without flaws. B. Russell pointed to the three main shortcomings of Aristotle's logic: the uncritical use of the subject-predicate form of description to universal utterances, the reassessment of syllogisms in comparison with other forms of logical proof, the absolutization of deduction and, accordingly, the underestimation of induction [10, 197-202]. In his criticism B. Russell used a very characteristic technique, namely, he considered traditional logic from the point of view of the logic of predicates of the first order. His position deserves approval. Criticism should be conducted from the standpoint of a certain theory. In this sense, the logic of predicates represents excellent possibilities. The fact is that from its heights traditional logic is nothing more than the logic of one-place predicates. It is not adapted to consider multiple-place predicates, i.e. relations. Of course, criticism of traditional logic can be carried out not only from the positions of the classical but also from various forms of non-classical logic.

The real revolution in logic was the creation of the logic of predicates, the formal theory of linguistic expressions, taking into account their subject-predicate structure. Properties and relations are understood, respectively, as single and n-local predicates of subjects (objects). At the suggestion of Frege (1879), language expressions are interpreted by means of quantifiers and propositional functions. The logic of predicates is fundamentally different from the logic of utterances abstracting from the structure of sentences. In the logic of predicates of the first order, predicates are considered, in the logic of predicates of the second-order – predicate of predicates, etc. The development of the logic of predicates of the first order was of fundamental importance for all logic. The creation of the logic of predicates is especially closely related to the names G. Frege, C.S. Peirce, B. Russell, D. Hilbert, T. Skolem, K. Gödel, and A. Tarski. Initially, in their works, first-order logic was considered in conjunction with second-order logic. Only in 1928 D. Hilbert and W. Ackermann presented the logic of predicates of the first order as an independent logical system [2]. In it example, the logicians comprehended the new conceptual depths of logic. The logic of predicates of the first order has a number of attractive features that are relevant for the matter of formalizing any science. Its consistency, completeness, and compactness is proved.

Later, logical revolutions happened quite often. The real logical revolutions were the creation, in particular, of intuitionistic, multi-valued, paraconsistent, modal, intentional, relevant and fuzzy logic. Pluralistic tendencies began to permeate all components of logic, in particular, its axiomatic parts, as well as the methods of proof. In the latter case, we are talking about methods of proof that have similar characteristics [11]. There are many such types of proofs, but the most known are the systems of Hilbert's calculus [3], the natural deduction [1; 7] and sequential analysis [1]. The most classical type of proof is the Hilbert axiomatic system, in which axioms and rules for the derivation of theorems from them are given. There are usually few such rules, in the simplest case, only one. The development of the non-Hilbert systems of proof in the mid-1930s, carried out by G. Gentzen and S. Jaskowski, showed that logical inference can be implemented in different ways. It does not exclude, but, on the contrary, implies pluralism.

The pluralism of logic did not become a denial of its unity. The point is that between logical systems there are transitions, in particular, limiting ones, which unite them into a single whole. Of course, the limit transitions should not be interpreted excessively rectilinearly, i.e. without taking into account the conceptual differences of more developed theories from less developed conceptions. In logic, such relationships are characteristic of many theories. If two theories are related to each other by a limiting transition, then we call the less developed of them the quasi-theory of a more developed concept. For example, traditional logic is the quasi-theory of the logic of predicates of the first order (the limit transition consists in the transition from multi-place to one-place predicates); multivalued logic is the quasi-theory of probabilistic logic (the transition from continuous truth values to discrete ones takes place); classical consistent logic is the quasi-theory of paraconsistent logic (a transition to excessive logical follow-up is made). The entire field of logic appears as numerous problem metamorphoses, one of the manifestations of which are limiting transitions. Logical league-theories express the unity of logic as a branch of science.

The development of logic was largely stimulated by its interdisciplinary connections. In fact, it turned out that in a logical sense all the stages of intratheoretical transduction, namely, deduction, adduction, induction, abduction, can be formalized. In our opinion, the same applies to the stages of intertheoretical transduction.

There is every reason to believe that any science can be supported by innovations of logicians. Very significant in this respect is the development of the logic of language games, first implemented by P. Lorenzen and K. Lorenz [8; 9]. For a long time, it seemed that language games were not subject to logic.

Nevertheless, logicians refuted this opinion. In this connection, J. Hintikka achieved particularly significant successes [4; 5]. Numerous other variants of the logic of language games [6] show that any varieties of reasoning are accessible to logical formalization.

Thus, there is no doubt that in the future logic will increasingly be incorporated into modern scientific knowledge as a formal and trans-disciplinary whole.

Reference

1. Gentzen, G. (1934-1935) Untersuchungen über das logische Schließen [Logical reasoning studies]. Mathematische Zeitschrift 39(2), 176–210. [In German].
2. Hilbert D., Ackermann W. (1950) [1928] Principles of Mathematical Logic. Ed. by R.E. Luce. Transl. by L.M. Hammond, G.G. Leckie, and F. Steinhardt. New York: Chelsie Publishing Company.
3. Hilbert, D. (1931) Die Grundlegung der elementaren Zahlenlehre [The foundation of elementary number theory]. Mathematische Annalen 104(2), 484–494. [In German].
4. Hintikka, J. (1973) Logic, Language-Games and Information: Kantian Themes in the Philosophy of Logic. Oxford: Clarendon Press.
5. Hintikka, J. and Sandu, G. (1989) Informational Independence as a Semantical Phenomenon. In Fenstad, J.E., Frolov, I.T., and Hilpinen, R. (Eds.). Logic, Methodology and Philosophy of Science. Amsterdam, Elsevier, 8, 571–589.
6. Hodges, W. and Väänänen, J (2019) Logic and games. The Stanford Encyclopedia of Philosophy. Available at: https://plato.stanford.edu/archives/fall2019/entries/logic-games/

7. Jaśkowski, S. (1934) On the Rules of Suppositions in Formal Logic. Poświęcone logice i jej historji [Dedicated to logic and its history] 1, 5–32.

8. Lorenzen, P. (1955) Einführung in die operative Logik und Mathematik [Introduction to Operational Logic and Mathematics]. Berlin, Göttingen, Heidelberg: Springer-Verlag. [In German].

9. Lorenzen, P., Lorenz, K. (1978) Dialogische Logik [Dialogical Logic]. Darmstadt: Wissenschaftliche Buchgesellschaft. [In German].

10. Russel, B. (1972) A History of Western philosophy. New York, London, Toronto, Sydney: A Touchstone Book, Simon and Schuster.

11. von Plato, J. (2018) The development of proof theory. The Stanford Encyclopedia of Philosophy. Available at: https://plato.stanford.edu/archives/win2018/entries/proof-theory-development/

Chapter 5. The nature of mathematics

5.1. Mathematical sciences and philosophy of mathematics

Mathematics (from Greek μάθημα – knowledge, study, learning) - one of the branches of science. It includes the following sciences: category theory, topology, and algebra, number theory and numerical analysis, geometry, mathematical and function analysis, probability theory, mathematical statistics, operations research, computer mathematics. The list contains only ten sciences, each of which in its turn contains a number of theories. For example, geometry includes projective geometry, non-Euclidean geometry, Euclidean geometry, and so on. Of course, one cannot say that this list exhausts the variety of mathematical sciences. However, in the first approximation, it presents this variety in quite a full form.

The history of the development of mathematics explains much of the nature of mathematical sciences. In its original ancient version, mathematics was represented by only two sciences, namely, arithmetic and geometry. The increase in the number of mathematical sciences was the result of centuries of development. In this process, the following four trends were clearly manifested. First, there was a generalization of mathematical knowledge, the result of which was the emergence of algebra, topology, and then the theory of categories. Secondly, the arithmetic and geometry themselves changed. In its current form, arithmetic is part of the theory of numbers, which in turn is at the root of functional analysis. Thirdly, mathematical disciplines arose that were initiated not so much inside mathematics as by its surroundings. These sciences include the study of operations and computer mathematics. Fourth, numerous connections between mathematical sciences have been revealed. It is to be supposed that within the framework of mathematics, interdisciplinary connections testify to its unity (compare algebraic geometry, number geometry, algebraic number theory, etc.).

To give an extremely concise description of mathematics, it is necessary to turn to the most general mathematical conception, which is the theory of categories. Otherwise, we would risk getting lost in details. A mathematical category is a collection of mathematical objects of the same type and mappings (morphisms) between them. Thus, it is necessary to distinguish between a class of objects and a class of morphisms. It is extremely important that these two classes are not equivalent. The fact is that morphisms are not somehow extracted from objects. Morphisms define the specificity (meaning) of objects. It is quite legitimate to assert that mathematics is the science of morphisms. This says the main thing. Nevertheless, the above definition of mathematics is not enough if guided by an unofficially established rule, according to which, in determining the specificity of a particular science, it is imperative to characterize its objects. In view of this norm, it seems that one can define mathematics as follows. Mathematics is the science of objects studied up to morphisms. However, this definition is already wrong. The fact is that mathematics is studying morphisms; everything else is beyond its sphere of competence. The expression "up to morphisms" suggests that there is something behind morphisms, from which the mathematicians abstract. Mathematicians do really study what is part of other sciences. Mathematics is an independent science it studies morphisms. Being of morphisms does not depend on any operation of abstraction.

The Greek word morphe means externality. When dealing with mappings, mathematics studies objects of the same externality. The sciences of morphisms are called formal. Certain morphisms are studied not by mathematics, but by logic. However, logic is not dealing with mathematical, but logical morphisms. Thus, mathematics is the science of special classes of morphisms. At this point, I only emphasize that all mathematical objects, be they numbers, figures, rings, fields, tensors, vectors, are defined by means of morphisms.

Every science needs a metascientific companion. This circumstance was understood in mathematics only at the turn of the 19th and 20th centuries. Precisely during this period, D. Hilbert put forward a program for the development of metamathematics. Of course, long before this, mathematicians met with great difficulties, the comprehension of which was sometimes delayed for centuries. Strictly speaking, they testify to the need for metamathematics. We give some examples. Within the framework of Euclidean geometry, the status of mathematical concepts remained unclear. Are there really points, straight lines, including parallel straight lines that go to infinity? The emergence of mathematical analysis drew attention to the notion of a limit. What are these quantities, called infinitesimal? The question of infinity became the subject of a headache for many generations of mathematicians, in particular, in connection with the creation of set theory. The question of the possibility and necessity of non-Euclidean geometries remained somewhat mysterious. A lot of controversies is connected with understanding the requirements to the axioms of mathematical theory, in particular, to their consistency, completeness, independence from each other. Numerous paradoxes of set theory, revealed at the beginning of the 20th century, filled the "cup of patience" of mathematicians. They energetically began to develop various metamathematical projects. The classical beginning of metamathematics was the programs of D. Hilbert's formalism, G. Frege and B. Russell's logicism, L. Brouwer's intuitionism.

In this connection, a circumstance deserving of special attention emerged. Metamathematics developed by professional mathematicians. Like other colleagues, they offered systems of axioms and proved theorems. To a certain extent, the line between sub- and metamathematics was obliterated. On the other hand, the problems of mathematics were vigorously discussed by those who came from philosophy. They, as a rule, did not prove any theorems, nevertheless, they gave them and other mathematical concepts profound characteristics. In fact, they considered the interdisciplinary relationship between mathematics and philosophy. The philosophy of mathematics is precisely the use of the achievements of philosophy in the interests of mathematics.

Within the framework of science as a whole, mathematics is closest in its content to logic and computer science. On the relationship of logic, mathematics and computer science, see section 4.1.

5.2. Intuitionism and constructivism

The creation by G. Cantor of the theory of infinite sets, which led to numerous paradoxes, stimulated the critical thought of many outstanding mathematicians. The greatest doubt was caused by the concept of infinity. A number of mathematicians, including L. Kronecker and H. Poincaré, offered constructive ideas as an antidote to the paradoxes of the "naive" set theory. It was meant that an object assuming the realization of an infinite number of acts cannot be constructed hence infinity is impossible. However, they failed to formalize their representations as a direction of metamathematics. This honor fell on the Hollander L.E.J. Brouwer [3]. He was very careful in handling philosophical constructions. Nevertheless, he preferred to bring a solid philosophical base to mathematics.

First, all truths are constructed in consciousness. They are not given initially. They must be worked out, designed. Language in comparison with consciousness is secondary. Secondly, the construction of truths is possible only insofar as a person has the original intuition of time. Whatever event a person is dealing with, he always encounters duality the synthesis of the sides of which are provided by the intuition of time.

Third, Brouwer believed that a person's consciousness, not being determined by any external circumstances, forms an arbitrary loosely becoming sequence. It is possible that the creations of this or that person will not be accepted by other people. Nevertheless, everyone is free in his original work.

Thus, the foundations of the Brouwer metamathematics are three propositions: 1) the primacy of the mentality in relation to language, 2) the intuition of time, which opens the door to understand the nature of constructions, 3) the freely becoming sequence of mathematical steps.

The basic idea of intuitionists is to understand both logical and mathematical concepts as constructs. The construct is recognized as existing only if it can be built. In classical mathematics, intuitionists believe, first, do not pay due attention to the question of the existence of its constructs. This aspect of mathematics is simply misunderstood. Secondly, the world of mathematics is recognized initially as something absolute and unchanging. Thirdly, the actual infinity is recognized as valid. Nevertheless, due to the time factor in the procedural respect, infinity is unattainable. Consequently, the actual infinity is an illusion, which is misleading. The intuitionist believes that no one is allowed to reach the end of a freely becoming sequence. Admissible is the abstraction of not actual, but of potential infinity. Thus, using the method of mathematical induction, we can constructively prove the existence of an arbitrarily large number. It seems that by insisting on the existence of an arbitrarily large number, the intuitionist contradicts himself: this number cannot be built in real-time. However, the intuitionist does not claim that the logical sequence of steps is made in real-time. Strictly speaking, he does not mean a real, but a logical time.

The ratio of intuitionists to logic is very specific. They do not deny it, but they do not consider it a prerequisite of mathematics. To think differently means to allow the existence of an outside force for mathematics. All positions of non-intuitionistic logic are tested for their suitability. Brouwer himself showed an example in this matter, having devoted his dissertation to criticizing the law of the excluded third, according to which either A or not-A is true. Intuitionists believe that significant shortcomings are characteristic of the classical understanding of literally all propositional connections (implications, disjunctions, etc.). Nevertheless, an intuitionistic interpretation of logical propositions is possible. Together they form intuitionistic logic, which was first introduced by A. Heyting.

What has been said about the specifics of intuitionistic mathematics is sufficient to recognize its uniqueness. Estimating the status of intuitionistic mathematics, I note the following circumstances. First, the thesis about the subjective nature of mathematics is rarely supported by modern scholars. Perhaps we should admit that insisting on the subjective nature of mathematics intuitionists absolutized the sphere of mentality. Secondly, it is hardly advisable to consider the intuition of time as the basis of all mathematics. Thirdly, it turned out that the freedom of mathematical creativity has its limits. Fourth, the attitude of intuitionists to their opponents from the field of mathematics and the philosophy of mathematics turned out to be unnecessarily critical. When comparing intuitionism with other areas of the philosophy of mathematics, one should abandon the scheme either-or. One of the pillars of intuitionism, A. Heyting, comparing the state of affairs in mathematics in the 1930s and 1960s, stated that initially, representatives of various mathematical trends considered as the only right the direction to which they belonged. The situation changed drastically by 1960.

> The spirit of peaceful cooperation has gained the victory over that of ruthless contest. No direction of research has any longer the pretension to represent the only true mathematics. The philosophical importance of research in the foundations of mathematics consists at least partly in the isolation of formal, intuitive, logical, and platonistic elements in the structure of classical mathematics, and in the exact determination no of their scope and their limitations. A new form of mathematics is born, in which we know at every moment whether we work on an intuitive basis or not, which part of the work is purely formal, and which platonistic assumptions we make. [4, 194].

Intuitionists did not manage to give their criticism of classical mathematics a complete character. Thus, the criticism of the abstraction of actual infinity was not explained to the fact of its known acceptability. On the other hand, opponents of intuitionistic mathematics failed to show its deficiency. D. Hilbert argued that taking away from mathematicians the law of the excluded third would be tantamount to prohibiting astronomers from using telescopes. However, such a statement is declarative. At this point, perhaps, it is appropriate to briefly describe the relationship between Hilbert and Brouwer, the leaders, respectively, of formalism and intuitionism in mathematics.

Hilbert, being a supporter of the construction of any mathematical formula in a finite number of steps, should be counted among the scientists who stood at the origins of constructivism, occupying a prominent place in intuitionism, whose claims, however, he considered excessive. Brower as a very emotional man sharply criticized the philosophy of mathematics of Hilbert. They did not succeed in reaching an agreement. Each of them sought to find the only true path in mathematics.

If the philosophy of mathematics does not begin with the principle of intuition, but with a constructive principle, then they deal with constructivism in mathematics. Thus, intuitionism in mathematics, on the one hand, and constructivism, on the other hand, do not coincide with each other. Along with the indicated difference, constructivism differs from intuitionism in its relation to language. Intuitionists put language after mentality. Constructivists, as a rule, understand this or that mathematical system like a language. Thus, they restore language in mathematics in those of its rights that are not recognized in intuitionism. The intuitionistic thesis of a freely becoming sequence is also, as a rule, not accepted by constructivists. It is understood that the design should be carried out according to certain rules, which are usually specified by some algorithms. The concept of potential infinity is also called into question. The process must have a valid end or it becomes aimless. As for the law of the excluded third, then constructivists treat him differently than intuitionists. Intuitionists reject it. Constructivists believe that if a constructive process is possible, then in its estimation one can use the law of the excluded third. Thus, for a number of its conceptual features, constructivism differs from intuitionism. [2].

Various variants of constructive mathematics are known. In particular, we are talking about the recursive mathematics of A.A. Markov [5], the constructive mathematics of E. Bishop [1], and the constructive theory of types of P. Martin-Löf [6].

In the recursive mathematics of Markov, in connection with the refinement of the concept of the algorithm, the concept of a normal algorithm is introduced. Normal algorithms are verbal, that is, designed to apply to words in different alphabets. The definition of any normal algorithm consists of two parts: the definition of the alphabet of the algorithm (to the words to which the algorithm will be applied) and the definition of its scheme. The scheme of a normal algorithm is a finite ordered set of substitution formulas, each of which can be simple or final. There are good reasons to believe that any normal algorithm is equivalent to some Turing machine, and vice versa – any Turing machine is equivalent to some normal algorithm. The recursive mathematics of Markov is especially effective when the basic objects of the theory admit a representation in the form of words in some alphabet.

E. Bishop believed [1] that both Brouwer's intuitionistic logic and the normal Markov algorithm are excessively radical requirements that limit the possibilities of constructive analysis. Brouwer and Markov recognized the priority of mathematics over logic, which led to the limitation of the merits of logic. Bishop suggested taking a pragmatic point of view. In each separate case, it is necessary to build a computational function and perform the corresponding calculations. However, at the same time, it is necessary to use all the possibilities, even if they contradict the set of principles of intuitionism and the recursive mathematics of Markov. This is a kind of pragmatic interpretation of constructive mathematics. The Swedish mathematician P. Martin-Löf charted a path that was to take into account the achievements of constructive mathematics of both Markov and Bishop [6]. He introduced objects of two levels. Roughly speaking, the objects of the lower level are built according to Markov. Objects of the highest level, types, are built according to Bishop. As we can see, constructive mathematics can develop in different ways, sometimes approaching, sometimes moving away from the provisions of Brouwer, Markov, and Bishop.

References

1. Bishop, E. (1967) Foundations of Constructive Analysis. New York: Mcgraw–Hill.
2. Bridges, D. and Palmgren, E. (2018) Constructive mathematics. The Stanford Encyclopedia of Philosophy. Available at: https://plato.stanford.edu/archives/sum2018/entries/mathematics-constructive/

3. Brouwer, L.E.J. (1975) Collected Works. Volume I. Philosophy and Foundations of Mathematics. Ed. by A. Heyting. Amsterdam, New York: North-Holland/American Elsevier.
4. Heyting, A. (1962) After thirty years. In Logic, Methodology and Philosophy of Science: Proceeding of the 1960 International Congress. Ed. by E. Nagel, P. Suppes, and A. Tarski. California: Stanford University Press, 194–197.
5. Markov, A.A., Nagornyi, N.M. (1984) Teoriya algorifmov [Theory of Algorithms]. Moskva: Nauka. [In Russian].
6. Martin-Löf, P. (1970) Notes on Constructive Mathematics. Stockholm: Almqvist and Wiksell.

5.3. Formalism

The founder of the formalism is the German mathematician D. Hilbert. Pushing this program out for the first time in 1899, he substantially reworked it in the 1920s. Moreover, worked on it until his death in 1942. He was not satisfied with either logicism or intuitionism. He believed that supporters of logicism vainly try to reduce mathematics to logic. Intuitionists overly narrow the sphere of mathematics, refusing many of its achievements, including the Cantor theory of infinite sets. Hilbert himself was very keen on mathematics. He wanted to preserve all achievements of mathematics. In this connection, the subject of his special attention was, along with genuine mathematical objects, so-called mathematical idealizations, for example, imaginary numbers, infinitesimal quantities, and actual infinity. Genuine mathematical objects are needed to describe real phenomena, Hilbert believed. However, what is the status of idealizations, for example, infinity?

In summary, let us return to our main theme and draw some conclusions from all our thinking about the infinite. Our principal result is that the infinite is nowhere to be found in reality. It neither exists in nature nor provides a legitimate basis for rational thought — a remarkable harmony between being and thought. In contrast to the earlier efforts of Frege and Dedekind, we are convinced that certain intuitive concepts and insights are necessary conditions of scientific knowledge, and logic alone is not sufficient. Operating with the infinite can be made certain only by the finitary.

The role that remains for the infinite to play is solely that of an idea — if one means by an idea, in Kant's terminology, a concept of reason which transcends all experience and which completes the concrete as a totality — that of an idea which we may unhesitatingly trust within the framework erected by our theory. [1, 190]

Reconstructing the course of Hilbert's thought, it can be generalized as follows. It is permissible to include in the theory only such idealizations, which do not violate its status. They have an auxiliary meaning. It is inadmissible to include in the theory idealization, which destroys it, i.e. make unacceptable contradictions in mathematics. Since idealizations do not describe real phenomena, they are invented by the person himself. In accordance with Kant's philosophy, man is able to invent transcendental and transcendent ideas. Unlike transcendental ideas, transcendent positions lead to contradictions. Consequently, mathematical idealizations have a transcendental character, that is, they are the result of the activity of reason. He, dealing with real phenomena, ascribes to them a transcendental schematic that does not coincide either with real phenomena or with the processes of consciousness. Hence, Hilbert concluded that formal mathematical methods should be formalized and symbols should be used. As for the justifications of mathematical theories, it is forced to be three-step. First, it is necessary to avoid the transcendent concepts in every way, which introduce contradictions into mathematical theories. Secondly, it is necessary to prove that the transcendental concepts, i.e., idealizations, are harmless, they only testify to the strength of the basic core of the theory. Thirdly, it is necessary to justify the consistency of the core of the theory. Ultimately, having avoided Scylla and Charybdis of empiricism and intuitionism, Hilbert found himself in his native mathematical domain. The reliability of the theory must be justified in the theory of mathematical proof.

The core of the Hilbert mathematics justification program includes three provisions: 1) classical mathematics should be axiomatized; 2) it is necessary to show its completeness and consistency by finite methods; 3) mathematicians have to show that mathematical innovations do not violate the harmony of mathematics, whose foundation is arithmetic of G. Peano. The program for substantiating mathematics was adopted by many outstanding mathematicians, in particular, K. Gödel, J. von Neumann, and P. Bernays.

Formalism met with significant difficulties, which were represented in the clearest form by K. Gödel in his two famous theorems (1931). According to Gödel's incompleteness theorem, if formal arithmetic is consistent, then there is a formally unsolvable sentence in it, i.e. such a formula A that neither A nor non-A can be deduced from the axioms of the system.

Gödel's incompleteness theorem applies to all formal systems that include the axioms of arithmetic. In these systems, as A, one can take a formula that expresses the consistency of formal arithmetic. In this case, the Gödel's theorem of consistency follows from the incompleteness theorem: there is no proof of the consistency of formal arithmetic by means of the formal system that contains it.

Gödel's theorems were initially perceived as proof of the failure of the formalism program. In any sufficiently rich formal axiomatic system, there are always true statements that are unprovable in its framework. Only gradually, it was found out that the program of formalism, as a whole is one of the variants of interpreting the ideals of mathematical knowledge. In it, one should distinguish: a) fruitful ideas, b) unjustified idealizations. Removal of these idealizations does not destroy the entire program of formalism but precise its actual content. The Hilbert program does not reduce to pseudo-problems; it is a real program of effective scientific research [6].

In 1936, the student of Hilbert G. Gentzen proved the consistency of arithmetic. A departure from the "hard" formalism program was that the usual principle of mathematical induction was generalized to a transfinite number ω_0. This generalized version of induction is not formalized in Peano's arithmetic.

It is impossible to formalize all mathematics, but this provision is not an obstacle to the formalization of its individual parts. It can be pointed out in this connection that set theory, based on the Zermelo-Fraenkel axioms, plus first-order logic allows one to formalize many branches of mathematics. As for the very logic of the first order, its completeness and consistency were proved by Gödel. The Japanese mathematician G. Takeuti succeeded in proving the completeness of certain parts of second-order logic and arithmetic [5].

G. Kreisel, S. Feferman, and S. Simpson received interesting results by Hilbert's program [3; 1, 284-298; 4]. These researchers seek, first, to identify those sections of classical mathematics that can be successfully formalized. Secondly, they reduce still not formalized mathematical theories or their parts to the already formalized.

It was shown that in the absence of acceptable idealizations, the length of mathematical conclusions increases. In non-standard models of mathematical analysis, along with real numbers, there are non-standard, including infinitesimal and infinitely large numbers. Nonstandard analysis can be considered as the development of Hilbert's idea of the need for ideal concepts.

Finally, it is extremely important that in physics, mathematical theories are used without fail, together with their ideal components (functions of a complex variable, the concept of infinity). When interpreting the results of physical measurements, idealizations are eliminated. This means that the Hilbert program has not only purely mathematical but also applied value.

Thus, the program of formalism is one of the most important areas of modern metamathematics. Nevertheless, the presence of problematic issues in it is beyond doubt. In our opinion, the formalists in vain want to reduce complex theories to simpler ones. In fact, this desire does not lead to actual successes.

References

1. Feferman, S. (1998) In the Light of Logic. Oxford: Oxford University Press.
2. Hilbert, D. (1926) Über das Unendliche [About the infinite]. Mathematische Annalen 95(1), 161-190. [In German].
3. Kreisel, G. (1983) Hilbert's program. In Philosophy of Mathematics. Ed. by P. Benacerraf and H. Putnam. Cambridge: Cambridge University Press, 207–238.
4. Simpson, S.G. (1988) Partial Realizations of Hilbert's Program. Journal of Symbolic Logic 53(2), 349-363.
5. Takeuti, G. (1987) Proof Theory: Studies in Logic and the Foundations of Mathematics. Vol. 81. Amsterdam: North-Holland.
6. Zach, R. (2019) Hilbert's program. The Stanford Encyclopedia of Philosophy. Available at: https://plato.stanford.edu/archives/fall2019/entries/hilbert-program/

5.4. Set-theoretical, type-theoretical and category-theoretical directions

Of great importance in the study of the nature of mathematics was the development of set theory. If it is the theory of sets that is the foundation of mathematics, then its study acquires strategic significance in the philosophy of mathematics. Knowing what the theory of sets is, you can say a lot about all mathematics.

According to the set-theoretical direction, first, other mathematical theories must be reduced to set theory. Secondly, the theory of sets itself must be strictly justified axiomatically. In the considered direction, set theory plays a special role, namely, as an ideal, the methodological norm of mathematics. Among the leaders of the set-theoretic direction, more often than others, G. Cantor, E. Zermelo, A. Fraenkel, and K. Gödel are called. The set-theoretic direction has much in common with logicism and, in particular, with formalism. In all three directions, the axiomatic method is welcomed in every possible way. Nevertheless, in methodological respect, the set-theoretic direction is autonomous; its ideals are of independent significance.

The continuum hypothesis states that there is no set whose cardinality is strictly between that of the integers and the real numbers. The axiom of choice is equivalent to the following statement: for every family X of non-empty sets, there exists a function f, which assigns to each set in the family one of the elements of this set. The continuum hypothesis is relevant in the validation of the axiomatics of set theory. The problem consisted of elucidating the possibility of either proving or refuting the axiom of choice and the continuum hypothesis. The clarity in this problem was introduced only in 1963 [4], primarily due to the works of K. Gödel and P. Cohen.

It was proved that in the Zermelo-Fraenkel axioms, the axiom of choice and the continuum hypothesis, as well as the negation of both propositions, are insoluble. This means that if the Zermelo-Fraenkel axioms are consistent, then one can add to them either one of the statements under consideration, or both, as well as either the negation of one of the propositions or the negation of both. One can even abandon the axiom of choice and the continuum hypothesis, but in this case, the theory of sets is impoverished. There are other ways of constructing axiomatic set theory, not mentioned by me. The conclusion from the above, especially when one considers that the Zermelo-Fraenkel axiomatics is not unique, is obvious: a number of different set theories are possible.

In this context, the Löwenheim–Skolem theorem is also worthy of note. It turned out that any axiomatic system is non-categorical, that is, it can be interpreted in different ways. Thus, the same theory can represent both countable and uncountable sets (an uncountable set, unlike a countable set, is not equivalent to the set of natural numbers). There is something like the principle of mathematical relativity. The nature of the set is not originally given. It is theoretically loaded in the sense that it depends on the axiomatic chosen and its interpretations.

It should be noted that, in the light of the difficulties encountered by the programs of logic and formalism, the age-old prosperity of axiomatic set theory raises some surprise. Formalists spend enormous efforts on proving the consistency of mathematical theories. But it turns out that there is another way, perhaps much more economical. We just need to pick up the axioms in such a way that they, on the one hand, block out various kinds of trouble, on the other hand, ensure the development of the theory, in particular, the proof of new theorems. Of course, certain difficulties will inevitably meet on this path, which cannot be foreseen. However, they can be overcome. The formulation of each axiom assumes the consideration of numerous conceptual subtleties. Let my formulate the Zermelo-Fraenkel axioms in the verbal form [9, 295-296].

1) Two sets are identical if they consist of the same elements.
2) There is an empty set.
3) If x and y are sets, then the unordered pair (x, y) is also a set.

4) The union of any set of sets is also a set.

5) There is an infinite set.

6) Any property formalized in the language of theory can be used to define a set.

7) It is possible to form a set of subsets of any set, i.e. the set of all subsets of a given set is a set.

8) Axiom of choice.

9) x does not belong to x.

Some of these axioms seem intuitively clear, for example, the first axiom. Others raise great doubts. Intuitively, for example, it is not entirely clear why one should introduce an idea of an empty set. However, with careful analysis, it turns out that all axioms are necessary insofar as in their absence it is not possible to develop the potential of set theory. Each axiom is an unobvious concept, the formulation of which presupposes an exceptional refined understanding of the essence of set theory. From this point of view, it is difficult to overestimate the scientific feat of Ernst Zermelo, who managed to work out the framework of the axiomatic set theory.

Not always, the set-theoretical direction is evaluated as one of the directions in the philosophy of mathematics. It seems that his supporters do not so frankly define their philosophical position, as, for example, logicists, intuitionists, and formalists. Nevertheless, this impression is deceptive. In fact, the set-theoretical direction is by no means neutral in philosophical terms. It includes a provision on the fundamental character of set theory, which, by definition, constitutes the basis of all mathematics, and relies on the axiomatic method, which is regarded as the conceptual core of all mathematics.

The theory of sets with all its advantages met with many difficulties. Called to free mathematics from paradoxes, she herself became their refuge. Particularly significant was the paradox of Russell [7, 130]. To formulate it, I use the notion of Russell's class R. It is the class of all classes, which are not members of themselves. Russell's paradox is the following contradiction: if R is not a member of itself, then its definition dictates that it must contain itself, and if it contains itself, then it contradicts its own definition as the set of all sets that are not members of themselves. For the derivation of this contradiction, no axioms and sentences of set theory are used, apart from the definition of the class. It turns out that the contradiction in question is characteristic directly for the initial foundations of the theory of the set. Overcoming Russell's paradox became the primary task of mathematicians.

B. Russell proposed the most original way to overcome the paradox he discovered. This is a theory of types, according to which all the concepts of logical and mathematical theories are located in a hierarchy [14]. The theory is based on the following idea: simple objects in this theory have type 0, classes of simple objects have type 1, and classes of classes of simple objects have type 2 and so on. Thus, no class can have itself as an element. The device of the theory of types is incompatible with the recognition of the relevance of the notion of a set of all sets that are not members of themselves.

The theory of types postulates the existence of a huge number of hierarchy levels whose independent status raises doubts among those scientists who believe that there is nothing else in the world than objects with their attributes whose values are determined in experiments. B. Russell was just such a scientist. Avoiding mentioned difficulties, he introduced the notion of the axiom of reducibility which, in fact, postulates the reducibility of an arbitrary function to the concepts of the first level. Then the principle of hierarchy that is actual for the theory of types is destroyed. As shown by F. Ramsey, the type hierarchy is completely redundant in the presence of the axiom of reducibility [13]. From the axiom of reducibility had to be abandoned. Nevertheless, this circumstance does not call into question the actuality of the provision that every term has a type and operations are restricted to terms of a certain type. Two well-known type theories are A. Church's typed λ-calculus and P. Martin-Löf's intuitionistic type theory.

At the beginning of the XX century, set theory and type theory were considered as the basis of all mathematical knowledge. In the second half of the last century, they acquired an influential rival, the category theory. The fundamental work in its formation was the classical work of S. Eilenberg and S. Mac Lane [5]. They needed a term that would generalize the term «type». This is precisely the term «category», borrowed from the philosophy of Aristotle. Of course, this is a mathematical, and not a philosophical category. For more than 10 years, until the appearance of pioneering works by A. Grothendieck in the late 1950s, category theory was not perceived as an independent theory but was regarded as a convenient language for considering the most generalized branches of mathematics, the meaning of which, in the final analysis, should be determined set-theoretic way.

The formation of the theory of categories as an independent mathematical science was completed by 1970. Especially important in this connection, are along with the work of Grothendieck, who introduced the concept of topos into mathematics, F. Lawyer's works. He realized that category theory is relevant not only for mathematics but also for logic. In this connection, it was reasonable to take category theory as a general formal conception. As for the philosophical interpretation of the theory of categories, it has acquired impressive forms, perhaps only in the last twenty years [12].

A category is understood as the unity of structures of mathematical objects with their continuous transformations, called morphisms. Corresponding examples are the notions of sets, topological spaces, and groups. Varieties of morphisms are isomorphism, endomorphism, automorphism, monomorphism, epimorphism, and bimorphism. They are also called arrows, i.e. transitions between structures. The concept of function is generalized to the concept of a functor, which is a map between categories.

Why did category theory not immediately gain citizenship rights in mathematics? Mathematicians have always known that algebra is the universal mathematical discipline. Nevertheless, why in this case it was not it, but the theory of sets, considered the foundation of mathematics? The fact is that in algebra, the focus is not on objects and their attributes, but on operations on objects. The nature of objects is not clarified. But it is the nature of objects that attracts paramount attention.

The category theory that inherited the potential of algebra, as well as of topology, was evaluated in the same way as algebra. Category theory study abstractions from the nature of mathematical objects. Even prominent representatives of category theory often claim that they study abstract structures. Reasoning about abstract structures is not so obvious and not as harmless as it seems at first glance. First, as a rule, it is not reported from what exactly is abstracted when introducing the notion of a structure. In this case, the nature of the structure itself remains unseparated. Secondly, and this is especially important, the conceptual side of the matter is not given due attention. In this respect, the successes of representatives of category theory are very revealing. Unlike their opponents, they realized that the notions of categories, morphisms, and functors do not impoverish the conceptual content of mathematics, but, on the contrary, substantially increase it. This circumstance found a clear expression in S. Awodey's article [1].

He notes that it has become a commonplace to recognize the exceptional importance in clarifying the foundations of mathematics by the three theories, set theory, type theory, and category theory. However, this does not reveal the relationship between them and their most important concepts, which are respectively sets, types and categories. Therefore, he considers transitions: sets ↔ types plus types ↔ categories plus sets ↔ categories and depicts it in the form of a triangle. Each of the concepts gets its interpretation within the framework of this triangle. Each of them has its own advantages. For example, the sets are most specific, while the categories are intended for direct study of structures. In this respect, they are more effective than the concept of type.

In my opinion, the idea of considering the correlation between the concepts of set, type, and category, is fruitful. It must be considered in the context of the conception of league-theories. The theory of types arose not accidentally, but as a reaction to the difficulties of naive set theory with its numerous paradoxes. In turn, category theory also arose not accidentally but was a reaction to the fragmentation of mathematical theories, not overcome because of their set-theoretic interpretation.

It is significant that each subsequent theory increased the conceptual potential of mathematics. However, it did not completely reject its predecessors. They were subjected to a new interpretation. Both set theory and type theory were now evaluated from the standpoint of category theory. Consequently, in fact, formed a league-theory:

$$T_{cat} \rightarrow T_{typ}\{T_{cat}\} \rightarrow T_{set}\{T_{cat}\}. \qquad\qquad 5.1$$

E. Landry characterizes the theory of categories as a formalized linguistic philosophical conceptual schematic [9]. In my opinion, the theory of categories is not philosophical, but a metamathematical theory, this, in the first place. Secondly, it is not only a linguistic but also a mental construction.

The question of the ontological status of mathematical objects deserves special attention. In this regard, the position of J.-P. Marquis seems to my very productive [12]. First, the nature of objects is characterized by the framework of category theory. Secondly, objects are characterized as morphisms. There are no such objects as, for example, natural numbers. There is the concept of a natural number. What this concept refers to depends on the context. Often mathematicians try to define mathematical objects in all their uniqueness. The correct way of reasoning is the determination of the types of mathematical objects, that are represented by signs. As for the interpretation of signs, it depends on the appropriate context. Thus, category theory sheds additional light on the ontological problems of mathematics.

The category theory allowed to largely ordering mathematical theories. It culminates in the search for the fundamental principles of mathematics. The nature of any class of objects is determined by the corresponding morphisms. This result is extremely nontrivial.

J.C. Baez and M. Stay managed to highlight the general scientific relevance of the theory of categories in a particularly striking manner [3, 66]. From the standpoint of category theory, logic, topology, physics, and computation theory are arranged in the same way. We add to this that in recent years, especially in connection with the development of the concept of the conjugate functor, category theory has been used quite successfully not only in natural sciences but also in the social sciences [6].

The development of category theory is by no means an ordinary fact in the history of the development of mathematics. In fact, it stimulates a number of innovations in the field of metamathematics.

References

1. Awodey, S. (2004) An answer to Hellman's question: does category theory provide a framework for mathematical structuralism. Philosophia Mathematica 12(1), 54-64.
2. Awodey, S. (2011) From sets to types to categories to sets. In Sommaruga, G. (Ed.). Foundational Theories of Classical and Constructive Mathematics. The Western Ontario Series in Philosophy of Science, Vol. 76. Dordrecht: Springer,113-125.
3. Baez, J. C. and Stay, M. (2011) Physics, topology, logic and computation: a rosetta stone. In New Structures for Physics. Ed. by B. Coece. Berlin: Springer, 95-174.
4. *Cohen, P.J. (2008) [1966]. Set Theory and the Continuum Hypothesis. Mineola, New York: Dover Publications.*
5. Eilenberg, S., Mac Lane, S. (1945) General theory of natural equivalences. Transactions of the American Mathematical Society 58(2), 231-294.

6. Ellerman, D. (2006) A Theory of adjoint functors – with some thoughts about their philosophical significance. In What is Category Theory? Ed. by G. Sica. Milano: Polymetrica, 127-183.

7. Frege, G. (1980) Philosophical and Mathematical Correspondence. Oxford: Basil Blackwell.

8. Hellman, G. (2003) Does category theory provide a framework for mathematical structuralism? Philosophia Mathematica 11(2), 129-157.

9. Kline, M. (1984) Matematika. Utrata opredelennosti [Mathematics. Loss of certainty]. Moskva: Mir. [In Russian].

10. Landry, E. (2002) Category theory as a framework for an in re interpretation of mathematical structuralism. In The Age of Alternative Logics. Assessing Philosophy of Logic and Mathematics Today. Based on the Conference on Philosophical Insights into Logic and Mathematics. Nancy, France, September 30 - October 4, 2002, 163-179.

11. Mac Lane, S. (1992) The protean character of mathematics. In The Space of Mathematics. Berlin: DeGruyter, 3–13.

12. Marquis, J.-P. (2019) Category theory. The Stanford Encyclopedia of Philosophy. Available at: https://plato.stanford.edu/archives/fall2019/entries/category-theory/

13. Ramsey, F.P. (1931) The Foundation of Mathematics and Other Logical Essays. London: Routledge and Kegan Paul, 1931.

14. Russell, B. (1908) Mathematical logic as based on the theory of types. American Journal of Mathematics 30(3), 222-262.

5.5. Platonism and fictionalism

Operating with mathematical theories, the scientist certainly introduces the notion of mathematical objects. As a result, the question of their nature is initiated. He attracted the attention of ancient philosophers. Of course, each of them, when interpreting the nature of mathematical objects, was guided by one or another philosophical theory. Many of these theories are forgotten. However, this does not apply to Plato's theory, who was guided by the concept of forms developed by him. The form was understood as the sample of a certain class of objects, capable of being autonomous from them. From this point of view, there is, for example, the form of a triangle, which does not coincide with made of this or that material, triangular objects. Plato believed that the world of mathematical objects is a world of mathematical forms that exist independently of people.

Mathematicians remember Plato much more often than, for example, physicists. Physicists compare their sensory experience with physical objects. It is difficult for mathematicians to compare sensory impressions to mathematical objects. In this regard, mathematicians, as evidenced, in particular, by the works of G. Frege and K. Gödel, is capable of actualizing the platonic representations. Why do eminent mathematicians sometimes reanimate platonism?

Frege believed that the work of the scientist consists not in creation, but in the discovery of truths. Truth exists independently of this or that person. « The thought we express by the Pythagorean theorem is surely timeless, eternal, unchangeable. » [4, 217]. Truths are real, but their reality is of a completely different kind than the reality of things. The same can be said about mathematical objects. Arguing about them, we introduce concepts, but not arbitrary, but true. The number, for example, 2 will remain so, regardless of the evolution of human beings.

The essence of Gödel's philosophical and mathematical views is as follows [5]. He compares mathematics to physics. It turns out that both sciences deal with objects that are understood in a nontrivial way. In physics, as an exemplary science, Gödel does not see anything that could cause him to doubt the consistency of mathematics as a theory about a particular reality. Both physicists and mathematicians have no direct access to reality. Mathematicians realize this access through intuition. There is no reason not to trust her.

Let me also mention platitudinous (abundant) platonism, according to which in every mathematical theory the notion of objects is inevitably introduced, and they must be accepted as real. M. Balaguer argues about a full-blooded platonism, which is defended and refuted no less successfully than anti-platonism [1].

Let me single out the conceptual core of mathematical platonism. 1) In mathematical theories, there are concepts of mathematical objects. 2) These objects are abstract because they do not have space-time certainty. 3) Mathematical reality is specific. It differs, for example, from physical reality. Should we agree with the supporters of mathematical platonism? They are right, but only in part.

Arguing about the nature of mathematical objects, one should take into account the status of mathematics. Mathematics is formal, not concrete. From a specific, for example, physical or economic, one aspect is singled out, while others are simply ignored. What is extracted does not exist by itself, autonomously. In my opinion, this fact is misunderstood by platonists. They do not take into account that mathematical objects are the result of formalization. These objects do exist, but not otherwise than as part of a concrete one. It is wrong to consider mathematical theories in themselves. It is imperative to emphasize their origins, which are contained in human activity, in their ability to isolate the formal.

Frege asserted that '2 × 2 is 4' is true and will remain so. Alas, he was wrong. The concept of truth is the property of people. Without theories of people, both truth and its antagonist, error, are impossible. Without humans, neither 2 × 2 = 4 nor 2 × 2 = 5 can be realized. By the way, one should not forget that any theory is improved, even one that claims that 2 × 2 = 4. The problem of mathematical platonism consists of insufficient accounting for the conceptual status of mathematics and its dependence on people.

In the works of platonists, mathematical objects are ideal forms. Proponents of fictionalism present mathematical objects in an even more exotic form; they consider them fictions. In historical terms, fictionalism goes back to the ideas of the skeptic Pyrrho of Elis (IV century BC). Skeptics refuse to consider the semantic meaning of words and sentences. In mathematics, where so much difficulty is associated with the definition of the nature of mathematical objects, fictionalism has found nutritional soil. After the appearance of the work of H. Field [3], it took shape as an independent mathematical direction.

M. Balaguer defines fictionalism as follows: 1) our mathematical propositions and theories talk about abstract mathematical objects; 2) such objects do not exist; 3) consequently, mathematical theories are not true [2]. Fictionalists deviate from the line of skepticism. The skeptic would say that it is impossible to prove either the truth or the falsity, for example, of the sentence «3 is an odd number ». A fictionalist confidently determines the falsity of this sentence in view of the fact that the numbers do not exist. Balaguer insists on the abstractness of mathematical objects, emphasizing the familiar closeness of fictionalism to platonism. However, strictly speaking, fictionalism does not need to insist on the abstractness of mathematical objects. The nature of mathematical objects appearing in mathematical texts is entirely determined by these texts. Unlike the supporters of mathematical platonism, fictionalists do not claim that abstract objects exist outside texts.

Field's book "Science without Numbers" made a strong impression on the philosophical community. It almost refuted universally accepted assertion that best scientific theories cannot do without mathematics. Field argued the opposite: in principle, science can do without mathematics, but it is useful because facilitates certain operations, for example, calculations.

The way of proof, elected by Field, consisted of translating the traditional exposition of Newton's theory of gravitation into another language. Usually, this theory is presented by the notions of spatial and time coordinates, the relationship between which is described by means of functions. Field identified these coordinates with the potential of the gravitational field, i.e. gave them a purely physical meaning, and replaced the function with equations containing operators of the second-order logical language. According to Field, he excluded mathematics from physics. Critics disagreed with his statement [7]. They argued that in fact, mathematics remained in physical theory; it was simply given a surrogate form.

It is essential that the fictionalists only partially abandon the concept of truth. Semantic truth is rejected because it is believed that mathematical sentences do not correspond to any referents. Syntactic and pragmatic truth remain in force. The truth of the mathematical propositions is defined as their consistency with the course of the historical development of mathematics. In this case, the truth appears in a syntactic guise. If it is argued that the use of mathematics is useful, then there is a transition to pragmatics, within which one can introduce an idea of pragmatic truth.

Fictionalists claim that they highly appreciate all the achievements of mathematics, not delusions. No matter how articulated the achievements of mathematics in other mathematical directions, they can, nevertheless, always be translated into a fictionalist language.

Most often against the fictionalists, an argument is advanced that, contrary to Quine-Putnam's thesis, they do not take into account the need for mathematics for empirical sciences. This accusation is denied: an appeal to mathematics is useful, for it facilitates many operations.

Fictionalists are also accused of not taking into account the objectivity of certain mathematical provisions. Suppose that two statements are considered: $2 + 2 = 4$ and $2 + 2 = 5$. Fictionalists are reproached for believing that both of these proposals are false. This is followed by Field's answer: $2 + 2 = 4$ is false in the semantic sense, but it is true within the history of the development of mathematics. As for the sentence $2 + 2 = 5$, it is false both in the semantic and in the historical sense.

Fictionalists are also accused of facing the dilemma of adopting either hermeneutic or radical fictionalism. Both choices put them in a difficult position. In the first case, it is difficult to hope that the dialogue that they realize will lead to significant results. In the second case, the fictionalists pretend to be intermediaries in contact with mathematicians, but this is hardly possible in view of their fundamentally different positions. Mathematicians do not think that they operate with fiction. The answer to both objections is the same: one should not present the position of the fictionalists in a perverted form. Arguments of fictionists are not for facilitated, but for quite professional discourse.

S. Yablou, perhaps, the main authority in the field of hermeneutic fictionalism, finishes one of his articles with such a passage [6]. Being engaged in the simulation, you can first interrupt this process, not wanting to be just a bearer of some belief in this or that situation. Simulation is understood as the buildup of mature discourse without assuming any semantic obligations. Secondly, you can stop, because faith in the truth of the situation is achieved. Thirdly, you can continue to imitate, but on condition that the belief in the situation under consideration is rephrased. However, the true fictionalist chooses the fourth way: he simulates in order to achieve a position, which corresponds to the facts. In reality, S. Yablou formulated the creed of a fictionalist: to simulate not far from mathematics, not gliding along its outer sides, but at its center.

Numerous critics of the fictionalists more than once were convinced that they cleverly refuted the opinions of their opponents. Every time, the fictionalists asserted that together with their critics they are building up the potential of the philosophy of mathematics avoiding false concepts. Sometimes the fictionalists remembered Occam's razor: do not multiply the essence beyond necessity.   It is enough, to consider mathematical objects as fictions.

In my opinion, fictionalism is indeed not devoid of weaknesses. In this connection, I give three arguments. First, among the fictionalists, there is an asymmetry between the theses about existence and truth. Semantic truth is rejected, which leads to the assertion that there are no mathematical objects. It seems to be all right. However, if syntactic and pragmatic truth is not rejected, why is the existence of mathematical objects in their syntactic and pragmatic quality not recognized? In fact, fictionalists recognize the existence of mathematical objects as units of discourse. In this case, arguing that mathematical objects do not exist, they make an obvious mistake. Secondly, fictionalists are extremely uncertain about the phenomenon of mathematical modeling. It is unacceptable to deny that there is mathematical modeling. Why is it so effective? The fictionalists do not see a reasonable answer to this question. Thirdly, the fictionalists pay insufficient attention to the nature of mathematics. If they did not avoid it, they would have to say a great deal about the nature of mathematical objects, the very things that they consider non-existent.

References

1. Balaguer, M. (1998) Platonism and Anti-Platonism in Mathematics. Oxford: Oxford University Press.
2. Balaguer, M. (2018) Fictionalism in the philosophy of mathematics. The Stanford Encyclopedia of Philosophy. Available at: https://plato.stanford.edu/archives/fall2018/entries/fictionalism-mathematics/
3. Field, H. (1980) Science without Numbers. Princeton, NJ: Princeton University Press.
4. Frege, G. (2003) The thought: a logical inquiry. In Logicism and the Philosophy of Language: Selections from Frege and Russell. Ed. by A. Sullivan. Peterborough, Ontario: Broadview Press, 201-218.

5. Gödel, K. (1983) What is Cantor's continuum problem? In Philosophy of Mathematics: Selected Readings. Ed. by P. Benacerraf and H. Putnam. New York: Cambridge University Press, 258–273.
6. Shapiro, S. (1993) Modality and ontology. Mind 102(407), 455-481.
7. Yablo, S. (2002) Go figure: a path through fictionalism. Midwest Studies in Philosophy 25(1), 72-1-2.

5.6. Structuralism, realism and naturalism

The question of the nature of mathematical objects has become a key one in the philosophy of mathematics. Some answers to it were considered above. Supporters of structuralism took a special position on this subject. Structuralists consider mathematical objects, for example, numbers, not by themselves, but exclusively as part of some structures. They avoid the question of the existence of mathematical objects or clarifies them as categorical errors. Thus, for example, two is no longer considered as a natural number detached from the structure of natural numbers, but as an identifier for the second place in the structure of natural numbers. Mathematical objects have not internal properties.

The development of mathematical structuralism was largely contributed by Paul Benacerraf, the author of two articles published for the first time in 1965 and 1973 respectively [2; 1]. In the article [2], he refutes the dogmatic trait of most mathematicians that the nature of numbers can be determined by means of set theory. Frege and Russell defined the number as the class of all classes equivalent to a given class. For example, the number 3 is the class of all classes containing three elements. According to Benacerraf, such a definition is untenable. The fact is that there are different ways of forming sets. Unambiguously, a mathematical object, for example, the number 3 cannot be determined. Thus, the set theory does not allow us to identify the number 3. The problem of identifying mathematical objects rises in full growth.

The question about the nature of mathematical objects is complicated by the epistemological difficulties. [1] In the theory of knowledge, causal relationships that unite specific sensually given objects are studied. According to platonism, mathematical objects, being abstractions, are excluded from causal relationships. Yet it is believed that they are directly related to the real causal processes. Again, there is a dilemma. It is difficult to answer the question: "How do we get access to abstract objects"?

Having formulated the problems in the best philosophical traditions, Benacerraf does not claim to resolve them. He subtly feels that each way invariably leads to difficulties. Such sensitivity is commendable. Nevertheless, the problems are put in order to achieve their resolution. Benacerraf operates on some projects rather than decisions.

The epistemological problem is mitigated by a constant appeal to the phenomenon of language. In fact, Benacerraf believes that the questions of cognition are resolved through an analysis of the use of language. In this choice, the influence of analytical philosophy and pragmatism is evident. But what about numbers?

On this account, Benacerraf has two projects. One is fictionalist the other structural. The structural project was considered earlier. According to the fictionalist project, without trying to identify the nature of the numbers, we simply have to admit that we operate with numbers in our linguistic practice. People use the names of numbers. This does not mean that they have referents.

Benacerraf himself admitted that in his article [2] he was only flirting with structuralism. The genuine apologists of structuralism are other authors. This is primarily S. Shapiro [15] and M. Resnik [14]. Unlike Benacerraf, these philosophers are not tempted by fictionalism. They believe that mathematical structuralism has lifted the veil over the question of the relationship between algebraic and non-algebraic theories. Traditionally it was believed that algebraic theories are generalizations of non-algebraic theories. The true content of algebra is reduced to other sciences, in which the nature of mathematical objects is uniquely determined. Shapiro and Resnik believe that the matter is fundamentally different. Conceptually, algebra dominates in mathematics. Therefore, all non-algebraic sciences must be illuminated by the light of algebra. Strictly speaking, in mathematics all structures are algebraic. In this regard, we can state that Shapiro and Resnik develop a structural-algebraic approach.

In my view, in one respect, mathematical structuralists are right: mathematics really studies structures. However, they do not take into account that, for all the legitimacy of the structural approach, it must be supplemented by an atomic approach, in which the structure is interpreted as being composed of atoms, which in this case are mathematical objects. Any conception including mathematical theory is a whole. Concepts are part of this whole. The theory itself acts as a transition from one concept to another. These transitions are cyclical in accordance with the nature of intratheoretical transduction. This means that one and the same concept is not in an unchanging status. This is what we had in mind, arguing that the structural approach should be complemented by the atomic one. Obviously, the structuralists absolutize the structural approach.

The question of the nature of mathematical objects is usually associated with a discussion of the fate of mathematical realism. The term 'realism' is based on the Latin realis - material. The material is not an ideal, not a platonic form. Therefore, realists distanced themselves from platonism. Hilary Putnam expressed the conviction that the acceptance of realism in mathematics is the only way from the transformation of mathematics into an inexplicable fairy-tale phenomenon [10, 60].

Mathematical realism finds wide support among philosophers, especially representatives of materialism and analytical philosophy. However, it meets with considerable difficulties. This is not surprising. Let me turn, for example, attention to the development of the concept of numbers: natural → rational → irrational → complex → hypercomplex → transfinite numbers. Involuntarily there is a doubt that all these numbers describe something real.

The most popular approach in the evaluation of mathematical realism is contained in the work of Penelope Maddy. [6] She tries to illustrate her conclusions on concrete mathematical material. Most often, she talks about set theory. Such a choice is not accidental; according to Maddy, the philosophy of set theory forms the basis of the modern philosophy of mathematics.

Maddy distinguishes three forms of realism: Robust, Thin realism, and Arealism [8]. Her own sympathies are clearly on the side of Thin realism. Representatives of Robust realism do not particularly delve into the subtleties of the theory. With respect to set theory, they consider that there are real sets; all concepts of set theory have their real analogs. However, this tranquil position is questioned by the methodology of maximization, which implies the achievement of the best theoretical result. Suppose that there is an initial theory, which is then modified. Consequently, the notions of reality change. The way out of the difficult situation, Maddie sees in Thin realism. It is clearly marked by the stamp of methodology and epistemology. Maddy illustrates the course of his thoughts with the introduction to the theory of sets of the axiom of choice. Against the axiom of choice, very many mathematicians objected, in particular, E. Borel, F. Bernstein, R.-L. Baire, A. Poincaré. Nevertheless, over the years, arguments around the axiom of choice have subsided. However, this did not lead to a rejection of realism. Mathematicians abandoned Robust realism in favor of sophisticated realism. Justification of the adoption of additional provisions is carried out within the theory.

Further, Maddy seeks to isolate the grounds by virtue of which there is a departure from Thin realism towards Arealism, which differs from Anti-realism. Arealism is not engaged in debunking realism. It is the result of the growing speed of doubts about the possibility of remaining on realistic positions. On the one hand, theories are becoming more sophisticated, which leads to an increase in the number of concepts that have an auxiliary value from the position of a sophisticated realist. On the other hand, in mathematics, the realistic position is much more difficult to realize than, for example, in physics. Not coping with these two circumstances, the mathematician proceeds to the position of Arealism.

Comparing the achievements and flaws of the three forms of realism, Maddy concludes that Thin realism differs from Robust realism more than from Arealism. When comparing Robust realism with Thin realism, the choice should be made in favor of Thin realism. There are appropriate grounds for this. If, however, Thin realism and Arealism are compared, then there is no reason to prefer one of them. Both kinds of realism are good because they do not allow deviations from the method of mathematics. Realizing this, many mathematicians are reluctant to take the position of either Thin realism or Arealism. If this choice is made, then everything is determined by convenience, taste, and preferences in the use of terms of truth, existence, and science.

Thus, Maddy, firstly, recognizes the necessity of adopting mathematical realism. Secondly, she believes that mathematical reality should be judged based on the most refined theories. I believe that Maddy is right. However, in her theory, there are moments of underdetermination. In this connection, I note several important circumstances.

It is generally accepted that ontological (objective) representation attests to reality. Such an approach considered natural for the vast majority of sciences. Why should a realistic approach not extend to mathematics? Because mathematics deals with formal objects? The fact is that they are extracted from the concrete. Returning through mathematical modeling to concrete theories, beginnings of mathematical objects are found in them. The triangle itself does not exist, but there are many triangular objects. Formal objects express the similarity of real concrete objects. Anyone who tries to understand the nature of mathematical objects regardless of their connection with specific objects makes a serious philosophical mistake.

Of course, there is nothing surprising in the fact that our ideas about mathematical reality are being improved. Refined realism does not pass by this circumstance. Judgments about mathematical reality would have acquired a proper foundation if it had always been taken into account that mathematics correlates with other sciences as a formal theory with concrete ones.

Above we have repeatedly faced with the need to take into account the status of mathematical theory and to assess its relationship with philosophy and other sciences. In this connection, one should turn to naturalism in mathematics, initiated by Willard Quine. Philosophy must develop in the same spirit as the natural sciences. [13, 185] Quine's naturalistic thesis as applied to mathematics raises the question of the relationship of mathematics to philosophy and other sciences. Quine's main claim is that the method of mathematics is the same as the methods of empirical sciences, whose leader is physics. Naturalism is the visiting card of the majority of analytical philosophers of mathematics. Particularly illustrative in this sense is the work of Penelope Maddy.

First, she points to the relevance of taking into account the specifics of the mathematical method; mathematics is not responsible for the supra-scientific tribunal and does not need to be substantiated beyond the bounds of the proofs and the axiomatic method [5, 184]. Secondly, Maddy legitimately indicates that applied mathematics acquires independence because of mathematical modeling, which is not a mechanical transfer of mathematics to other sciences [7]. Thirdly, she recognizes the independence of the philosophy of mathematics. Quine rejected the first philosophy. But there is a second philosophy; in particular, it is the philosophy of mathematics [9]. Fourthly, mathematicians often work without regard to the philosophy of mathematics, which indirectly indicates its uniqueness. The standards of the philosophy of mathematics should not be imposed on mathematicians.

It seems to me that Maddy, as well as other naturalistic philosophers, have unanswered the following pressing questions. 1) Is philosophy useful for mathematics? 2) What is the specificity of the philosophy of mathematics, does it go beyond the axiomatic method? 3) Is the failure of mathematicians to fulfill the standards of the philosophy of mathematics fruitful? I will try to find answers to these urgent questions.

Quine is right; mathematics does not need a backup from purely speculative positions, not determined by the content of mathematics itself. Equally right, Maddy, indicating the need for a philosophy of mathematics. To a lesser extent, her judgment on the primacy of mathematics over the philosophy of mathematics deserves approval.

To begin with, we note that the intratheoretical methods of mathematics are of a formal nature. This circumstance distinguishes them from the methods of natural and axiological theories. It is not so, that mathematics is limited exclusively to the deductive method, which is given an axiomatic form. Is mathematics involved in the experimental data? Yes, it is involved, but indirectly, namely, in so far as it formalizes the adductive method.

Considering the relation between mathematics and the philosophy of mathematics, one should take into account not only the ascent from mathematics to the philosophy of mathematics, as Maddy does, but about the movement in the opposite direction, from the philosophy of mathematics to mathematics. The philosophy of mathematics in isolation from its foundation, i.e. of mathematics, is also able to wither. It seems to me that P. Maddy did not pay sufficient attention to the relative independence of the philosophy of mathematics. First, the philosophy of mathematics is a general formal mathematical theory. This means that it accumulates the achievements of all mathematical theories, and then extends them to individual theories. Secondly, through its contacts with the philosophy of science, i.e. with the formal metatheory of all existing sciences, she is able to draw new ideas from non-mathematical theories. Let me give a concrete example. The idea of the need for a mature dialogue has come to the philosophy of mathematics not from mathematics, but from hermeneutics with its reliance on humanitarian disciplines.

Mathematics takes a worthy place in the commonwealth of sciences. This, in fact, is the main content of mathematical naturalism. This term has an obvious drawback, it excessively brings mathematics closer to the natural sciences, somewhat alienating it from the social sciences. Thus, the strength of the doctrine of naturalism in mathematics is its focus on taking into account the inter-theoretical connections of mathematics with the achievements of other sciences.

I will have to address once again the question of the empirical content of mathematics. In the 20th century, on many questions of the philosophy of science, neopositivists, critical rationalists and analytical philosophers competed sharply. However, in one question they were one: in the composition of the scientific theory, the most important is the experiment. Nevertheless, with regard to mathematics, this thesis has puzzled many. There is no experiment in mathematics. How can we combine, on the one hand, the lack of experiments in mathematics, on the other hand, its recognition as a defining feature of scientific theories? The way out of the difficult situation was proposed by two iconic figures, the critical rationalist Imre Lakatos and the analytical philosopher Willard Quine. They initiated the emergence of quasi-empiricism as a mathematical direction.

As a supporter of the theory of falsification, Lakatos had to justify the variability of mathematical knowledge. Unshakable knowledge does not happen, including in mathematics. Falsificationism is a program for all sciences. The revision of knowledge is forced by "hard facts"; therefore, something like this should be in mathematics. Mathematics differs from exemplary empirical sciences. Nevertheless, it shares the falsification with them. Consequently, it has a quasi-empirical character. Lakatos introduced the idea of heuristic falsifiers [4, 39]. His argument was that a well-formed formal theory is irrefutable. It becomes refutable when compared to informal theories. However, he did not consider the specifics of the relationship between formal and informal theories.

Quine argued in a different vein. The totality of sciences is a single whole, the boundary conditions of which are our sensory experience [11, 38]. Scientific practice confirms and refutes the proposals of all sciences forming a single whole. That is why mathematics falls into the category of empirical sciences. One of the most characteristics of Quine's statements is that numbers and functions appear in the physical theory as genuinely as hypothetical particles [12, 149]. We are talking about the obligatory use of mathematics in modern science. This statement is usually qualified as Quine-Putnam's argument about the inevitability of mathematics in science. [3, 11]

In my opinion, the views of Quine and Lakatos share an inherent disadvantage. They did not carefully consider those intertheoretical relations that unite mathematics with natural and axiological sciences. It is not enough to talk about the whole, it is necessary to find out the correlation of its parts. The essence of the matter is this: mathematics is a formal science, but it is bound by inseparable ties with informal disciplines. Empiricism, characteristic of mathematics, should be called formal. The experiment as a direct intervention in the course of events is possible only in a field subject to natural and axiological theories. However, if it takes place, then it does not pass without a trace for mathematics.

References

1. Benacerraf, P. (1983) Mathematical truth. In Philosophy of Mathematics: Selected Readings. Second Ed. Ed. by P. Benacerraf and H. Putnam. Cambridge: Cambridge University Press, 403–420.

2. Benacerraf, P. (1983) What numbers could not be. In Philosophy of Mathematics: Selected Readings, 272–294.

3. Colyvan, M. (2001) The Indispensability of Mathematics. New York: Oxford University Press.

4. Lakatos, I. (1998) A renaissance of empiricism in the recent philosophy of mathematics. In New Directions in the Philosophy of Mathematics: An Anthology. Ed. by T. Tymoczko. Prinstone: Princeton University Press, 29–48.

5. Maddy, P. (1997) Naturalism in Mathematics. Oxford: Clarendon Press.

6. Maddy, P. (1990) Realism in Mathematics. Oxford: Clarendon Press, 1990.

7. Maddy, P. (2008) How applied mathematics became pure. The Review of Symbolic Logic 1(1), 16-41.

8. Maddy, P. (2005) Mathematical existence. The Bulletin of Symbolic Logic 2(3), 351-376.
9. Maddy, P. (2007) Second Philosophy: A Naturalistic Method. Oxford: Oxford University Press.
10. Putnam, H. (1983) What is mathematical truth? In Philosophy of Mathematics: Selected Readings, 55-65.
11. Quine, W. (1953) From a Logical Point of View. Cambridge: Harvard University Press.
12. Quine, W.V. (1981) Theories and Things. Cambridge, Massachusetts: Harvard University Press.
13. Quine, W.V. (1968). Ontological Relativity. Journal of Philosophy, 65(7), 185–212.
14. Resnik, M. (1997) Mathematics as a Science of Patterns. Oxford: Clarendon Press.
15. Shapiro, S. (199) Philosophy of Mathematics: Structure and Ontology. Oxford: Oxford University Press.

5.7. Social constructivism. League-theories of mathematical directions

The review of philosophical and mathematical directions we conclude with an analysis of social constructivism. Its status is determined by the connection of mathematics with the social sciences. With the greatest enthusiasm, the legitimacy of social constructivism is defended by Reuben Hersh [4] and Paul Ernest [2].

R. Hersh expressed his view in the theses as follows [3].

1) Mathematics is peculiar to man. It is a part of human culture and does not correspond to the Frege concept of an abstract, timeless, objective reality.

2) Mathematical knowledge is subject to error. Like science, mathematics can grow on the background of errors and their correction.

3) There are different versions of proof and accuracy. Standards of accuracy may depend on time, place and other circumstances. The use of computers in formal proof, in particular, in the proof of the theorem in 1977 on four colors, is one example of the emergence of an unconventional standard of accuracy of evidence.

4). Empirical evidence, computational experiment and proof using probabilities - all this can help us decide what exactly one should believe in mathematics.

5) Mathematical objects are a special kind of socio-historical object. Contrary to the pretensions of postmodern detractors of mathematics, it should not be recognized as merely a new form of literature or religion.

Unfortunately, Hersh does not clearly define the status of mathematical objects. In my opinion, he recklessly characterizes mathematical objects as socio-historical entities. Strictly speaking, only those objects that are conceptually reproduced in the social sciences are socio-historical. Mathematical objects are not such things. Our remark shows that the term social constructivism is unsuccessful, for it should be left for the social sciences. Realizing this, some authors use the term radical constructivism. Authors who hold approximately the same views as Hersh often qualify themselves as supporters of practically oriented realism. However, many authors refer to practical orientation mainly to emphasize their antirealistic position.

It should be noted that terms such as practice and social should be used with caution. Any activity, including mathematical activity, may well be recognized as practical. Practice is a goal-setting activity. A mathematician sets certain goals, it cannot be denied. Nevertheless, all these goals are conceptually comprehended exclusively in the mathematics itself, and not in the social sciences. In mathematics, there is nothing social. There is no reason to identify mathematics with the social sciences. It is another matter that the connections between mathematics and the social sciences must be carefully considered. They are provided through appropriate modeling.

Let me turn now to the concept of social constructivism of P. Ernest. This philosopher is most concerned with the teaching of mathematics [1]. Being impressed by the works of J. Piaget, he believes that the key to teaching mathematics is the philosophy of mathematics. However, traditional philosophical and mathematical directions, in fact, ignore the problems of teaching mathematics. Therefore, he seeks to develop a special form of the philosophy of mathematics, characterizing it as social constructivism. According to Ernest, the rationale for the necessity of mathematics is reduced to the following six provisions.

1) Knowledge is not passively assigned, but actively constructed.

2) Knowledge does not open the ontological reality, but functions as part of an empirical organization by the man of his world.

3) The theories constructed by man must correspond to physical and social reality.

4) This goal is achieved through scientific predictions, testing them and overcoming failures.

5) As a result, theories based on social harmony are constructed, and samples and rules for the use of language are developed.

6) Mathematics is the theory of forms and practices that arise with the language.

Unlike R. Hersh, P. Ernest, in characterizing mathematical objects, puts forward language, not mentality. However, of course, their concepts are very similar to each other.

Social constructivism was initiated by the critical rationalist Imre Lakatos. Constructivists learn from him to assess the status of mathematics from the standpoint of fallibilism (a mathematician can be wrong) and falsificationism (irrefutable knowledge is unscientific). As a result, mathematical knowledge is given a fluid character, the very one on which representatives of the historical school in science insisted (Popper, Lakatos, Kuhn, Feyerabend). Many advocates of social constructivism are also keen to take into account the lessons of the two Copernican changes that took place in the philosophy of the 20th century, language and pragmatic. In both these twists, the analytical philosopher L. Wittgenstein played an active role. It is not by chance that he is also recognized as one of the initiators of social constructivism in mathematics.

In my opinion, social constructivists in their derivations should rely on a thorough analysis of the correlation of mathematics with the social sciences. However, that is exactly what they do not do. Mathematics, undeniably, is a form of people's activity, but not a social one, but a formal one. If mathematics is straightforwardly proclaimed social activity, then it, in fact, is identified with the social sciences, and this is a serious mistake.

After considering a dozen mathematical directions, it is advisable to present their contents in a systematic way. The abundance of mathematical directions shows that they cannot be unified. Pluralism in the field of metamathematics has taken place! It does not deserve to be blamed, for it provides an increase in the potential of the philosophy of mathematics. However, of course, not all pluralism deserves approval. Pluralism is bad when it leads to conceptual anarchism. New directions are being proclaimed, but no inter-theoretical relations are established between them. In this case, pluralism only leads to discontent, and not to the desired problematic union. Then, the actual task is the ordering of mathematical directions.

To begin with, I will single out groups of mathematical directions. In the first group of mathematical directions, it is reasonable to include intuitionism, constructivism, formalism, and structuralism. In these areas, the emphasis is on considering the structure of the mathematical theory. Unfortunately, this is done without resorting to methods of conceptual transduction.

In the second group of mathematical directions, I propose to include a set-theoretic, type-theoretical, category-theoretical direction, and structuralism as an algebraic-theoretical direction. In the considered mathematical directions, the status of general mathematical theories is brought to the forefront.

In the third group of mathematical directions, it is reasonable to include realism, fictionalism, and platonism. In these mathematical directions, the nature of mathematical objects is considered.

In the fourth group of mathematical directions, it is reasonable to include logicism, quasi-empiricism, social constructivism and naturalism. The questions considered within the framework of these directions, one way or another, refer to the relationship of mathematics with other branches of science, namely, with logic, physics (in the case of quasi-empiricism), social disciplines and philosophy (naturalism).

Which group of mathematical directions for a particular researcher is of paramount importance depends on his goals. Preferences are determined by the research objectives. According to them, some weight can be assigned to each direction. The corresponding ordering can also be carried out within each individual mathematical direction (MD). A possible relationship between mathematical directions is presented in Table 5.1.

Table 5.1. League-theories of MD

N	League-theories of MD with indication of local ratings	Rank weights of groups of MD
I	(10) formalism → (8) constructivism → (7) intuitionism → (6) structuralism	10
II	(10) category-theoretical direction → (8) type-theoretical direction → (6) set-theoretical direction → (4) structuralism	8
III	(10) realism → (7) fictionalism → (5)	5

	Platonism	
IV	(10) naturalism → (9) logicism → (6) quasi-empiricism → (5) social constructivism	4

In the first group of mathematical directions, I prefer the formalism, which expresses the structure of the mathematical theory more fully than its rivals do. With respect to the second group of mathematical directions, I prefer a category-theoretic direction, because the theory of categories is superior in its degree of generality to type theory, set theory, and algebra. In the third group of mathematical directions, I give preference to realism. He has shortcomings, but not so striking as platonism and fictionalism have. Finally, in the fourth group of mathematical directions, I give preference to naturalism insofar as, ultimately, mathematics owes its success to philosophy more than to logic, physics and the social branches of science.

In determining the rank weights of league-theories of mathematical directions, their historical significance in the development of mathematics is taken into account. The quantifications indicated in Table 5.1 expresses the author's preferences. The quantifications of the reader, of course, will be another. It is important to emphasize that there is a method of ordering mathematical directions that makes it possible conceptually master mathematical pluralism.

Thus, the set of mathematical directions is the most important field of problematization of the nature of mathematics. This field should be mastered purposefully, without eclecticism.

References

1. Ernest, P. (1991) Philosophy of Mathematics Education. London: Falmer Press.
2. Ernest, P. (1998) Social Constructivism as a Philosophy of Mathematics? New York: State University of New York Press.
3. Hersh, R. (2006) Introduction. In 18 Unconventional Essays on the Nature of Mathematics. Ed. by R. Hersh. New York: Springer, vii-xvi.
4. Hersh, R. (1997) What is Mathematics, Really? Oxford: Oxford University Press.

5.8. Intertheoretical and interdisciplinary relations of mathematics

So far, this or that mathematical theory was understood as an independent whole, not come into contact with other theories. In reality, any mathematical concept is involved in intertheoretical relationships. Here is an illustrative example. Euclid first introduced the axiomatic construction of geometry. Over the past 23 centuries, Euclidean geometry has been improved many times, including in the twentieth century. By common opinion, remarkable success was achieved by D. Hilbert [5]. However, even after this, improvements in Euclidean geometry continued. Especially significant works were noted by G. Birkhoff [1] and A. Tarski [7]. If you want to understand in detail the essence of Euclidean geometry, you should build the appropriate league-theory.

The second example relates to set theory. Invented in 1870 by G. Cantor, set theory was subsequently improved many times, in particular, by Zermelo, Fraenkel, Bernays, and Gödel [3]. Again, we need to build the corresponding league-theory.

The theory of models occupies a prominent place in mathematics. It studies the relationship between syntactic languages and their interpretations. The theory of models was consistently developed by A. Tarski. Guided by the theory of models, one can consider Euclidean geometry as an interpretation (model) of Lobachevski's geometry. This relation allowed E. Beltrami and F. Klein to justify the consistency of Lobachevski's geometry. The main achievement of the theory of models was to clarify the relationship between the various mathematical sciences, i.e. theories that cannot be included in the same league-theory.

Thus, mathematicians successfully develop the correlation not only theories of the same type, but also of different types. Heterogeneous theories are in the mirror of each other. Compare, for example, on the one hand, the algebraic topology and, on the other hand, the topological algebra. In the first case, the initiative belongs to topology, and in the second - to algebra.

A wide range of relations connects mathematics with other branches of science, for example, with physics. This time we are talking about interdisciplinary relations. Each science uses only its own, and not mathematical language. Between all scientific languages, there is a certain equivalence. In this connection, they are related to the language of mathematics. This circumstance opens wide opportunities for the development of interdisciplinary connections of mathematics with other sciences.

For example, the history of physics shows that, in principle, its refined conceptuality is really connected with mathematics.

This conceptuality is difficult to imagine without the use in classical mechanics of mathematical analysis, in the general theory of relativity of non-Euclidean geometry, in the quantum theory of vector algebra.

Interesting morality lies in the famous story with John Jeans, who in 1910 argued that physicists do not need to study the theory of groups because it will never find application in physics [2, 351]. Now the group-theoretic direction occupies a central position in physics. The theory of groups is necessary, in particular, for the systematics of elementary particles and the formulation of the principles of invariance. The case of Jeans shows that the question of the specifics of mathematics, demanded by a certain science, is highly unusual. There is no universal mathematics, which would be suitable for all cases. The conceptual essence of this or that science is not any mathematics, but only one that has actual similarity with it. This circumstance, perhaps, explains why beyond the limits of physics, for example, in biology, the effectiveness of mathematics is diminishing. It is not ruled out that a form of mathematics adequate to the nature of biological phenomena has not yet been found. In this regard, certain hopes are placed on fractal geometry.

Jean's case can also be understood as follows: any mathematical discipline will be used outside of mathematics. This statement, I think, is too categorical. The diverse world of mathematics only partially intersects with other sciences. However, a detailed analysis of this contact reveals that not only the given mathematical discipline but, to a certain extent, mathematics in general, is in contact with this or that science. Any mathematical discipline, not being completely autonomous within the framework of mathematics as a whole, involves this whole in interdisciplinary relations.

There is always such a mathematical system, which is particularly relevant for the development of a particular science. For example, the study of operations and the theory of games represent interesting possibilities in the mathematization of axiological sciences [6]. The study of operations is designed to identify optimal solutions. In the theory of games, conflict situations, oppositions of two or more players are studied. Mathematics is being introduced into the field of axiological sciences to the extent that it has succeeded in developing a mathematical theory of optimal processes.

The theory of optimal processes can be used to model both natural phenomena and the actions of people. The essential difference between the two is, however, that unlike natural processes, people in their actions are guided by certain values and strategies of behavior. The successes of the mathematical theory of games are indicative of many things. First, there is no reason to build bastions between mathematics and the humanities. Secondly, the concept of the game itself must be understood taking into account the status of mathematics. Unfortunately, the concept of games so popular among philosophers is often interpreted as a triumph of arbitrariness, which is supposedly alien to any formalization. The actual state of affairs does not confirm this understanding of the game. By the way, if in fact, absolute arbitrariness were possible, even it would have been modeled with mathematical means, not without success. In terms of understanding the value content of human actions, as well as the concept of the game, it is important not to oppose mathematics to the humanities, but to strengthen their union.

In my opinion, the effectiveness of mathematics is determined by its ability to express in the conceptual form some aspects of human life. Mathematical modeling is the key to understanding the imaginary incomprehensibility of mathematics. In a review article by R. Frigge and S. Hartmann, various interpretations of the nature of mathematical models are considered [4]. They are considered as substitutes for studied objects, then the result of clever abstractions and idealizations, then the prerequisites of future theories, then fictions. In my opinion, all these interpretations have one and the same, and a significant drawback. In one form or another, the features of the substantive sciences are transferred to mathematics. In fact, the essence of mathematical modeling is that mathematics deals with morphisms, which unite it with other branches of science.

References

1. Birkhoff, G.D. (1932) A set of postulates for plane geometry (based on scale and protractors). Annals of Mathematics 32(2), 329-345.
2. Dyson, F. (1965) Matematika i fizika [Mathematics and Physics]. Uspekhi fizicheskikh nauk [Advances in Physical Sciences] 85(2), 351–364. [In Russian].
3. Fraenkel, A. A., Bar-Hillel, Y., and Levy, A. (1973) Foundations of Set Theory. Second rev. ed. Amsterdam: North-Holland.
4. Frigge, R., Hartmann, S. (2018) Models in science. The Stanford Encyclopedia of Philosophy. Available at: https://plato.stanford.edu/archives/sum2018/entries/models-science/
5. Hilbert, D. (1950) [1902]. The Foundations of Geometry. Transl. by E.J Townsend. Second edition. La Salle, IL: Open Court Publishing.

6. Ross, D. (2019) Game theory. The Stanford Encyclopedia of Philosophy. Available at: https://plato.stanford.edu/ archives/win2019/entries/game-theory/

7. Tarski, A. (1959) What is elementary geometry? In Henkin L., Suppes P., Tarski A. The Axiomatic Method. With Special Reference to Geometry and Physics. Amsterdam: North-Holland, 16–29.

Chapter 6. The nature of computer science

6.1. Scientific status of computer science

Around the nature of computer science, there is fierce debate. Most often, it is recognized as a mathematical or technical science. William Rapaport considered various definitions of the nature of computer science in an exceptionally voluminous and detailed review. He himself summarized them as follows. [1, 69-152]

> I said that our survey suggests that there is no simple, one-sentence answer to the question: What is computer science? If we were to summarize the discussion in this chapter in one sentence, it would look something like this:
>
> Computer science is the scientific (or STEM) study of:
>
> what problems can be solved,
>
> what tasks can be accomplished,
>
> and what features of the world can be understood . . .
>
> . . . computationally, that is, using a language with only:
>
> 2 nouns ('0', '1'),
>
> 3 verbs ('move', 'print', 'halt'),
>
> 3 grammar rules (sequence, selection, repetition),

and nothing else,

and then to provide algorithms to show how this can be done:

efficiently,

practically,

physically,

and ethically.

But this definition is hardly a simple sentence!
[2, 152].

As you know, STEM is a term used for a group of disciplines - science, technology, engineering, and mathematics. Rapaport, apparently, believes that informatics is an interdisciplinary scientific study of the topics allocated to them. This is a very popular point of view on the nature of informatics as a science.

My point of view is that computer science is a kind of formal branches of science [1]. Its status as a science can be defined as laconically as the status of mathematics, physics, and economics.

Why is computer science a science? Because it is realized according to the methods of intratheoretical and intertheoretical transduction. In this respect, it is very similar to mathematics and logic. If informatics were not guided by methods of deduction, adduction, induction, abduction, problematization, discovery, interpretation and ordering, then there would be no reason to recognize it as a science.

Why is computer science formal science? Because it has the degree of universality that is not inherent in natural and axiological sciences. The same is characteristic of all formal sciences, philosophy, linguistics, logic, and mathematics.

Why is computer science not mathematics, despite the fact that it deals with algorithmic calculations? Because it takes on a new commitment in comparison with mathematics, namely, computing through computers. This circumstance distinguishes computer science from logic and mathematics, its two closest conceptual neighbors in science as a whole.

Why is computer science not a natural science? Because it does not limit itself to the study of exclusively natural, for example, physical processes.

Why is computer science not a technical science, despite the fact that it deals with computers? Because it studies not computers as such, but computing processes performed by computers. Computers as technical artifacts are studied in the framework of computer technology. Computers as goods are studied in the economy, and not in any other science. Computers, respectively, in computer science, computer technology, and economics are far from the same thing. In all three cases, computers are representations of certain theories. Theories are different, and therefore representations of computers, that is, the computers themselves are different. It is wrong to consider that in all cases computers are representations of only certain technical theories.

Why is computer science not a social science? Because it does not concentrate its attention solely on the characteristics of social processes.

Why is computer science not an art? Because unlike art, it does not deal solely with the fictional world.

Why is computer science not an interdisciplinary science? Because such sciences do not exist at all. Interdisciplinary relations are a characteristic of the correlation of certain sciences, and not of some independent science that rises above them. Interdisciplinary connections of physics and biology do not indicate a science that is neither physics nor biology. Of course, for computer science a wide range of interdisciplinary connections is characteristic. However, the same is inherent in any science; it is not a feature exclusively of computer science.

Is it right to consider computer science as a branch of science? Why not? It has become an extremely extensive field of scientific knowledge. There is no such branch of science, in whose box it could be squeezed.

References

1. Kanke, V.A. (2017) Metascientific and philosophical reasons to define the status of computer science. Automatic Documentation and Mathematical Linguistics 51(3), 101-107.
2. Rapaport, W.J. (2018) Philosophy of Computer Science. Draft, 2004-2018. Available at: https://cse.buffalo.edu/~rapaport/Papers/phics.pdf/

6.2. Passions around information

In a number of countries, particularly France, Germany and Russia, the term 'informatics' is used instead of the term computer science. This use of words suggests that the subject of informatics is information. As noted by Pieter Adriaans, «the term 'information' in colloquial speech is currently predominantly used as an abstract mass-noun used to denote any amount of data, code or text that is stored, sent, received or manipulated in any medium». [1]. Rudhzero Gilyarevskyi, the leading Russian expert on the topic of information, defines it as follows: «information - 1) the semantic content of information transmitted by one person to another or to many people, materialized in data that serves to convey information because direct communication, between people in another way is not carried out; 2) a widely used term for the designation of feedback through various kinds of signals in nature and technology, introduced by N. Wiener as the basic concept of cybernetics; 3) what reduces the degree of uncertainty (entropy, according to K. Shannon) of the knowledge of the addressee of an object or phenomenon; 4) in philosophy - the reflection of various aspects and elements of the surrounding world». [4, 113] As a rule, supporters of this point of view emphasize the ubiquity of information; it has flooded all sciences and society as a whole. [1; 3-5] Modern society is informational.

In my opinion, the very idea of information as an abstract mass-noun is erroneous, not consistent with the status of sciences. As repeatedly noted earlier, there are grounds for distinguishing between natural, axiological and formal sciences. There are no universal sciences. Natural and axiological sciences, of course, are marked by a distinct stamp of specificity. They clearly do not dominate the claims for universality. As for the formal sciences, they deserve closer analysis in the context of the search for a universal science. Philosophy, linguistics, logic, mathematics and computer science are formal, but not universal sciences. Each of these sciences deals with some similarities in all other sciences. However, they do not replace other sciences. Every formal science has a certain specificity, not absolute universality. In this connection, special attention should be given to philosophy, on whose behalf enthusiasts of universal science often speak.

Philosophers repeatedly designed systems that they considered universal and attributed to all sciences. Such, for example, is the dialectic of Georg Hegel. The so-called universal sciences invariably fell into a mess if they ignored the structure of the sciences. The dialectics of Hegel, ultimately, was not found in any of the sciences. However, what is there in them? In any theory, principles, laws, and variables are revealed. The appeal to them makes it possible to express a certain level of similarity of all existing theories. Those levels of similarity that distinguish linguistics, logic, mathematics and computer science are not represented in philosophy. This circumstance points to the specific nature of philosophy. The lessons of the development of philosophy throw a certain light on the possibility of constructing the concept of information and, accordingly, of informatics.

All the content of theories, i.e. their principles, laws, variables, and methods of managing them, can be called information. Of course, it is possible to do so, but this action will have a purely nominal character. A new word will not lead to the formation of a new theory. An attempt to reveal the meaning of information will lead to the need to operate with the concepts of principle, law, and variable. It is possible to denote by the term information all contents of computer sciences. Again, the case will be limited to a nominal share. An attempt to clarify the meaning of the concept of information will not allow going beyond the concepts of data, algorithms, languages, programming paradigms, and programs. Information turns out to be identical to computer science. Accordingly, the philosophy of information comes down to the philosophy of computer science. Scientific recognition of a certain degree of similarity can take place only when it is characteristic of the sciences. Otherwise, it is merely proclaimed. In my opinion, this is the case with the proclamation of the universality of information.

As for the works of Claude Shannon and Norbert Wiener, then, of course, they did not develop computer science as some universal discipline. Shannon energetically implemented interdisciplinary connections between technical sciences and mathematics [6]. The unit of measure used by him, bit, is the units of measurement of some technical signals, not information as such. Wiener carried out interdisciplinary connections between mathematics, on the one hand, and technical, economic and biological theories, on the other. His famous expression «information is information, not matter or energy» [7, 132] gave rise to some confusion. Some researchers, by analogy with energy and mass, tried to present information as a phenomenon that can be transmitted in space and time.

Luciano Floridi, opening discussion on the philosophy of information delineated 18 'Open Problems' in the philosophy of information [2, 560-575]. He believed that all of them could be resolved only within the framework of a special philosophy of information. In my opinion, in order to find a reasonable answer to them, it is sufficient to turn to correctly understood theories of implementing algorithms by means of computers. Below I consider a single draft of the answer to all 18 problems of Floridi.

Problem 1. The elementary problem: what is information? You can do without using the term information. However, it will not be a mistake to regard the information as a computer program together with the results of its implementation.

Problem 2. The 1/0 problem: dynamics of information? It should be about building programs and implementing them.

Problem 3. Is a grand unified theory of information possible? There is no such theory and, presumably, will not. I mean that there is not and there will not be a single computer program for all cases of life.

Problem 4. How can data acquire their meaning? They acquire their meanings in the process of building and implementing programs.

Problem 5. How can meaningful data acquire their truth-values? They are true if they are inherent in the most developed program.

Problem 6. Can information explain the truth? No, it cannot. The program is true if it is the best.

Problem 7. Can information explain meaning? No, it cannot. Meanings are realized in the process of writing and implementing programs, as well as their further improvement.

Problem 8. How far can cognition be analyzed in terms of information processing at some level of abstraction? Each program is an expression of some degree of similarity of the processes under consideration. This means that it represents these processes. Other degrees of similarity are beyond her control.

Problem 9. Can natural intelligence be analyzed in terms of information processing at some level of abstraction? Artificial intelligence is certain programs and their implementations, which are characterized by different degrees of similarity, rather than levels of abstraction.

Problem 10. *Can natural intelligence be satisfactorily implemented nonbiologically?* Of course, it can. In particular, this is the case when implementing artificial intelligence programs through a computer. Of course, one should take into account that inanimate objects do not have thinking.

Problem 11. *Can an informational approach solve the mind-body problem?* It is successfully solved in biology and axiological theories. At the same time, the information approach also has a certain importance.

Problem 12. *How can information be audited if information cannot be transcended?* Information is verified through improved programs. Unsuccessful programs are rejected.

Problem 13. *Should epistemology be based on a theory of information?* Epistemology is a generalization of the achievements of all sciences including computer science. Computer science acts as an equal among equals. It does not dominate the theory of knowledge.

Problem 14. *Is science reducible to information modeling?* Of course no. Science is much richer than informatics, no matter how it is understood.

Problem 15. *What is the ontological status of information?* Computer theory, like all other scientific concepts, has an ontological, mental and language representation. In the case of an ontological representation, objects are selected in the form in which they are presented in the program and its implementation.

Problem 16. *Is there information in reality without life?* Computer programs are widely used in the natural sciences.

This just means that there is no need to correlate them only with biological and social processes.

Problem 17. Can nature be informationalized? Nature does not need it. It is inherent in that degree of similarity with other processes, which finds its expression in computer programs relevant to the natural sciences.

Problem 18. Do computer ethics have a philosophical foundation? As a formal science, computer science does not have ethical content. Nevertheless, it is necessary to express the ethical potential of all axiological theories. In this regard, it is legitimate to assert that computer science has ethical relativity. Understood correctly philosophical ethics generalizes the ethical achievements of all axiological theories. These achievements are relevant to the implementation of the ethical relativity of computer science.

References

1. Adriaans, P. (2018) Information. The Stanford Encyclopedia of Philosophy. Available at: https://plato.stanford.edu/archives/fall2018/entries/information/
2. Floridi, L. (2004) Open problems in the philosophy of information. Metaphilosophy 35(4), 554-582.
3. Floridi, L. (2011) The Philosophy of Information. Oxford: Oxford University Press.
4. Gilyarevskyi , R.C. (2016) Informatsionnaya sfera [Information sphere]. Sankt-Peterburg: Professiya. [In Russian].

5. Lenski, W. (2010) Information: a conceptual investigation. Information 1(2), 74-118.
6. Shannon, C.E. (1948) A mathematical theory of communication. Bell System Technical Journal 27(3), 379-423.
7. Wiener, N. (1961) Cybernetics: Or Control and Communication in the Animal and the Machine. Second rev. ed. Cambridge, Massachusetts: MIT Press.

6.3. Scientific methods of computer science

The question of methods of computer science is still open. In this regard, below will be considered several projects, sponsored by experts in computer science. My position is that methods of informatics are methods of conceptual transduction. Below I will try to show the legitimacy of such a position.

Gordana Dodig-Krnkovich believes that computer science, continuing the traditions of other scientific disciplines, itself gained a critical weight, which makes it possible to consider it a full-fledged science [4]. She believes that based on already known knowledge, a certain hypothesis is chosen. It allows you to make predictions. They are tested, after which the initial hypothesis is changed to some extent and a choice is made between competing theories. We note that both intratheoretical and intertheoretical transduction falls into the field of vision of Dodig-Krnkovich. The logic of her reasoning seems to me to be correct. Nevertheless, unfortunately, Dodig-Krnkovich does not list the scientific methods of computer science. She believes that science has different methods. The method of mathematics, natural, social and human sciences is respectively deduction, hypothetical-deductive method, hypothetical-deductive method plus hermeneutics, and, finally, hermeneutics. According to the logic of reasoning by Dodig-

Krnkovich, all these methods are characteristic of computer science. With this statement, we cannot agree. Methods of informatics are deduction, adduction, induction, abduction, problematization, discovery, interpretation, and ordering. This is a complex method. Four methods are intratheoretical (4M), the other four methods are the intertheoretical (4M+). Methodological complex of computer science = 4M + 4M+.

The understanding of the scientific method that has become traditional for many modern scholars as the implementation of experiments and observations + induction + deduction + confirmation or refutation of theories is characteristic of many experts in computer science, in particular, for J.G Kemeny [6] and W.G. Rapaport [7, 180].

Many authors, paying considerable attention to the justification of the scientific nature of computer science, dispense without enumerating its methods [2; 5; 8]. Three authors list nine incorrect understandings of the status of computer science, in particular, when mistakenly reducing it to programming or excluding from it the latest research, for example, AI. Only one case mentions concepts related to methods. «**Once you master a core knowledge base including variables, sequencing, conditionals, loops, abstraction, modularization, and decomposition, you will be a computing professional.** This is a woefully incomplete characterization of what computing professionals need to know. The concepts listed are all programming concepts, and programming is a small subset of CS» [3, 32].

Meanwhile, in my opinion, all erroneous understandings of computer science, first, are connected with a superficial understanding of the methods of computer science. It remains for us to state our position on the methods of informatics.

Previously it was repeatedly noted that the formal, natural and axiological sciences share the same methods, i.e. methodological complex 4M + 4M⁺. In the case of formal sciences, this complex is presented in a formal form. Understanding this circumstance causes many researchers difficulty. They tend to interpret the content of methods in a universal manner, without taking into account the characteristics of formal sciences. Formal sciences deal with objects that differ substantially from those of natural and social sciences. Experiment as the transformation of objects in the formal sciences is impossible. It is possible to experimentally transform elementary particles, but not numbers. I turned to the topic of the experiment, not by chance. The fact is that understanding of the status of informatics largely depends on his understanding.

Thus, like all other sciences, computer science is guided by the methodological complex $4M + 4M^{+.}$ Of course, it is necessary to take into account that in computer science this complex is presented in a specific form. This fact is usually misunderstood. Computer science does not repeat the methods of the natural and axiological sciences but provides their accompaniment with formal means available to it.

References

1. Denning, P. (2005) Is computer science science? Communications of the ACM 48(4), 27-41.
2. Denning, P. (2007) Computing is a natural science. Communications of the ACM 50(7), 13-18.

3. Denning, P.J., Tedre M., Yongpradit P. (2017) Misconceptions about computer science. Communications of the ACM 60(3), 31-33.
4. Dodig-Crnkovic, G. (2002) Scientific Methods in Computer Science. Proceeding of the Conference for the Promotion of the Research in IT in New Universities and at University Colleges in Sweden. Suecia: Sköwde, 126-130.
5. Eden, A.H. (2007) Three paradigms of computer science. Minds and Machines 17(2), 135-167.
6. Kemeny, J. G. (1959). A Philosopher Looks at Science. Princeton, NJ: D. van Nostrand.
7. Rapaport, W.J. (2018) Philosophy of computer science. Draft, 2004-2018. Available at: https://cse.buffalo.edu/~rapaport/Papers/phics.pdf/
8. Turner, R. and Angius, N. (2017) The philosophy of computer science. The Stanford Encyclopedia of Philosophy. Available at: https://plato.stanford.edu/archives/spr2017/entries/computer-science/

6.4. The paradigm of computer science and the thesis of Church-Turing

Many scientists tried to express the basic, exemplary content of computer science. In this regard, they often talked about the paradigm of this science. In our opinion, computer science is guided by the same methods as any other science. What distinguishes it from other sciences does not consist of methods but in the content of the concepts. Consider two other actual points of view on the nature of computer science.

According to P. J. Denning and P.A. Freeman, the paradigm of computer science differs from the paradigms of mathematics, science, and engineering [2]. In this regard, they talk about the computing paradigm and represent its dynamics as a sequence of five stages: Initiation → Conceptualization → Realization → Evaluation → Action [2, 29]. Initiation is understood as elucidating the possibility of representing the processes being studied as informational. Conceptualization consists in the implementation of previously developed conceptual models. Evaluation is reduced to a critical evaluation of the results of Realization. Action translates the achieved results into the world, beyond the limits of informatics.

A.H. Eden and R. Turner presented the dynamics of computer science in a different sequence: Metaprograms → Programs → Hardware [3, 16]. They believe that the three stages in the deployment of the potential of computer science differ from each other in the degree of their abstractness. Metaprograms are all in particular, algorithmic calculations that open the possibility of creating programs. Metaprograms are more abstract than programs and hardware, and the most specific is hardware.

In my opinion, the intratheoretical cycle of the deployment of the content of computer science includes the following stages: Paradigms of computations → Programming paradigms → Programs → Implementation of programs → Evaluation of the results of program implementation → Introduction of corrections into the paradigms of computations and the programming paradigm. The content of these steps can be explained by using concepts about the methods of conceptual transduction. Paradigms of computations → programming paradigms → program = deduction. Implementation of the program = adduction. Evaluation of the results of program implementation = induction. Making adjustments in the paradigm of computing and the programming paradigm = abduction.

It is not difficult to see that the three theories of understanding the nature of computer science, presented above, largely coincide with each other. However, there are fundamental differences between them. Unlike P. J. Denning and P.A. Freeman, I believe that conceptualization takes place at all stages of the deployment of the content of computer science. Unlike A.H. Eden and R. Turner, I believe that the stages of intratheoretical transduction of computer science differ from each other not by the degree of abstraction, but by their place in the cycle of cognition. Then, the paradigm of computer science is the cycle of intratheoretical transduction.

Computer science arose not accidentally, but due to the development of quite certain scientific trends. Since antiquity, mathematicians have developed the notion of an algorithm. In the XVII century. G. Leibniz set the task of developing a formalized language that could be used in computer calculations. B. Russell in the 1900s, studying the problem aspects of set theory, developed a theory of types. In 1928, D. Hilbert and W. Ackermann presented the problem of solvability in a clear form [4, 19]. The formula is decidable if in the given formal system it is either itself provable or its negation. The function is computable if there is an algorithm, i.e. a finite sequence of operations that process every object x for which a function f is assigned to an object f(x) and is not applicable to any x for which f is not defined. In 1931, K. Gödel proved the incompleteness of any formal system containing a significant part of formal arithmetic. In doing so, he used the concept of a recursive function. In 1936, A. Church developed a theory of lambda-calculus based on the theory of types B. Russell. In the same year, A. Turing and E. Post proposed independently of each other an algorithm for realizing effective computability, conjugated with the concept of an abstract mathematical machine, i.e. not embodied in the gland. In 1941, K. Zuse, based on the lambda-calculus of Church, built the first computer. The birth of computer science took place!

Comprehension of the concept of computable function led to an unexpected result. It was found that this concept organically combines the notion of a recursive function, lambda-calculus, and Turing algorithm. This circumstance suggested an emphasis on the principles of informatics. It was in this connection that three theses were formulated.

The Turing thesis: an abstract Turing machine is capable of performing any operations that obey certain rules and in this sense are purely mechanical.

The Church's thesis: the functions of natural numbers are effectively computable only if they are lambda-definable. Often the theses of Turing and Church are generalized into one position.

The Church-Turing thesis: if there is an algorithm, its equivalents are the Turing machine, recursively defined functions, or closed lambda-expressions.

In my opinion, the Church-Turing thesis is nothing but the main principle of computer science. This is its meaning. It has been repeatedly noted that, the Church-Turing thesis is unprovable. This opinion does not seem to us solid. The successes of computer science clearly show in its favor. That is why scientists do not abandon it.

References

1. Davis, M. (1965) The Undecidable. Kleene and Rosser (lecture note-takers). New York: Raven Press.

2. Denning, P. J. and Freeman, P. A. (2009). The profession of IT. Computing's paradigm. Communications of the ACM, 52(12), pp. 29-31.
3. Eden, A.H. and Turner, R. (2007) Problems in the ontology of computer programs. Applied Ontology 2(1), 13-36.
4. Hilbert, D., Ackermann, W. (1972) Grundzüge der Theoretischen Logik [Basics of Theoretical Logic]. 6. Aufl. Berlin, Heidelberg: Springer. [In German].
5. Kleene, S.C. (1967) Mathematical Logic. New York: Wiley.

6.5. The development of computer theory: the language aspect

Every theory is a multitier process. This circumstance finds a very vivid manifestation in computer science. In this case, I mean, first, its language aspect. In modern computer science, on the way from algorithms to computers, diverse languages are used. The researchers had to go from the first-generation language to the fifth-generation languages. Languages of the first and second generation are languages whose content is mainly determined by the characteristics of the computer. Languages of the third, fourth and fifth generation are exempt from rigid attachment to computers. Their connection with the computer code of computers is provided by the translators. They themselves vary within the limits that are inaccessible to the languages of the first and second generation. Third-generation languages allow you to write a program for the central processing unit directly. The fourth-generation languages consist of statements similar to languages studied in linguistics. These are, in particular, Perl, PHP, Python, Ruby, and SQL. Languages of the fifth generation contain visual tools that help create programs. This, for example, Mercury and Prolog.

The division of programming languages into generations largely refines their conceptual description. In the same connection, it should be noted that there is a broad connection between programming languages. The number of languages is estimated in thousands. Of course, not all of them are popular in the same degree. Nevertheless, the abundance of programming languages amazes the imagination of a person.

Éric Lévénez presented the history of the development of programming languages for the period 1954-2018 in the form of a very impressive visual image [2]. The history of each individual language is depicted in the form of a straight line, which unites its stages of development. The second essential circumstance is that the line of development of languages crosses each other. This means that they do not develop independently of each other. This circumstance is manifested in the fact that programming languages adopt certain features from each other. Thus, there are certain similarities between the languages Python, Swift, C #, Ruby. Once seeing visual images É. Lévénez, I was struck by their similarity with the schemes used by me. In my opinion, the use of the concept of league-theory allows us to understand the history of the development of programming languages. The history of the development of each programmed language appears as a certain league-theory. For example, the league-theory of development of the Java language can be written as follows:

Java 7 → Java 6 → Java 5 → Java 4 → Java 3 → Java 2 → Java 1.

Of course, every dialect of the language, for example, Java 6, can also be represented as a certain league-theory. Macro league-theory of the Java language consists of seven of its micro league-theories. As for the intersections of programming languages, they express interdisciplinary connections. Conceptual metamorphoses in computer science occur according to the laws of conceptual transduction.

Continuing the assessment of programming languages, I turn to program paradigms. The 'programming paradigm' concept was introduced into computer science in 1979 by Robert Floyd [1]. He cited three times philosopher T. Kuhn the author of the paradigm theory. Floyd connected the concept of the programming paradigm primarily with two other factors, namely, first, with the originality of the programming languages, and secondly, with the need to highlight the conceptual bases of the efforts made by the programmer. We should pay tribute to R. Floyd – he managed to determine accurately the epistemological status of programming paradigms.

Programming paradigms are a way to classify programming languages based on their features. Languages can be classified based on multiple paradigms. Often there are two paradigms of programming, imperative and declarative. The imperative paradigm acts as a set of instructions. An object-oriented programming paradigm is usually referred to as imperative programming. Declarative programming is not guided by instructions but on specifications. For example, functional programming refers to the declarative programming paradigm. No one knows how many programming paradigms there are. There are also various options for introducing generic and species differences into the system of paradigms of programming. Nevertheless, it is obvious that the development of the concept of 'programming paradigm' led to a significant improvement in computer science, in particular, to a better understanding of the status of various programming languages. Most of them turned out to be multi-paradigmatic. It is significant that when writing a specific program, the programming language is used to express a completely defined, and not arbitrary, programming paradigm. Applied to program languages, the programming paradigm plays the role of a principle. In any theory, principles are of fundamental importance. Therefore, the progressive significance of the separation of programming paradigms is evident.

As for the expression 'programming paradigm', it has become very popular in computer science. Probably, he received here citizenship rights for many years. The programming paradigm is understood as a style of thinking and language. I prefer to talk about principles in computer science. The term 'paradigm' is usually used with reference to the American philosopher T. Kuhn. He believed that in all sciences for a long time some samples remain, despite their inconsistency with new scientific facts. However, in computer science, we see a fundamentally different situation. Almost every day the programming languages are improved. There is no such inertia of scientific thinking, for which T. Kuhn insisted.

Thus, the history of the development of computer science is very vividly represented in its language aspect.

References

1. Floyd, R.W. (1979) The paradigms of programming. Communications of the ACM 22(8), 455-460.
2. Lévénez, É. (2019) Computer Languages History. Available at: https://www.levenez.com/lang/

6.6. Program as stage of conceptual transduction

Paradigms and programming languages provide the ability to create programs. They are a sequence of instructions intended for execution by the processor. Of course, their understanding is associated with a number of problematic issues. The central one is, perhaps, the question about the theoretical and scientific nature of the programs.

This question was carefully considered by William Rapaport [3, 557-577]. He singled out the positions of supporters and opponents of the thesis about the theoretical nature of programs. H.A. Simon and A. Newell have proven themselves as active advocates of the recognition of the theoretical nature of computer programs [4; 5]. J. H. Moor and P. Thagard, by contrast, deny the theoretical nature of the programs [2; 6]. All these authors distinguish 1) real phenomena, 2) their theories, 3) models of real phenomena and 4) programs. H.A. Simon and A. Newell emphasize the existence of a connection between programs and theories. This connection, in their opinion, is so close that it is necessary to recognize the theoretical nature of the programs. J. H. Moor and P. Thagard recognize the relationship between programs and theories, but it does not abolish the uniqueness of programs. This means that programs, by their very nature, are not theories. The positions of the four authors are similar in one respect. All four interpret the nature of theories and models in the context of semantics. Theories and models are mappings of real phenomena. However, the theories are more abstract than models.

In my opinion, the above-mentioned researchers wrongly, firstly, are ascribing to computer science the ascent from the abstract to the concrete. Secondly, they use the semantic concept. Thirdly, the theory is separated from its stages and representations. The status of the program should be evaluated in the context of the theory of conceptual revolution. In this connection, it becomes immediately apparent that the program is one of the stages of conceptual transduction, i.e. computer theory. It is unjustifiable to contrast the theory stage to the theory itself. As for reality, it is not a stage of the theory, but its representation. It is inappropriate to contrast the representation and stage of the theory, in particular, reality and program. Within the theory of conceptual transduction, there is no need to introduce the concept of a model. Samples of algorithms, programming paradigms, and programs express the device of any representation of computer theory, in particular, reality. The concept of a model appears in computer science when researchers come from the traditional understanding of semantics. Rejection of this understanding also means abandoning the concept of the model.

Thus, the program is a stage in the development of computer theory. Program is not a theory as such, but a certain part of it. However, by its nature, the program is completely related to theory.

The stages of program development are 1) design, 2) constructing, 3) testing and 4) maintenance (elimination of identified defects). Typically, computer programs are stored in non-volatile memory until requested to be executed by the computer user. At the request of the user, the program is loaded into the random access memory. Then, it is brought directly to the central processor by the operating system. There comes the stage of execution of the program, which is called the process. The results of the process are usually displayed on the monitor screen.

How does the program relate to its execution? Often, not particularly getting into the conceptual subtleties, the execution is seen as a concretization of the program. However, as already noted, the transition from the abstract to the concrete is the legacy of an untenable theory of abstraction. Another theory is to understand the execution as an isomorphic mapping of the program. This position is protected, for example, by D. Chalmers [1]. Its main idea is that the physical system performs a calculation if its causal structure reflects the formal structure of the calculation. With such a position, it is difficult not to agree.

Let me sum up the analysis. The main condition for understanding programs is their successful incorporation into the line of conceptual transitions that are characteristic of computer science. Ultimately, the significance of programs is determined by their place in the cycle of intratheoretical, and then the intertheoretical, transduction.

References

1. Chalmers, D.J. (1994) On implementing a computation. Minds and Machines 4(4), 391-402.
2. Moor, J. H. (1978) Three myths of computer science. British Journal for the Philosophy of Science 29(3), 213–222.
3. Rapaport, W.J. (2018) Philosophy of computer science. Draft, 2004-2018. Available at: https://cse.buffalo.edu/~rapaport/Papers/phics.pdf/
4. Simon, H. A. (1996) Computational theories of cognition. In The Philosophy of Psychology. Ed. by W. O'Donohue and R. F. Kitchener. London: SAGE Publications, 160-172.

5. Simon, H.A. and Newell, A. (1956) Models: their uses and limitations. In The State of the Social Sciences. Ed. by L.D. White. Chicago: University of Chicago Press, 66-83.

6. Thagard, P. (1978) Why astrology is a pseudoscience. PSA: Proceedings of the Biennial Meeting of the Philosophy of Science Association 1, 223–234.

6.7. Nature of the computer

After clarifying the nature of the program, it is also advisable to address the question of the nature of the process executed by the central processing unit. In this regard, usually talk about the nature of the computer. William Rapaport, after examining dozens of definitions of the nature of the computer, reduced them to six definitions, of which the most significant is the following: «A computer is a physically plausible implementation of some model of computation». [2, 399] The simplest definition of a computer is that it is a physical or technical device. Anyone who aspires to clarify the nature of the computer must, first, consider the relationship of logic, mathematics, computer science, technology and physics; secondly, the ratio of algorithmic models of computations, programs, and processes; thirdly, the ratio of computer science with theories of thinking. These theories lead to the field of cognitive sciences, in particular, psychology. Alan Turing was the first to connect the nature of the computer and the human intellect [5]. With him begins the tradition of comparing the computer with the intellect of man. It was most actively discussed by John Searle [3; 4].

First, I note that the computer is neither a physical device nor a technical device. The specificity of the computer in the form, in which it appears in computer science, is not explained either in physics or in technology. It finds its explanation exclusively in computer science. Therefore, it must be recognized that a computer is an object of purely computer science.

Above, in determining the nature of the computer, the expression 'physically plausible implementation' was used. The computer is not a physical object, therefor in determining its nature it is not appropriate to use the adjective 'physically'. Here the question arises as to the appropriateness of the expression 'plausible implementation'. Implementation is the process of execution. The term 'implementation' used in this case is quite appropriate. It is hardly advisable to use 'embodiment' instead of 'implementation'. The use of the term 'embodiment' would imply that the changes taking place with the central computing unit would be clearly tangible. Nevertheless, they are not such.

Implementation is a very real process, but not so obvious, as, for example, the physical interaction of bodies. What does it mean? The nature of all-natural objects is such that people can attribute them technical, economic and computer processes. Such a peculiar nature of natural objects always aroused the astonishment of researchers. It really exists and is not just a fiction of scientists. A computer is a computer-scientific object to which a program is attributed.

Scientists, evaluating the specifics of the computer, usually come from a syntax-semantics dichotomy. This position is typical, for example, for John Searle. He believes that for the brain, in contrast to the computer is characterized by a unity of syntax and semantics that is not available to the computer. Consequently, the brain is not a digital computer [4]. In my opinion, the brain can be a computer in case it is used solely for the performance of some computer programs, attributed to it. In all other cases, the brain is not a computer.

The brain of a computer scientist is certainly also a thing, but it fundamentally differs from a computer. The human brain is a creative thing; the computer is an auxiliary thing. The human brain develops all the concepts and methods of transduction cycles, including the attribution of programs to computers. The share of the computer remains only the execution of programs. The cycle of intratheoretical transduction is much richer than one of its stages, namely, the execution of the program by the central computing unit. The processor is not able to go beyond this stage. The difference between the brain and the computer is explained through the theory of conceptual transduction, and not the syntax-semantics dichotomy.

It is interesting that objecting Searle, a large group of computer scientists tried to present the computer's work in the most meaningful way. This is the concept of John Hayes, who believes that a computer is a «machine which performs computations» [1, 390]. Nevertheless, it should not be forgotten that only a person and not a computer as an auxiliary tool, does calculations in the full volume.

From the foregoing, it follows that the computer does not think. The very formulation of the question of man's thinking seems somewhat amusing. However, the question was initiated by outstanding scientists A. Turing, so it should be treated with all seriousness. The following assertion of A. Turing is indicative: «I believe that at the end of the century the use of words and general educated opinion will be altered so much that one will be able to speak of machines without expecting to be contradicted». [5, 442]

Thinking is the process of conceptual transduction in its mental form, free from all emotions and feelings. Only a man can carry out this process, but not a computer. Turing disputed this conclusion. Guided by the scientific method, he proposed the now widely known test. The expert asks questions in an impersonal form, for example, in writing, a computer and a person. For the selected period, the expert should identify the computer and the person. If he does not succeed, he must recognize the identity of both of them. The computer that passed the test is similar to the person with whom it was compared. The decisive mistake of A. Turing is that he regards the computer as an independent thing, outside of that whole within which he has meaning. The computer is a representation of the theory, which was created not by him, but by his creators. A person does not compete with a computer, but with a person using a computer. It is not a computer that defeats the world chess champion, but the creative collective of people that it represents.

The thesis about computational thinking is the result of a misunderstanding of computer theory. In this case, it seems quite legitimate to compare experimentally the human and computer. This idea has a pronounced positivistic character. For Turing, one of the founders of computer science, such a position is quite natural.

Thus, from the perspective of the theory of conceptual transitions, the question of computer thinking gets obvious resolution. The computer does not think. It is not necessary to distinguish strong and weak intellect. The Latins under intellect understood the thinking ability of man. Computers do not have the ability to think, even in a weakened form. Of course, this circumstance doesn't question the excellent achievements of computer science. In alliance with other sciences, computer science ensures the steady development of mankind.

References

1. Hayes, J.P. (1997) What is a computer? An electronic discussion. The Monist 80(3), 389-404.
2. Rapaport, W.J. (2018) Philosophy of computer science. Draft, 2004-2018. Available at: https://cse.buffalo.edu/~rapaport/Papers/phics.pdf/
3. Searle, J. R. (1980). Minds, brains, and programs. Behavioral and Brain Sciences 3(3), 417–457.
4. Searle, J.R. (1990) Is the brain a digital computer? Proceedings and Addresses of the American Philosophical Association 64(3), 21-37.
5. Turing, A. (1950) Computing machinery and intelligence. Mind 59(236), 433-460.

6.8. The nature of visualization

The reader has evidently already noticed that we are striving to explain the nature of all computer things and processes by referring to the theory of conceptual transduction. Having reached the computer, you cannot avoid discussing the nature of the monitor. A computer monitor is an output device, which displays information in a pictorial form. In this case, the process of visualization assumes a decisive role. I am turning to the consideration of its nature. In this regard, the statement of Chris Johnson is indicative.

Too often, creators of visualization technology
do not spend enough (or indeed any) time

endeavoring to understand the underlying science they are trying to represent, just as application scientists sometimes create crude visualizations without understanding the algorithms and science of visualization. To establish mutually beneficial peer relationships with application scientists and to create effective visual representations, visualization scientists need to spend more time understanding the underlying science, engineering, and medical applications. [3, 14]

There is no doubt that a consistent theory of visualization is needed. However, in this connection, there is a shortage of detailed concepts. Nevertheless, one of the theories is undoubtedly worthy of attention. This is a study of Agustin Araya «Hidden side of visualization» [1]. He, in turn, relies on the study of the German philosopher phenomenologist Edmund Husserl, who in his quest to develop a unified image of science, attached paramount importance to the three epoch-making scientific strategies, namely, the geometry of Euclid, the mathematized physics of Galileo and the analytical geometry of Descartes [2].

The specificity of Euclidean geometry lies in the fact that scientists operate with ideal forms as limiting cases of ontological reliability and use the axiomatic method. Within the framework of Galilean physics, the world of Euclidean idealizations unites with the world of bodily things and empirical dimensions. Mathematics becomes the language of physics. Descartes, applying algebraic methods to geometry, developed analytical geometry. As a result, geometry acquires a metric (countable) form that can be applied to any empirical world. Thanks to the innovations first Galileo, and then Descartes, it becomes possible to visualize any processes. They significantly multiplied due to the capabilities of computers. Digital operations allow the creation of digital bodies and places that act as surf. «A surf is a collection of pixels on a computer window whose purpose is to realize a geometrical surface representing something. We can say that surfs are the building blocks from which visualizations are constructed. » [1, p. 69]. Thus, according to Araya, the conceptual trend of visualization provided with epochal innovations of Euclid, Galileo, and Descartes, culminated in computer visualization.

Araya does not repeat the conclusions of Husserl but essentially modifies them. In this connection, he refers to the ontology of M. Heidegger and the pragmatism of J. Pitt [1, 60, 84, 89]. Heidegger regarded man as an exemplary ontological being. Pitt insisted on the relevance of the practical life of man. As for Araya himself, he gives priority to the historical-ontological perspective [1, 35]. In this regard, I consider it possible to call the theory of visualization developed by him a historical-ontological conception.

Let me now turn to my conception of visualization, which follows from the theory of conceptual transduction. In this connection, I, first, emphasize the paramount importance of the principle of theoretical representation. Consideration of all questions should begin with the reference to the status of the theory. The second step is that I am considering the possibility of various presentations of theories. Them, as you know, can be quite a lot. The presentation of the theory can be and object, and language, and mental, and procedural, and behavioral. As soon as this circumstance is recorded, it immediately becomes clear that visual images are one of the forms of representation of the theory.

The successes of scientific visualization are ensured by the achievements of all sciences. A person sees not only physical objects but also biological organisms and people carrying out economic processes. Visual impressions are determined by the theories of man. As the theories develop, visual impressions become more and more conceptually saturated. It is enough to use a certain search engine to discover on the Internet numerous visual images related to the most diverse sciences. To understand them, a developed scientific theory is required. In quantum field theory, Feynman diagrams are widely used. They are not photographs of real phenomena, but their visual image. Strictly speaking, this is not geometric, but a physical image. Geometry achievements can be used to interpret the content of Feynman diagrams, but not otherwise than within the interdisciplinary connections of quantum field theory and geometry, for example, topology. For physical visualization, physicists, and not geometers, are primarily responsible. Economists are responsible for economic visualization.

Visualization is a form of representation of the theory, which, in many respects, uses the capabilities of the organs of vision. However, this circumstance should not be absolutized, considering, for example, that the device of the organs of vision has decisive significance in the matter of visualization. All the wealth of theories is visualized. However, this is not so much due to the physiological capabilities of our eyes, but because of the theoretical relativity of our senses. Many animals, for example, eagles, have unique organs of vision, in many ways superior to the human eye. Nevertheless, they do not possess a high degree of theoretical relativity that is characteristic of the human eye.

Araya, developing the views of Husserl, believes that visualization is determined mainly by geometry. Of course, in the field of visualization, the achievements of geometry are extremely important. Nevertheless, visualization is not reduced to geometry. The text that the reader sees now is also a visual image. It is also any photograph, or any equation written on paper, the meaning of which is determined not by geometry.

In conclusion of the section, I note that computer science, has attached great importance to the visualization theme, was extremely helpful in exposing one widely spread myth about the nature of science. It consists in the fact that science in its development, more and more immersed in the world of abstractions and idealizations, moves away from the real world, in particular, from sensory impressions. This circumstance E. Husserl regarded as a crisis of science [3]. In my opinion, he was in many ways right. Nevertheless, for the sake of justice, it should be noted that in many respects he exaggerated the shortcomings of science. In spite of Husserl, science never lost sight of the sensual world of man. Unfortunately, this world not always found the proper assessment. In this connection, the theoretical relativity of all visual perceptions is of decisive importance. Their true meaning is revealed only when the visual images are considered as representations of the corresponding theories. In the case of computer science, this means that they acquire additional specificity in accordance with its formal status.

References

1. Araya, A.A. (2003) Hidden side of visualization. Techné 7(2), 27-92.

2. Husserl, E. (1970) The Crisis of European Sciences and Transcendental Phenomenology: An Introduction to Phenomenological Philosophy. Evanston: Northwestern University Press.
3. Johnson, C.R. (2004) Top scientific visualization research problems. IEEE Computer Graphics and Visualization 24(4), 13-17.

6.9. Status of computer and information ethics

As a formal science, computer science is an interdisciplinary partner of all existing sciences. There is an impression of its ubiquity. In this connection, the conviction grows that computer science has a pronounced ethical component. However, in our opinion, such a position is superficial.

The ethical project is known since time immemorial. Throughout the centuries of development of philosophy, he was repeatedly modified. Invariably the central importance in it was the procuring of maximizing the prosperity of not only the individual person but also all stakeholders. However, how to understand prosperity? It varies from one axiological theory to another. In economics, prosperity is understood as maximizing the profits of entrepreneurs and the wages of employees and workers. In pedagogy, prosperity is the maximization of the learning competencies of students. In many technical sciences, prosperity is interpreted as increasing the productivity of technical artifacts.

It is essential that the notion of prosperity is organically exclusively for axiological theories, but not for natural and formal conceptions. It is impossible to introduce the concept of prosperity, for example, neither in physics nor in mathematics.

Physical objects, for example, elementary particles, do not achieve prosperity. Numbers, being mathematical objects, also do not have the characteristics of prosperity. Therefore, it seems that natural and formal theories have nothing to do with ethics. However, in reality, it is not so. Maximizing their prosperity, people cannot do without resorting to natural and formal theories. They are certainly used in the interdisciplinary connections of axiological theories. It is therefore incorrect to consider that non-axiological theories are completely indifferent in ethical terms. Natural and formal theories have ethical relativity, but unlike axiological concepts, they do not have an ethical principle as such. This circumstance is manifested in the fact that the principle of maximizing the prosperity of all stakeholders is incompatible with the principles of natural and formal theories. However, it is organic for all axiological theories.

From what has been said above, the corresponding conclusion follows: the conception of computer ethics, developed by many researchers [1; 7], is devoid of clear scientific meaning. Computer science has ethical relativity [6].

Let me turn now to the conception of information ethics. Those authors, who believe that there is universal science, informatics, often introduce the idea of a special, namely, information ethics. This position is typical, for example, for Krystyna Gorniak [4] and Luciano Floridi [3]. However, computer science as a universal science does not exist at all. It follows that there is no information ethics.

Thus, the concepts of both the ethics of computer science and information ethics are not consistent. The real significance has only the ethical relativity of computer science.

Another urgent issue relates to the correlation between philosophical ethics and the ethical relativity of computer science. Should we use the ethical systems known from philosophy, such as Kant's deontological ethics, Bentham-Mill's utilitarianism, and J. Dewey's pragmatism, when discussing topics related to computer science? Unfortunately, all these systems do not properly use the potential of axiological theories, in particular, scientific understanding of the principle of maximizing the prosperity of all stakeholders. Given this circumstance, philosophical ethical systems are unacceptable to use uncritically. They certainly need a proper modification. After that, they are legitimately used to develop an in-depth understanding of the ethical relativity of computer science.

Finally, it must be borne in mind that the discussion of ethical issues pertaining to informatics is certainly accomplished in a certain philosophical way. In the era of pluralism, this cannot be avoided. These interpretations are often made on behalf of the main philosophical trends, in particular, analytical philosophy [8], phenomenology [5] and hermeneutics [2].

Many authors, when discussing ethical issues, for example, relating to the problems of the Internet, do not take into account the place of computer science in interdisciplinary relations. Frequently discussed issues of computer security are not the prerogative of computer science alone. They initially refer to certain axiological theories, for example, psychological, economic, political, legal or military conceptions.

References

1. Bynam, T. (2018) Computer and information ethics. The Stanford Encyclopedia of Philosophy. Available at: https://plato.stanford.edu/archives/sum2018/entries/ethics-computer/

2. Capurro, R. (1990) Ethik und Informatik. Die Herausbildung der Informatik für die Praktische Philosophie [Ethics and computer science. The development of computer science for practical philosophy]. Informatik-Spectrum 13(2), 311-320. [In German].

3. Floridi, L. (199) Information ethics: on the philosophical foundation of computer ethics. Ethics and Information Technology 1(1), 37-56.

4. Gorniak, K. (1996) The computer revolution and the problem of global ethics. Science and Engineering Ethics 2(2), 177-190.

5. Introna, L. (2017) Phenomenological approaches to ethics and information technology. The Stanford Encyclopedia of Philosophy. Available at: https://plato.stanford.edu/archives/fall2017/entries/ethics-it-phenomenology/

6. Kanke, V.A. (2018) The metascientific and philosophical bases of information ethics. Automatic Documentation and Mathematical Linguistics 52(1), 1-6.

7. Moor, J. (1999) Just consequentialism and computing. Ethics and Information Technology 1(1), 65-69.

8. Moor, J. (1985) What is computer ethics? Metaphilosophy 16(4), 266-275.

Chapter 7. The nature of physics

7.1. Physics specifics

Physics (from Ancient Greek φύσις phýsis 'nature') is a very authoritative branch of science. It is often claimed that physics is a science that studies the matter and its motion and behavior through space and time. However, such definitions are questionable insofar as the terms are used, in particular, the concept of matter, regardless of the specific content of individual physical theories.

Physics consists of many separate theories; their number is not known to anyone. One thing is certain. There are many such theories. To define physics, it is necessary to study their similarities. It is desirable that they were few. For example, it would be tedious to list all the objects that physics studies, elementary particles, and condensed matter. The number of physical laws is also huge. In the search for solving the criterion for the definition of physics, it is reasonable to refer to the principles. Most often in physics, the principles of variational action, invariance, and actions are used. Given this circumstance, it is advisable to offer the following definition of physics: physics is a branch of science, all the theories of which are guided by the principles of variational action (first of all, by the principle of least action), of invariance, and of short-range interaction.

The entities of physics are objects only, but not persons. From the standpoint of physics, all persons are objects and, therefore, do not differ from them. All physical objects possess properties, in particular, potential and kinetic energy, masses, charges, forces, impulses, accelerations, speeds, lengths, and durations.

Physical knowledge is multiplied in the process of intratheoretical and intertheoretical transduction. Since an experiment is part of a theory, it is not right, as is often done, to distinguish between theoretical and experimental physics. What is meant by theoretical physics are physical theories, with an emphasis on prediction and its method, the deduction. While the methods of adduction, induction, and abduction paid little attention. Experimental physics is a theoretical physics with an emphasis on the factualization stage and its method, namely, the adduction. Scientific methods of physics are the methods of conceptual transduction, i.e. the deduction, adduction, induction, abduction, problematization, discovery, interpretation and ordering of league-theories.

Often in physics, there are special and general theories. General theories express similar features of special concepts. Strictly speaking, these are formal theories as part of physics. In this quality, they, unlike, for example, from mathematics and computer science, do not go beyond the limits of physics. In physics, formal theories are known as mechanics. I mean, above all, classical mechanics, relativistic mechanics, quantum mechanics, and quantum field theory. However, mechanics do not exhaust physics, which includes other formal theories, for example, thermodynamics, and statistical physics.

The origins of all formal physical theories are special physical theories. They all relate to one or another type of physical interaction. Each type of interaction is characterized by some subtypes. In our case, it suffices to list the types of interactions; these are electromagnetic, weak, strong, and gravitational interactions.

To assess the status of modern physics, its historical steps are extremely important. As physics developed, it became clear that less developed theories did not take into account some concepts of more developed theories. A comparison of theories allows revealing the disadvantages of less developed theories. In classical mechanics, Newton did not take into account the principles of the short-range action, the quantum nature of the actions, and the birth and death of particles. Of the three indicated principles, only the principle of the quantum nature of actions was taken into account in the nonrelativistic quantum mechanics of Heisenberg-Schrödinger. In the relativistic quantum mechanics of Dirac-Gordon-Fock, two principals were taken into account, the principle of short-range action and the principle of quantum actions. Only in quantum field theory, all three of the above principles were taken into account.

It was in physics in a vivid form that it was established that a developed theory is the key to a less developed form. Today, quantum field theory (Tqft) is the key to understanding quantum (Tqm), relativist (Trm) and classical mechanics (Tcm). This circumstance can be expressed as follows:

$$T_{qft} \rightarrow T_{qm} \rightarrow T_{rm} \rightarrow T_{cm}. \qquad 7.1$$

A less developed scientific theory is always a limiting case of a more developed theory. This circumstance was noticed by Wolfgang Pauli in 1938. He noted that in physics the later stages of its development do not nullify the value of the earlier stages, but only indicate the limits of applicability of these earlier stages, including them as limiting cases of the new physics system [2, 10]. The possibility of limit transition from a more developed theory of T_{n+1} to a less developed T_n does indeed often exist:

$$\text{Lim } \varepsilon \rightarrow 0 \ Tn+1 = Tn \ , \qquad 7.2$$

where ε is the deforming parameter. In the case of transition from relativist to classical mechanics, it is ε = v/s, where v is the speed of movement of physical objects, and c is the speed of light in a vacuum.

In the transition from quantum to classical mechanics, ε = h/S, where h is the Planck constant, and S is the action.

Albert Einstein an Leopold Infield also emphasized the priority of a developed theory over a less developed one.

> The new theory shows the merits as well as the limitations of the old theory and allows us to regain our old concepts from a higher level. This is true not only for the theories of electric fluids and field, but for all changes in physical theories, however revolutionary they may seem. [1, 158]

The successes of physics are impressive. Nevertheless, in the development of physics, there are also numerous difficulties, to which we turn in the following texts.

References

1. Einstein, A. and Infeld, L. (1950) [1938] The Evolution of Physics. London: The Scientific Book Club.
2. Pauli, W. (1975) Fizicheskiye ocherki [Physical Essays]. Moskva: Nauka. [In Russian].

7.2. Principles and laws of classical mechanics

Few doubts that by the creation of classical mechanics set out in Newton's «Mathematical Principles of Natural Philosophy» (1687), he accomplished a scientific feat. The name of the book is somewhat strange. Obviously, Newton created a new physical theory. In this case, mathematics played a significant, however, auxiliary, interdisciplinary role. As for the beginnings of classical mechanics, they deserve a special discussion. Of course, Newton faced the greatest difficulties in discussing the principles of his theory. In this regard, the well-known three Newton's laws attract special attention, especially the first one, according to which if the forces acting on the body balance each other, then it is in a state of rest or uniform rectilinear motion.

At first glance, this law is a consequence of Newton's second law: $F_i = m_i a_i$. If the sum of the forces Fi is equal to zero, then at a constant body mass m, its acceleration a is also zero. However, this opinion is wrong. The fact is that the forces entering Newton's second law must be active, real. This is not the case in some reference system. Judgments about laws presuppose an initial view of reference systems. The fact is that physicists have to deal with interacting objects. This circumstance is expressed in the concept of a reference system. It can be understood in two ways. Newton understood the reference system as a closed collection of objects. This means that they do not interact with other objects and, therefore, also systems. In the case of a closed reference system, all forces are active. It is known which bodies are their source. Forces can be measured. In physics, closed reference systems are called inertial.

Another situation occurs when an open one is considered, i.e. non-inertial reference system. In this case, there is not enough data to describe the behavior of physical objects. Newton's first law is necessary in order to distinguish inertial reference systems from non-inertial reference systems. The meaning of this action is not derived from any principle. In fact, Newton's first law is not a law. It turns out that in its rational features, it is a principle. In fact, there are two, not three of Newton's laws. This circumstance is clearly understood by those physicists who, instead of Newton's first law, prefer to talk about the principle of inertia. Its positive meaning is that it is always necessary to search for those forces that are characteristic of closed systems. On this point, there is a wonderful example related to the discovery of the planet Neptune. Its presence was predicted because without taking into account its influence on the planet Uranus, it was impossible correctly to predict behavior of this planet. Unexpected changes in the orbit of Uranus led A. Bouvard to deduce that its orbit was subject to gravitational perturbation by an unknown planet [1]. He skillfully used the concept of a closed or inertial reference system.

In my opinion, the naming of a closed reference system as inertial is not a good language action. The fact is that the meaning of such terms as body inertia and inertia forces is not always understood correctly. The term 'inertial frame of reference' suggests that its meaning is closely related to the concepts of inertia of the body and inertial forces. This is not true.

Body inertia is often characterized as a property of bodies [3, 221]. However, the properties of physical bodies must necessarily be measured and calculated in certain units of measurement. Nevertheless, there is neither one nor the other. Therefore, there is no reason to introduce the notion of the inertia of physical objects. It is not by chance that the inertia of the body is not presented in any formula of mechanics. Physical bodies have mass, but not inertia. Mass is measured in kilograms. To explain the behavior of physical objects, the concept of inertia is not required; the concepts of force, mass, and acceleration are sufficient.

We now turn to the phenomenon of inertial forces. Passengers, for example, when accelerating and slowing down the car, sincerely believe that they are affected by inertia forces. However, in the English-language literature, they are called fictitious forces and there is every reason for this. To verify this, it is enough to refer to the D'Alembert principle, according to which if an additional inertia force is applied to an active force acting on a body and a coupling reaction, then the body will be in equilibrium [2; 4, 90]. The forces of inertia are not real forces; they are introduced only to the extent that they contribute to applying simpler static methods to the solution of dynamic problems. It is no more than an artificial method, which does not turn fictitious forces into real ones.

We now turn to another fundamental feature of Newtonian mechanics, namely, to the determinism. Forces are recognized as the only agents that can cause some changes. In science, people often look for the answer to the question: "Why does Event A occur? » It usually means that an event is a consequence of a certain interaction. Why does the moon rotate around the earth? Thanks to gravitational forces. It seems to be given a comprehensive explanation of the behavior of the moon. However, it is not. Forces are determined by laws, and they, in turn, are determined by principles. Given this circumstance, it is necessary to distinguish between intensional determinism and causal one. The explanation of the origin of a certain event is complete only when intensional determinism is supplemented by a causal one.

According to the mechanics of Newton's laws are not deduced. Therefore, on its behalf, it is logical to proclaim force determinism. The situation is fundamentally different in the reformulation of classical mechanics, which Lagrange carried out in 1788. Here the laws of mechanics, appearing under the name of the Euler-Lagrange equations, are derived from the principle of least action. Forces are interpreted as negative gradients of potential energy. This means that energy determinism comes to the fore. However, it should not be taken for simplicity. In my opinion, the deductive dominance of the principle of least action over the laws of dynamics should be perceived as a special kind of determinism, namely, intensional. Meaning intensional determinism generally underestimated. Often, determinism is understood exclusively in its force version.

Thus, in my opinion, the foundations of Newton's mechanics include three principles: 1) the principle of least action, 2) the principle of a closed frame of reference, 3) the principle of determinism.

Reference

1. Bouvard, A. (1821). Tables astronomiques publiées par le Bureau des Longitudes de France [Astronomical tables published by the Bureau des Longitudes de France.]. Paris: Bachelier. [In French].
2. D'Alembert, J. le R. (1743) Traité de Dynamique, dans lequel les Lois de L'Equilibre & du Mouvement des Corps sont Réduites au plus petit Nombre Possible [Treaty of Dynamics, in which the Laws of Balance & Movement of Bodies are Reduced to the Smallest Possible Number]. Paris: David L'Aîné. [In French].
3. Inertia. (1983) Fizicheskiy entsiklopedicheskiy slovar' [Physical Encyclopedic Dictionary]. Moskva: Sovetskaya entsiklopediya. [In Russian].

4. Lanczos, C. (1970). The Variationel Principles of Mechanics. Forth ed. New York: Dover Publications Inc.

7.3. Development of space and time conceptions

In physics philosophy courses, as a rule, the nature of space and time is considered. Our position is that there is no space and time, but the length of physical objects (Δr) and the duration of physical processes (Δt). All physical theories contain these characteristics. There is nothing in them that could be called space and time. Therefore, they are not. You can use the term 'space' to denote the entire set of lengths of objects. However, space is not a special physical substance or an attribute of physical bodies. The term 'time' can be used to refer to the entire set of durations, but it is not a substance or a sign of physical objects. You can use the term 'matter' or 'objective reality' to refer to all physical objects, but the matter will not differ from physical objects. When using the terms 'matter', 'space' and 'time' prerequisites are created for the formation of fictions. If lengths would interact with each other, then, one must assume, they would form a systemic formation, which it would be reasonable to call space. Accordingly, durations, which interact, would form time. Nevertheless, the interaction does not exist in the case of lengths, nor in the case of durations. No space and time as system objects. In the text below, I use the terms space and time in the sense I have clarified.

I. Newton insisted on the existence of absolute, true, mathematical space and time in his «Mathematical Foundations of Natural Philosophy» [4, 77]. There was no reason for such a conclusion. The mechanics created by Newton stated that, firstly, the length and duration of bodies in all inertial reference systems are the same, i.e. they are invariants. Secondly, as

349

invariants, they do not depend on physical interactions. Based on these two characteristics of lengths and durations, it is impossible to conclude in any way that absolute space and time exist. This circumstance was noticed by I. Newton's main opponent Gottfried Leibniz.

Leibniz considered the length and duration as the measurable attributes of things. Time is the order of sequences, and space is the order of coexistence [6, 17]. Leibniz did not give up the concepts of space and time as systemic entities. Note that Newton and Leibniz, two geniuses of the science of the XVII century, in their reflections on the nature of space and time continually referred to the wisdom of the creator of the universe, although it could and should have been done without it.

By rethinking the contents of mechanics Emmy Noether made an extremely important point in the entire discussion of the space-time perspective. It turned out that, to every differentiable symmetry generated by local actions there corresponds a law of conservation. [5] Conservation of energy corresponds to time invariance. Conservation of linear momentum corresponds to translation invariance. Conservation of angular momentum corresponds to rotation invariance. In fact, it should be allocated not two, space and time but three factors. Physicists, as a rule, do not pay due attention to this circumstance.

Relativistic mechanics, also known as Einstein's special theory of relativity, led to significant changes in views about space and time. The concept of absolute space and time was archived. It turned out that not the length and duration, taken separately, are invariants but the interval composed of them (Δs): $(\Delta s)2 = c2 \ (\Delta t)2 - (\Delta r)2$. The introduction of four-dimensional coordinates led to the concept of space-time. Hermann Minkowski believed that «space itself and time itself turns into a shadow and only a kind of their union preserves independence» [3, 1]. In fact, the difference of three-dimensional lengths from one-dimensional durations has not been canceled. Once again, we have to deal with the widespread misunderstanding of the relationship between mathematics as a formal science and physics. To understand the ontological significance of mathematical concepts and conclusions, one should proceed from the status of physics. Physics as a non-formal science has in its relationship with mathematics decisive importance. In relativistic mechanics, the fallacy of the concept of absolute simultaneity was shown. In its absence, the concept of absolute time is inappropriate.

Many controversies are associated with the explanation of the nature of lengths and durations by means of forces. Eugene Fenberg convincingly revealed the dynamic nature of relativistic space and time effects [1]. Nevertheless, one important circumstance should be taken into account. The dynamics of the processes explain the variability of relativistic space and time effects. Nevertheless, there is no reason to say that length and duration are generated by forces or energy.

Quantum mechanics has led to another change in the ideas of physicists about lengths and durations. This time it turned out that they, like all other physical characteristics, have probabilistic values, uncertainty, and discreteness. The frequently discussed doubts about the discreteness of time were dispelled by H.-D Zeh and J. Hilgevoord [7; 2].

An extremely important stage in the development of space-time representations in physics turned out to be associated with the successes of quantum field theory. The consistent development initially quantum electrodynamics, and then of the quantum theory of electroweak interactions and quantum chromodynamics showed that the nature of the lengths and durations bears the imprint of this or that type of interaction. This circumstance was also expressed in the relativistic gravitational theory of A. Einstein. Space and time characteristics of gravitational phenomena turned out to be significantly different from other types of interactions. It is reasonable to assume that this feature of them is determined by gravitational interactions.

In the context of the problems discussed, it is also reasonable to recall the theory of superstrings, in which multidimensional spaces are considered, for example, 10-dimensional []. With each success of string theory, multidimensional spaces seem less and less fantastic.

The history of the development of space and time representations shows that more advanced theories update these theories in a decisive way. However, this happens only if their content receives an adequate interpretation. In this regard, the development of the philosophy of physics is crucial.

References

1. Fenberg, E.L. (1975) Mozhno li rassmatrivat' relyativistskoye izmeneniye masshtabov dliny i vremeni kak rezul'tat deystviya nekotorykh sil? [Can the relativistic change in the scales of length and time be considered the result of the action of certain forces?]. Uspekhi fizicheskikh nauk [Successes of Physical Sciences] 115(80, 709-730. [In Russian].

2. Hilgevoord, J. (2002) Time in quantum mechanics. American Journal of Physics. 70(3), 301-306.
3. Minkowski, H. (1909) Raum und Zeit [Space and Time]. Leipzig, Berlin: Teubner. [In German].
4. Newton, I. (1846) Newton's Principia: The Mathematical Principles of Natural Philosophy. New York: Published by Daniel Adee.
5. Noether, E. (1918). Invariante Variationsprobleme [Invariant problems of variation]. Nachrichten von der Gesellschaft der Wissenschaften zu Göttingen. Mathematisch-Physikalische Klasse, 235–257. [In German].
6. The Leibniz-Clarke Correspondence. Ed. by H.G. Alexander. Manchester, 1956.
7. Zeh, H. D. (2009) Time in quantum theory. In Compendium of Quantum Physics. Ed. by D. Greenberger, K. Hentschel, and F. Weinert. Berlin: Swinger, 786–792.

7.4. Invariance principles and conservation laws

As is well known, in physics, principles that express the interrelation (correlation) of certain features of processes are of paramount importance. What principles of physics deserve primary attention? It is essential that the principles of physics were realized not in any but in a quite definite way. According to the principle of least action, physical processes are carried out in such a way that the magnitude of the action (S), which is calculated according to the formula 7.2 given below, turns out to be extreme, usually minimal:

$$S = \int_{t_1}^{t_2} L dt, \qquad 7.2$$

L – Lagrange function (Lagrangian), which in the framework of classical mechanics is equal to the difference of kinetic and potential energy.

Of course, it is also important to understand the mechanism for implementing the principle of least action. It is the process of interaction. In addition, how is the interaction process? This question is important. Let me try to answer it. Interacting objects exchange, for example, energy, masses, and charges. Interestingly, the attributes exchanged between interacting objects are dynamic. Objects do not exchange lengths, durations or speeds. When taking into account the exchange nature of the physical interaction, the assumption of conservation laws is quite natural. If object A transferred some attribute to object B, then it did not disappear, but only changed its affiliation. Dynamic characteristics do not disappear but only pass from one object to another. This fact is recorded by the laws of conservation, for example, the laws of conservation of energy, mass, momentum, angular momentum, electric and other charges.

As you can see, there is a close relationship between the dynamics of processes and the laws of conservation. The preservation of certain quantities is always realized in the processes of interaction. Moreover, as it turned out, conservation laws correlate with symmetry operations. The Greek word 'symmetry' literally means proportionality. In physics, symmetry is understood as such a change in the system, in which some of its features remain unchanged, i.e. are invariants. In this regard, the following relationships are relevant.

1. Time invariance is in accordance with the law of conservation of energy.

2. Translation invariance is in accordance with the law of conservation of linear momentum.

3. Rotation invariance is in accordance with the law of conservation of angular momentum.

These correlations, of course, are not obvious. What is its meaning? Finding an adequate answer to this question is not easy. However, as we see, it is quite possible.

Earlier it was noted that there is a subordination between the physical parameters; the primary is dynamics, not kinematics: the dynamics determine the kinematics. Proceeding from this circumstance, it becomes obvious that time change is causing by acts of energy exchange. Accordingly, the length change is determined by the acts of exchange of the pulse. Finally, the change of angular characteristics is determined by the transfer of angular momentum. Therefore, my conclusion is as follows: symmetry ergo dynamics. Compare: Jun Sakurai said, «dynamics ergo symmetry». [1, 9]

It should be noted that the above-described correlation between variations of kinematic variables in the composition of the principle of least action and conservation laws is often characterized with reference to the homogeneity of time and space, as well as the isotropy of space. Supposedly, from the homogeneity of time follows the law of conservation of energy, from the homogeneity of space – the law of conservation of momentum, from the isotropy of space – the law of conservation of angular momentum. In this case, the homogeneity of time is understood as the equivalence of all moments and periods of time, the homogeneity of space as the equivalence of all regions of space, and the isotropy of space as the equivalence of properties of space in all directions. In my opinion, this explanation is not true.

The fact is that the principles of the theory are by definition omnipresent. It is wrong to say, for example, that in one area of space, they are correct, and in the other, they are wrong. It is untenable to say that the law of conservation of energy follows from the homogeneity of time. Agreeing with this statement, it will be necessary to consider that along with the homogeneity of time there is also its heterogeneity, which is supposedly incompatible with the law of conservation of energy. However, it is impossible to introduce the correct definition of time heterogeneity. The law of conservation of energy is in correlation not with the homogeneity of time, but with all of its nature. Contrasting the homogeneity and heterogeneity of time, as well as the homogeneity and heterogeneity of space, as well as the isotropy and anisotropy of space, is untenable.

The principles of invariance are usually appreciated by physicists. In this regard, the conclusion reached by the Nobel laureate Eugene Wigner deserves attention: «the progression from events to laws of nature, and from laws of nature to symmetry or invariance principles, is what I meant by the hierarchy of our knowledge of the world around us.» [2, 30].

Thus, according to Wigner, cognition is a three-step process: single events → laws → principles of invariance. Of course, he is largely right. However, it may be appropriate to complete his output. As emphasized above, in physics there is no more important concept than the original dynamic principle. Given this circumstance, the Wigner scheme should be extended: *single events → laws → principles of invariance → dynamic principle.*

356

In addition, of course, it is necessary to take into account that the Wigner cognition scheme relates only to one stage of transduction, namely, to the abduction. If we bear in mind the scientific explanation (deduction), then it does not end but begins on the contrary with a dynamic principle: a dynamic principle → principles of invariance → laws → single events. Thus, the dynamic principle is more relevant than the principles of symmetry. Symmetry is determined by dynamics.

In three sections, the conceptual structure of classical mechanics was considered. In this connection, some conclusions are relevant. As a physical theory, classical mechanics includes the following concepts: 1) dynamic principle, 2) principles of invariance, 3) laws, including conservation laws, 4) individual events. The nature of physics cannot be understood without distinctions of dynamic and kinematic features. It is extremely important that all concepts be interconnected with each other. This connection is implemented as a process, a transition. In this connection, it is imperative to recall the four conceptual transitions — deduction, adduction, abduction, and induction.

The physical explanation implements as a deduction: dynamic principle → principles of invariance → laws → single events.

Physical discovery commits as an abduction: empirical principles → deductive principles.

It is impossible to go directly from explanation to discovery. An intermediate link between them includes certainly experiment or observation. Conceptually, they are adduction: hypothetical variables → experimental variables (facts).

The variables obtained in the experiment and observation, i.e. the facts open the way to the establishment of inductive laws and principles. This operation is induction: inductive variables → inductive laws → inductive principles.

The full cycle of physical cognition is a peculiar cycle: deduction → adduction → induction → abduction.

Finally, when thinking about the structure of classical mechanics, one should always keep in mind that there are no special mechanical phenomena that could be opposed to electromagnetic, weak, strong, and gravitational events. Mechanics deal with the similarities that are typical for different types of interactions.

References

1. Sakurai, J.J. (1960) Theory of strong interactions. Annals of Physics 11(1), l-48.
2. Wigner, E.P. (1967) Symmetries and Reflections. Bloomington and London: Indiana University Press.

7.5. How geniuses mastered abduction in relativistic mechanics

Intratheoretical transduction is realized through four methods, namely deduction, adduction, induction, and abduction. The first three methods are often discussed in the scientific literature. Few people doubt their relevance. The method of abduction is rarely discussed by anyone. It is crucial in understanding the mechanisms of scientific creativity, which usually associates with various kinds of intuitive guesses. Below we question this opinion, considering the history of the creation of relativistic mechanics. The reader will find the necessary reference material in [1; 2]. Our consideration of this question is intended to shed additional light on the nature of the method of abduction.

In 1865, James Maxwell was able to present the basic laws of electromagnetic phenomena. Oliver Heaviside managed to present them in the most economical form, in the form of four equations. Both believed that electromagnetic waves were disturbances of the ether, whose nature was not explained. Another difficulty was that Maxwell's equations were non-invariant regarding inertial reference systems. They contradicted the principle of relativity, from which no one was in a hurry to refuse.

The Michelson-Morley experiment of 1887 did not record the presence of the ether wind, which was supposed will arise due to the motion through the Earth's ether. The results of the experiment have questioned the very existence of ether. In case of denial of the existence of ether, significant difficulties arouse in understanding the nature of electromagnetic waves, as well as the fact of the constancy of the speed of light in all inertial reference systems.

The negative result of the Michelson-Morley experiment was explained by George Fitzgerald and Hendrik Lorentz, who postulated a reduction in the length of charged particles in the direction of their movement through the ether. However, unfortunately, the length reduction mechanism itself was in many ways invented artificially, not confirmed experimentally. Lorentz also succeeded in replacing the Galilean transformations by others, which did not contradict the principle of relativity of electromagnetic phenomena. They were known J. Larmor. It is believed that he first drew attention to the fact that they in a new way raise the question of the nature of time.

The transformations considered were improved by Henry Poincaré and named by him the Lorentz transformations. He first noted that the Lorentz transformations satisfy the requirements of a mathematical group. His other achievement was that he quite clearly presented a mechanism for measuring relativistic durations, which implies synchronization of clocks located in different places of inertial reference systems. It was already 1905. For 16 years, physicists failed to bring into agreement with each other all the components of the theory of electromagnetic phenomena.

Albert Einstein proposed two fundamentally new ideas. First, the principle of relativity should be preserved, insisting on the invariance of the electromagnetism equations with respect to all inertial reference systems. Secondly, and most importantly, the principle of short-range action is introduced, according to which physical interactions cannot be transmitted at a speed greater than the speed of light in a vacuum. The principle of short-range action seems at first glance doubtful. Perhaps, as Lorenz believed, future experiments will have disproved it. Poincaré also doubted the fruitfulness of the ideas of Einstein. However, in the scientific community, the popularity of ideas of Einstein grew. An increasing number of physicists understood that it was A. Einstein, who succeeded in uniting numerous notions of electromagnetic theory into a harmonious whole. Now the Lorentz transformations were deduced directly from the principles of relativity and invariance. There was no need to recognize the existence of ether and, therefore, it was not necessary to explain the absence of the ether wind. The reduction of the lengths and the slowing down of the durations were also deduced directly from the principles of the theory.

Einstein clearly surpassed his colleagues, no doubt outstanding physicists in one respect. He was the only one who understood that it was necessary to update not the laws, but the principles of the theory. Abduction suggests exactly that. Was the discovery of Einstein just a happy guess? Obviously not. He clearly took into account the results of numerous experiments in which it was confirmed that the velocity of propagation of electromagnetic waves never exceeds the speed of light in a vacuum. Einstein himself, who recognized the relevance of empirical research, nevertheless, never emphasized the direct significance of these studies in his abductive decisions. In fact, he was a true master not of intuitive innovations but completely rational abductive decisions.

Abduction does not occur from scratch, its paths are not obvious. Nevertheless, ultimately, a scientific search will certainly lead to the rut, movement along which allows you to update directly the principles of a partially outdated theory.

References

1. Brown, H.R. (2003) Michelson, Fitzgerald and Lorentz: The origins of special relativity revisite. Bulletin de la Société Des Sciences et Des Lettres de Łódź, Volume LIII; Série: Recherches sur Les Déformations, XXXIX, 23–35.
2. O'Connor, J.J. and Edmund, F.R. (1996) Special Relativity. The MacTutor History of Mathematics archive, School of Mathematics and Statistics, University of St. Andrews.

7.6. Foundations of quantum mechanics and pluralism

The development of quantum mechanics led to an unprecedented revolution in science. It clearly surpassed the conceptual highscores of relativistic mechanics. The most important feature of quantum mechanics is that quantum and probabilistic representations are organically combined with each other. Consider in this connection the wave function of a free particle moving along the x-axis:

$$\psi = e^{-\frac{i}{\hbar}(Et - p_x x)} \qquad\qquad 7.4$$

E is energy, t is time, p_x is momentum in the direction of the x-axis, x is the coordinate.

Expression 7.4 is significant in many ways. The deep meaning lies in the fact that it is written through an exponential function. Usually, features of things are given one after another, in a disconnected form. They are united only by scientific laws. In the case under consideration, there is a different situation, because exponential function used represents a complex of features. Something similar is not observed outside of quantum physics.

The second feature of the expression 7.4 consists in the fact that it contains the Planck constant ($\hbar$). It indicates, firstly, the quantum nature of the processes, and secondly, the limit at which non-quantum physics is untenable. This occurs when the magnitudes of actions have the same scale as the Planck constant.

The third feature of expression 7.4 is that it contains the imaginary unit (i). In this case, it has not an imaginary, but a very real meaning. The fact is that the squares of both positive and negative numbers are positive numbers. The squares of imaginary numbers are equal to negative numbers. These squares are often used to describe wave processes that do not strengthen but weaken each other. Such processes are considered in quantum mechanics.

The fourth feature of equation 7.4 is that it is an expression not of probabilities, but amplitudes of the probabilities of quantum processes. In classical physics, the probabilities of processes are represented directly. In quantum physics, their base is singled out in the form of a probability amplitude, which opens up the possibility of calculating the probabilities of quantum magnitudes.

The fifth feature of the expression 7.4 is that it allows you to calculate the average magnitudes of physical parameters <F >:

$$<F> = \int \psi^* F \psi \, dV. \qquad 7.5$$

In classical physics, laws are written in the form of some analytical expressions. It does not emphasize that the magnitudes of variables appearing in them are their average magnitudes. However, the state of affairs really looks that way. This circumstance was fully revealed due to quantum mechanics.

The sixth feature of the concept of the wave function is its organic combination with the principle of superposition of quantum states. If functions ψ_i , where i = 1 ... n, are admissible wave functions, then their linear superposition also describes a certain state. From the standpoint of classical physics, such a state of affairs is in principle impossible; it essentially coarsens the actual state of affairs in the world of physical phenomena. The actual consequence of quantum superposition is the presence of entangled states. After the interaction of two quantum objects with each other, each of them carries information about his partner. In classical physics, it is believed that this information is missing. The concept of entangled states explains many of the paradoxes of quantum mechanics, for example, Schrödinger's cat. The principle of quantum superposition indicates the systemic nature of quantum processes. Its remarkable feature is the equality of the integral given below to unity.

$$\int_{-\infty}^{+\infty} |\psi|^2\, dV = 1. \qquad\qquad 7.6$$

It can be shown that the quantum principle of superposition leads to two more consequences that are important. Any observable quantity is an eigenvalue of the Hermitian linear operator. If the operators do not commute with each other, the values of variables described by them are related by an uncertainty relation. One of these relations is the Heisenberg formula:

$$\Delta x \Delta p_x \geq \frac{\hbar}{2}. \qquad\qquad 7.7$$

My intentions do not include a detailed description of all conceptual features of quantum mechanics. We note only that in the best manuals on quantum mechanics, for example, in the book of P. Dirac, they are presented in an extremely consistent form [6].

It is time to turn to the amazing features of all physical theories, especially quantum mechanics. The interpretation of their content is never unambiguous. In this regard, physical pluralism is inevitable.

In the final part of his Nobel lecture, R. Feynman made a significant statement «that a good theoretical physicist today might find it useful to have a wide range of physical viewpoints and mathematical expressions of the same theory (for example, of quantum electrodynamics) available to him. This may be asking too much of one man. Then new students should as a class have this» [9, 708]. Today the topic of pluralism is one of the most acute in any science, including physics. The more meaningful the theory is in conceptual terms, the more different, in many respects, alternative points of view. R. Feynman rightly insists on the need for knowledge of many points of view, but he does not regulate in any way to handle them. Methods of ordering theories were considered by us in section 1.5. We use them in relation to various interpretations of quantum mechanics. This book is not possible to consider them in detail. Therefore, we restrict ourselves to bringing tabular information. They are sufficient to explain the way of mastering physical pluralism.

Table 7.1. Interpretations of quantum mechanics

№	Interpretation title	Authors	General provisions
1	Copenhagen	N. Bohr, W. Heisenberg	The wave function refers to a separate quantum object. The behavior of quantum objects cannot be separated from the measurement results. The measurement causes the collapse of the wave function; hidden parameters are

			not possible.
2	Ensemble [3; 2]	A. Einstein, L.E. Ballentine, D.I. Blokhintsev	The wave function refers to statistical ensembles, and not to individual particles. The main function is not the wave function, but the density operator.
3	De Broglie-Bohm [5; 4]	L. de Broglie, D. Bohm	Quantum mechanics describes the behavior of particles driven by a wave.
4	Stochastic [11]	E. Nelson	Quantum-mechanical motion is determined by some averaged properties of stochastic microscopic (vacuum) space-time.
5	Multiworld [7, 9]	H. Everett	The universal wave function represents the entire physical universe. Separate physical worlds are formed as a consequence of measurement processes. By choosing this or that alternative, people do not destroy other physical worlds, the reality of which is manifested in

			interference patterns.
6	Many consciousnesses [13; 1]	H.D. Zeh, D. Albert, B. Loewer	The same thing as the many-world interpretation of quantum mechanics plus an understanding of the consciousness of the experimenter as an active physical factor.
7	Modal [11]	B.C. van Fraassen	The wave function does not describe many worlds, but one world whose capabilities are manifested in measurements.

For brevity, I have indicated only seven interpretations of quantum mechanics. Nevertheless, a knowledgeable physicist has at least two dozen of them. What to do with these interpretations, avoiding both eclecticism and a one-sided point of view? First, they should be distributed among different series of theories, which in this case are interpretations of quantum mechanics. Secondly, assign them local ratings. Third, the weights of those criteria according to which a series of theories were formed should be determined. Fourth, by multiplying the local ratings by the weights of the criteria of the critical series of theories, the researcher has at his disposal the top ratings of interpretations that will be the basis for him to work with them. Probably, he will turn primarily to those interpretations that have the highest rating. This rule is also relevant to the teacher.

In the conditions of shortage of study time, he should undoubtedly decide on those interpretations of quantum mechanics that it is advisable to study in a student audience.

Of exceptional importance is the determination of criteria for comparing different interpretations of quantum mechanics. They are not clearly distributed across individual interpretations. Often they are inherent in several interpretations simultaneously, but not with the same degree of relevance.

Table 7.2. Comparison of interpretations of quantum mechanics [10, 152]

Interpretations	Process dynamics	Wave function is real	No collapse of wave functions	No hidden parameters	Locality	No active consciousness
Copenhagen	−	−	−	+	−	+
Ensemble	//	−	+	//	−	+
De Broglie-Bohm	+	+	+	−	−	+
Stochastic	−	−	+	+	−	+
Multiworld	+	+	+	+	+	+
Many consciousnesses	+	+	+	+	+	−
Modal	−	+	+	+	−	+

The concepts indicated in table 7.2 are formulated in such a way that their confirmation, marked with the + and - symbols, is evaluated positively and negatively, respectively. The symbol // means that, within the framework of the interpretation, no clear meaning has been worked out regarding the concept under consideration. From the content of table 7.2, it follows that the many world interpretation has numerous advantages. Nevertheless, whether it is the best can only show a specific calculation. Very much depends on the purpose of the study. Depending on it, one or another interpretation of quantum mechanics may come to the fore.

The centuries-old history of the development of quantum mechanics shows that there is not and can hardly be the only true interpretation of quantum mechanics. Anyone who tries to abolish quantum-mechanical pluralism inevitably limits his understanding of quantum mechanics. Trying to avoid this it is necessary to criticize tirelessly various interpretations of quantum mechanics. The absolute majority of physicists go that way. However, they do not use the opportunities that the concept of league-theory opens up. A review of various interpretations of quantum mechanics does not reach the goal if it does not end with the construction of the corresponding league-theory. This is a program that the author of this book did not implement either. I present it exclusively as a proposal, inspired by the interpretation of pluralism in various sciences. In my opinion, this program offers certain positive prospects that have not yet been realized.

References

1. Albert, D., and B. Loewer. (1988) Interpreting the many worlds interpretation. Synthese 77(2), 195-213.
2. Ballentine, L. E. (1988) Quantum Mechanics: a Modern Development. New Jersey: World Scientific Publishing Company.
3. Blokhintsev, D.I. (1977) Klassicheskaya statisticheskaya fizika i kvantovaya mekhanika [Classical statistical physics and quantum mechanics]. Successes of Physical Sciences 122(4), 745-757. [In Russian].
4. Bohm, D. A. (1952) Suggested interpretation of the quantum theory in terms of «hidden» variables. I. Physical Review 85(2), 166-179.
5. De Broglie, L. (1927) La mécanique ondulatoire et la structure atomique de la matière et du rayonnement [Wave mechanics and the atomic structure of matter and radiation]. Journal de Physique 8(5), 225-241. [In French].
6. Dirac, P.A.M. (1930) Principles of Quantum Mechanics. Oxford: The Clarendon Press.

7. Everett, H. (1957) Relative state formulation of quantum mechanics. Review of Modern Physics 29(3), 454-462.
8. Everett, H. (1973) The theory of the universal wave function. In De Wit, B., and Graham, N. (Eds.). The Many-Worlds Interpretation of Quantum Mechanics. Princeton, NJ: Princeton University Press, pp. 3-140.
9. Feynman, R.P. (1966) The development of the space-time view of quantum electrodynamics. Science 153(3737), 699-708.
10. Kanke, V.A. (2014) Istoriya, filosofiya i metodologiya yestestvennykh nauk [History, Philosophy and Methodology of Natural Sciences]. Moskva: Yurayt. [In Russian].
11. Nelson, E. (1985) Quantum Fluctuations. Princeton: Princeton University Press.
12. Van Fraassen, B. C. (1991) Quantum Mechanics. Oxford: Clarendon Press.
13. Zeh, H.D. (1970) On the interpretation of measurements in quantum theory. Foundation of Physics 1(1), 69-76.

7.7. Measurements in quantum mechanics and the role of consciousness

The problem of measurement is relevant for any physical theory. Immediately there is a rather complicated question about the place of human consciousness in the processes of measurement of physical quantities. People take measurements not by chance, but in accordance with their theories. In one form or another, the measurement process is clearly mediated by the minds of physicists. It is possible, that this mediation will be more or less significant. Consider in this regard the development of physical knowledge according to classical, relativistic and quantum mechanics.

In classical mechanics, measurement is understood as fixing the values of certain parameters that exist before the measurement process. The measurement process does not affect the measured parameters. In this regard, there is no reason to consider the consciousness of physicists as a dynamic factor that determines the measurement results.

In relativistic mechanics, the situation with the understanding of the measurement process is somewhat more complicated, especially in connection with measurements of lengths and durations. In classical mechanics, they are considered invariant with respect to all reference systems. Now it turns out that they are different from one system to another. People are free to choose and design such reference systems that are not found in nature. Consequently, at least in part, the physical situations depend on the decisions that the experimenters make. People themselves can act like physical objects. Their consciousness is not a physical object. It is significant that the measurements considered in this case do not destroy the observed objects.

Quantum mechanics has brought with it numerous innovations related mainly to the concept of probability and the unusual features of quantum mechanical dynamics. In quantum mechanics, it is assumed that every time measurement of a quantum system registers the eigenvalues of Hermitian operators. The measurement leads to a significant transformation of the state of the quantum object involved in the measurement. It ceases to be himself. There is nothing like this in the worlds described by classical and relativistic mechanics. Having made a conscious decision to make a measurement, the researcher is to some extent responsible for transforming a very real physical situation. In this regard, some famous researchers believe that consciousness is responsible for the process of quantum measurement. This position was especially vigorously advocated by John von Neumann.

> But in any case, no matter how far we calculate
> – to the mercury vessel, to the scale of the
> thermometer, to the retina, or into the brain, at
> some time we must say: and this is perceived by
> the observer. That is, we must always divide the
> world into two parts, the one being the observed
> system, the other the observer. In the former, we
> can follow up all physical processes (in principle at
> least) arbitrarily precisely. In the latter, this is
> meaningless. ... That this boundary can be pushed
> arbitrarily deeply into the interior of the body of
> the actual observer is the content of the principle
> of the psycho-physical parallelism — but this does
> not change the fact that in each method of
> description the boundary must be put somewhere,
> if the method is not to proceed vacuously, i.e., if a
> comparison with experiment is to be possible.
> Indeed experience only makes statements of this
> type: an observer has made a certain (subjective)
> observation; and never any like this: a physical
> quantity has a certain value. [2, 419–420].

Von Neumann's point of view was strongly supported by Eugene Wigner, who believed that «as seen from von Neumann's brilliant analysis of quantum mechanical measurement, even the laws of quantum mechanics with all their consequences cannot be formulated without addressing consciousness» [3, 202]. The question of consciousness occupies an extremely prominent place in the multiworld interpretation of the quantum mechanics of Dieter Zeh. «According to the twofold localization of consciousness, there

373

are two kinds of subjectivity: The result of a measurement is subjective in that it depends on the world component of the observer; it is objective in the sense that all observers of this world component observe the same result. The question of whether the other components still "exist" after the measurement is as meaningless as asking about the existence of an object while it is not being observed. It is meaningful, however, to ask whether or not the assumption of this existence (i.e., of an objective world) leads to a contradiction». [4, 74]. Michael Mensky connects especially high hopes with the inclusion of the theme of consciousness directly into the foundations of quantum mechanics. He not only connects the separation of the quantum state into components with the consciousness of the observer but also even fully identifies them with him, believing that as a result, the nature of consciousness is clarified [1].

For the sake of further, we consider the following chain of phenomena of interest to us: quantum objects — measuring devices used by the researcher — the brain of the researcher as a physical object — the consciousness of the experimenter. The fact of an interaction of the studying quantum objects and measuring devices is beyond doubt. This process, which was rather incomprehensible at the dawn of the development of quantum mechanics, is explained today by the phenomenon of decoherence. As is known, the device captures one or another quantum alternative. That is why it is relevant as a device in the study of quantum phenomena.

The human brain can obviously be considered as a physical object. However, without further explanation, it is obvious that it is not adapted and, therefore, is not suitable for quantum-physical measurements. It is equally indisputable that, as a physical object, the brain substance, like any other physical objects, has a quantum nature. This circumstance can be considered in the case of characterization of the nature of the brain substance as a physical phenomenon. Nevertheless, it is not directly related to the process of quantum-mechanical measurements.

It is time to turn to the characteristics of the consciousness of the experimenter. Consciousness is of mental nature. What does it mean? The brain substance, first of all, the cortex of the big hemispheres acts as a representation of the theory of the physicist. Using, for example, sound waves, a physicist can present the theory in a language form. The physical carrier of the mentality of man is his brain. The physical carrier of the language of a physicist is sound waves. In both cases considered, the principles, laws, and variables of physics are expressed. With them, obviously, quantum objects cannot interact. A quantum object, for example, an electron, does not interact with the principle of least action or with the Euler-Lagrange equation. This means that consciousness cannot be included in the following cause chain: a quantum object — a device of measurement — a medulla. Meanwhile, all supporters of the active role of consciousness in the processes of measurement, in fact, insist on such inclusion. Their erroneous decision is due to a misunderstanding of the nature of consciousness. Consciousness is not a physical object.

The activity of consciousness is usually associated with the decisions that people make and implement. From this point of view, it is certainly legitimate to assume that each physicist is an active being. However, at the same time, it is necessary to give the most accurate description of his actions. As a scientist, he realizes the potential of physics. In particular, in this regard, he uses physical instruments to detect quantum alternatives. It is not the case a physicist does this by chance or by whim. He does this solely for the development of a physical theory. To the best of his ability, he reveals the conceptual wealth that is inherent in physical objects. The principles and laws of physics, he is not free to change. In the physical world, he is able to express yourself exclusively as a physical object. For the above reasons, he prefers to do this by means of special physical devices, rather than his body or the medulla.

Contrary to the opinion of E. Wigner, consciousness is not included in the foundations of quantum mechanics. It is correct to assume that physicists cognize these bases more and more thoroughly, but they do not create them. Quantum alternatives belong directly to physical phenomena, to all those metamorphoses that are determined by mutual transitions between the three types of quantum states, namely, pure, entangled, and mixed.

The decisive mistake of all supporters of the active role of the experimenters' consciousness in physical dimensions is that they do not consider this as a representation of physical theories. And yet consciousness is precisely this representation, nothing else.

References

1. Mensky, M.B. (2005) Kontseptsiya soznaniya v kontekste kvantovoy mekhaniki [The concept of consciousness in the context of quantum mechanics]. Uspekhi fizicheskikh nauk [Advances in the physical sciences] 175(4), 413-435. [In Russian].
2. Von Neumann, J. (1955) Mathematical Foundations of Quantum Mechanics. Princeton; Princeton University Press.

3. Wigner, E.P. (1967) Symmetries and Reflections. Bloomington and London: Indiana University Press.
4. Zeh, H.D. (1970). On the interpretation of measurement in quantum theory. Foundations of Physics 1(1), 69–76.

7.8. Foundations of quantum field theory. Problem of interactions

To date, quantum field theory (QFT) is the most developed physical theory. Physicists have made vigorous efforts to develop it since the late 1920s. Only decades later they achieved decisive success. QFT of electromagnetic phenomena was created by the end of 1940 and the corresponding theory of weak and strong interactions after another quarter of a century [9; 10]. The first of QFT was quantum electrodynamics, created in 1948-1949. The main contribution to its development was made by S. Tomonago, R. Feynman and J. Schwinger, Nobel Prize Laureates in Physics in 1965. By 1973, a consistent QFT of weak interactions was created, and it turned out that, despite their uniqueness, they should be considered together with electromagnetic interactions. The greatest contribution to the development of the QFT of electroweak interactions was made by S. Weinberg, A. Salam, S. Glashow (Nobel Prize for 1979), G' t Hooft and M. Veltman (Nobel Prize for 1999). The QFT of strong interactions (quantum chromodynamics) was also created in the mid-1970s. The main contribution to its development was made by D. Gross, F. Wilczek and D. Politzer (Nobel Prize in Physics for 2004). Unfortunately, a full-fledged QFT of gravitational interactions has not yet been created.

The study of the history of the development of QFT shows that it absorbs many of the achievements of its predecessors, namely, classical and quantum mechanics, as well as A. Einstein's relativistic electrodynamics.

The Lagrange formalism, in which the principle of stationary action is of primary importance, was inherited by QFT from classical physics. The achievements of relativistic electrodynamics are also taken into account. Since we are talking about fields, which are by definition volumetrically distributed systems, then the volume element (dv) is entered into the integral required for the calculation of the action (S): S = $\int L dv dt$.

Especially close is the relationship of QFT with quantum mechanics. In this regard, of particular importance is the development of such a concept, which would have, in relation to a field, merits similar to those characteristic of the wave function in quantum mechanics. It is in this connection that the concept of an operator-valued function is introduced. Operator valued function A is a function whose values A(t) are operators depending on the variable t. It can be a real or complex value, a vector from the region of a topological space, an element of a certain set. By analogy with quantum mechanics, permutation relations for conjugate variables are constructed, expressed by commuting and non-commuting operators. At the same time, the permutation relations of the birth and annihilation operators of particles are of central importance. In contrast to quantum mechanics, QFT is relevant not only for systems with a constant number of particles. That is why QFT is the basis of the physics of elementary particles.

Until now, I have argued in an exceptionally risky manner, unwittingly creating for the readers the idea that there is a direct transition from pre-quantum physics to QFT. In fact, there is no such transition. The inheritance lines noted by me are some heuristic prerequisites that are relevant to the creation of QFT. Their realization is impossible except through the cycles of conceptual transduction.

In order to avoid misunderstanding, we note that QFT is fundamentally different from quantum mechanics. This circumstance is especially clearly seen in the difference between the wave function and the operator-valued function. The wave function is the amplitude of probability, not the operator. It is under the influence of operators, which leads to the selection of the values of the observed parameters. An operator-valued function has an initial operator nature. Only after some mathematical manipulations, it turns into an operator acting in the Hilbert space of quantum field states. In both quantum mechanics and QFT, the concept of a Hilbert space is used, which in contrast to the Euclidean space admits infinite dimension. However, we are talking about different types of Hilbert space.

Of course, the development of QFT is accompanied by numerous problematic aspects. Perhaps the two most important of them are the following two problems: first, the nonequivalence of the representations of the mathematical apparatus, secondly, the difficulties associated with choosing a variant of quantum ontology, of the nature of the entities with which quantum field theory deals [2; 7]. Researchers face great difficulties even when characterizing objects of quantum mechanics. However, compared to the state of affairs in QFT the situation in quantum mechanics is relatively simple. The representations used in quantum mechanics, in particular, the Heisenberg matrix and the Schrödinger wave, are equivalent to each other. It is permissible to use each of them. The representations of QFT are nonequivalent. In these conditions, firstly, it is difficult to isolate the interpretation that most adequately represents physical reality. Secondly, as a rule, it turns out that no presentations are perfect.

It is also difficult to establish the validity of judgments about particles and fields. [6] Some authors deny the legitimacy of using the concept of a particle [4], others do not recognize fields [1]. There are authors who prefer to assert the reality of exclusive structures [8]. The fourth group of authors opposes particles, fields, and structures. They recognize the reality of properties inherent in more fundamental things than fields and particles.

In my opinion, the main line of development of quantum field theory should not consist of the negation of some ideas in favor of others. It is important to understand the advantages and disadvantages of each of the representations. The situation in quantum field theory resembles the situation in quantum mechanics. Different interpretations of the theory complement each other.

The concept of interaction occupies an exceptionally prominent place in quantum field theory. The mechanism of quantum-field interaction is most clearly expressed in the formulation of the theory using Lagrangians. With each of the Lagrangians, correlate some type of quantum objects, particles. The interaction itself is described by the addition to Lagrangians the particle interactions. The interaction leads to a change in the dynamic characteristics of the particles, in particular, the mass and charge. However, when calculating their values, infinitely large quantities arise, which causes confusion. Experimental data indicate the finite value of any physical parameter. Naturally, physicists had to find ways to pacify the infinity. It should be noted that on this path they achieved remarkable success. The concept of renormalization has become crucial. In accordance with it, operating with the values of physical parameters, they should be normalized to the experimentally observed values.

It is, of course, extremely difficult to present the procedure for renormalization in a simple form. However, in general terms, it can be done. The essence of the situation under consideration is that the equations of quantum field theory contain bare characteristics, for example, mass and charge, and additions to them, which are determined by the interaction of particles with certain fields. Both bare and additive characteristics are not observed in the experiment. In this regard, the idea is born of attributing to them such a form that the result would be experimental values. Of course, it is important not to leave the field of adequate scientific knowledge. This goal is achieved, firstly, by the very fact of using the Lagrangian formalism Second, as the coefficients of the counterterms used to adjust the expression of the full Lagrangian, interaction constants are used, which depend on the energy scale of the particles under study. This circumstance indicates the specific physical meaning of the counterterms they are not arbitrary. Third, the renormalization is performed only for systems that obey the principle of gauge invariance (see the next section). Thus, a number of factors indicate the physically meaningful nature of renormalization. Nevertheless, the use of infinite magnitudes in it is of great concern to many physicists.

Paul Dirac in 1975 said as follows «I must say that I am very dissatisfied with the situation, because, this so-called good theory does involve neglecting infinities which appear in its equations, neglecting them in an arbitrary way. This is just not sensible mathematics. » [5, 184]. Even Richard Feynman, one of the founders of the renormalization procedure, expressed doubts about the legality of it. «I think that the renormalization theory is simply a way to sweep the difficulties of the divergences of electrodynamics under the rug. I am, of course, not sure of that» [3, 707].

Dirac's position was determined by his exceptionally high estimate of the importance of mathematics for physics. Following Newton, he believed that the foundations of a physical theory should be of a purely mathematical nature. In this case, the role of the physical experiment is belittled. For physics, mathematics is an auxiliary theory. It should also be noted that the dissatisfaction of Dirac and Feynman is largely determined by their metaphysical position. It is expressed in the fact that researchers underestimate what has already been achieved; they direct their eyes somewhere far away beyond its limits. However, at the same time, an urgent problem, which denotes not an imaginary, but a short-term perspective, is not put on the agenda.

References

1. Baker, D. J. (2009) Against field interpretations of quantum field theory. British Journal for the Philosophy of Science 60(3): 585-609.
2. Baker, D.J. (2015) The Philosophy of Quantum Field Theory. Available at: http://philsci-archive.pitt.edu/ 11375/1/QFToup.pdf/
3. Feynman, R.P. (1966) The development of the space-time view of quantum electrodynamics. Science 153(3737), 699-708.

4. Halvorson, H. and Clifton, R. (2002) No place for particles in relativistic quantum theories? Philosophy of Science 69(1), 1-28.

5. Helge, S.K. (1990) DIRAC: A Scientific Biography. Cambridge et al.: Cambridge University Press.

6. Kuhlmann, M. (2010) The Ultimate Constituents of the Material World – In Search of an Ontology for Fundamental Physics. Frankfurt: ontos Verlag.

7. Kuhlmann, M. (2018) Quantum field theory. Stanford Encyclopedia of Philosophy. Available at: https://plato.stanford.edu/archives/win2018/entries/quantum-field-theory/

8. Roberts, B. W. (2011) Group structural realism. The British Journal for the Philosophy of Science 62 (1), 47-69.

9. Weinberg, S. (1977) The search for unity: notes for a history of quantum field theory. Daedalus 106(4), 17–35.

10. Weisskopf, V. (1981) The development of field theory in the last 50 years. Physics Today 34(11), 69-85.

7.9. Gauge invariance, spontaneous symmetry breaking, and asymptotic freedom

In physics, calibration fields are extremely important, which by definition satisfy certain transformations (the symmetry groups). The so-called gauge invariance is that the interactions predicted by the theory do not depend on the choice of the value of a certain physical parameter. The chosen value of the parameter plays the role of a certain scale clarifying the content of the theory, its peculiar calibration. There is global and local gauge invariance. In contrast to global, the local invariance depends on spatial and temporal coordinates. Historically, first was considered global invariance of electromagnetic and gravitational phenomena. In particular, it was shown that the law of conservation of electric charge corresponds to the global gauge invariance of the equations of electrodynamics [1, 165]. However, at the same time, the dynamic mechanism for the implementation of this law remained unclear. Similar to the state of affairs in electrodynamics, the situation in the theories of weak and strong interactions looks like: global gauge invariance points to the law of conservation of charges inherent in these interactions.

The situation with the dynamics of physical processes has been significantly clarified due to the concept of local gauge invariance. Let me explain its main idea by the example of the wave function, $\psi(x) = e^{i\varphi(x)}$ the phase, φ (x) of which depends on the space-time coordinates, x. Whether a quantum equation will be invariant when replacing $\varphi(x) \to \varphi(x) + \alpha(x)$. Will, but only if there are terms in the equation that exactly compensate for the additions that arise by taking into account α (x). These terms are called the gauge field. Gauge fields appear in the form of massless bosons, i.e. particles with a spin of 1 and not having mass. These are the photons for electromagnetic interactions, W +, W-, Z_0 – bosons for weak interactions, gluons for strong interactions.

Attention to the heuristic capabilities of the concept of local gauge invariance in QFT has increased dramatically thanks to an article by Chen Yang and Robert Mills [13]. The estimation of Jun Sakurai of the idea of introducing vector fields based on local gauge invariance is very indicative.

This is a very profound idea – perhaps the most profound idea in theoretical physics since the invention of the Dirac theory. It essentially states that, if we have a conservation law of some internal attribute, there must necessarily exist a vector-type interaction corresponding to it in order that the conservation law in question be consistent, with the concept, of localized fields. To borrow Schwinger's words, internal attributes should have "dynamical manifestations." To put this idea more succinctly, internal symmetry ergo dynamics. It puzzles the author that the idea so profoundly physical has received so little attention in the past five years. [10, 9]

Another extremely important milestone in the development of QFT was the establishment in 1971 of the renormalizability of the local-gauge theories by Gerard 't Hooft [7].

Systematically, physicists linked together all the foundations of quantum field theory, including the Lagrange formalism, the principle of least action, gauge invariance, renormalization, and the mechanism of physical interactions. Moreover, these bases were the same for electromagnetic, weak and strong interactions. This combination of the foundations of QFT makes a strong impression because it points to the nontrivial organic integrity of the theory.

Unfortunately, for a long time, the concept of gauge invariance could not be effectively used in the theory of weak interactions. Particles that claimed the role of interaction quanta had mass. This contradicts the concept of local gauge invariance. The way out of a difficult situation with reference to weak interactions was found thanks to the idea of spontaneous symmetry breaking [3; 11; 12].

The concept of spontaneous symmetry breaking is peculiar. In fact, it fixes the correlation of the equations of motion with the specific states to which they lead. If the system is in an unstable state, then it goes into one of the possible states. All other states are now inaccessible to it; therefore, the original symmetry is broken. This happened due to the initial instability of the system, passing randomly into one of its possible states. Emphasizing the moment of chance, they talk about spontaneous symmetry breaking. The term 'spontaneous symmetry breaking' cannot be called successful. The fact is that the symmetry of the equations of motion remains so as it was. The set of transitions to different states agrees perfectly with it. In one case, one state is realized, in the other state, another. Therefore, they turn out to be equally probable, manifestations of the initial symmetry of the laws (equations of motion).

Thus, the spontaneous breaking of symmetries expresses the fact of the generation of some particles. It is desirable that the weak interaction quanta have masses. In 1964 six physicists at once, among whom was Pieter Higgs, suggesting a mechanism of spontaneous symmetry breaking. Some fundamental particles, in particular, weak interaction quanta, interact with a scalar field; as a result, they acquire energy, which corresponds to the mass of a certain value [2; 5; 6]. For historical reasons, the name of the Higgs boson was assigned to the particles of the scalar field. The Higgs boson was discovered in 2012 [8].

When studying the strong interactions of hadrons consisting of quarks and gluons, physicists encountered new difficulties. The high intensity of interactions was considered an obstacle to the use of renormalization. In this case, physicists also found a way out of a difficult situation. The point is that the charge and, accordingly, the interaction parameter is effective quantities. They depend on the polarization of the vacuum. According to the theory of strong interactions (quantum chromodynamics), the polarization of the quanta of gluon interactions is superimposed on the polarization of vacuum, and the two types of polarization act in different directions. As the distance between quarks decreases, the effective interaction parameter tends to zero. This is the phenomenon of asymptotic freedom [4; 9], for the discovery of which David Gross, Frank Wilczek, and David Politzer won the Nobel Prize for 2004. At high energies of hadrons, quantum chromodynamics is used most successfully. At lower hadron energies, asymptotic freedom does not manifest itself in a bright form. This leads to difficulties when using the apparatus of quantum chromodynamics.

Since the theory of electromagnetic, weak, and strong interactions is based on local gauge invariance in a uniform manner, attempts are made to create a unified theory. The gauge group for electroweak interactions is well known; it is the SU (2) × U (1) group. The gauge group of strong interactions is the SU (3) group. The union SU (3) × SU (2) × U (1) does not have a clear physical meaning. Perhaps it indicates a non-trivial circumstance: the uniformity of theories of various types of interactions should not be exaggerated. The absence of a consistent quantum theory of gravitational interactions leads to the same conclusion. One thing is certain: physicists in the process of nearly a century-old development of QFT created a kind of conceptual tapestry that can be improved, but not destroyed. New physical theories ripen on a very solid basis.

References

1. Bettini, A. (2008) Introduction to Elementary Particle Physics. Cambridge, UK: Cambridge University Press.

2. Englert, F. and Brout, R. (1964) Broken symmetry and the mass of gauge vector mesons. Physical Review Letters 13(9), 321-323.

3. Glashow, S. (1959) The renormalizability of vector meson interactions. Nuclear Physics 10(2), 107-117.

4. Gross, D. J. and Wilczek, F. (1973) Ultraviolet behavior of non-abelian gauge theories. Physical Review Letters 30 (26), 1343-1346.

5. Guralnik, G. S., Hagen, C. R., and Kibble, T.W.B. (1964) Global conservation laws and massless particles. Physical Review Letters 13 (20), 585-587.

6. Higgs, P.W. (1964) Broken symmetries and the masses of gauge bosons. Physical Review Letters 13(16), 508-509.

7. Hooft, G.'t. (1971) Renormalizable lagrangians for massive Yang-Mills fields. Nuclear Physics B35(1), 167-188.

8. New results indicate that particle discovered at CERN is a Higgs boson. Press Release from CERN, 2013.

9. Politzer, H. D. (1973) Reliable perturbative results for strong interactions. Physical Review Letters 30(26), 1346-1349.

10. Sakurai, J.J. (1960) Theory of strong interactions. Annals of Physics 11(1), I-48.

11. Salam, A. and Ward, J.C. (1959) Weak and electromagnetic interactions. Nuovo Cimento 11(4), 568-577

12. Weinberg, S (1967) A model of leptons. Physical Review Letters 19(21), 1264-1266.

13. Yang, C. N. and Mills, R.L. (1954) Conservation of isotopic spin and isotopic gauge invariance. Physical Review 96(1), 191–195.

Chapter 8. The nature of chemistry

8.1. About metachemistry and philosophy of chemistry

Every scientific discipline goes through the difficult path of its formation to the accompaniment of positivistic ideas: nothing but clear knowledge, no philosophy. As a result, a theory appears "what the mother gave birth to," that is, conception without philosophical clothing. Inevitably, sometimes quite quickly, the number of difficult to solve problems increases. Then they recall philosophy, first, in order to cope with these problems. The history of the development of physics is very indicative in this respect. As soon as such problematic theories as the special theory of relativity and quantum mechanics appeared in its arsenal, the number of works devoted to the philosophy of physics began to grow like an avalanche. Suddenly it became clear that even the great physicists of the scale of Albert Einstein and Niels Bohr could not do without philosophizing.

I mentioned physics far from an accident. The fact is that philosophically, chemistry has been in the shadow of physics for a relatively long time. Therefore, at the beginning of the XX century, philosophical disputes in chemistry did not acquire the acute form that was characteristic of physics with its highly unusual ideas, such as the relativity of space and time and the probabilistic behavior of particles. Philosophically, chemistry lagged behind physics by at least thirty years. The formation of the philosophy of chemistry as an independent discipline was clearly delayed.

In 1997, the International Society for the Development of the Philosophy of Chemistry was founded, publishing since 1999 the journal «Foundations of Chemistry». Since 1995, the magazine «HYLE - International Journal for Philosophy of Chemistry» has been published, devoted to the philosophy of chemistry, also having an international character. It is widely believed that in the mid-1990s there was a constitution of the philosophy of chemistry in a fundamentally new capacity [4]. It is hardly worth disputing this opinion. Nevertheless, with all the successes achieved in the field of the philosophy of chemistry, its development is not without significant difficulties.

As before, I distinguish the philosophy of science from metascience, or, for a given case, metachemistry from the philosophy of chemistry. Metachemistry is an expression of progress taking place directly in chemistry. At the same time, the philosophy of chemistry can and should be perceived as a donor in relation to metachemistry science. The philosophy of chemistry includes chemistry in the general metascience, which generalizes the achievements of all sciences without any exception. As a rule, the absolute majority of researchers do not distinguish between metachemistry and philosophy of chemistry. However, this rule has exceptions.

Gaston Bachelard developed the view that because of overcoming the image of chemistry created by Lavoisier, «Metachemistry would be like metaphysics» [1, 45]. «Metachemistry would be to metaphysics in the same relation as chemistry to physics» [1, 45]. This position was vigorously supported by Alfred Nordmann: «Physics and metaphysics articulate a timeless, perhaps quantitative ontological framework, chemistry and metachemistry study genuine qualitative change, that is, processes that cannot be represented as displacements of material points» [3, 361]. It is difficult to agree with this position because metaphysics does not directly relate to physics. As Auguste Comte and Rudolf Carnap correctly noted, metaphysics is beyond scientific knowledge. There is no reason to detract from the status of physics as a science, attributing to its metaphysics.

As for the term 'philosophy of chemistry', it indicates both philosophy and chemistry. The currents of knowledge go to the philosophy of chemistry, at least from two sides. However, both sources do not shine with crystal clarity. Modern philosophy, which is the result of centuries of effort, is overloaded with metaphysical, that is, unscientific, provisions. There is nothing surprising. It took shape in those centuries when science was in its infancy. Outstanding philosophers were not always experts in the philosophy of science. Unfortunately, this state of affairs has been preserved in philosophy to the present day. It defines the desire for universal laws, which, as it turns out on closer examination, are not necessary for the chemistry. Metaphysical means do not create a philosophy of chemistry; moreover, they significantly complicate its constitution.

At first glance, it seems that the way out of this situation is a reliance not so much on philosophy as on the philosophy of science. However, unfortunately, the philosophy of science is overloaded with all the same metaphysical moments. Scientists cannot do without them when they talk about science in general, without entering into the subtleties of individual sciences, physics, chemistry, biology, economics and all the rest. We have to admit that modern philosophy is largely embraced by antiscientific syndrome. It, of course, is contraindicated to the philosophy of chemistry. From what has been said, a quite definite conclusion follows: the philosophy of any science, including chemistry, must have a scientific character.

As already noted, the currents of knowledge go to the philosophy of science not only from philosophy but also from chemistry. However, in the aspect of interest to us, and chemistry is far from perfect. It does not suffer from the anti-scientific syndrome in any significant way but has its own weakness, namely, the anti-philosophical syndrome. It is manifested in the desire to do without any philosophy. In chemistry as such, philosophy really has nothing to do. Chemistry is chemistry; there are no gaps in it for other sciences. Nevertheless, this does not mean that it should be isolated from other sciences, especially from the philosophy of chemistry. The fact is that any science, including chemistry, does not exist by itself. Chemistry is a relatively independent structural unit of the network of scientific disciplines with which it is in interdisciplinary connections. Chemists need and logic, and mathematics, and computer science, and linguistics, but especially the philosophy of chemistry, which is the awareness of the conceptual nature of chemistry itself. Socratic "know yourself" refers to any science, in relation to chemistry; it just leads to both metachemistry and the philosophy of chemistry. In addition, here a new difficulty becomes known. Chemists are accustomed to being guided by the standards of chemistry, not the philosophy of chemistry.

Many philosophers of chemistry point out the estrangement of the traditional philosophy of science, on the one hand, and chemistry, on the other. «Philosophy of chemistry has been the poor cousin of the philosophy of science for most of the twentieth century» [2, 58]. Bernadette Bensaude-Vincent offers some dilemma in this regard «Philosophy *of* Chemistry or Philosophy *with* Chemistry? » [2]. She emphasizes that philosophers, with their attentive attitude to chemistry, could significantly develop many categories of metaphysics. Bensaude-Vincent pays special attention to the possibility and necessity of 'thing turn'. «By 'thing turn' I mean that things, the most familiar and ordinary things that we encounter in daily life, provide a unique angle for raising and discussing philosophical issues» [2, 75]. Of course, interdisciplinary relations between the philosophy of science and chemistry need further development. The following path is of decisive importance: chemistry – metachemistry – philosophy of chemistry – philosophy of science, both in the forward and in the opposite direction. For now, it resembles an unkempt path in the mountains rather than a city track.

References

1. Bachelard, G. (1968) The Philosophy of No: A Philosophy of the Scientific Mind. New York: Orion Press.
2. Bensaude-Vincent, B. (2014) Philosophy of chemistry or philosophy with chemistry. HYLE – International Journal for Philosophy of Chemistry 20(1), 58-76.
3. Nordmann, A. (2006) From metaphysics to metachemistry. In Baird, D., Scerri, E. and McIntyre. L. (Eds.). Philosophy of Chemistry. Synthesis of a New Discipline. Dordrecht: Springer, 347-362.
4. Schummer, J. (2006) The philosophy of chemistry: from infancy toward maturity. In Baird, D., Scerri. E. and McIntyre. L. (Eds.). Philosophy of Chemistry. Synthesis of a New Discipline. Dordrecht: Springer, 19-42.

8.2. Two dogmas: reductionism and anti-reductionism

As a rule, authoritative manuals on the philosophy of chemistry contain sections on the possibility of reducing chemistry to physics. The dominant concept is anti-reductionist. It is set out in detail in the review by Jaap van Brakel [8]. The opposite, namely, the position of reductionism is presented in the most developed form of Hinne Hettema [2; 3]. It received very solid support from Eric Scerri [6]. At the beginning of his article, he cites statements from a number of eminent scientists, in particular, P. Dirac, W. Heitler, P. Oppenheim, E. Nagel, H. Reichenbach, in favor of the concept of reduction. They adhered to the line of positivism. Criticism of this line was largely related to the rejection of the concept of reduction and the strengthening of the position of anti-reductionism, to which Scerry himself joined [6, 126]. However, success on this path turned out to be dubious. This circumstance forced Scerry to abandon the concept of anti-reductionism in favor of the conception of reductionism. At this point, it is time to move on to the conception of Hettema, which, as already noted, presented arguments in favor of reductionism in the most presentable way.

The Hettema research program includes three crucial points. First, it comes from the concept of reduction that the neopositivist Ernest Nagel developed. Suppose we consider two theories T1 and T2. The theory of T1 can be reduced to the theory of T2 only if, firstly, these theories are comparable with each other, secondly, all the concepts of the first theory can be derived from the second theory, and this means that, thirdly, conformity rules should be formulated, combining both theories. The requirements that Nagel makes to the reduction are formulated in a rigid manner, in particular, it is necessary to follow the logic of first-order predicates. In the proposed form, the Nagel theory is not very productive in realizing the reduction of some theories to others. In this regard, Hettema seeks to give it a more flexible character. For this purpose, he addresses the structuralist concept of the dynamics of knowledge [1; 7].

Structuralists interpret theory as a hierarchy of interrelated models reflecting the phenomena under study. Mathematically, each model is represented by formulas (structures) built based on set theory. The mathematical structure is included in the substantive theory only with the correspondence rules that establish the connection between mathematics and the phenomena under study. After that, it acquires the status of a non-mathematical structure. The following are models of three types. The class of potential models (M_p) represents the conceptual structure of the theory. The class of actual models (M) represents empirical laws and is a subclass of potential models. The class of partial potential models (M_{PP}) contains exclusively non-theoretical terms. An idea is also introduced about a) a class of constraints C connecting different models of the same theory, b) a class of relations L uniting models of different theories, c) a class of admissible approximations between different models (A). The formal-theoretical part of the theory forms its core (K): K = <M_p, M, M_{pp}, C, L, A>. The minimal part of the theory (T) connects the core of the theory with the area of its application I: T = <T, I>.

The scientific revolution is interpreted as the destruction of the core of the theory. The relation between theories, for example, the previous T_1 theory and the new T_2 theory, is considered as the possibility of reducing K_1 to K_2. If such a reduction succeeds, then the theories T_1 and T_2 are considered comparable. Otherwise, they are recognized as incommensurable with each other. The reduction is understood as a justification for the validity of the interpretation of T_1 as an approximation to T_2. Structuralists were able to translate the discussion of the problem of the commensurability of theories from the field of purely conjectural reasoning into the mainstream of scientific research. They did not prove the fallacy of the thesis of Kuhn-Feyerabend of the incommensurability of the theories but largely questioned him. As a rule, structuralists seek to justify the commensurability of scientific theories. Reductionism entails more than anti-reductionism.

Hettema, referring to some chemical theory, in particular, to the absolute reaction rate theory, shows that all of its concepts receive a quantum interpretation. As a result, Hettema comes to the following conclusion.

> It would seem that this approach is capable of reconciling both our intuitions about how reduction should work in practice with actual examples from science, and show that a number of confusing debates in the philosophy of chemistry could have been avoided altogether.

> This reconstruction of the notion of reduction fulfills a number of interesting desiderata: it supports the unity of science as an overall epistemic structure, and can make sense of some actual problematic cases of reduction from the philosophy of chemistry. The limitation on incommensurability inherent in this approach also limits the scope of feasible pluralisms in the philosophy of chemistry, and focuses our attention instead on a more precise formal characterization of the resulting epistemic structures [3, 20].

Perhaps this position is too optimistic. Describing the program of H. Hettema, Olympia Lombardi notes that it contains certain points that might give rise to perplexity. ... The reductive links do not supply a global reduction but only local and partial reductions of particular theories of chemistry. They introduce relevant idealizations and approximations that establish loose and non-continuous connections between theories. They even draw concepts out of their context and re-use them in a manner inadmissible to the theory to which the concepts originally belong. These links provide a liberal notion of reduction, which could even be made compatible with non-reductionist positions. But once the concept of reduction has been relaxed in such a way, we are entitled to ask why the relationship is still called 'reduction' instead of 'inter-theory link', and how to justify Hettema's insistence on conceptualizing this kind of loose links as reductive in the Nagelian sense. [4, 137]

Let me return to the position of E. Scerri. He, one of the most authoritative representatives of the anti-reductionist tradition, had to admit his mistakes made by him in interpreting the conceptual content of the periodic table of Mendeleev. He concluded that philosophers often draw far-reaching conclusions without proper preparation.

Let me make a general comment about philosophy of science which has been made many times before but which is especially pertinent in the present case. There is a tendency for philosophers of science to obtain their knowledge of science from textbooks, which inevitably present impoverished accounts of the particular fields that they are describing. Of course it is not difficult to understand this tendency, which stems from the fact that philosophers are generally not sufficiently technically proficient to cope with the latest research on the subject and prefer to fall back on the version of the science that they themselves learned during their earlier scientific education. [6, 141].

It is time to give my own interpretation of the programs of reductionism and anti-reductionism. I am talking about the possibility of reducing quantum chemistry to quantum mechanics. The latter is unconditionally attributed to physics. In my opinion, this is a serious mistake. Quantum mechanics was originally developed in physics. Nevertheless, as mechanics, it has a formal character. In its present state, mechanics express the similarities of not only physical but also chemical theories, in particular, quantum chemistry. This means that it is wrongfully to consider mechanics as a physical theory. The link between quantum chemistry, on the one hand, and quantum mechanics, on the other hand, is not a link between chemistry and physics. This is the connection of two theories, special (quantum chemistry) and formal (quantum mechanics). Quantum mechanics, being turned to chemistry, acquire a selective, namely, chemical content. You can forget about quantum physics at this stage of analysis. Reduction and anti-reduction make sense if the relationship between quantum and classical chemistry is considered. In connection with the clarification made, it becomes obvious that supporters of anti-reductionism in chemistry, often, defended not the bastions of chemistry, but by classical chemistry. The relevance of the research of H. Hettema is not in the fact that he strengthened the building of reductionism, but in the fact that he broke through new gaps in the fortifications of pre-quantum chemistry. Not surprisingly, E. Scerri has left the ranks of the so-called anti-reductionists, who often speaks on behalf of obsolete chemistry.

One more circumstance should be noted. Physics and chemistry are branches of science that consist of an uncountable number of individual theories. Consistent thinking takes place only when the relation of basic theories is considered, and not the branches of science, the content of which is not properly defined. The fact of relatedness of physics and chemistry, which is expressed in quantum mechanics, of course, is of current importance. It does not put chemistry in a subordinate position relative to physics. Chemistry is the science of substances, their composition, structure, properties, and mutual transformations. In this quality, it goes beyond the limits of physics. The concept of branches of science does not sufficiently characterize the status of those basic theories that today belong to physics and chemistry.

In my opinion, the core of chemistry is the process of multiplying and developing its basic theories. They can be both commensurate and incommensurable. In this place, it is reasonable to recall the concept of league-theory. It is which most adequately expresses the commensurability of theories. The reductionist program with its positivist past is clearly outdated. This dogma is not overcome by the propaganda of its opposite, i.e. anti-reductionism. The fact is that in both cases those theories are not defined whose connection they seek to express. The concepts of reductionism and anti-reductionism are useless if only the relationship between quantum mechanics and quantum chemistry is considered.

References

1. Balzer, W., Moulins, C.U., and Sneed J.D. (1987) An Architectonic for Science. The Structuralist Program. Dordrecht: Reidel.
2. Hettema, H. (2012) Reducing Chemistry to Physics: Limits, Models, Consequences, Groningen: Rijksuniversiteit Groningen.
3. Hettema, H. (2015) Reduction for a dappled world: connecting chemical and physical theories. In Scerri, E., McIntyre, L. (Eds.). Philosophy of Chemistry, Boston Studies in the Philosophy and History of Science 306. Dordrecht: Springer, 5-22.
4. Lombardi, O. (2013) Hinne Hettema: Reducing Chemistry to Physics: Limits, Models, Consequences, Groningen: Rijksuniversiteit Groningen, 2012, xxvi+453 pp. HYLE– International Journal for Philosophy of Chemistry 19(1), 135-137.
5. Nagel, E. (1961) The Structure of Science. London: Routledge and Kegan Paul.
6. Scerri, E.R. (2015) The changing views of a philosopher of chemistry on the question of reduction. In Scerri, E., McIntyre, L. (Eds.). Philosophy of Chemistry, Boston Studies in the Philosophy and History of Science 306. Dordrecht: Springer, 125-143.
7. Sneed, G.D. (1971) The Logical Structure of Mathematical Physics. Dordrecht: Reidel.
8. Van Brakel, J. (2014) Philosophy of science and philosophy of chemistry. HYLE – International Journal for Philosophy of Chemistry 20(1), 11-57.

8.3. Theoretical relativity of practice

Many authors in the interpretation of the nature of chemistry come from the primacy of practice. This primacy is manifested in the fact that practice is singled out as an independent factor that dominates everything else that enters the world of chemistry. In this regard, the theory is most often in relation to the practice in the role of its poor relative. Even the authors, who rightly emphasize the current importance of chemical theories, nevertheless, put practice ahead of them. «In chemistry it's clear that making new molecules is a very, very different enterprise from analyzing what is in nature. And that synthesis creates in its practitioners different ways of looking at the world, in which theory building is not central. Making things is». [6, 332] Immediately before this quote, Roald Hoffmann quite rightly notes that in neopositivism and critical rationalism, obviously insufficient attention is paid to chemical experiments and the production of new chemicals. This criticism suggests that 'making things' should find an adequate expression in the philosophy of chemistry. Nevertheless, it is possible that chemistry is devoid of the primacy of the production of things. This position is unacceptable for Bernadette Bensaude-Vincent, who sees the future of the philosophy of chemistry in the 'thing turn' [1], just as in the philosophy of technology dominate 'thingly turn' [11, 3].

Pierre Laszlo «starts from the premise that the philosophy of chemistry needs to be primarily a philosophy of action. Its main task is to reflect on what chemists do, in their actual practice; not to bother with an ontological strawman, the fictional derivation from physics»; in accordance with this setting he proclaims 'hands-on knowledge' [8, 93]. Rein Vihalemm speaks energetically on behalf of the 'practice-centered approach'. «Chemistry, especially its historical practice, has in the philosophy of science in recent decades attracted more and more attention, influencing the turn from the vision of science as a timeless logic-centered system of statements towards the history- and practice-centered approach» [13,91]. At the same time, the practice-centered approach is vigorously opposed not only to the logic-centered but also to the theory-centered approach [13, 94, 96]. Romano Harré believes that in the twenty-first century such a fruitful practical tendency is reborn, which took place in the sixteenth and seventeenth centuries [4, 88].

The practice-centered approach is implemented based on various philosophical systems. Vihalemm does this on behalf of Marxism [12]. Joseph Earley comes from American pragmatism [2]. Harré emphasizes the importance of the works of the late Ludwig Wittgenstein [3]. Laszlo focuses on the abduction of Charles Sunders Peirce and the concept of implicit knowledge Michael Polanyi [8]. Bensaude-Vincent notes the relevance of the ideas of Gaston Bachelard and Pierre Duhem [1].

It is time to explain why I, guided by the principle of theoretical representation (manifestation), as a result, do not welcome the practice-centered approach. The fact is that something, be it a thing or a practical action, taken outside the theory, cannot be determined. It becomes a metaphysical fiction. Outside of the theory, there are no electrons, no chemical bonds, and no rules for the synthesis of new substances. There is only that what a part of the most developed theories is. Things, processes and problems that are postulated as being outside theories do not exist in the scientific sense of the word. There is not and cannot be a theory-centered approach. The theory cannot be the center of anything, insofar as it does not possess an environment.

The practice is not outside theory. By virtue of this, it is necessary to determine its place in the theory. The practice is nothing but factualization, in particular, observation and experiment. At first glance, such a statement is clearly insufficient. They say factualization can be carried out, on the one hand, for the sake of developing the theory, on the other hand, for the sake of practical results. Let me explain what was said by a simple example.

The coach of an athlete seems to be a theorist, and his ward is a practitioner. However, upon closer examination, it turns out that the distinction made between the practitioner and the theorist is not consistent. If the trainer's theory is not brought to the factualization stage, then it remains just a deductive prediction, nothing more. Such a prediction is not a full-fledged theory. The athlete, in turn, implements another stage of the theory, namely, the factualization. The theory has become more complete, but it is still not fully-fledged. As repeatedly noted earlier, a full-fledged cycle of intratheoretical conceptual transduction involves four steps, not only prediction and factualization but also data processing and abduction. It turns out that both the trainer and the athlete make their own contribution to the development of the theory. The trainer is strong in deduction, induction, and abduction, and the athlete is in adduction, performed by the factualization.

For theorists often take deductive scientists. However, in order to be a full-fledged theorist, it is not enough to be well versed only in the deduction. From this point follows conclusion, the prospering of people is ensured only in one way, namely, by the steady development of the potential of scientific theories. This conclusion fully applies to chemistry. The people involved in chemistry are called upon to envelop fully the potential of scientific chemical theories. They are not capable of anything else. It is remarkable that they possess this ability. By developing chemical theories, they produce new chemical reactions and new substances. Those and others are manifestations of theories and outside of them have no meaning. Chemists need not a practice thing, but a theory turn. However, of course, theory of things turn does not mean the cultivation of outdated understandings of the nature of science, including chemical, theories. The failures of the neopositivistic and critical-rationalistic projects for the development of scientific theories do not mean that it is necessary to belittle the significance of the institution of theories to one degree or another. The meaning of the above will become clearer after a brief description of those philosophical directions that have particularly energetically attracted attention to the concept of practice.

The second and eleventh theses of K. Marx on Feuerbach's philosophy read as follows

> The question whether objective truth can be attributed to human thinking is not a question of theory but is a **practical** question. The question whether objective truth can be attributed to human thinking is not a question of theory but is a practical question. Man must prove the truth — i.e. the reality and power, the this-sidedness of his thinking in practice. The dispute over the reality or non-reality of thinking that is isolated from practice is a purely *scholastic* question. ...

> Philosophers have hitherto only *interpreted* the world in various ways; the point is to *change* it. [9]

The program of Karl Marx – change the world for the better based on practice, has not been implemented with success in any country. Why? Because the proposed method of ascent from the abstract to the concrete understood as a transition from one contradiction to another, did not have the proper scientific weight. Without a correct theory, any melodious words turn out to be an empty slogan. An attempt to proclaim the primacy of practice ended in a bluff.

The founders of American pragmatism also declared the primacy of practice. They performed it more successfully than Marx did. Peirce proclaimed pragmatic maxim: «Consider what effects, that might conceivably have practical bearings, we conceive the object of our conception to have. Then, our conception of these effects is the whole of our conception of the object» [10, 293]. How exactly should practical bearings be considered? According to the scientific method: abduction – deduction – induction. It is not difficult to see that practical bearings, in fact, relate directly to the theory. Peirce did not single out this circumstance in a clear way. That is why he is to a certain extent "guilty" of declaring the primacy of the practice.

The notions of theory and practice were spread in different angles by William James and John Dewey. The scientific theory was understood as «an instrument: it is designed to achieve a purpose – to facilitate action or increase understanding» [7, 33]. There is no strict justification for the need for instrumentalism in either James or Dewey. They, especially Dewey, in no way sought somehow to diminish the merits of scientific theories. However, pragmatists were clearly not ready to include the practice directly in the context of theories. Pragmatist analyzes of the relationship between practice and theory, as a rule, boil down to the proclamation of instrumentalism in the form of a declaration. The content of scientific theories themselves is not considered in detail. This is characteristic of all authors who, one way or another, proclaim the primacy of practice, in particular, for Wittgenstein and Bachelard. In all cases, it turns out that the more the practice is alienated from scientific theories, the more it is deprived of any acceptable meaning.

Let me, not without pleasure end the next section with the remarkable conclusion of Roald Hoffmann: «A theory is then a special gift, a gift for the mind in a society (of science, not the world) where thought and understanding are preeminent. A gift from one human being to another, to us all» [5, 11]. Perhaps we do not fully understand that this gift does not need any other props, except our scientific enthusiasm.

References

1. Bensaude-Vincent, B. (2014) Philosophy of chemistry or philosophy with chemistry. HYLE – International Journal for Philosophy of Chemistry 20(1), 58-76.
2. Earley, J.E. (2015) Pragmatism and the philosophy of chemistry. In Scerri, E., McIntyre, L. (Eds.) Philosophy of Chemistry, Boston Studies in the Philosophy and History of Science 306. Dordrecht: Springer, 73-89.
3. Harré, R. (2014) New tools for philosophy of chemistry. HYLE – International Journal for Philosophy of Chemistry 20(1), 77-91.
4. Harré, R. (2016) Realism and the turn to practice. Foundations of Chemistry 18(2), 88–89.
5. Hoffmann, R. (2003) Why buy that theory? American Scientist, 91(1), 9-11.
6. Hoffmann, R. (2007) What might philosophy of science look like if chemists built it? Synthese 155(3), 321-336.
7. James, W. (1975) [1907] Pragmatism: A New Name for some Old Ways of Thinking. Cambridge, MA: Harvard University Press.

8. Laszlo, P. (2014) Chemistry, knowledge through actions? HYLE – International Journal for Philosophy of Chemistry 20 (1), 93-116.

9. Marx K. (2002) [1845] Theses on Feuerbach. Marxists Internet Archive. Transl. by C. Smith and D. Cuckson. Available at: www.marxists.org/

10. Peirce, C.S. (1978) How to make our ideas clear. Popular Science Monthly 12, 286–302.

11. Verbeek, P.P. (2005) What Things Do, Philosophical Reflections on Technology, Agency and Design. Philadelphia, Pennsylvania State University Press.

12. Vihalemm, R. (2011) Towards a practical realist philosophy of science. Baltic Journal of European Studies 1(9), 46–60.

13. Vihalemm, R. (2015) Chemistry and the problem of pluralism in science: an analysis concerning philosophical and scientific disagreements. Foundations of Chemistry 18(2), 91-102.

8.4. Scientific chemistry methods

As part of the philosophy of chemistry, scientific methods are considered extremely rare. This situation is difficult to explain. Perhaps a significant number of chemists believe that the issue of the status of scientific methods of chemistry has lost its relevance. Of course, such an assumption raises great doubts.

The scientific methods I understand as a way to manage some notions of the theory in accordance with certain rules. These notions are principles, laws, and variables. First, it is advisable to refer to these notions.

In chemistry, variables are features of atoms, molecules, and compounds. Any chemical object is a combination of features. In stating this situation, one should pay special attention to the following three circumstances. As it became known due to quantum chemistry, some variables are related by uncertainty relations. Such a relationship is characteristic, for example of the impulse and length as well as of the energy and duration of the processes. The second unusual circumstance is that the signs of quantum chemical objects in the expressions of wave functions are given in the form of some complexes, for example, like this: $Et - p_x x$. Thirdly, quantum signs appear in two qualities: first as part of the wave functions as signs of pure and entangled states, and then, after measurements, as signs of mixed states. Signs, on the one hand, of pure and entangled states, on the other hand of mixed states, are significantly different from each other.

It is time to move on to characterizing the laws, which I understand as such relationships between variables that are not principles. In a deductive attitude, laws are deduced from principles. In an inductive relation, on the contrary, the principles follow the laws. An interesting controversy took place about the status of chemical laws. Opponents regard two questions. The first question is do chemical laws have at least partially a different epistemological status than physical laws. The second question: should chemical laws be idealizations? Maureen Christie and John R. Christie answer the first question with a positive yes, and the second question negative no [3; 4]. Rein Vihalemm gives the opposite answers to the same questions [10].

In my opinion, arguing parties, focusing on the correlation between chemistry and physics, did not pay enough attention to the status of the philosophy of science. Due to its formal nature, philosophy of science does not express the specific features of chemistry and physics, respectively. The philosophical and etymological status of the laws of physics and chemistry is by definition the same. In this regard, it is useless to put physics as an example of chemistry, as R. Vihalemm does, or to pay special attention to features of chemistry that are not defined by any physical context (M. Christie and J. R. Christie).

Vihalemm, insisting on the uniformity of all scientific laws, emphasizes that they certainly have to deal with idealizations [10, 18]. M. Christie and J. R. Christie, adhering to a realistic position, are not inclined to attribute the indispensable belonging of idealizations to chemical laws [3]. There is a widespread position that idealization coarsens reality. Then the ability to use effectively idealizations is an incomprehensible mystery. In my opinion, in a detailed analysis, it always turns out that idealizations effectively used do not lead away from reality, but, on the contrary, bring it closer to it. In this regard, I support the position of M. Christie and J. R. Christie. However, in each particular case, it is necessary to show truly that idealizations do have real content. It is significant for example that the idea of ideal gases allows us to express some common features of many gases in those cases when the forces of interaction between molecules are small. Joachim Schummer gave an interesting U-turn of the discussion of the nature of chemical laws:

> ... The concept of laws of nature derived from methodological and metaphysical ideas of science that do not fit with modern chemistry. ... Chemistry (like probably all the experimental sciences) largely follows methodological pluralism in which

universal laws of nature or even a Theory of Everything cannot be the primary end of science. Instead, a multitude of models are used by necessity, depending on the specific subject matter and the kind of questions asked (which are derived from a variety of scientific goals), and which as well as prediction and various forms of explanation also include classification and synthesis. Reintroducing the notion of 'laws of nature' would misunderstand the methodologically different tradition of chemistry and inadequately develop the philosophy of chemistry after the model of mathematical physics. [8, S99]

I agree with Schummer that the notion of universal law is outdated. However, I see no reason to refuse the concept of the law. The model is a conceptual representation of some phenomenon. Law, unlike a model, is not a representation of anything. It is no more and no less than the ratio between some features of objects. It is directly this relation, and not it is mapping, in particular, mathematical or computer. The development of science leads to a more thorough understanding of the nature of laws, but not to their abolition. On the concept of the model, see 8.5.

It is time to turn to the nature of the principles of chemistry. The status of the most advanced chemistry, in particular, quantum chemistry, convinces that its principles are similar to the principles of quantum physics. These are the principles of stationary action, invariance, and short-range action. In the framework of pre-quantum physics, these principles do not appear in a distinct form. In this regard, we have to admit that she did without principles. The word principle was used, but on closer examination, what was called a principle was not really a principle. Le Chatelier's principle is widely known, according to which a system that is out of equilibrium tends to return to it. As it turned out, Le Chatelier's principle is not satisfied in thermodynamics [7, 173-174].

As already noted, the purpose of scientific methods is to manage the concepts of principles, laws, and variables. My position is known to the reader. It consists in the fact that in the case of managing concepts of a theory a scientist implements successively the methods of deduction, adduction (the method of conducting observations, experiments and the implementation of practical acts), induction and abduction. Of crucial importance is not the beginning of the cycle, for which, for example, the method of abduction can be chosen, as Ch.S. Peirce did, or the method of deduction, and the completeness of the cycle, which includes four links. The current understanding of the scientific method, as the review article by Hanne Andersen and Brien Hepburn shows, is not unique. They note the relevance of the ideas about the scientific method, which is characterized by them mainly in the context of opposition, on the one hand, deductive and, on the other hand, inductive method. The characteristic of this opposition does not lead to any definite characteristic of the scientific method. The question "What is the scientific method?" remains unanswered. At the same time, the authors strongly oppose the legend of a single, universal scientific method, the idea of which, they say, is widely used erroneously in the education system [1, 6.1].

In the same vein, Steve Weinberg argues,

Not only does the fact that the standards of scientific success shift with time make the philosophy of science difficult; it also raises problems for the public understanding of science. We do not have a fixed scientific method to rally round and defend. I remember a conversation I had years ago with a high school teacher, who explained proudly that in her school teachers were trying to get away from teaching just scientific facts and wanted instead to give their students an idea of what the scientific method was. I replied that I had no idea what the scientific method was, and I thought she ought to teach her students scientific facts. She thought I was just being surly. But it's true; most scientists have very little idea of what the scientific method is, just as most bicyclists have very little idea of how bicycles stay erect. In both cases, if they think about it too much, they're likely to fall off. [11, 85]

In the conditions of the variability of scientific knowledge, giving it a practical character and increasing pluralism, the very idea of the scientific method, in particular, the sequence of deduction - adduction - induction - abduction is a misunderstanding. Assume that it is. In this case, I would like to know what exactly an alternative to the scientific method became. If «most scientists have a little idea of what the scientific method is», then what exactly do they know in the most exhaustive way? After all, it is no coincidence that humanity is proud of them. S. Weinberg does not shy away from the above question. He argues that scientists implement philosophical zing-principle. «...There is a kind of zing – to use the best word I can think of – that is quite unmistakable when real scientific progress is being made» [11, 87]. S. Weinberg considers that the example of the zing operation is the introduction of T.D. Lee and C.N. Yang of the principle of parity violation in the case of describing weak interactions of K-mesons [11, 87].

I believe that in reality, Lee and Yang did not perform the intuitive action of zing, but a completely explainable act of abductive reasoning. Physicists have experimentally discovered such phenomena that could not be explained by the already existing theory of weak interactions. At the same time, they knew that in order to achieve a correct explanation, it was necessary for one way or another to make changes to the principles of the theory. Lee and Yang managed to identify these changes earlier than other physicists did. Thus, they acted highly expedient. Contrary to the concept of the zing principle, which S. Weinberg calls the philosophical for no apparent reason, I will dare to assert that any scientific act on the reorganization of the theory, with its proper scientific explanation, falls into one of four headings, either abduction, or deduction, or adduction or induction. Perhaps there are other form of transduction than listed ones. In this case, they must be named. Following the proponents of the zing concept, it is not enough to argue that scientific progress is provided by some intuitive acts of uncertain nature. The refusal of the scientific method is the way to assert intuitivism.

In my opinion, completely legitimate criticism of giving to scientific methods a priori and universal features should not be brought to the negation of the very concept of the scientific method. It is indisputable that scientists' ideas about deduction, adduction, induction, and abduction are constantly changing. It is equally indisputable that in the works of eminent scientists, in particular, the Nobel Prize winners throughout the 20th century and up to the present, all these four methods are revealed. Many critics of the scientific method themselves cannot do without it. This is also true with respect to Steve Weinberg, who argues about the correlation of theory and experiment, which «often go on at the same time, strongly influencing each other» besides, «these are the theories that can be tested by experiment, and can be falsified» [11, c. 89]. These statements clearly show that the eminent physicist argues not in an arbitrary manner, but in the context of the scientific method. It is in it that the relationship between theory and experiment is concerned.

In my opinion, there is every reason to assert that chemists are consistently guided by scientific methods. The opposite position leads to absurd conclusions because it seems that chemists are not aware of the rules, according to which they predict the course of chemical processes, carry out observations and experiments, process measurement results and improve the principles of theories. Chemists are really guided by the methods of deduction, adduction, induction, and abduction. They do not use them in the blind. Insisting on this conclusion, I, nevertheless, believe that the method of abduction, the purpose of which is to update outdated deductive principles, is mastered worse than other methods. Clarifying its content, I turn to the history of the invention by D.I. Mendeleev of the periodic system of chemical elements.

According to the memoirs of Ivan, son of Mendeleev, crucial to the invention of his father had the work of J-B. Dumas, Ch. F. Gerhardt and especially S. Cannizzaro [9]. Many chemists before Mendeleev were guided by the idea that the properties of chemical elements have a certain periodicity, depending on atomic masses. It was difficult to develop this idea in a systematic way insofar as the chemists' ideas about atoms, molecules and ways of experimentally determining atomic and molecular masses left much to be desired. It was in this respect that S. Cannizzaro succeeded, who, in his reasoning, proceeded from the hypothesis of A. Avogadro, according to which equal volumes of gases at the same temperature and volume contain the same number of molecules. By weighing the above volumes of gases, it was possible to determine the multiplicity of masses of molecules and, accordingly, the atoms that makeup them. The results obtained by S. Cannizzaro significantly stimulated new searches for D.I. Mendeleev. «In a short time, I reviewed a lot of sources, compared a huge amount of material. I had, however, to make a great effort in order to separate the main information from the secondary information in the available data, to decide to change a number of generally accepted atomic weights, to retreat from what was recognized then by the greatest authorities » [9]. Ivan Mendeleev sums up the discovery of his father as follows: «The discovery of the periodic law for its creator was not a happy event, not an unexpected success. No, the search for the basic law of the world of atoms was a conscious philosophical striving, a task set from the very beginning. The creator of the periodic law went on the siege of this mystery of nature systematically, from his first works, gradually and consistently narrowing the circle, until, as a result of tireless vital work with the help of the highest rise of creative thought, he finally took the fortress by storm» [9].

Mendeleev was convinced of the correctness of his discovery only after he managed to present the full cycle of intratheoretical transduction in its unity. Relying on adduction and induction, he perfected the deductive part of his theory. Predicted the existence of previously unknown elements and their atomic masses. If there were inconsistencies between deduction and induction, then after additional research, Mendeleev corrected either the deductive or the inductive parts of his theory. Mendeleev excelled his many predecessors precisely in the presentation of the unity of the intratheoretical transduction cycles that he implemented. Not all of his predictions were confirmed by experiments. However, his predictions were more accurate than forecasts of his contemporaries.

We also note the following nontrivial circumstance. Every eminent scientist implements a certain bunch of theories. For Mendeleev, it was the league-theory Dumas – Gerhardt – Cannizzaro – Mendeleev. In the competition of scientific theories, the combination of concepts that, in the most developed form represents complete cycles of intratheoretical conceptual transduction, triumphs over.

The question of intertheoretical relations in chemistry, of course, is also directly related to the scientific method of chemistry. In this connection, the question of commensurability, or, conversely, the incommensurability of theories, is of key importance. As is known, the thesis of the incommensurability of theories was most vigorously cultivated by T. Kuhn. If the theories are incommensurable, then the question of intertheoretical relations is largely meaningless. Scientists have no choice but to be content with the consideration of individual theories, not bringing them into contact with each other. However, eminent scientists usually do not recognize the validity of the thesis of the incommensurability of theories. In this connection, the conclusions reached by the physicist S. Weinberg and the chemist R. Hoffmann are very indicative. S. Weinberg writes, «Nowhere have I seen any signs of Kuhn's incommensurability between different paradigms. Our ideas have changed, but we have continued to assess our theories in pretty much the same way: a theory is taken as a success if it is based on simple general principles and does a good job of accounting for experimental data in a natural way» [11, 196]. In my opinion, the development of classical, relativistic and quantum physics and chemistry did not lead to the abandonment of the scientific method in the field of the estimation of intertheoretical relations.

Hoffmann considers the main milestones in the development of chemical bonding theory, in particular, G. Lewis theory with the concept of a shared electron pair, then the theory of L. Pauling, in which the concept of a shared electron pair received a quantum interpretation, then the concept of orbitals of density functional theory, in whose development he himself took an active part.

> Kuhn saw incommensurability as being the consequence of two competing paradigms, and he distinguished incommensurabilities of language, and of standards of evidence. I think incommensurability is no problem whatsoever to chemists. Differences in language are there, the result of different paradigms, but more so of history, and of education. Yet people, eager to make things, with no handwringing on how problematic it all is, graft one way of understanding onto another. So, to return to that electrostatic/quantum mechanical conundrum, a couple of decades down the line there is one language (of charges attracting, and of quantum mechanical explanations) which even though it is deeply inconsistent at its core, is rich enough to provide productive extrapolations. [6, 330]

How to explain the existence of unity between different theories in case they form an ascending line of development of scientific knowledge? Primarily, by the fact that even the least detailed theory correctly expresses some features of the phenomena under study. The correct method is inherited by future theories. That is why it is inappropriate to deny the existence of continuity between them. The arguments of Kuhn about the incommensurability of theories do not sufficiently take into account their continuity.

A remarkable example of the commensurability of chemical theories is carried out by P.W. Atkins, who compare of molecular-orbital and valence-bond theories [2,147-148]. He carefully identifies their similar and different features. These two theories complement each other. It should be borne in mind that they are not reducible to each other. One of these theories is not a limiting case of the other. Depending on the specific situation, preference may be given to one or another theory. As for the theories of Lewis and Polling mentioned above, the first theory is a classical approximation to the second theory. The situation in chemistry resembles the situation in physics. The theory of inter-theoretical transduction should take into account not only related theories when one of them is a limiting case of the other, but also complementary conceptions. Preference is always given to those theories that have the greatest conceptual power. «The theory of theories goes like this: A theory will be accepted by a scientific community if it explains better (or more of) what is known, fits at its fringes with what is known about other parts of our universe and makes verifiable, preferably risky, predictions» [5, 9].

Thus, it is undoubted that in the conceptual structure of chemistry its scientific methods occupy one of the central places. Refusal from them is equivalent to the refusal to understand chemistry as a scientific discipline.

References

1. Andersen, H., Hepburn, B. (2016) Scientific method. The Stanford Encyclopedia of Philosophy. Available at: https://plato.stanford.edu/archives/sum2016/entries/scientific-method/
2. Atkins, P.W. (1974) Quanta – A Handbook of Concepts. Oxford: Clarendon Press.
3. Christie, M., Christie, J. R. (2003) Chemical laws and theories: a response to Vihalemm. Foundations of Chemistry 5(2), 165–174.
4. Christie, M., Christie, J. R. (2000) 'Laws' and 'Theories' in chemistry do not obey the rules. In Bhushan, N., Rosenfeld, S.M. (Eds.). Of Minds and Molecules: New Philosophical Perspectives on Chemistry. Oxford: Oxford University Press, 34–50.
5. Hoffmann, R. (2003) Why buy that theory. American Scientist 91(1), 9-11.
6. Hoffmann, R. (2007) What might philosophy of science look like if chemists built it? Synthese 155(3), 321–336.
7. Münster, A. (1970) Classical Thermodynamics. Transl. by E.S. Halberstadt. London: Wiley–Interscience.
8. Schummer, J. (2014) The preference of models over laws of nature. Chemistry European Review 22(S1), S87–S101.
9. Trifonov, D.N. Kak Mendeleyev otkryl periodicheskiy zakon [How Mendeleev discovered the periodic law]. Available at: http://www.chem.msu.su/rus/elibrary/trifonov/ivan-mendeleev.html/ [In Russian].
10. Vihalemm, R. (2003) Are laws of nature and scientific theories peculiar in chemistry? Scrutinizing Mendeleev's discovery. Foundations of Chemistry 5(1), 7–22.
11. Weinberg, S. (2001) Facing up. Science and Its Cultural Adversaries Cambridge, Massachusetts London: Harvard University Press.

8.5. Manifestations of chemical theories: models and inverse problems

In the new sections, I seek to show that the principle of theoretical representation makes it possible to clarify significantly the content of many questions of metachemistry. In this regard, I turn to quantum chemistry, which is currently the most advanced chemical theories. Lev A. Gribov and Swetlana P. Mushtakova presented the foundations of quantum chemistry in a noteworthy form [3, 79-106]. They seek to present in a clear-cut way the realization of the conceptual potential of quantum chemistry, in which, as is known the central place is occupied by the concept of the wave function and the Schrödinger equation. The main line of argument of the two authors is that they strive to express the sequence of those stages that express the progress of quantum chemistry. At first glance, it seems that its initial link should be the Schrödinger equation, from which some laws can be derived. Nevertheless, according to the argument of L.A. Gribov and S.P Mushtakova potential of quantum chemistry is realized quite intricately. Figuratively speaking, in quantum chemistry, researchers who want to go forward have to move backward.

> Any experiments with micro-objects are always only macroscopic and indirect. In other words, it is impossible in principle to 'climb' inside an atom or molecule with any measuring device. One can check the correctness of a statement only in one way: calculate a macroscopic effect based on a microscopic model of an object, and then compare the result with a real experiment. [3, 27-28]

This means that one has to solve inverse problems, moving not from models to experimental results, but on the contrary, from these results to models. To solve these inverse problems, models are necessary. In this case, in accordance with the conceptual nature of quantum mechanics, it is necessary to rely on the principles of complementarity and correspondence developed by Nils Bohr.

According to Bohr, «evidence obtained under different experimental conditions cannot be comprehended within a single picture, but must be regarded as complementary in the sense that only the totality of the phenomena exhausts the possible information about the objects» [2, 40]. The complementarity principle, which gets its more accurate expression in the Heisenberg uncertainty relations, leads to the need to recognize the pluralism of the models used. Indeed, it is necessary to express the correlation of pairs of independent variables, for example, coordinates and impulses, energy and duration. The statement of N. Bohr, in my opinion, should be clarified as follows. Quantum mechanics, including in relation to chemistry, provides a unified picture of various patterns. In addition, the following crucial circumstance should be taken into account. Not any parameters are mutually additional, but only such variables, the commutator of operators of which is not equal to zero.

N. Bohr believed that «the correspondence principle expresses the tendency to utilise in the systematic development of the quantum theory every feature of the classical theories in a rational transcription appropriate to the fundamental contrast between the postulates and the classical theories» [1, 849]. Gribov and Mushtakova modifies the content of the correspondence principle, without committing themselves to an obligation, to consider the ratio of quantum and classical chemistry. According to their understanding, the correspondence principle indicates the need to associate model concepts and parameters with experiments based on human senses [3, 101]. Quantum chemistry is an effective theory if researchers achieve consistency between the results of direct measurements and the values of variables obtained indirectly, namely, through calculations using models.

The book of Gribov and Mushtakova testifies to the significant effects of the proposed methodology. While appreciating it merits, I tend to associate it effectiveness with methods of intratheoretical conceptual transduction. In my opinion, L.A. Gribov and S.P. Mushtakova presented in a very presentable form nothing but the stage of abduction in quantum chemistry, focusing on the process of updating models. After using the induction method in understanding the results of macroscopic experiments, the stage of abduction begins. If it is implemented, then in the process of deduction direct predictions are carried out.

The methodology for solving inverse problems in many ways explains what is in quantum chemistry considered as real. The evaluation criterion is not only the measurement results but also the content of the theory as a whole. Realized are not only mixed states that are subject to direct measurements, but also pure and entangled states. Pure and entangled states are not manifest directly in dimensions, but they are represented in them in a hidden, implicit form. Implicit becomes explicit in the process of solving inverse problems. This process largely explains what and how is observed in chemistry [5; 6; 8].

The methodology for solving inverse problems also largely clarifies the status of the models. Under the model most often, understand the mapping of some original entities, which is designed to contribute to a better conceptual understanding of these entities [9,131]. Models can be both real and conceptual. In modern science, researchers especially use mathematical and computer models [11]. The base of the models is originals. The model-original relationship is by definition semantic. It is perceived by researchers, as a rule, as something self-evident. In my opinion, this ratio should be questioned. The semantic relationship is not something given initially; it occurs if the correlation of some manifestations of the theory, in particular, objective, mental and linguistic, is considered. In content, they are identical, for they are manifestations of the same theory, but differ in form, which is determined by a particular material carrier. Material carriers, for example, language and mentality of people differ from each other.

It follows from the above that the essence of mathematical and computer models is not in their semantic relation to originals. Of decisive importance is their dual status, firstly, interdisciplinary, secondly, abductive. An acute need for models arises at the stage of abduction in the process of updating the deductive foundations of the theory. This is how the search for the right ways to concretize the principles and laws of the theory. Not all models are allowed to the deduction stage, but only those that adequately represent the results of experiments that have already been performed. Presumably, they are considered relevant to new prediction processes with their characteristic deduction method. Models are manifestations of the principles and laws of the theory at the stage of unfolding the potential of theory through the method of abduction. The solution of inverse problems is the method of abduction in action. It is not the case that researchers put models in place of theories. Models exist only as part of the theory.

The nature of mathematical and computer models is not in their semantic relevance. They are designed to reveal the true potential of chemical theories, which is present in them in a hidden form. They do not add to these theories anything alien to them. Mathematics and computer science, being formal sciences, reveal similar features of the natural and axiological sciences and give them new impulses of development. Just because of the latter circumstance, the use of mathematical and computer models in chemistry becomes relevant. Mathematical and computational chemistry is chemistry in its own form. The terms 'mathematical chemistry' and 'computer chemistry' are partly misleading because there is an erroneous impression that in both cases something alien is added to chemistry.

Any scientifically sound chemical theory is mathematical [7]. With the same success, it can be shown that any scientific chemical theory contains in its specific form, sometimes rather undeveloped, the potential of computer science. If they talk about mathematical and computational chemistry, they mean, in fact, the use of avant-garde achievements of mathematics and computer science in chemistry. Nevertheless, this circumstance does not get its expression in terms of 'mathematical chemistry' and 'computational chemistry'.

Manifestations of the theory can be holistic and partial. Models are holistic manifestations of the theory; they are not necessarily divided into the object, language, mental, procedural, dynamic, practical, and any other representations. The list of partial manifestations of the theory can be quite extensive. In my opinion, none of these manifestations should be absolutized. The endless dispute between realists and anti-realists, theorists and practitioners, as a rule, is marked by absolutizing or, on the contrary, by underestimating some partial manifestation of the chemical theory [4, 318-325]. There is no way to prove the indispensable advantage of one partial manifestation of a chemical theory over another. Of course, each of them must be considered in the context of conceptual transduction. I illustrate this fact with an example of understanding the language manifestation of the theory and expression 'Water is H_2O'.

As Michael Weisberg convincingly showed «there is not any strict sense in which water is H_2O, because exactly what water is depends on the context in which 'water' is uttered» [10, 345]. This means, in particular, that in ordinary language the term 'water' is understood differently than in the language of chemistry. Fully agreeing with Weisberg, let me comment on his conclusion from the standpoint of the theory of conceptual transduction.

As part of any theory, language is its specific manifestation. It expresses all the richness of the theory, but in a specific language, and not, for example, in a mental form. This conclusion does not apply to linguistics, according to which 'water' is a noun and in this quality does not differ from, for example, 'table' or 'star'. Linguistics does not care about the distinction of those informal theories, ordinary and scientific, in which the word 'water' is used. At the linguistic level, people reach agreement on the word 'water' relatively easily. Disagreements arise when not formal, but substantive, in particular, chemical theories are considered. In this situation, a more developed theory is the key to a less developed understanding. The owner of more advanced theory of T_2 is building a league-theory $T_2 \rightarrow T_1\{T_2\}$. He, interpreting T_1 from the standpoint of T_2, understands it's both strengths and weaknesses. The owner of a more advanced theory understands the supporter of a not so perfect theory. However, the latter does not understand his interlocutor, because he does not know the strengths of the interlocutor's theory. Thus, there is a hierarchy of meaningful languages, which includes both recognized scientific theories and everyday concepts. In the context of this hierarchy, the expression 'Water is H2O' does not have a clear meaning. Only the most advanced scientific theories have this meaning.

References

1. Bohr, N. (1925) Atomic theory and mechanics. Nature (Suppl.) 116, 845-852.
2. Bohr, N. (1958) Atomic Physics and Human Knowledge. New York: John Wiley.
3. Gribov, L.A., Mushtakova S.P. (1999) Kvantovaya khimiya [Quantum chemistry]. Moskva: Gardariki. [In Russian].
4. Kanke, V.A. (20140 Istoriya, filosofiya i metodologiya yestestvennykh nauk [History, philosophy and methodology of natural sciences]. Moskva: Yurayt. [In Russian].
5. Mulder, P. (2011) Are orbitals observable? HYLE – International Journal for Philosophy of Chemistry 17 (1), 24-35.
6. Ostrovsky, V.N. (2005) Towards a philosophy of approximations in the 'exact' sciences. Hyle – International Journal for Philosophy of Chemistry 11(2), 101-126.
7. Restrepo, G., Villaveces, J.L. (2012) Mathematical thinking in chemistry. HYLE – International Journal for Philosophy of Chemistry 18 (1), 3-22.
8. Schwarz, W.H.E. (2006) Measuring orbitals: provocation or reality? Angewandte Chemie International Edition 45(10), 1508-1517.

9. Stachowiak, H. (1973) Allgemeine Modelltheorie [General Model Theory]. Wien, New York: Springer. [In German].
10. Weisberg, M. (2006) Water is *Not* H_2O. In: Baird, D., Scerri, E., McIntyre, L. (Eds.) Philosophy of Chemistry. Boston Studies in the Philosophy of Science, vol. 242. Dordrecht: Springer, 337-345.
11. Weisberg, M. (2013) Simulation and Similarity – Using Models to Understand the World. New York: Oxford University Press.

8.6. Revolutions in the development of chemistry

Chemistry as a branch of science is a very extensive whole. Covering it with one look is extremely difficult. An interesting attempt was made on this score by N.E. Ablesimov. He identified eight chemical disciplines, which cover 58 subdisciplines [1]. These eight disciplines are inorganic chemistry, organic chemistry, analytical chemistry, physical chemistry, biochemistry, medical chemistry, geochemistry, technical chemistry. There are many other classifications of chemical disciplines and subdisciplines. The exact number of both disciplines and subdisciplines of chemistry is not known. Despite this circumstance, obvious that it is not enough just to state the diversity of chemical knowledge; it needs a consistent understanding. In this connection, the review paper by José Chamizo deserves special attention.

He presents the entire history of the development of chemistry as a sequence of five revolutions. Based on the concept of scientific revolution T. Kuhn, Chamizo in relation to each revolution indicates, firstly, the main instruments, secondly, the main concepts, thirdly, disciplines and subdisciplines [2, 163]. Instruments are listed first not by chance. The fact is that following other authors J.A. Chamizo believes that in recent years and from different traditions has been recognized that instruments play a key role in the changes that occurred in the development of sciences [2, 161]. The use of new instruments opens new territories sometimes without having any underlying theory [2, 160]. Chamizo does not deny the value of the theory. Nevertheless, the theory is in the shadow of his quite definite approach. Since the key role in this approach is given to instruments, it should be called an instrumental approach.

In my opinion, the opposition, on the one hand, of instruments and experiments, on the other hand, the theory is untenable. The fact is they form a whole. If instruments are distinguished from it, then scientific revolutions are merely stated as self-evident facts. They are not a natural result of the development of scientific knowledge. However, it is necessary to recognize, that they are not just happy accidents. Recognizing this, one should address the role that theories play in chemistry. In my opinion, Roald Hoffmann very correctly noted, «the most impotent role for theory in chemistry is to provide a framework in which to think, to organize knowledge» [3, 33]. If the instruments are extracted from this framework, then they become an independent self-sufficient force, they are told primacy over all other parts of the whole. In the absence of this extraction, instruments occupy a definite place in the theory, namely, they belong to the factualization stage, i.e. to experiments, observations, and practices that are carried out in accordance with the method of adduction. All supporters of the instrumental approach, first, do without any framework. Secondly, they do not recognize the practical function of the theory. Third, they believe that the theoretical approach is outdated. However, in reality, the theoretical approach is not outdated. In the absence of theories, the nature of, for example, Multinuclear FT, NMR, and Scanning Tunneling Microscope is unclear. Equally incomprehensible are the measurement results and their purpose. Initially, not only objects but also instruments are theoretical.

It follows from the above that an attempt to systematize chemistry should be carried out on behalf of the dynamics of theories, which finds its expression in the intertheoretical transduction. Moreover, here it immediately turns out that the statement of certain chemical disciplines and subdisciplines is not complete without a fair share of speculation. The fact is that the up-down analysis: chemistry as fields of science → chemical disciplines → chemical subdisciplines, does not reach the foundation of chemistry, which are the individual theories and their bundles (league-theories). Rising from the bottom to up, one can avoid the speculation mentioned above. Of course, such an analysis involves a huge array of raw data. The number of fundamental chemical theories is extremely difficult to estimate. Presumably, it should be no less than thousands of theories. I am not ready to follow the recipe I proposed to the full. Nevertheless, without losing sight of it, I dare to characterize the frequently used ways of classifying various fields of chemistry.

Primarily, we should talk about disciplines of purely chemical content. In this regard, as a rule, inorganic and organic chemistry is called. Then each of them is divided into subdisciplines. Thus, inorganic chemistry includes the chemistry of metals, complex chemistry, solid-state chemistry, crystallography, structural chemistry, colloid chemistry. Organic chemistry includes, in particular, the chemistry of aromatic compounds, of heterocyclic compounds, of polymers, of small molecules, of fullerenes.

Often analytical chemistry is considered as a separate chemical discipline. In fact, analytical chemistry is some part of any chemical discipline and subdiscipline. She is by definition dealing with the stage of factualization, with its method of adduction. Wanting to be consistent, researchers should distinguish along with analytical chemistry deductive, inductive and abductive chemistry. Nevertheless, such types of chemistry are not distinguished. Analytical chemistry should not be recognized by chemical discipline, comparable in its status to inorganic and organic chemistry.

Sometimes, mainly for educational purposes, emit general chemistry. It is designed to express the similarities between inorganic and organic chemistry. As such, general chemistry is a formal chemical discipline. This means that it has no value independent from organic and inorganic chemistry.

The next step in classifying areas of chemistry is to consider its interdisciplinary connections. In this regard, in particular, physical, geological, biological, technical, mathematical and computational chemistry are distinguished. In this connection, physical chemistry is of particular interest.

Primarily, it should be noted that physics and chemistry have a common methodological basis. Compare, for example, physical and chemical thermodynamics, as well as physical and chemical quantum theory. They have a common structure. This means that both thermodynamic and quantum chemistry are not physical chemistry. Quantum chemistry is a modern stage in the development of inorganic and organic chemistry. Thermodynamic chemistry at the end of XIX became an important stage in the development of non-quantum, i.e. classical chemistry. Physical chemistry rightly includes photochemistry and surface chemistry. In both cases, chemists are forced to take into account the influence of physical factors on the phenomena they are studying. This means that in this case, we are talking about interdisciplinary connections between chemistry and physics.

In the case of geochemistry, biochemistry, environmental chemistry, and medicinal chemistry, we are talking exclusively about interdisciplinary connections. They do not lead to the formation of new chemical disciplines. Biochemistry is not a special chemical discipline, comparable in its status to organic chemistry, but its known part focused on biology. Accordingly, technical chemistry is focused on technical sciences.

The ratio of chemistry with mathematics and computer science also has its own characteristics. Chemists do not study objects of mathematics, for example, triangles and numbers. However, of course, they use the achievements of mathematics, as well as computer science. This use leads to the development of chemical disciplines, but not the formation of independent chemical disciplines. Mathematical and computational chemistry does not exist along with organic and inorganic chemistry.

As for the term 'theoretical chemistry', it is extremely unfortunate to the extent that any chemical discipline or subdiscipline is theoretical. By virtue of this, it is illegal to consider theoretical chemistry as a chemical discipline.

Thus, much of what is traditionally considered a chemical discipline is not such one. At the beginning of the section, I have a list of eight chemical disciplines, which are often considered the main ones. In fact, from them, only inorganic and organic chemistry are genuine chemical disciplines.

The review allows us to proceed to the main milestones in the development of chemistry. They are always the achievements of individuals who developed certain theories. In this regard, I decided to use the conclusions of the remarkable Moscow chemist Peter M. Zorkiy. He called for his students 10 names, respectively, titans of chemistry and the greatest chemists, as well as 20 names of great chemists [4, 300]. The table below lists the names of only titans of chemistry in chronological order, indicating their discoveries. This will be enough to determine the way to assess the development of chemistry.

Table 8.1 Ten Titans of Chemistry

Years	Chemists	The main contribution to the development of chemistry
1662	R. Boyle	Discovered the Boyle-Mariotte law, developed the method of chemical experiment and created the prerequisites for the formation of scientific chemistry.
1777-1787	A. L. De Lavoisier	He refuted the phlogiston theory, developed the theory of combustion, discovered the law of mass conservation during chemical reactions, and developed a nomenclature of chemical elements known to him.
1808	J. Dalton	Developed the theory of atoms.
1802-1848	J.J. Berzelius	Developed an electrochemical theory, discovered the atomic masses of a number of elements, discovered several new elements, and developed a system of chemical elements.
1850-1896	F.A. Kekule	Developed the theory of chemical structure. He made a significant contribution to the development of organic chemistry.
1869-1871	D.I. Mendeleev	Created a periodic system of the chemical elements.
1876-1878	J.W. Gibbs	Developed the theory of chemical thermodynamics.
1884	J. H. Van 't Hoff	Discovered the laws of chemical dynamics.

| 1939-1947 | L. C. Pauling | Made a fundamental contribution to the development of quantum chemistry, especially the concept of chemical bonding. |
| 1942-1979 | R. B. Woodward | Made an outstanding contribution to the development of synthetic and organic chemistry. |

Strictly speaking, the three-stage classification of chemistry: chemistry as a branch of science – chemical disciplines – chemical subdisciplines, has significant drawbacks. It is an attempt to express the richness of chemistry, without referring to the foundation of chemistry, consisting of a variety of theories. Such an attempt is inevitably laden with scholastic moments. In a more distinct form, they are presented in the concept of T. Kuhn's scientific revolutions. His excursions into the history of the development of physics and chemistry are clearly insufficient to formulate the full-fledged theory of scientific revolutions. The invention of new theories is of fundamental importance in the development of any branch of science, including chemistry. They can be detailed in different ways, more or less carefully. The most large-scale (macroscopic) structure of development appears as a sequence of several, for example, three or five, scientific revolutions. The conceptual weight of a scientific revolution depends on the degree of detection of their microscopic basis. In any case, not the concept of a macroscopic scientific revolution is fundamental to an understanding of the development of chemistry.

In conclusion, I present the structure of chemistry as a branch of science. This seven-step structure differs significantly from the traditional, i.e. three-step.

Table 8.2 Seven-step structure of chemistry

Steps	Classification Units	Examples

1	Field of science	Chemistry
2	Chemical disciplines	Inorganic and organic chemistry
3	Chemical subdisciplines	Components of inorganic and organic chemistry, for example, metal chemistry, chemistry of fullerenes.
4	Formal chemistry	General chemistry
5	Methodologically oriented chemistry	Classical chemistry, quantum chemistry, thermodynamic chemistry.
6	Content-oriented donor-oriented chemistry (chemistry in its interdisciplinary connections with the content sciences)	Some sections of physical chemistry, for example, chemistry of solid surfaces, as well as geochemistry, biochemistry, medical chemistry, technical chemistry, agricultural chemistry, environmental chemistry, judicial chemistry
7	Formal donor-oriented chemistry (chemistry in its interdisciplinary connections with the formal sciences)	Mathematical chemistry, computational chemistry, philosophy of chemistry, as well as linguistic chemistry and logical chemistry

References

1. Ablesimov, N.E. (2005) Sinopsis khimii: Spravochno-uchebnoye posobiye po obshchey khimii [Synopsis of Chemistry: Reference and Training Manual for General Chemistry]. Khabarovsk: Dal'nevostochnyy goudarstvennyy universitet putey soobshcheniya. [In Russian].

2. Chamizo, J.A. (2017) The fifth chemical revolution: 1973–1999. Foundation of Chemistry 19 (2), 157-179.
3. Hoffmann, R. (1974) Theory in chemistry. Chemistry & Engineering News 72(30), 32-34.
4. Zefirova, O.N, Lubnina, I.E., Lunin, V.V. (2006) Prepodavaniye istorii khimii v Moskovskom universitete: lektory i ikh kursy. chast' iii (pamyati professora P.M. Zorkogo) [Teaching the history of chemistry at Moscow university: lectors and their courses. part iii (in memory of professor P.M. Zorkoy)]. Vestnik Moskovskogo universiteta. Seriya 2. Khimiya [Moscow University Chemistry Bulletin] 47 (4), 298-302. [In Russian].

8.7. Ethical relativity of chemistry

In the philosophy of chemistry, considerable attention is paid to ethics. [2-4; 7]. «...Chemists are inevitably involved in disputes about values. They would badly fail if they were not prepared to reflect on the values, develop and analyze moral and political arguments, build moral judgments and perform responsible actions, all of which belong to the domain of ethics» [2, 1]. Jeffrey Kovac sees the origins of the ethics of chemistry in four ways. First, all chemists are part of some communities; secondly, chemists belong to a particular profession with its wide range of ethical obligations; thirdly, chemists are part of some institutions, for example, universities, research laboratories, and corporations; fourthly, all chemists are part of the human community, and therefore have the same moral obligations as other people [8, 317-318].

Therefore, the involvement of chemists in solving ethical issues is beyond doubt. Nevertheless, when trying consistently to present a union of chemistry and ethics, many problematic aspects arise. The main one is that chemical theories themselves do not contain any values, i.e. preferences, invented not by nature, but by people. In quantum chemistry, there are no values and, accordingly, no ethics. Values are organic exclusively for axiological sciences. In the natural sciences, they are not. Kovac recognizes this. Nevertheless, he believes that, in contrast to the pure sciences, applied sciences have a value content [8, 314]. This kind of reasoning is widespread in the scientific literature, but, in my opinion, it is erroneous, because researchers do not receive the correct expression of the interdisciplinary connections of the natural, in our case chemistry, and axiological sciences.

Chemists often carry out orders, for example, physician as representatives of the axiological science. In this case, the values are set by physicians, not by chemists. These values were originally on the side of medicine and remain in the same place, and do not go over to the side of chemistry. The values of medicine are the values of medicine, not chemistry. Values do not migrate from axiological theories to natural ones. They cannot be transmitted like impulses and energies. That what is counted in this case is determined by interdisciplinary relations. Chemistry, being one of their sides of this relationship, does not become an axiological science. It has ethical relativity insofar as it is necessary for the realization of those values that appear in axiological theories. The ethical principle in the form of the principle of maximization of the prosperity of all stakeholders is present exclusively in axiological theories. Chemists, being involved in ethical matters, however, due to the division of labor in society are not the main performers of the desired axiological goals. In this regard, they have no choice but to enter into a fruitful alliance with representatives of axiological disciplines. However, according to my observations, the absolute majority of chemists who are interested in the development of ethical affairs strive to be independent. They do not develop the interdisciplinary chemistry relationship properly. The ethical relativity of chemistry cannot be developed otherwise than through the realization of appropriate interdisciplinary relations.

The second discrepancy is that chemists in their interest in ethical affairs need to turn to an arsenal of ethical ideas. Their addressee is ethics developed within the framework of philosophy. This, in particular, is an areological, deontological, utilitarian, Marxist, pragmatic, phenomenological, hermeneutic and poststructuralist ethics. It is extremely difficult to operate with this pluralism of ethical concepts. Unfortunately, ethicists have failed to provide chemists with an acceptable version of scientifically oriented generalization of philosophical and ethical pluralism. In the absence of such, most chemists avoid turning to philosophical ethics. Exceptions to this rule are rare. One of them is the article by A. Martin, A. Iles and C. Rosen [10]. An attempt to use the achievements of utilitarian and deontological ethics is commendable. However, the authors of the mentioned article did not pay enough attention to the shortcomings of the two ethical systems on which they focused.

The desire to do without the philosophical and ethical systems is widespread among authors considering the ethical relativity of chemistry. In this respect, the article by T. Børsen and S.N. Nielsen is indicative. These authors come from 'common-sense morality'. «Common-sense morality is an ethical theory differing from many other ethical theories by not providing universal answers or decision methods. The ethically correct action is context dependent, where one must independently evaluate their options and choose what seems ethically most correct in a context of conflicting concerns. As the name 'common-sense' implies, this ethical theory cherishes common-sense and believes in the ability of humans to make judgments that are as informed and as reasoned as possible. On one hand, common-sense morality accepts that established ethical approaches reflect legitimate ethical concerns. On the other, it does not insist on only one ethical principle but instead emphasizes ethical reflection and common-sense. Common-sense can be understood as what Aristotle named *phronesis* – practical wisdom and functioning judgment. Phronetic judgment strives after the good life and the individual or collective ability to define actions pointing in that direction, in a context of contradictory but legitimate values» [1, 9]. In my opinion, ethics in all its guises deserve not a common-sense, but a fully developed scientific orientation. In fact, T. Børsen and S. N. Nielsen implement it. All the virtues that they attribute to common-sense morality, in fact, belong to scientific ethics. However, their approach is not perfect. In particular, this refers to the identification of nine fundamental ethical values, namely: autonomy, safety and security, justice, utility, humility, social stability, and respect for nature.

Where do these values come from? In the scientific approach, they can be singled out exclusively from axiological theories that are part of more than a dozen axiological branches of science. In the ethical values listed above, the values of individual axiological theories are hard to see, for example, technical, economic, sociological, and so on. What kind of science dealt with justice or utility; why is the autonomy of the individual not accompanied by the autonomy of society; why is social stability proclaimed, despite the fact that it is sometimes inappropriate, for example, in non-democratic society? My position is that the allocation of specific ethical values that differ from the values of axiological disciplines is inappropriate. It always blocks the conduct of a thorough analysis of interdisciplinary relations of chemistry with the axiological sciences.

At the beginning of the section, the argument was considered by J. Kovac, which links the ethical obligations of chemists with their affiliation to various societies. As you know, in this regard, a variety of ethical codes is extremely common [9]. It should take into account an extremely important circumstance: the regulation of the activities of a community has, as a rule, economic, political, legal, sociological, but not chemical ground. The reference to the social obligations of chemists does not argue in favor of chemical ethics. It argues in favor of, for example, economic and sociological ethics.

My main conclusion is that chemistry has ethical relativity, which must be realized through interdisciplinary connections of chemistry with axiological theories. At the same time, it is necessary to take into account the scientific, rather than the metaphysical, the potential of philosophical ethics [6, 442-458].

References

1. Børsen T., Nielsen, S.N. (2017) Applying an ethical judgment model to the case of DDT. HYLE – International Journal for Philosophy of Chemistry 23(1), 5-27.
2. Børsen, T., Schummer, J. (2016) Editorial introduction: ethical case studies of chemistry. HYLE–International Journal for Philosophy of Chemistry 22 (1), 1-8.
3. Ethical case studies of chemistry, part III. (2018), ed. by T. Børsen and J. Schummer, special issue of HYLE: International Journal for Philosophy of Chemistry 24(1).

4. Ethics of chemistry (2001/2002). Ed. by J. Schummer. Special issue of HYLE – International Journal for Philosophy of Chemistry 7(2); 8(1).
5. Jeffrey, I. S. (2015) Ethics and responsible conduct of research within the chemical community. Ideas and experiences worth sharing. Accountability in Research 22(60, 303-306.
6. Kanke, V.A. (2014) Istoriya, filosofiya i metodologiya yestestvennykh nauk [History, Philosophy and Methodology of Natural Sciences]. Moskva: Yurayt. [In Russian].
7. Kovac, J. (2004) The Ethical Chemist: Professionalism and Ethics in Science. Upper Saddle River, NJ: Prentice Hall.
8. Kovac, J. (2015) Ethics in science: The unique consequences of chemistry. Accountability in Research 22(6), 312-329,
9. Kovac, J. (2018) American chemical society codes of ethics: past, present, and future. HYLE – International Journal for Philosophy of Chemistry 24(10), 79-95.
10. Martin, A., Iles, A., Rosen C. (2016) Applying utilitarianism and deontology in managing bisphenol A risks in the United States. HYLE–International Journal for Philosophy of Chemistry 22(1), 79-103.

8.8. Aesthetic relativity of chemistry

There is every reason to believe that chemistry has not only ethical but also aesthetic relativity. This means that its achievements can and are really used in art. The interdisciplinary relations of chemistry with art testify to the aesthetic relativity of chemistry. Compared with the recognition of the aesthetic relativity of chemistry, the thesis about the relevance of chemical aesthetics is much stronger [5; 8]. It is this thesis that makes up the leitmotif of the articles of two special issues of the journal 'Hyle' [1]. It means that chemistry itself, regardless of art history, has an aesthetic content.

In distinguishing the aesthetic relativity of chemistry and chemical aesthetics, understanding the status of aesthetics is crucial. If by its status aesthetics relates exclusively to art criticism, then there is no basis for recognizing chemical aesthetics, as well as for the whole set of regional aesthetics, each of which correlates with a certain science (compare: physical, technical, legal, etc. aesthetics). If aesthetics is a formal science, expressing the similarity of all sciences, then the idea of the totality of regional aesthetics, for example, of mathematical and physical aesthetics that go beyond the limits of art, is quite legitimate. Thus, before discussing chemical aesthetics, it is necessary to determine the status of aesthetics.

According to Gideon Engler, such concepts of classical aesthetics as symmetry, simplicity, order, coherence, and unity [3, 28-31] are widely used in science in its construction and improvement. However, crucial is the perception of the studied structures as a whole. «At a first glance, art and science seem to occupy separate worlds. However, a closer examination of these disciplines reveals a meaningful similarity between them. This is manifested by basic perceptive and creative acts of the mind and is apparent through a unique experience: the aesthetic appreciation of structures in these disciplines. A notable outcome of this feature is its compatibility with the Gestalt approach to the functioning of the mind [2, 207].

In my opinion, G. Engler, as well as those outstanding scientists, whom he cites in support of his position, in particular, P. Dirac, R. Penrose, S. Weinberg, do not take into account the extremely important circumstance. Symmetry, simplicity, order, coherence, and unity can really be found in various sciences, in particular, in art history, physics, mathematics, and chemistry. However, the fact is that in each of the sciences they are subject to different principles. The principle of least action in chemistry and, for example, the principle of the sublime as an antidote against vulgarity in art history, these are fundamentally different concepts. In this regard, it immediately turns out that there is no reason to bring under the same heading the symmetry of molecules and the beauty of the face. As for the conclusion about the uniform perception of structures, it is also untenable. In each science, the relationship between the whole and its parts are studied, but this is done in fundamentally different styles. Gestalt psychology does not define these styles. It deals exclusively with the perception of the whole in psychology. In addition, there are other psychological trends, such as humanitarian and cognitive psychology, which also study the psychological whole. Gestalt psychology does not have the privilege of studying the whole even in the field of psychology. Moreover, it does not have this privilege outside of psychology.

Another way to substantiate the aesthetic content of any science is to introduce the concept of 'aesthetic induction' of a non-empirical property [7; 3]. «In fact, one can distinguish at least two kinds of, one of an emotive or affective and one of a cognitive nature» [4, 299]. Emotive induction accompanies cognitive induction and as a result, contributes to the advancement of the truth [4; 6; 7]. Aesthetics is embedded in all sciences, with attention to sensory cognition. As you know, this argument goes back to the ideas of I. Kant. As it turns out, it does not hold water. The fact is that every theory has various forms of manifestation, including linguistic, sensual (emotive), behavioral, and many others. They express the potential of the same theory, which is primarily determined by its principles. One theory corresponds to its various manifestations. According to the McAllister-Kuipers concept, a separate theory consists of other concepts. This is not really the case.

So far, I have considered approaches that are designed to substantiate the aesthetic content of all the sciences, including chemistry. It is time to turn to attempts to justify the need for chemical aesthetics from the standpoint of chemistry. In this regard, I appreciate the desire of Pierre Laszlo to highlight the foundations of chemical aesthetics. 'Beautiful' arguments about chemical aesthetics are untenable if its foundations are not distinguished. P. Laszlo highlights the bases of chemical aesthetics in the following order: «(1) the natural is more beautiful; (2) the artificial is more beautiful; (3) the invisible is yet more beautiful than the visible; (4) the need for visualization is unavoidable; the beauty of chemistry stems from (5) an inner logic and (6) its unpredictability; (7) any change is handsome on account of its invariant elements; (8) the beauty in any change is the fleeting instant; the beauty of chemistry is that it is (9) a science of the complex and (10) a science of the simple; (11) a new contemporary art has been born» [5, 11]. Unfortunately, strictly speaking, there is nothing purely chemical on any of these grounds. An inner logic and invariant elements are present in any scientific theory. This means that Laszlo did not identify the specificity of chemical aesthetics.

I am not aware of such a theory in which the peculiarity of chemical aesthetics could be derived directly from the fundamental chemical principles. That is why I put at the forefront not chemical aesthetics, but aesthetic relativity of chemistry. Of course, my denial of chemical ethics does not in any way limit the need to study a wide range of relationships between chemistry and aesthetics as an expression of the main achievements of art. The connection of chemistry with aesthetics is beyond doubt. Its full development implies adequate understanding.

References

1. Aesthetics and visualization in chemistry. (2003) Ed. by T.I. Spector & J. Schummer. Special issue of HYLE – International Journal for Philosophy of Chemistry 9(1), 9(2).
2. Engler, G. (1994) From art and science to perception: the role of aesthetics. Leonardo, 27(3), 207-209.
3. Engler, G. (1990) Aesthetics in science and in art. The British Journal of Aesthetics 30(1), 24-31.
4. Kuipers, T.A.F. (2002) Beauty, a road to the truth. Synthese 131(3), 291–328.
5. Laszlo, P. (2003) Foundations of chemical aesthetics. Hyle – International Journal for Philosophy of Chemistry 9(1), 11-32.
6. McAllister, J.W. (1996) Beauty and Revolution in Science. Ithaca, NY: Cornell University Press.
7. McAllister, J.W. (1998) Is beauty a sign of truth in scientific theories? American Scientist 86(2), 174–183.
8. Parsons, G. (2012) The aesthetics of chemical biology. Chemical Biology 16(5-6), 576–580.

Chapter 9. The nature of earth science

9.1 Earth science, geology, and philosophy

The term 'geology' (from ancient Greek γῆ, *gē* ("earth") and -λογία, *-logia*, ("study of", "discourse") was first used by the Italian Ulisse Aldrovandi (1603). [1] It is similar to the terms 'biology', 'psychology', 'technology', and 'sociology'. Nevertheless, in contrast to them, the term geology does not mean a separate branch of science, but a group of disciplines in earth science. Earth science is understood as a branch of science in which the composition, structure, and history of the Earth, as well as other planets and their natural satellites, are reproduced by means of specific concepts. Geology is the study of solid Earth, the rocks of which it is composed. The main object of the study of geology is the lithosphere. The hydrosphere, atmosphere, and biosphere are objects of study of other earth sciences.

V.E. Khain and A.G. Ryabukhin assert that «at present, geology numbers more than 100 independent scientific disciplines formed in the process of differentiation and integration of the geological sciences» [3, 270]. In fact, the number of geological disciplines is unknown. Nevertheless, it is obvious that they are quite a lot.

It is generally accepted that geology is the most developed part of earth sciences. Therefore, when characterizing the specifics of earth science, as a rule, they primarily refer to the achievements of geology. I will not break this tradition. Thus, my main findings are for the most part not only geology but also earth science.

A review of the literature shows that «[e]arth science has received relatively little attention from philosophers of science. ...[M]ost of earth science is *terra incognita* to philosophers.» [4,213] This circumstance is partly due to the difference between earth science and basic sciences. «Unlike more fundamental sciences, earth science is characterized by explanatory pluralism: earth scientists employ various forms of narrative explanations in combination with causal explanations.» [4,213] There is no reason to say that earth science departs from the ideals of science, usually prescribed to physics. Nevertheless, in earth science, they are not represented as distinctly as in physics. [2] This circumstance is an insurmountable barrier for those researchers who are inclined to evaluate the scale of earth science by the standards of the formal philosophy of science. This means that with respect to earth science, the metascientific approach is at a premium. As a rule, authors of articles and books about the philosophy of earth science are experts of the earth science itself.

Metageology – the science of geology. Often, metageology identifies with the philosophy of geology. Strictly speaking, such identification is untenable. The philosophy of geology expresses the connection of geology with the philosophy of science. It means that philosophical concepts are considered as symbols of geological concepts. This symbolization is carried out in the interests of geology. If symbolization were carried out in the interests of philosophy, then it would be a question of the geological orientation of the philosophy of science. It is necessary to distinguish geological orientation on philosophy and philosophical orientation on geology. Geological orientation means that the main, acceptor discipline is geology. At the same time, philosophy serves as a donor discipline. In the case of a philosophical orientation on geology, philosophy is the main discipline. An example of geological orientation is the search by many Soviet researchers on behalf of dialectical materialism in the geology of dialectical contradictions, which, by the way, have never been discovered. Another example of geological orientation is the transfer to geology from the philosophy of science the concept of paradigm developed in the framework of the philosophy of science by T. Kuhn.

The relevance of geological orientation on philosophy is determined by at least two circumstances. First, the philosophy of science sometimes very fruitfully accumulates in itself the impulses of knowledge emanating from many disciplines. This means that referring to the philosophy of science can contribute to the use of achievements of other sciences in geology. Secondly, within the framework of the philosophy of science, ideas can be developed that are the works of philosophers without reference to the content of individual sciences. Sometimes these kinds of ideas are quite relevant.

As for metageology, it is not a geological orientation on philosophy. It uses concepts exclusively of geology. The purpose of metageology consists of a comprehensive study of the conceptual content of geology, its variables, laws, and principles. Unfortunately, I have to admit that in the geological literature, as a rule, the due characteristic is not given to the philosophy of geology and to metageology. Often instead of the philosophy of methodology metageology appears. This is the case when, in fact, researchers either do not turn to philosophy at all or only sporadically. Of course, both the metageology and philosophy of geology are full of numerous problematic aspects. Many of them are discussed in the following articles.

References

1. Aldrovandi, U. (2004) Four Centuries of the Word Geology - Quadricentenario della parola geologia: Ulisse 1603 in Bologna. Bologna: Minerva Edizioni. [In Italian].
2. Inkpen, R. (2009) The Philosophy of Geology. A Companion to the Philosophy of History and Historiography. Ed. by A. Tucker. Oxford: Blackwell, 318-329.
3. Khain, V.E., Ryabukhin, A.G. (1997) Istoriya i metodologiya geologicheskikh nauk [History and Methodology of Geological Sciences]. Moskva: Izdatel'stvo Moskovskogo gosudarstvennogo universiteta. [In Russian].
4. Kleinhans, M.G., Buskes, C.J.J., and de Regt, H.W. (2010) Philosophy of earth science. In Philosophies of the Sciences: A Guide. Ed. by F. Allhoff. Oxford: Blackwell, 213-236.
5. Šešelja, D. and Weber, E. (2012) Rationality and irrationality in the history of continental drift: Was the hypothesis of continental drift worthy of pursuit? Studies in History and hilosophy of Science, Part A 43(1), 147-159.

9.2. Specific and methods of geology

In the vast majority of works devoted to the philosophy of geology, the question of the difference between geology and physics is considered. The prevailing trend is that on the one hand, they seek to avoid the reduction of geology to physics. On the other hand, it is recognized that, unlike biology, geology is closely related to physics. For a long time, the trend in question, as well as its opposites, could not be justified. The situation has changed dramatically for the better after the development of a synergistic approach. [2; 5; 8] Its use is akin to the application of mathematics with an emphasis on certain classes of nonlinear equations, namely, those that allow us to imagine the processes of achieving non-equilibrium states, the output of which is due to bifurcations and as a result leads to the formation of new structures. Bifurcation explains how the similarity of geological and physical processes, and their difference from each other. It turned out that to express their continuity it is necessary to turn to a sophisticated mathematical apparatus. It provided the development of dynamic geology, in which the originality of geological processes is most clearly represented.

Abstract and nongeological physical mechanisms are a necessary and important component of the initial axiomatics when solving dynamic geology problems, in particular, when predicting the preparation, occurrence, and aftermath of a seismogenic tectonic faulting. It follows that any natural macro-fracture can form directly in an initially *quasicontinuous* medium. At the pre-destruction stage, such a medium unavoidably becomes a *coarsely discrete fractal* one. Multiple micro- and meso-fractures occur in the medium and surround the resultant macro-fracture; they are more or less "scattered" under a bulk distributed load, while they are localized in a multidirectional in-plane load (cut). [4, 312]

The relationship between physical and geological concepts is very peculiar. According to Shamil Mukhamediev, many physical concepts, for example, strength, tension, nonlinearity, are transferred from physics to geology, and their meaning is distorted so much that researchers are unable to observe the canons of science. This means that the principles of geology mistakenly are given a priori, irrespective of the laws of physics, in particular, the laws of conservation. [6, 367] Geology, an independent discipline, but not so much that it was considered as completely autonomous in relation to physics. Just as programming should certainly be considered in combination with computer technology, geology is unthinkable without its correlation with physics.

The use of a synergistic approach in geology forced scientists to re-evaluate the status of geology methods. In my opinion, this was not without unacceptable extremes.

Among the enthusiasts of the synergetic approach, the position prevails that it is time to introduce the idea of a new paradigm of geology. The most energetically this point of view is developed by Dmitriy Egorov [1]. He believes that the inductive-actualistic paradigm should be replaced by a synergistic one.

Alfred Naimark and Anatoly Ryabukhin insist on replacing the inductive method with the deductive one. «Dynamic geology as a poly- and interdisciplinary study of near-surfacial and deep earth processes is in the process of its most important conceptual turning point in its overall history, from the classical inductive-empirical paradigm to the new, hypothetical-deductive one. » [7, 341]

Shamil Mukhamediev claims that «by the geological type of thinking we mean the method of cognition based on induction, i.e. on the transition from private knowledge to general. This method is associated with the generalization of the results of observations and experiments, it helps to search for the truth, but does not necessarily guarantee its achievement. The exact sciences are more inherent in the method of deduction, i.e. the transition in the process of cognition from general knowledge of a certain class of objects and phenomena to private and individual knowledge. Methods of induction and deduction are more complementary than mutually exclusive. » [6, 352, note]

Kleinhans, Buskes, and de Regt distinguish between three methods, inductive, law-based, deductive, effects-based, and abductive or inference to the best explanation based on causes. In this regard, they believe that «[unlike] more fundamental sciences, earth science is characterized by explanatory pluralism». [3, 213] «Finally, we will highlight a methodological strategy that is typical of the geosciences: *abduction or inference to the best explanation.* » [3, 214]

In my opinion, the views of the cited authors testify to their misunderstanding of the essence of intratheoretical transduction. Otherwise, Egorov would not have to look for a replacement for the inductive method. Due to the need to process experimental data, an inductive method cannot be dispensed with. As for the synergistic method, it does not exist as such. Methods of synergetics are all the same methods of conceptual transduction.

Contrary to Naimark and Ryabukhin, induction and deduction methods from time immemorial function in science, including geology, in close unity. Geology has never done without a deductive method. It is legitimate to talk about strengthening his position in geology, but not about the transition from an inductive method to a deductive one.

Mukhamediev quite rightly points to the complementarity of inductive and deductive methods. But he erroneously proclaims exclusively induction by the method of geology and does not give a characteristic of close unity, and not just the complementarity of induction and deduction.

I also cannot agree with some conclusions of Kleinhans, Buskes, and de Regt. They rightfully point to methods of induction, deduction, and abduction. However, contrary to their assertion, the presence of three methods does not indicate the pluralism of knowledge. Pluralism would take place if it were possible to get by either by induction, or by deduction, or by abduction. But in reality, scientists are always forced to use these methods in unity with each other. Intratheoretical transduction as a unity of the methods of deduction, adduction (this method should also be remembered), induction and abduction, is one. As for causal explanations, they take place within the framework of induction, rather than abduction. Finally, abduction does not dominate the three other methods of intratheoretical transduction. In the cycles of intratheoretical transduction, the initiative passes from one method to another. In addition, it should be borne in mind that abduction is characteristic of all sciences, and not just Earth sciences.

Methods of geology are methods of conceptual transduction. Throughout the development of geology, these methods are constantly being strengthened. There is no need to replace them with other methods.

References

1. Egorov, D.G. (2004) Izmeneniye paradigm v sovremennykh naukakh o Zemle [Paradigm Shifts in Modern Earth Sciences]. Moskva: Akademiya. [In Russian].
2. Hobbs, B.E., Ord. A. (2014) Structural Geology: The Mechanics of Deforming Metamorphic Rocks. Amsterdam et al: Elsevier.
3. Kleinhans, Maarten G., Buskes, Chris J.J., and de Regt, Henk W. (2010) Philosophy of Earth Science. In Philosophies of the Sciences: A Guide. Ed. by F. Allhoff. Oxford: Blackwell Publishing Ltd, 213-236

4. Koronovskii, N. V., Naimark, A. A., Zakharov, V. S., and Bryantseva, G. V. (2015) On the geological and physical mechanisms of natural processes in dynamic geology problems. Moscow University Geology Bulletin, 70(4), 305–313. doi:10.3103/s0145875215040067

5. Mandelbrot, B. (2013) Fractals and Chaos: The Mandelbrot Set and Beyond. New York, NY: Springer Science & Business Media

6. Mukhamediev Sh.A. (2016). O diskretnom stroyenii geosredy i kontinual'nom podkhode k modelirovaniyu yeye dvizheniya. [On discrete structure of geologic medium and continual approach to modeling its movements]. Geodinamika i tektonofizika 7 (3), 347–381. doi:10.5800/GT-2016-7-3- 0213.

7. Naimark, A.A., Ryabukhin, A.G. (2010) Dynamic geology on the border of two general scientific paradigms. Moscow University Geology Bulletin 65(7), 335–342.

8. Turcotte, D.L. (1997) Fractals and Chaos in Geology and Geophysics. Cambridge, Cambridge University Press.

9.3. Geological theory

In all sciences, the concept of the theory is central. In this regard, it is advisable to consider the concept of geological theory. Any theory is a coherent set of notions driven by man through conceptual transduction. According to Vladimir Frolov, «in geology with the theory, as with the laws, the deficit» [2, 35]. However, the definition of a theory given by Ivan Sharapov, he calls the most complete and logically strict [2, 35]. It really is of great interest. «The theory is a fairly complete, internally consistent system of new (for the time of its occurrence), logically true ideas in general and nomological statements in particular, and a system that has descriptive, nomological explanatory, heuristic, extrapolative, pragmatic and erothematic abilities. Each theory must objectively reflect reality and meet the requirements of completeness, consistency, novelty, provability, fact stability, simplicity and efficiency. The theory differs from a hypothesis by its actual truth (the hypothesis is true not in fact, but only logically) » [4, 58].

In my opinion, the considered definition of a theory is not flawless. In particular, the expression of «logically true ideas» is in doubt. First, the theory consists of concepts, namely, variables, laws, and principles. It is untenable to argue that along with them there are also ideas. Secondly, the reference to logic is also inappropriate. Logic is a special formal science with which geology is in interdisciplinary relations, but it is not present in geology itself. Thirdly, the reference to the truth of ideas is lacking clarity. It is unclear what exactly is meant by truth. A modern researcher is unlikely to call the views of the adherents of neptunism and plutonism true, but they were so at one time. Ivan Sharapov, in fact, defines the nature of the most relevant theory. There are other theories that also should not be overlooked.

Frolov, arguing about the deficit of theories, obviously also has in mind only the most developed theories. The reference to the consistency of the theory also past the target. All theories are contradictory to one degree or another. The nature of the theory is determined not by the absence of contradictions in it, but by the strategy of scientific research, which makes it possible to resist them, reducing the degree of inconsistency so undesirable for scientists. As for the emphasis on nomological statements, i.e. focused on the laws, he does not take into account the relevance of the provisions about principles and variables. The theory is not limited to laws.

According to Ivan Sharapov, the theory should objectively reflect reality. Here, obviously, the theory is to a certain extent contrasted with reality: on the one hand, there is a reality, and on the other hand, there is a theory. Such opposition is characteristic of the theory of copying, in our opinion, long obsolete, because it does not take into account the conceptual content of reality itself. The point is not that theory is likened to mentality and language, but that all three spheres — mentality, language, and objects — are conceptually similar. Many of the functions that Sharapov attributes theories are relevant. However, he attributes too much to it. In particular, it is illegal to call a theory at once descriptive and effective. Geology as a natural science discipline is descriptive, but not pragmatic and not effective. As for hypotheses, they are not logically true knowledge, but assumptions that are tested for theoretical soundness. The possibility of their inclusion in the interpretational series of scientific theories is being studied.

I will also address the question of the theoretical relativity of any geological knowledge. Victor Khain and Anatoly Ryabukhin believe that «many theoretical developments in geology cannot, strictly speaking, be considered theories. For example, the doctrine of geosynclines is in fact an empirical conception» [2, 187].

With all possible certainty, I note that in geology, as well as in any science, any statement is theoretical. From this point of view, attempts to bring some knowledge outside the theory by means of phrasing «strictly speaking», «mainly» or «at the basis» are untenable. Of course, there are theories of various levels. Nevertheless, in geology, there is nothing but theories.

Empirical judgments are impossible in principle to formulate outside the theory. It is obvious that a person who is not knowledgeable about geology will not be able to formulate a single empirical judgment, much less say something intelligible about geosynclines. It is true that theory is not limited to the experiment, which is only one of the stages of conceptual transduction. However, already at the experimental stage, the geologist is in theory. A geologist, like a representative of any other science, must be constantly focused on perfecting the theory through full-fledged conceptual transduction. In polemics with colleagues, he is obliged to criticize the weak points of their theories. However, it is unacceptable to deny the theoretical nature of any views.

Exceptionally interesting ideas regarding the concept of the geological theory are being developed by Alfred Naimark. He should be credited drawing the attention of the geological community to the phenomenon of the theory, which he reported, perhaps, more than any other geologist draws. Therefore, it makes sense to turn directly to his views. I will note the provisions that Naimark highlights in italics. [3, 178-185] For the convenience of the reader, I will number the provisions.

> 1) «It is discussed, no more and no less, as the question of '*what* is the truth': what is the process of geotectogenesis evolving and how does it evolve *in fact*».

> 2) «Factual argumentation is not capable, due to the inexhaustibility of observational material and the variety of its possible interpretations, to lead to any definite decision, equally convincing *for all* solution of the issues discussed».

3) «Process *models* are reviewed, compared, accepted or disputed»

4) «Any concept necessarily in some way corresponds to reality, but in some way, it does not agree with it».

5) «Concepts in their attitude to reality differ *not* in verity, but only in the *degree* of their conformity or inconsistency with reality».

6) «Any experimental facts in any study are always perceived not completely objectively, but according to what the accepted theories prescribe».

7) «A fact is always a reflection of material objects, phenomena, processes in something different from reality».

8) «Objectivity and authenticity of any empirical fact is always relative».

9) «Any created natural science theory is based on certain hypothetical constructions».

10) «Experience in general cannot unambiguously and definitively verify the truth of a particular theory».

11) «The validity of any natural science theory is always problematic *in principle*».

12) «Theories are confirmed or refuted not by empirical, but only by theoretical facts of science».

13) «Only the greater effectiveness of the subsequent application gives the new concept wide recognition and leadership. ... The purpose of a natural science concept is justified to the extent that it is effective in explaining, reconstructing and predicting natural processes».

14) «The direct purpose of ... models are 'not to be true', i.e. not to display reality absolutely and precisely, but to be comfortable for the effective solution of certain tasks».

The main feature of the position of A.A. Naimark is trying to combine the concept of correspondent truth with the idea of a theoretical load of facts. However, these two positions are not compatible with each other. Either the isolation of reality from theory is recognized, or itself is perceived exclusively in a theoretical context. Facts are not just loaded with theory but are precisely its concepts. In Argument-12 Naimark distinguishes empirical facts from theoretical ones, and yet any fact is theoretical, without one or another theory nothing can be said about facts at all. There are authors who separate experiments from theory. Naimark rightly criticizes their position; nevertheless, he distinguishes between empirical and theoretical facts.

Naimark in Argument-4 expresses the widespread view that the theory is in some way consistent and in some way not true. Despite the seeming obviousness of this provision, it is untenable. We cannot say anything about something that the theory does not correspond because this something has not been expressed in theory. We are not able to distinguish theories by the degree of their correspondence to reality (Argument-5). By comparing theories we can only establish a different degree of their relevance. Theories are compared, not theories with facts.

Dissatisfied with the concept of truth, Naimark refers to the concept of efficiency (Arguments-13). However, it can be regarded precisely as the establishment of the truth of the theory. Within the framework of philosophical pragmatism, many authors do just that.

The main disadvantage of A. Naimark is the point that he does not compare theories with each other. He compares theories not with facts, but with tasks. He never comes to comparing theories directly with each other. In this case, the hypothetical nature of the theories that Naimark identifies with the models turns out to be self-sufficient. It is not limited to anything. The hypothetical nature of science is mainly determined by the operation of abduction. However, it is mediated by deduction, adduction, and induction. This means that hypothetical human activity is relevant only in certain limits.

Finally, the last remark. If the theories are considered on their own, and not as part of a series of conceptions, then it is hardly possible to limit uncontrolled relativism.

References

1. Frolov, V.T. (2004) Nauka geologiya: filosofskiy analiz [Science Geology: a Philosophical Analysis]. Moskva: Akadimiya.
2. Khain, V.E., Ryabukhin, A.G. (1997) Istoriya i metodologiya geologicheskikh nauk [History and Methodology of

Geological Sciences]. Moskva: Moskovskiy gosudarstvennyy universitet publ. [In Russian].

3. Naimark, A.A. (2006) Polveka diskussii fiksistov i neomobilistov: analiz real'nosti ili gipotez, poiski istiny ili "udobnoy" teorii?   [Half a century of debate between fixists and neomobilists: an analysis of reality or hypotheses, the search for truth or a "convenient" theory?]. Vestnik KRAUNTS. NAUKI o Zemle 2(8), 177–188. [In Russian].

4. Sharapov, I.P. (1989) Metageologiya (nekotoryye problemy) [Metageology (Some Problems)]. Moskva: Nauka, 1989. [In Russian].

9.4. Principles and laws in geology

Principles are the most informative concepts of geology. They always are concepts of the upper tier of the deductive chain. In the deductive chain, laws are below principles. Through deduction, the meaning of the principles is transferred to the laws and also to individual variables. Unfortunately, the principles are not always given the attention they deserve. This remark also applies to geology. I think it makes sense to take into account lessons of stratigraphy.

The number of named stratigraphic principles ranges from three to twenty or more. The authors from the Russian city of Voronezh, perhaps, found a middle ground, focusing on 11 principles [4, 22]. To streamline principles of stratigraphy significant work was done by Sergei V. Meyen in the 1970s. [5]. Starting from the Steno principle, which makes it possible to establish a relation to stratigraphic units earlier / later, S.V. Meyen quite rightly drew attention to the fact that this is done using the principles of Huxley and the chronological interchangeability of attributes (this principle is often called the Meyen principle). Finally, he prefaced the Steno principle with the principle of objectivity and uniqueness (the Khalfin - Stepanov principle). In a letter dated 07.03.1982 S.V. Meyen summed up his perennial reflections as follows: «1) we allocate stratigraphic units in a single section; 2) we establish their preferred (or temporary) order (this is Steno); we compare the cuts on homotaxis; 4) if somewhere attributes are laterally changeable, then we introduce interchangeability (i.e., obtain homotaxis through transformation)» [cit. by: 7, 86]. In our opinion, this is not about the highest level of abstraction, but about the initial stages of stratigraphic deduction. Anyway, S.V. Meyen brilliantly showed the building of principles in a deductive line. To listen, it looks like this: the Khalfin-Stepanov principle → the Steno principle → the Huxley principle → the Meyen principle.

Of course, various researchers are building a deductive line in different ways. Naturally, a particularly large conceptual load falls on the principle that is put at the head of the deduction. In the theory of Meyen, it is the Khalfin – Stepanov principle. The group of Voronezh authors begins with the principle of uniformitarianism, and from it proceeds to the principle of the irreversibility of geological changes [4, 22-24]. The Khalfin – Stepanov principle appears only in third place. As for my position, I would put in the first place the principle of theoretical relativity, or conceptual transduction (all geological phenomena are reproduced conceptually through operations of deduction, adduction, induction, abduction) and the principle of dynamism (the nature of all geological processes must be explained by dynamic mechanisms). The principle of uniformitarianism is derived from the principle of theoretical relativity, and the principle of irreversibility from a dynamic principle, because time is a manifestation of interactions.

My example with stratigraphy is indicative of the need to build a deductive line of principles. It is hardly possible to imagine any geological science without this line. This is a certain epistemological rule that deserves the close attention of researchers. Without its use, geological science looks faded, especially against the background of mathematics and physics with their developed apparatus of principles.

Finally, I note that in modern science, principles, as a rule, are extremes. Something is either minimal (for example, the magnitude of the action in physics), or maximally (in particular, the expected utility in technical sciences). It seems that the search for extreme principles in geology is behind schedule.

It's reasonable to move from principles to laws. By definition, a geological law is the ratio of geological variables not derived from each other. The geological law does not include variables of non-geological nature. This circumstance is often misunderstood. Ivan Sharapov noted, «the majority of nomological statements (laws, principles, patterns) in geology relate to the composition of rocks and minerals and are of a physicochemical nature. The specificity of geological processes by these statements is not revealed» [6, 92–93]. Said inaccurately, physical and chemical laws are not part of geology, which is why they do not express its specificity. Within geology, physical laws function as symbols of geological laws. By themselves, they are not geological laws.

V.E. Khain and A.G. Ryabukhin share the conviction that geology is characterized by physicochemical laws, patterns, and finally, specific geological laws [3, 192-194]. In fact, geology is characterized exclusively by geological laws and, of course, they all express the specifics of geology.

V.T. Frolov adheres to the dogma of the need to distinguish between empirical and theoretical laws. However, empirical law is also theoretical. All laws are theoretical. It is legitimate to contrast deductive and inductive laws within certain limits, but not theoretical and empirical laws.

Frolov, like many other authors, attaches the utmost importance to the universality of laws. Criticizing the content of geological laws, he constantly emphasizes their non-universality [2, 4–5; one]. Universal laws do not exist at all. Any law is effective only as part of a certain cycle of knowledge. It should be considered in its framework. It does not matter if the law is modified with the new cycle of knowledge. Law is a ratio of variables that must necessarily be considered in relation to a specific situation. This is the case in any science, including geology. Contrary to the widespread dogma in physics, there are no universal laws.

Trying to find an approach to assess adequately the status of geology as a science, Frolov introduces two quantitative indices for the laws of separate geological sciences, assessments for theoreticity and historicity (speculativeness) [2, 6]. Theoreticity is considered a positive meaning, and the historicity– negative. The sum of the two indicators is 10. V.T. Frolov confers high points on the theoretical nature of crystallography, mineralogy, and geochemistry, while low points are awarded tectonics – 1.5 and geohistory – 1.

In my opinion, Frolov approach is not consistent. Of course, theories with all their laws can be compared with each other and in this regard, to introduce certain rating scales. Nevertheless, we must not forget that the comparison suggests some basis for comparison. Suppose that a problem series of theories are compared: $T_1 \rightarrow T_2 \rightarrow T_3 \rightarrow T_4$. The degree of closeness of the first three theories to T4 may well be estimated by the corresponding indicator. A comparison of theories belonging to different problem series has its own characteristics. It can be argued that mineralogy is effective for some research tasks and stratigraphy for others.

Now about the criteria of theoreticity. In my opinion, it is not quantifiable. Any theory is theoretical at 100 percent. If non-theoretical components are present, they should be removed through scientific criticism. It is unacceptable to consider them as part of the theory as such. Another mistake of V.T. Frolov is that he obviously unreasonably brings together historicity and speculativeness. Historicity is an actual feature of any scientific theory, which, unlike speculativeness, should not be eradicated from a scientific concept.

I now turn to the question of the number of geological laws. Frolov mentions the rather curious result of the study of Sharapov, who discovered only 11 laws in the two-volume geological encyclopedia, «and most of the statements that claimed this level were debunked and partially attributed to empirical generalizations. It is significant that of the eleven laws, the overwhelming part (ten) is related to material sciences, mainly to mineralogy, geochemistry, and petrology, and only one – the Golovkinsky -Walter law faces to geology itself, namely, to stratigraphy » [2, 4]. This text, which seems to me curious, deserves a special comment.

Primarily, I am rehabilitating the relevant empirical generalizations as laws. If in them there is a connection of variables, then they are not illusory, but real laws, namely, empirical laws. It is nothing flawed in them. In the new cycle of knowledge, they can be adopted as hypothetical deductive laws.

How many geological laws exist? Really just a few? My answer to this question is so: in geology, the number of laws is incalculable. Why? Because any scientific research is not without laws. Otherwise, it is not a scientific work. Let us give an elementary example on this point.

Consider the ratio

$$E = P + R, \qquad\qquad 9.1$$

E is the mass of water evaporated over the ocean, P is the mass of precipitation, R is the mass of water provided by the river flow.

Expression 9.1 is the law of hydrology. It is clarified by modern scientists. No matter how refined the model of the water cycle, its understanding is carried out by means of some law. The situation is similar to any other geological phenomenon, the laws of which are specified.

Unfortunately, many researchers strive to reduce a particular geological science to a few numbers of laws. As a rule, they fail. As a result, they begin to doubt the scientific nature of geology. For these doubts, there is no valid base. Geology needs no justification. It functions as a set of laws that are constantly being improved.

References

1. Frolov V.T. (2000) O nauke geologii. Stat'ya 1: Zakony v geologii [On the science of geology. Article 1. Laws in geology]. Vestnik Moskovskogo universiteta. Seriya 4. Geologiya (6), 3–10. [In Russian].
2. Frolov, V.T. (2004) Nauka geologiya: filosofskiy analiz [Science Geology: a Philosophical Analysis]. Moskva: Akadimiya.

3. Khain, V.E., Ryabukhin, A.G. (1997) Istoriya i metodologiya geologicheskikh nauk [History and Methodology of Geological Sciences]. Moskva: Moskovskiy gosudarstvennyy universitet publ. [In Russian].

4. Kholmovoy, G.V., Ratnikov, V.Yu., Shkul, V.G. (2008) Teoreticheskiye osnovy i metody stratigrafii [Theoretical Foundations and Methods of Stratigraphy]. Voronezh: Voronezhskiy gosudarstvennyy universitet. [In Russian].

5. Meyen, S.V. (1989) Vvedeniye v teoriyu stratigrafii [Introduction to the Theory of Stratigraphy]. Moskva: Nauka. [In Russian].

6. Sharapov, I.P. (1989) Metageologiya (nekotoryye problemy) [Metageology (Some Problems)]. Moskva: Nauka, 1989. [In Russian].

7. Zhamoyda, A.I. (1995) Sergey Viktorovich Meyyen i teoreticheskaya stratigrafiya (k 60-letiyu so dnya rozhdeniya) [Sergey Viktorovich Meyen and theoretical stratigraphy (on the occasion of his 60th birthday]. Stratigraphy. Stratigrafiya. Geologicheskaya korrelyatsiya 3(4), 83–94. [In Russian].

9.5. Geological time and space

Geology is often referred to among the historical sciences, i.e. sciences, in which one of the central notions is the concept of time. Geological time is a set of durations of geological processes expressing their specificity. It has become commonplace for many philosophical works to emphasize the central place in the geology of the concept of time. Nevertheless, the problem character of time is extremely rarely considered. In this regard, the ideas of Kirill V. Simakov are a pleasant exception. He points out, in particular, that «all attempts made so far to introduce quantitative estimates of the temporal parameters of geological phenomena were initially doomed to failure, because they proceeded from a false premise, stating that the concepts of geological (paleobiospheric) and physical (ordinary) time were identical» [4, 493–494]. This is the whole point - it is necessary to understand the specifics of geological time, its fundamental difference from physical time.

Different points of view are expressed about the relationship between physical and geological time. Some researchers leave this ratio without any attention at all. They enthusiastically consider the geochronological time scale, characterizing the duration of eons, eras, periods, and epochs in millions of years. Physical time is simply superimposed on the geological history. Many researchers emphasize the integrative-systemic nature of geological time. This point of view was especially vigorously developed by Igor Krut. [3, 97] However, just emphasizing the integrative-systemic nature of geological time is not enough to characterize its specificity. This specifity, in fact, does not get enough clear expression. Krut emphasized that elementary times are components of integrative time [3, 85-86]. Of course, there is a connection between elementary and integrative durations. Nevertheless, it is impossible in principle to go from elementary to integrative durations.

The question of the transition from elementary times to integrative characteristics remains, it seems to me, unresolved in the works of Simakov. He, however, should be credited with a clear understanding of the exceptional uniqueness of geological time, which «develops not on the basis of direct observations and measurements of the course of real processes, but by building and studying retrospective models» [4, 103]. However, it remains unclear how exactly time should be allocated in retrospective models of the geological processes. It remains for me to state my own point of view. [1, 105-117]

Firstly, as the history of the development of geology shows, it is quite acceptable to characterize geological processes by means of physical time units. However, do not calm down on this. It is important to understand that physical time should be considered as a symbol of geological time. Secondly, in contrast to the physical, the geological time comes into the field of view of the researcher, not in the radiological measurement of time, but for example, in lithological or stratigraphic time. Thirdly, it is necessary to understand exactly how this or that geological time is measured. Actually, this circumstance is precisely the obstacle in the comprehension of geological time. My proposal is that alternating durations should be evaluated as stages of an approach to some final stage. For example, within the Cenozoic era, seven epochs are considered: the Holocene, Pleistocene, Pliocene, Miocene, Oligocene, Eocene, and Paleocene. If we quantify each of these epochs as advancing to the beginning of the Mesozoic era, then the corresponding units of geological time will be determined. For these purposes, the units of physical time will be insufficient.

As for the concept of space, much less attention is paid to it in geology than to the concept of time. Nevertheless, the question of the specifics of not only geological time, but also geological space is quite legitimate. Above, when discussing the nature of geological time, there were identified difficulties associated with the distinction of physical and geological time. A similar difficulty exists with respect to the concept of geological space. It is illegal that geological space is often identified with physical space. The latter is an attribute not of geological, but of physical objects. My understanding of the concept of geological space is as follows.

First, I note that the attribution of physical lengths to geological objects, although permissible, is nevertheless not enough. Secondly, it should be borne in mind that the physical lengths from the standpoint of a geologist are symbols of geological lengths. Two types of lengths are not equivalent to each other. Thirdly, the introduction to the geology of the concept of geological distance is quite appropriate. If the physical length is interpreted in the context of a geological theory, then, when transformed, it loses its physical features and becomes a geological parameter, for the measurement of which the usual meters and multiple units are unsuitable for all. Fourth, if you wish, you can enter an idea of the units of measurement of geological lengths.

Soviet philosophers considered time and space as attributes of the geological form of the movement of matter. As is known, within the framework of dialectical materialism in accordance with the ideas of F. Engels, the concept of the forms of movement of matter occupies a prominent place. In this regard, soviet geologists began to use the concept of 'geological form of movement of matter'. However, with its philosophical substantiation, the matter dragged on, right up to the writings of Michal B. Kedrov. By the end of the 1950s, the concept of the geological form of the movement of matter is quite firmly established in the philosophy of science of the Soviet period [2; 5].

For the sake of justice, it should be noted that neither philosophers nor geologists have ever managed to make the concept of a 'geological form of movement of matter' a scientifically acceptable view. Their failure is not an accident. The fact is that the concept under consideration should be coordinated with the status of scientific knowledge. In this case, it is necessary to take into account the existence of two dozen branches of science, one of which is Earth science. However, there is no reason to attribute to each branch of science some form of movement of matter. Both the conception of matter and the conception of the movement of matter is controversial. Modern researchers emphasize the specificity of geological processes, which is characterized by the geological conceptions. In their arsenal, there is no concept of geological form of the movement of matter.

References

1. Kanke, V.A. (2011) Formy vremeni. Izdaniye tret'ye [Forms of Time. Third edition]. Moskva: Librokom publ.
2. Kedrov, B.M. (1959) O sootnoshenii form dvizheniya materii v prirode [On the Relationship between the Forms of Motion of Matter in Nature]. In Filosofskiye problemy sovremennoy nauki [Philosophical Problems of Modern Science]. Moskva: Nauka publ, 137–211. [In Russian].
3. Krut, I.V. (1975) Vvedeniye v obshchuyu teoriyu Zemli: Urovni organizatsii geosystem [Introduction to the General Theory of the Earth: Levels of Organization of Geosystems]. Moskva: Mysl'. [In Russian].
4. Simakov, K.V. (1999). Vvedeniye v teoriyu geologicheskogo vremeni. Stanovleniye. Evolyutsiya. Perspektivy. [Introduction to the Theory of Geological time. Becoming. Evolution. Perspectives]. Magadan: SECC FEB RAS publ.
5. Zubkov, I.F. (1979) Problema geologicheskoy formy dvizheniya materii[The Problem of the Geological Form of Motion of Matter]. Moskva: Nauka publ.

9.6. Mobilism and fixism: protracted confrontation

The theory of plate tectonics occupies a prominent place in modern geology. It goes back to the ideas of Alfred Wegener, who put forward in 1912 the hypothesis of continental drift. Wegener did not have enough facts at his disposal to convince the geological community of the relevance of the hypothesis. The decisive arguments in favor of the hypothesis of the travel of continental plates were obtained in a decade (1956-1966). The discovery of the periodic inversion of the Earth's magnetic field testified in favor of the drift of continental formations. Numerous data from marine geology, in particular, the discovery of the existence of a grandiose system of mid-ocean ridges and rifts, also successfully agreed with the new theory, which was finally formed in 1965-1967 and got the name of the theory of plate tectonics. As is usually the case with the most meaningful theories, it allowed harmonizing with one another numerous experimental facts, many of which were first predicted and then actually observed.

The theory of plate tectonics throughout its history of existence has had an implacable rival the theory of fixism, the doctrine of an invariable, fixed position of continents. Unlike fixism, the theory of plate tectonics allows not only vertical but also the horizontal movement of continents (continental plates). This theory is considered the embodiment of mobilism. Thus, two scientific directions, mobilism, and fixism, were formed in geology. The most amazing thing is that in their confrontation the winner has not yet been identified. What does this indicate? The conservatism of a certain part of geologists or the ineradicable pluralism of geological knowledge?

Trying to overcome the indicated problematic situation, geologists met with significant difficulties. They did not have at their disposal such a philosophical concept that would make it possible to effectively compare the achievements and shortcomings of mobilism and fixism. In this regard, the following recognition of a large group of prominent philosophers of science is very significant:

> However, the fact of the matter is that we have no well-confirmed general picture of how science works, no theory of science worthy of general assent. We did once have a well developed and historically influential philosophical position, that of positivism or logical empiricism, which has by now been effectively refuted. We have a number of recent theories of science which, while stimulating much interest, have hardly been tested at all. And we have specific hypotheses about various cognitive aspects of science, which are widely discussed but wholly undecided. If any extant position does provide a viable understanding of how science operates, we are far from being able to identify which it is. [2, 142]

Nevertheless, various ways were proposed for assessing geological trends, primarily mobilism with its theory of plate tectonics. In particular, great hopes were pinned on the concept of scientific revolutions of Thomas Kuhn. But the bright hopes did not materialize. In particular, Rachel Laudan showed that there is no reason to consider theory of plate tectonics a paradigm in her understanding of Kuhn. [3] First, before the strengthening of the position of modilism, there was no normal science. Secondly, after this strengthening, criticism of modilism by the fixists continued.

Dunja Šešelja and Erik Weber took a different line of argument. They believe that there are four crucial criteria under which the theory is worthy of pursuit in a strong sense. These criteria are 1) the presence of significant explanations, 2) inferential density, 3) programmatic character and also 4) theoretical growth and the growth of the programmatic character. [6, 151] The theory of continental drift satisfies these criteria, therefore, it is worthy of pursuit. "[I] t was irrational to reject its pursuit as unworthy" [6, 147]. D. Šešelja and E. Weber believe that the mobilists are always right in a dispute with the fixists.

Pablo Pellegrini admits the absence of a final winner in the dispute between mobilists and fixists. He believes that this is not about specific geological theories, but about two dominant thinking styles in geology that dominate theories. «[T]he acceptance or rejection of a scientific theory can only be understood within a broader cultural context which defines what is acceptable or not. Indeed, each style of thought possesses its own frame of validity, that is to say, its own tools to define what kind of theories are acceptable. » [4, 94]

Emphasizing the particular importance of styles of thinking as the basis of historical analysis, Pellegrini goes beyond geology, namely in the field of sociology. In my opinion, his position suggests that geologists are not able to separate sociological factors from geological ones. In my opinion, the actual state of things is fundamentally different. Anatoly Ryabikhin, considering the dispute between mobilists and fixists, is limited to presenting exclusively geological arguments. Ultimately, the divergence of views between mobilists and fixists is based on a different understanding by them of the correlation of vertical and horizontal movements in the Earth's tectonosphere. [6] Sociology does not dominate over geology.

In my opinion, the situation under consideration indicates the need to combine the achievements of mobilism and fixism. Their confrontation reminds me of a discussion around wave-particle dualism in physics. It was possible to overcome it only after, in quantum mechanics, in contrast to the state of affairs in classical physics, the illegality of opposing the concepts of wave and particle was proved. In my opinion, a similar situation takes place in geology. In their classic version, mobilism and fixism are opposed to each other. The situation changes if they are considered in the context of the systemic nature of the Earth. In this case, mobilism and fixism act as some approximations with an emphasis on either horizontal or vertical movements in the Earth's tectonosphere.

My final remark concerns the criteria for scientific theory. In my opinion, the vast majority of philosophers, including Thomas Kuhn, present them in a very blurry form. They do not reach the stages of conceptual transduction. Turning to the works of prominent mobilists and fixists, it is easy to establish that they are constantly improving their theories, consistently using, in particular, methods of intratheoretical transduction. Methods characterize scientific theories much more concretely and thoroughly than, for example, those criteria that attracted the attention of Dunja Šešelja and Erik Weber.

References

1. Krill, A. (2011) Fixists vs. Mobilists in the Geology Contest of the Century, 1844-1969 Trondheim, Norway: A. Krill.
2. Laudan, L., Donovan, A., Laudan, R., Barker, P., Brown, H., Leplin, J., Wykstra, S. (1986) Scientific change:

Philosophical models and historical research. Synthese 69(2), 141–223. doi:10.1007/bf00413981

3. Laudan, R. (1978) The recent revolution in geology and Kuhn's theory of scientific change. In PSA: Proceedings of the Biennial Meeting of the Philosophy of Science Association, Vol. 1978, Volume Two: Symposia and Invited Papers, 227-239.

4. Pellegrini, P. A. (2019) Styles of thought on the continental drift debate. Journal for General Philosophy of Science 50(1), 85-102. doi:10.1007/s10838-018-9439-7

5. Ryabukhin, A.G. (2006) 'Fiksizm-Mobilizm' - diskussii o prioritete vertikal'nykh i gorizontal'nykh dvizheniy v tektonosfere zemli (metodologicheskiye aspekty) ['Fixism – Mobilism' – discussions about the priority of vertical and horizontal movements in the Earth's tectonosphere.] Vestnik Moskovskogo universiteta. Seriya 4. Geologiya (3), 3–8. [In Russian].

6. Šešelja, D. and Weber, E. (2012) Rationality and irrationality in the history of continental drift: Was the hypothesis of continental drift worthy of pursuit? Studies in History and Philosophy of Science Part A 43(1), 147-159.

Chapter 10. The nature of biology

10.1. Biological theories are not elusive

Biology (from ancient Greek βίος – 'life' + λόγος – 'teaching, science') is a branch of science consisting of six dozen biological disciplines, each of which consists, in turn, of subdisciplines. Like other branches of science, biology consists of separate theories united in league-theories. In this regard, it is obvious that decisive importance in characterizing biology should be given to the concept of 'theory'. Immediately it turns out that this concept causes many biologists, including outstanding ones, to have big doubts. Werner Callebaut began his excellent review article by stating, «the concept remains elusive» [1, 413]. In my opinion, in biology, there is nothing more specific than theory. I adhere to this position insofar as everything that is part of the biological theory is its manifestation. The manifestation of a theory cannot be more obvious than the theory itself. However, what is the theory? A theory is the management of principles, laws, and variables by means of deduction, adduction, induction and abduction methods. Of course, in the case of biological theory, principles, laws, and variables, as well as methods, have an exclusively biological content. Such, for example, are Mendel's principles of genetic heredity and Darwin's natural selection principle. In biological theory, there is no other than biological content.

Unfortunately, biologists, as a rule, define the concept of a biological theory irrespective of the theory of conceptual transduction. So, D.C. Krakauer et al. believe that «scientific theories seek to provide simple explanations for significant empirical regularities based on fundamental physical and mechanistic constraints» [5, 269]. However, physical and mechanistic limitations are directly related solely to physical theories, and not to biological concepts. In addition, the emphasis on 'simple explanations' is insufficient, because, first, the explanation process is not clarified. Secondly, it also remains unclear why one should always insist on simple explanations. Whatever the explanations, the scientists it is necessary to rely on not only simple but also more refined types of explanations.

A review of the literature devoted to the concept of the theory shows that the acquired opposition of theory to experiment, followed by practice, is widespread. In the past three decades, theories are very often opposed to models. These types of oppositions are so popular that they have acquired the character of tradition. Overcoming them appears as a kind of innovation. In this connection, the statement of Root Gorelick is indicative:

> Theory is vital in science, including evolution and ecology, yet is seldom defined. Theory is often amorphously described as anything abstract or mathematical, or is simply defined as the opposite of empirical work. By contrast, I explicitly define theory as the formation of testable hypotheses, while defining empirical work as hypothesis testing. This pair of definitions highlights the false dichotomy between theory and empirical work insofar as models, mathematics, and methods do not fall in either category, but instead provide the operational link between theory and empirical work. [2, 1]

Of course, Gorelick attempts to overcome the opposition of theory and experiment. However, in my opinion, it is partial, because there remains a disconnection between theory and experiment; they, being brought into contact with each other, nevertheless remain on opposite sides of the barricades, artificially erected between them. The experiment is part of the theory, which is why it should not be opposed to theory. The experiment goes after prediction and prepares data processing. Methodologically, this means that adduction follows deduction and opens the way to induction. Methods turn out to be commensurate with each other solely because they are part of the same unity, which is precisely the theory. Otherwise, they would be incommensurable with each other.

The question of the nature of the models should also be solved in view of their commensurability with other parts of the theory. In my opinion, the withdrawal of models outside the theory is illegal. They represent the manifestation of relevant, in these case, biological, theories, taking into account the achievements of the formal sciences, namely, logic, mathematics and computer science. These achievements are not accepted thoughtlessly, but only to the extent that they formally express the features of biological phenomena themselves. Contrasting models with theories is a relapse of formalism. The value of the formal sciences is absolutized. This happens to the extent that the relationship between the formal sciences and the non-formal sciences is misunderstood. If the foundations of the biological theory appear in the outfits of the formal sciences, in particular, the mathematical and computer sciences, then they do not cease to be biological phenomena.

Of particular interest is the attempt to present the genesis of the concept of the theory from antiquity to the present day in philosophy and science, including biology, made W. Callebaut [1]. Rarely does anyone venture on such obligatory excursions and conclusions. Callebaut believes that the opposition of theory and practice goes back to Plato. He particularly appreciated the theoretical sciences. Frances Bacon rehabilitated the value of experiment and practice. The neopositivist and critical-rationalistic versions of the philosophy of science faced significant difficulties, which became especially apparent due to the philosophy of science Thomas Kuhn. Thus, obvious innovations have emerged in the understanding of the phenomenon of scientific theory. In this regard, attention is drawn to the lack of understanding of the theory as a syntactic or semantic event, so vividly represented in physics. After all these failures, the theory has ceased to be considered a priority scientific event. Nevertheless, a decisive rejection of it is clearly wrongful, for otherwise, it would not avoid an all-out fragmentation of science in connection with the ever-increasing flow of experimental data. W. Callebaut sees a way out of the extremely difficult situation in science, including biology, in the «positive program for 'naturalizing theorizing'» [1, 413]. In this regard, some ways are suggested for improving obsolete ideas about the relevance of theorizing [1, 425-427]. Certain hopes are pinned on the success of cognitive sciences, it is proposed to move from explanation to understanding, use analogies and metaphors, be tolerant of in/consistency, be guided by environmentally friendly thinking. These steps allow you to move closer to a perspectivist theoretical biology [1, 426].

The analysis of W. Callebaut is commendable. He managed to express some trends of thought shared by many modern philosophers and biologists. However, in my opinion, they are loaded with unacceptable aspects. Especially often manifested lack of familiarity philosophers of science and scientists with the achievements of the philosophy of science. I dare to assert that many authors, in words, rejecting the theory, did not really do it. Any proposal from the field of biology, with meaning, is certainly theoretical. Any experimenter, asserting something, for example, about genes, has a certain idea about their nature. This means that he, perhaps not fully aware of this, is guided by some theory. A biologist, as well as his colleague from any other field of science, cannot «jump out» from the theory. He may limit himself to certain types of experimental work, but its meaning is not autonomous from theory. There is nothing in science that precedes theory.

Modern understanding of the nature of scientific theories is the result of centuries of development. It consists not in abandoning the phenomenon of theory in favor of the practice, experiment or models, but in its all-round development. A theory that does not avoid speculative metaphysical arguments or does not allow, in spite of promises and excessive ambitions of its creators, to present a full-fledged scientific image of a certain phenomenon, must certainly be rejected. The scientist must find it an alternative. This is the core of his scientific work. Without scientific theory, a scientist is not a scientist.

Biologists in their scientific work constantly encounter numerous problem situations, whose flow does not stop. As a rule, the list of principles used, their relationship of subordination is controversial. Some experimental data are contrary to recognized laws. Logical, mathematical, computer models are not as effective as we would like. Everywhere there is a pluralism connected, in particular, with various levels of biological organization that cannot be contained in the bed of universal theories.

Massimo Pigliucci rightly notes that there are various ways of 'Doing Theory' in Biology [6]. On my own behalf, I would add to this conclusion that in science there is no such path, moving along which it would be possible not to make a theory. In science, including biology, it is impossible to do without deduction, adduction, induction, abduction, as well as the methods of intertheoretical transduction: problematization, discovery, interpretation, ordering. There is no such science or philosophical direction, which would disprove the relevance of these eight methods. Inductive preferences of the positivists and neopositivists did not abolish deduction. The deductive preferences of critical rationalists have not abolished induction. The pragmatic preferences of many analytical philosophers have not abolished the institution of theory. The anarchist methodology of Paul Feyerabend did not abolish scientific methods. Appeal to mathematical and computer models did not abolish the originality of the natural and axiological sciences.

If a biologist is not well versed in the vicissitudes of the development of scientific knowledge, he constantly risks being in the ravines of various kinds of dichotomies and trichotomies: deduction – induction, theory – practice, rationalism – empiricism, syntactics – semantics – pragmatics, theory – models, neopositivism – critical rationalism – naturalism, etc. The lack of scientific and philosophical competence of the biologist prevents his scientific work.

On the one hand, he has to evaluate very carefully the achievements that take place directly in biology. At the same time, the most advanced theories are the key to understanding less developed theories. This is the main content of metabiology. The philosophy of biology takes place when its interdisciplinary connections with the philosophy of science are realized in the interests of biology. For the designation of interdisciplinary connections of the philosophy of science and biology, implemented in the interests of philosophy, the term has not yet been coined. As a rule, researchers do not distinguish between metabiology and philosophy of biology. Meanwhile, between them, there is a fundamental difference. In some researchers, metabiology prevails over the philosophy of biology [4; 7], others come to the forefront of the philosophy of biology [3; 8]. The need for metabiology and the philosophy of biology has always been in biology. It acquired particularly acute forms due to the need to reconcile genetics and evolutionary theory. It is not by chance that the emergence of a developed form of the philosophy of biology is associated with the beginning of the 1970s. [3]. Of great importance in the development of the philosophy of biology and metabiology are the journals, in particular, «*History and Philosophy of the Life Sciences*», «*Biological Theory*», «*Philosophy and Theory in Biology*».

References

1. Callebaut, W. (2013) Naturalizing theorizing: beyond a theory of biological theories. Biology Theory 7(4), 413–429.
2. Gorelick, R. (2011) What is theory? Ideas in Ecology and Evolution 4(4), 1-10.
3. Griffiths, P. (218) Philosophy of biology. The Stanford Encyclopedia of Philosophy. Available at: https://plato.stanford.edu/archives/spr2018/entries/biology-philosophy/
4. Hull, D. (1974) Philosophy of Biological Science. Englewood Cliffs, New Jersey: Prentice-Hall.
5. Krakauer, D.C., Collins, J.P., Erwin, D., Flack, J.C., Fontana, W., Laubichler, M.D., Prohaska, S.J., West, G.B., Stadler, P.F. (2011) The challenges and scope of theoretical biology. Journal of Theoretical Biology 276(1), 269–276.
6. Pigliucci, M. (2013) On the different ways of «doing theory» in biology. Biological Theory 7(4), 287–297.
7. Ruse, M. (1973) Philosophy of Biology. London: Hutchinson.
8. Serrelli, E. (2020) Philosophy of Biology. Internet Encyclopedia of Philosophy. Available at: https://www.iep.utm.edu/biology/

10.2. Principles of biological theories

Persistent attempts to present biological knowledge in a systematic manner were undertaken in antiquity (Hippocrates, Aristotle), and continue to the present day. In this regard, the correct construction of the structure of biological theories is crucial. The most capacious conceptual units of the biological theory are principles. They are crucial in the processes of biological explanations. What are the principles guided by biologists? In connection with this question, first, attention should be paid to Francis Crick's dogma, according to which «the central dogma of molecular biology deals with the detailed residue-by-residue transfer of sequential information. It states that such information cannot be transferred back from protein to either protein or nucleic acid» [1, 561]. As noted by Crick, the principle he identified, and the speech, obviously, is precisely about the principle, and not about dogma, allowed to give a uniform explanation to numerous isolated facts. «In such a situation well-constructed theories can play a really useful part in stating problems clearly and thus guiding experiment» [1, 561]. The Crick principle permits the transfer of biological information between DNA, RNA, and protein only in certain directions. In this regard, it is of some restrictive nature. Another circumstance is also extremely important. Crick considers six ways of a possible transfer, for example, DNA → RNA and RNA → DNA, each of which sets a specific direction of biological metabolism. This means that there is not one, but six principles for the transfer of biological information. F. Crick is reasonable to consider the discoverer of the principle of multi-directional transfer of biological information. Biological processes cannot take place without such a transfer.

The main contender for the laurels of the second basic principle of biology is the principle of inheritance, according to which genetic information is transmitted from parents to their descendants. Let us call this concept the principle of Mendel, whose merits in disclosing the secrets of biological inheritance are generally recognized. The principle of inheritance, like the principle of transfer, is implemented in various ways. The inheritance is based on the processes of doubling, combining and distributing genetic material that determines the phenotype of organisms.

The genotype and phenotype also depend on the ways of implementing Darwin's principle of natural selection. «Darwin's genius was that he first saw in nature the principle of natural selection, the natural historical mechanism of the evolution of living beings" [5, 79]. The meaning of the principle of natural selection is that it takes into account the notion of a reference frame for biology. As is known, this concept is widely used in physics. Strictly speaking, all physical phenomena have a definite meaning not on their own, but relative to some reference system. Something similar is also characteristic of biology. All biological phenomena are relations. Outside the frame of reference, embodied by the environment, biological phenomena do not have any meaning. It is also significant that, like other principles of biological theory, the principle of natural selection is implemented in various ways. There is no only one right way. I will also note that the principle of natural selection expresses the correlation of biological phenomena not only with physical, chemical, geological and biological systems. Reference systems can also be technical, social and many others, in a word, axiological.

Therefore, the bases of biological theories are three principles, firstly, the principle of the directional transfer of

Crick's biological information, secondly, the principle of Mendel's inheritance, thirdly, the principle of Darwin's natural selection. These three principles seem to be relevant to all biological objects, including viruses, bacteria, and archaea. They represent the first, most fundamental level of biological principles. As noted earlier, they are all implemented not in one, but in many ways. Despite their selectivity, these principles are not as variable as the principles accompanying them. Let me call these principles the principles of the second level. Their nature deserves special discussion. In this regard, the position of Lucas Mix seems to me relevant. «I lay out a rule of thumb— the proper activity criterion—and a three-part typology of binary, range, and preference for understanding definitions of life. The resolution of "optimal" function within a scientific framework presents the central challenge to creating a successful definition of life» [4, 1]. Any organism realizes some form of activity with varying degrees of success. The actual task is to express this circumstance properly, i.e. through principles. They, as a rule, are expressed not as functions, but as functionals, and therefore are extremals. In my opinion, they were successfully presented by V.P. Fursova, A.P. Levich, and V.L. Alekseev. In particular, they call the principles of optimal construction, maximum individual reproductive success for the individual, the maximum mass of biological progeny, the maximization of reproductive efforts, the maximization of generalized entropy, the maximum energy used, maximum total respiration [2].

The principles of the second level are many. This is not surprising, because they represent the originality of biological objects, in particular, species, in the most specific way. However, there is every reason to believe that, with respect to each level of biological organization, depending on the specific situation, only some second-level principles are of decisive importance. The degree of their relevance is variable. For example, in the evolution of vertebrate organisms from fish to warm-blooded animals, there is a tendency to a decrease in the number of offspring and an increase in its survival. The principle of maximum reproductive success of an individual is characteristic of all species, but its degree of relevance may be less or more.

In my opinion, the possibility of methodological unification of biological principles is crucial in understanding the nature of biological knowledge. Principles really exist and constitute the basis of this knowledge. Biological principles are not related to each other deductive relationships. They differ in the degree of relevance. However, they are not derived from each other. The deductive manifestation of principles appears in the form of laws, i.e. certain relationships between variables. The deductive line – of principles → laws → variables is no less characteristic of biology than of physics.

The biological principles of the second level and all of them have a distinct phenotypic character, demonstrate the peculiarity of biology in its comparison with physics, chemistry, and geology. They do not act as a manifestation of the principle of least action and do not complement it. They complement the principles of Crick, Mendel and Darwin. In my opinion, phenotypic principles can be called by the name of Wilhelm Johannsen, who was one of the first to draw a clear demarcation line between the genotypes and the phenotypes [3].

In natural science, there is a clear demarcation line dividing biology from physics, chemistry, and geology. A formal generalization through the principle of least action is possible for non-biological natural sciences. Biology cannot be included in this line of generalization. Biology is clearly moving away from all three of its closest neighbors in the field of natural science knowledge.

References

1. Crick, F. (1970) Central dogma of molecular biology. Nature 227(5258), 561-563.
2. Fursova, P.V., Levich, A.P., Alekseev, V.L. (2003) Ekstremal'nyye printsipy v sovremennoy biologii. biologicheskikh nauk [Extreme principles in mathematical biology] Uspekhi sovremennoy biologii 123 (2), 115-137. [In Russian].
3. Johannsen, W. (1911) The genotype conception of heredity. American Naturalist 45(531), 129-159.
4. Mix, L.J. (2014) Proper activity, preference, and the meaning of life. Philosophy and Theory in Biology 6(1), 1-16.
5. Timofeev-Resovskiy, N.V. (1996) Genetika, evolyutsiya i teoreticheskaya biologiya [Genetics, evolution and theoretical biology]. In Tyuryukanov, A.N., Fedorov, V.M., Timofeev-Resovskiy, N.V. Biosfernyye razdum'ya [Biosphere thoughts]. Moskva: RAYEN, 77-82. [In Russian].

10.3. The development of biological theories (on the example of modern synthesis)

In each branch of science, there are theoretical complexes defining their main content. In biology, such a complex is modern synthesis. Its founders are Jean-Baptiste Lamarck, author of the book "The Philosophy of Zoology" (1809) and Charles Darwin, author of the book "The Origin of Species" (1859) [1; 9]. Both researchers understood that, firstly, animals in some way adapt to the environment, and secondly, the signs acquired by them in the process of their adaptation to the environment are of certain importance for the fate of both emerging new species and individual individuals. The decisive difference in their views consisted of a different understanding of the mechanism of the relationship of the processes inherent directly to the organisms and, on the other hand, to their relationship with the external environment. Lamarck believed that changes that occur with organisms due to their interactions with the environment are inherited. He believed that the internal changes of organisms are a manifestation of their inherent vitality, which determines the chain of being.

Darwin also needed somehow to estimate the inheritance of traits acquired by new offspring from their parents. Nevertheless, he avoided assertions that they are inherited through some deterministic process. Recognizing that the offspring has a tendency to inherit the variations of their parents, he, without haste with categorical judgments, gave the floor to statistics.

Thus, both researchers remained largely unaware of the nature of the processes internal to the body. As is known, this uncertainty was dissipated as genetics developed. Biologists are faced with the need to pair the three approaches, Lamarckism, Darwinism, and genetics. It is in this connection, thanks primarily to the books of T. Dobzhansky, E. Mayr, and J. Huxley [2; 10; 3], the theory of modern synthesis was developed. Since the book of J. Huxley was mainly popularizing, it is reasonable to consider the two main founders of the theory of modern synthesis T. Dobzhansky and E. Mayr, whose books were published respectively in 1937 and 1942. Their theoretical positions did not coincide in everything, but they agreed on the main thing, namely, that evolution takes place through the natural selection of features determined genetically.

The theory of modern synthesis is not a separate theory of one author, but a generalization of a complex of theories, many of which were developed both before and after the work of T. Dobzhansky and E. Mayr. In this regard, biologists are constantly faced with the same problem, namely, they need somehow to express the progress of the theory of modern synthesis. It is most often characterized by the concepts of 'extended evolutionary synthesis' and 'post-modern evolutionary syntheses'. Extended evolutionary synthesis takes into account multilevel selection, transgenerational epigenetic inheritance, niche construction, evolvability, and several concepts from evo-devo [13; 12]. Post-modern evolutionary synthesis seeks to present adequately the results of the comparative genomics and systems biology [8; 9]. Both directions have numerous supporters. Consideration of their extensive arguments is not part of my task. I will focus on attempts at the philosophical evaluation of the need to adhere to the standard theory of modern synthesis.

Massimo Pigliucci and Leonard Finkelman examined the controversial significance of a number of newly discovered factors, in particular, epigenetic inheritance, for the theory of modern synthesis. They concluded that, firstly, the main provisions of modern synthesis remained unshakable, therefore, in the sense of T. Kuhn, there was no paradigm shift; secondly, a fundamentally new epistemological situation arose, to characterize which they use the concept of Kuhn's disciplinary matrix. [12, 2] As you know, T. Kuhn called the set of obligations shared by scientists [8, 182] a disciplinary matrix. [8, 182] The concept of a disciplinary matrix is intended to clarify the concept of a paradigm.

A paradigm shift in biology would have occurred if scientists preferred Lamarckism to Darwinism. Eva Jablonka and Marion Lamb are often blamed for this preference, in connection with their book on the genetic, epigenetic, behavioral, and symbolic variation of the history of life [4]. They themselves explained their position as follows: «We agree with Godfrey-Smith that the change that is occurring in evolutionary theory is not a Kuhnian revolution, but will argue that there are good reasons for thinking that the new facts and ideas coming from cell biology, molecular biology and developmental biology, although not revolutionary within the framework of their own domains, do have radical, revolutionary, implications for evolutionary theory». [5, 455]. Francesca Merlin in the context of discussing the same problems comes to a much less radical conclusion: «I argue that biologists can continue to talk about chance mutations according to what I call and define as the notion of "evolutionary chance," which I claim is the Modern Synthesis' consensus view and a reformulation of Darwin's most influential idea of "chance" variation. Advances in molecular genetics are therefore significant but not revolutionary with respect to the Modern Synthesis' paradigm». [11, 1]

One of the leaders of post-modern evolutionary synthesis Eugene Koolin demonstrates a rather peculiar position: «The Modern Synthesis is no longer a viable framework for evolutionary biology, and a "postmodern synthesis" will have to replace it»; «the fate of Darwin's theory is the same as that of other major scientific theories of old that become approximations, sometimes, applicable under special circumstances, within new, more comprehensive theoretical constructs»; «the new developments in evolutionary biology by no account should be viewed as refutation of Darwin. On the contrary, they are widening the trails that Darwin blazed 150 years ago and reveal the extraordinary fertility of his thinking» [6, 800]. Koolin compares biology with physics and Darwin's theory with Newton's theory. He means that, just as Newtonian mechanics is the limit case of quantum physics, the theory of modern synthesis is a limit case of the theory of post-modern evolutionary synthesis.

Let me state the problematic situation that arose in connection with the discussion of the fate of modern synthesis. It consists in the fact that researchers have to deal with a huge variety of theories. This diversity is mastered in one way or another. First, Lamarckism and Darwinism are often contrasted. Secondly, a more developed version of it is added to the classical theory: modern synthesis → advanced synthesis; here we see the relevance of the three-link transition: modern synthesis → extended synthesis → post-modern synthesis. Thirdly, it is proposed, as Pigliucci and Finkelman do, to use the concept of Kuhn's disciplinary matrix to understand the pluralism of theories. Fourthly, it is proposed to link the various theories with each other through the passage to the limit (E. Koonin).

The fourth approach seems to be the most promising. In the other three approaches, in fact, the connection of theories is either not considered at all, or their generalization is put in place of individual theories, in the form, for example, of extended synthesis. Unfortunately, this does not consider the path that leads from individual theories to generalizations. Meanwhile, it is individual theories that make up the basis of their generalizations, the number of which may be large. From this point of view, it is not enough to restrict ourselves to the idea of three large blocks of theories, corresponding respectively to modern synthesis, extended synthesis, and post-modern synthesis.

Conscious use of the fourth approach involves a direct appeal to a bunch of theories, league-theories. Some generalization of theories does not reduce to just one league-theory. Thus, in my opinion, the development of pluralism of theories should be carried out through a system of league-theories, each of which fixes, as a rule, an emphasis on one of the factors, which may be, for example, multilevel selection or a certain epigenetic effect. Until biologists turn to the dynamics of league-theories, their understanding of the synthesis of theories will not be sufficient. Strictly speaking, it is not the synthesis of theories that is carried out, but their development. It is not the case that they are synthesized, i.e. unite, genetics and Darwin's theory of evolution. Modern synthesis is the result of the development of either genetics or Darwin's theory and not their sum.

References

1. Darwin, C. (1859) On the Origin of Species. London: John Murray.
2. Dobzhansky, T. (1937) Genetics and the Origin of Species. New York: Columbia University Press.
3. Huxley, J. (1942) Evolution – The Modern Synthesis. Cambridge: MIT Press, 2010.
4. Jablonka, E, Lamb, M.J. (2005) Evolution in Four Dimensions: Genetic, Epigenetic, Behavioral, and Symbolic Variation in the History of Life. Cambridge, MA, US: MIT Press.

5. Jablonka, E., Lamb, M.J. (2007) The expanded evolutionary synthesis—a response to Godfrey-Smith, Haig, and West-Eberhard. Biology and Philosophy 22(3), 453–472.
6. Koolin, E.V. (2009) Towards a postmodern synthesis of evolutionary biology. Cell Cycle 8(6), 799–800.
7. Koonin, E.V. (2009) The Origin at 150: is a new evolutionary synthesis in sight? Trends in Genetics 25 (11), 473–475.
8. Kuhn, T. (1970) [1962] The Structure of Scientific Revolutions. Second edition, with postscript. Chicago: University of Chicago Press
9. Lamarck, J-B, de. (1809) Philosophie Zoologique, ou Exposition des Considérations Relatives À L'histoire Naturelle des Animaux [Zoological Philosophy, or Exhibition of Considerations Relating to the Natural History of Animals]. Paris: Chez Dentu [et] L'Auteur. [In French].
10. Mayr, E. (1942) Systematics and the Origin of Species from a Viewpoint of a Zoologist. Cambridge: Harvard University Press.
11. Merlin, F. (2010) Evolutionary chance mutation: a defense of the modern synthesis' consensus view. Philosophy and Theory in Biology 2(3), 1-22.
12. Pigliucci, M., Finkelman, L. (2014). The extended (evolutionary) synthesis debate: where science meets philosophy. BioScience 64(6), 511–516.
13. Wade, M. (2011). The neo-modern synthesis: The confluence of new data and explanatory concepts. BioScience 61(5), 407–408.

10.4. Explanation in biology

The topic of explanation occupies a prominent place in all sciences, including biology. English 'explanation', French 'explication', German 'Erklärung', Russian 'ob"yasneniye' means the same thing, namely, to make something more understandable, purer. To explain something means to give the most complete information about it. If the information is incomplete, fragmentary and does not form a single whole, then something appears vague, not fully explained. From this point of view and in the light of the theory of conceptual transduction developed by me, something is clarified if it is included in all links of conceptual transduction, including interdisciplinary relations. In this case, information about a certain phenomenon will be the most complete and, therefore, exhaustive.

Suppose that we are talking about some variable, it should be understood as part of scientific laws and principles. Nevertheless, this is not enough. The variable is not explained if the method of its measurement in experiments and in practice is not defined. In this regard, it turns out that in the case of an explanation of variables, it is also necessary to take into account the factualization stage.

The situation with the explanation of the principles of the theory looks somewhat different. Unlike variables, they are not part of the laws. However, does this mean that the principles need no explanation? Of course not. Considering the principles, it is necessary to identify, firstly, their necessity, secondly, their verity. Otherwise, the researcher risks being guided by principles that do not protect him from delusions, but, on the contrary, will plunge him into them. The explanation of the principles is largely achieved through the method of abduction. Through this method, the principles are updated and improved. Moreover, this means that the degree of their verity is growing. Of course, the full significance of a principle will not be clarified if its deductive force is outside the zone of consideration. Thus, systematic, it turns out that in order to explain the nature of the principles, all four levels of intratheoretical transduction are needed, namely, prediction, factualization, data processing, and updating of obsolete principles. It immediately becomes clear that one cannot do without the stages and methods of intertheoretical transduction. If the content of a principle is explained by means of an outdated theory, it will not be recognized by experts of more advanced theories. This means that the content of the principle should also be detected based on intertheoretical transduction, therefore, as part of leaguetheory. However, this is not enough. The nature of the principle should be explained also in view of the status of the science of which it is an integral part. This status remains misunderstood if interdisciplinary relationships are not considered. Consider the Crick principle as an example. A researcher who adheres to the line of physicalism may try to reduce it to the physical principle of least action. Consequently, it is necessary with exhaustive completeness to identify the difference between the physical principle and the biological one. This cannot be done without direct reference to interdisciplinary relations.

Thus, the explanation is realized by eight conceptual transduction methods. Unfortunately, this circumstance, as a rule, is not properly taken into account.

In a review article by James Woodward, the types of explanations are considered, firstly, the deductive-nomological model, secondly, the statistical relevance models, thirdly, causal mechanical models, fourthly, unificationist models [12]. The deductive-nomological model was developed most fully by Carl Hempel [4]. It is, of course, a rather obvious absolutizing of the deduction method. This method is most often absolutized by critical rationalists, in particular, Karl Popper. Hempel, being an outstanding logician, as a neo-positivist, clearly underestimated the relevance of the experiment and of its method, adduction. It is not surprising, therefore, that as applied to the topic of explanation, he occupied critical rationalistic positions, and close to some analytical philosophers with their prevailing logical background. The deductive-nomological model explanation is not sufficient to ensure the completeness of the explanation. The methods of adduction, induction, and abduction in the explanation are no less relevant than the method of deduction. It should be noted that in the framework of the deductive-nomological model, the inductive statistical explanation is also recognized, but it is understood in a deductive manner. This means that the difference between deduction and induction does not receive its expression.

The basis of statistical relevance models is the requirement to be guided by statistical calculations. This requirement is fully justified insofar as probabilistic representations are very characteristic of the most developed modern sciences, in particular, for quantum field theory in physics, genetics in biology. However, it should be borne in mind that the statistical model does not cancel the methods of conceptual transduction, but only gives them a new look. Often it turns out to be very relevant. However, in all cases, it is necessary to clarify the relevance of the statistical explanation.

The relevance of causal mechanical models goes back, at least, to positivists, in particular, John Stuart Mill insisted on the need for causal explanations [7]. Nowadays, Wesley Salmon most vigorously protects the need for causal mechanical models. [11] Supporters of causal mechanical models insist on the need for dynamic theories that give an answer not only to the question "How do phenomena occur?", But also to the more topical question "Why do they occur in this way?" [6] The strengthening of the position of causal mechanical models in science was largely due to the mechanics of Newton, in which the forces were the causes. In the axiological sciences, the motives of people as principles of their actions are usually considered the causes of the events. Analytical authors, as a rule, insist on the presentation of the full mechanism of action. A vivid example of this is the translation of a protein in which transfer of amino acids necessary for protein synthesis is carried out by transfer RNA. The requirement to use the causal (deterministic) mechanism in explaining phenomena is quite consistent. However, it must be borne in mind that not all relationships are causal. For example, the transition - principles → laws are not causal, but intensional (notional) in nature.

The value of unificationist models is seen in the fact that they are trying to achieve an explanation of as many facts as possible using the same pattern of derivation [5]. Nevertheless, in all sciences the increasing importance of the pluralism of theories constantly makes itself felt. This circumstance is clearly a challenge to the program of supporters of unificationist models.

So far, I have considered the concept of explanation in the form in which it is cultivated in the general philosophy of science. Now I turn to the theories of the philosophers of biology. All of them, striving to follow in the wake of the general philosophy of science, seek to express the peculiarities of biological knowledge. How exactly they do this, undoubtedly, deserves special attention.

John Dupré pays special attention to the disunity of science, meaning, in particular, that the branches of science differ from each other; there are also significant differences between micro and macro theories [5]. The criticism of reductionism is quite consistent. My objection concerns the thesis of the disunity of science. Conceptual transduction methods are relevant to all sciences and scientific theories. This circumstance, in my opinion, compels us to use the expression 'disunity of science' with care. Modern science has a unity that, however, is combined with pluralism.

Following William Dray [2] David Resnik distinguishes how-possibly and how-actually explanations. He strongly emphasizes the heuristic power of how-possibly explanations. «An explanation is a how-possibly explanation if and only if it 1) lacks adequate empirical support, but 2) still satisfies other explanatory virtues» [10, 143]. How-possibly explanations really are relevant in biology. However, why? To this question, in my opinion, Resnik did not give an answer. It is obvious in the light of the theory of conceptual transduction.

Seeking to improve the existing theory and initiating a new cycle of knowledge in this connection, any researcher begins with a prediction. They are precisely how-possibly explanations that should be justified including empirically. How-possibly explanations have scientific relevance only if they are the beginning of a new cycle of knowledge. In this capacity, they certainly accompany how-actually explanations. By virtue of what has been said, how-possibly and how-actually explanations really form an inseparable pair.

How-possibly explanations attract the attention of many researchers. The prevailing point of view is that they themselves are not complete [1]. At the same time, attempts to prove their maximum fullness continue. Christopher Pearson argues that if how-possibly explanations are considered as part of some explanatory strategy, and then they may well be considered complete [9]. «At the center of the strategy context is the notion of an explanatory strategy. A strategy is a general approach for achieving some practical aim. Strategies set out the terms, resources, and constraints that one will use in attempting to achieve some end. Strategies, moreover, can be abstracted away from any particular implementation of them; they lie, that is, at a higher level of abstraction relative to their instantiations. Consequently, strategies are also distinguishable from any particular implementation of them with respect to matters of evaluation. One may fail to achieve some end by executing a particular course of action, while still recognizing that the strategy adopted was appropriate for achieving the end» [9, 6]. Pearson justifies his position by referring to the success of the Wilhem His mechanistic strategy, which made a significant contribution to the development of embryology at the end of the 19th century, and in opposition to the phylogenetic concept. In my opinion, Pearson overlooks several relevant factors from the standpoint of the theory of explanation.

First, no matter how understood the strategy, it should be evaluated from the standpoint of its most developed conception. Hardly biologists today recognize such conception. If not, then the explanations carried out within the framework of a mechanistic strategy are not rightly considered complete. Secondly, the mechanistic strategy should be evaluated in the framework of interdisciplinary relations of embryology and mechanics, within the framework of which mechanics is a donor discipline. Thirdly, and this, perhaps most importantly, attempts to present some explanatory strategy bypassing the methodological structure of biological theories are doomed to failure. In the case of underestimation of the relevance of the methods of intratheoretical and intertheoretical conceptual transduction, the scientific explanation is based on the rules that are set largely a priori, without taking into account the centuries-old lessons of various sciences, including biology.

Michel Morange seeks an explanation for scientific pluralism. He clarifies its existence on three bases. «The first is the ambiguity of the questions raised, which can be understood in different ways and require different answers. One recurring ambiguity concerns the local or general nature of the questions (and answers). The second explanation is in the historicity of life, which makes every situation unique, and may require different models for the explanation of apparently similar situations. Another cause of this plurality is the existence of long-lasting competing traditions of explanations» [8, 31]. Let me consider these three arguments.

Of course, the questions may be very different, but in themselves, they do not give rise to various types of explanations. Giving the answer to any question, the researcher evaluates it in the context of his theory. It is possible that many questions will be clarified through one theory.

The historicity of life also does not always initiate pluralism of answers. All biological theories are historical. Pluralism occurs only when evolution leads to sharp metamorphoses, i.e. supervention takes place.

The presence of long-lasting competing traditions, for example, confrontations of holism and particularism, phenomenological and dynamic theories, really leads to a pluralism of types of explanations. However, in this case, one should always distinguish between pluralism imaginary and real. Imaginary pluralism can be overcome by criticism. M. Morang gives an example of pluralism of opinions when following a reductionism program, some researchers evaluated genetic factors from the standpoint of physics, and others of chemistry [8, 40]. Strictly speaking, both of these positions are scientifically untenable. Therefore, in this case, there is no genuine pluralism.

In my opinion, pluralism takes place insofar as nature itself is diverse. Nature is structured in such a way that there is not and cannot be the only interpretation of quantum mechanics or the nature of genes. Pluralism of unfounded opinions must be overcome by their criticism. The pluralism of nature cannot be undone.

As we see, the scientific explanation is considered in biology in the absence of close contact with the methods of conceptual transduction. This circumstance deserves a critical assessment. I see no reason for abandoning conceptual transduction in the field of biology. The methods of explanation in biology are the same in form as in physics, chemistry, and geology. Nevertheless, they differ in content, for they have an exclusively biological nature. The key to the scientific explanation in biology is the theory of conceptual transduction.

References

1. Bokulich, A. (2014) How the tiger bush got its stripes: 'how possibly' vs. 'how actually' model explanations. The Monist 97(3), 321-338.
2. Dray, W. (1957) Laws and Explanation in History. Oxford, Oxford University Press.
3. Dupré, J. (1983) The disunity of science. Mind 92(367), 321-346
4. Hempel, C., (1942) The function of general laws in history. Journal of Philosophy 39(2), 35-48.

5. Kitcher, P. (1989) Explanatory unification and the causal structure of the world. In Kitcher, P. and W. Salmon W. Scientific Explanation. Minneapolis: University of Minnesota Press, 410-505.

6. Mayr, E. (1961) Cause and effect in biology. Science. New Series 134(3489), 1501-1506.

7. Mill, J. S. (1874) A System of Logic. New York: Harper and Brothers.

8. Morange, M. (2015) (Is there an explanation for … the diversity of explanations in biological studies? In Braillard, P.-A., Malaterre, C. (Eds.). Explanation in Biology, History, Philosophy and Theory of the Life Sciences 11. Dordrecht: Springer Science + Business Media, 31-46.

9. Pearson, C. (2018))How-possibly explanation in biology: lessons from Wilhelm His's 'simple experiments' models. Philosophy, Theory, and Practice in Biology 10 (4), 1-15.

10. Resnik, D.B. (1991) How-possibly explanations in biology. Acta Biotheoretica 39(2), 141-149.

11. Salmon, W. (1984) Scientific Explanation and the Causal Structure of the World. Princeton: Princeton University Press.

12. Woodward, J. (2017) Scientific Explanation. The Stanford Encyclopedia of Philosophy. Available at: https://plato.stanford.edu/archives/fall2017/entries/scientific-explanation/

10.5. Biological ontology

In his comprehensive review article on the problem of biological individuality, Thomas Pradeu identifies five approaches, namely, questiondependence, antianthropocentrism, hierarchization, continuity, and transitions [6]. Each of these approaches deserves support. On the other hand, Pradeu highlights five recent objections to philosophical accounts of biological individuality: monism, theory-centrism, ahistoricity, disciplinary isolationism, and conceptual uncertainties. Theory-centrism is interpreted as the tendency only to discuss problems.

As it is known, theory-based (not theory-centered - V.K.) individuation goes back to the concept of ontological relativity developed by Willard Quine: all objects are theoretical [8; 7, 20]. There is no alternative to this position, because all our knowledge, including practical, is ultimately theoretical. The practice is a manifestation of the theory. Biologists, in particular, David Hull, orienting themselves to the study of W. Quine, hold a quite consistent position [3]. Quine was very laconic in characterizing ontological relativity. In fact, we should talk about the fact that all objects with which scientists, including biologists, deal, are manifestations of the relevant theories.

The shortcomings of monism, ahistoricity, and conceptual uncertainties, are revealed only through the analysis of the content of theories. Of course, such an analysis cannot clarify the shortcomings of the theory-based approach itself. The theoretical relativity of biological ontology sets the framework for the consideration of the problem of individuality in biology. It is significant that Pradeu examines various biological theories, in particular, microbiology, evolutionary biology, ecology, developmental biology. It is impossible to identify the issue of biological individuality, for example, holobionts without careful study of the conceptual system of ecology.

It is generally accepted that an individual is that which exists as a distinct entity. Literally individual means that which is independent and not divisible. However, this definition is clearly outdated, because, as a rule, a biological individual has some internal structure. In my opinion, when determining the individual, the following circumstances should be taken into account. First, an individual is an attributive integer, for it appears as a combination of some features. In accordance with the Russell-Whitehead logical atomism, any feature is a characteristic of an object in accordance with the formula 'S is P'. A scientist always operates on some variables. They belong to certain individuals. The scientific analysis leads from variables to objects, but only if the variables form integrative nodes, which are called individuals. Secondly, each individual acts as a system. It is known to possess properties that are not inherent in its parts. Of course, there is a definite connection between the parts of the system and it as a whole. There is no system without its parts. In this regard, it is said that parts of the system supervene itself [4]. The fundamental difference of the system from its parts leads to the need to determine individuals in accordance with the level of analysis performed. In accordance with the system level, there is access only to systemic entities. Since there is no access to parts of the system, they are not individuals. They acquire this distinctness if the type of research that provides access to them is realized. Thus, a particular type of individual is always correlated with the type of analysis.

In modern biology, gene-centered, cell-centered, organism-centered, population-centered, species-centered approaches are widely distributed. The debate between Richard Dawkins and Stefen Gould is indicative in this regard, in which Dawkins adhered to a clearly defined gene-centered approach, and Gould attached greater importance to the organism-centered approach and to the overall multi-level selection [9]. It is extremely important to understand that the possibility of different ontological approaches, each of which is distinguished by its particular conceptual focus, leads to inevitable pluralism. There is no such author, who would demonstrate the presence of the only correct separate approach or a combination of approaches. Biological ontology is pluralistic. This circumstance manifests itself in different ways, not only in connection with the presence of different approaches.

Individuals have to be judged by the most advanced theories that head the corresponding league-theory. Assume that the league-theory $T_3 \rightarrow T_2 \{T_3\} \rightarrow T_1 \{T_3\}$ is considered. Its content compels to consider as true those individuals who figure in the theory of T_3. Individuals of the theories T_3, T_2 and T_1 are invariant to each other only insofar as these concepts are combined in the same league-theory. If not, then the individual theories T_3, T_2, and T_1 are different from each other. There is also pluralism here, but incidentally, insolvent from a scientific point of view. Mature knowledge is relevant in the biological ontology to the same extent as in all biology.

One of the central places in biological ontology is the question of the ratio of taxonomic units, especially of the organism and the species. On this account, there are various topical hypotheses. David Hall developed the species-as-individuals hypothesis, according to which species are similar to organisms, like them, they have a certain temporal and spatial history and have internal cohesion. Organisms have cohesion due to biological and chemical processes, and species through the processes of gene flow, homeostasis, and common selection pressure [2].

Matthew Barker and Robert Wilson define the species as homeostatic property cluster kinds [1]. The species, unlike individual organisms, does not have an integrative cohesion, which is explained by the disconnection of the populations that make up the species. In this regard, Celso Neto seeks to bring the necessary clarity to the question of the relationship between individuals and species. His decisive idea is that the identity of the individuals that make up the species is defined by nothing else but cohesion [5]. «Cohesion is what keeps things together into a single "whole," making them "parts" of a specific individual. These considerations lead me to conclude that the concept of "cohesion" plays an important theoretical role in individuality: it refers abstractly to identity criteria for individuals. Such a concept refers to whatever makes an individual the one and the same individual it is, indicating what this individual must have in order to remain the same individual. ... When saying that an individual is cohesive, we are referring to the fact that its identity necessarily relies on part-whole relationships occurring in space and time. In sum, the role of that term is not only to refer to identity criteria for individuals but also to indicate that such criteria are satisfied by spatiotemporal relations, whatever they may actually be» [5, 41-42]. Below I will attempt to express the relationship between individuals and species from fundamentally different positions than those which advocate by Hall, Barker and Wilson, and Neto.

Reading the works of all these authors it is difficult to get rid of the idea that they, considering the relationship between individuals and species, underestimate the status of biological theories. It seems that it is permissible to argue about biological entities irrespective of theories. In fact, it is only through theories that we have access to an understanding of the identity of both individuals and species. The topic of biological identity is meaningless if one does not consider the nature of biological principles, in particular, the principles of Crick, Mendel, Darwin and Johannsen. Believing that the identity of individuals is determined, for example, by processes of gene flow, the authors overlook the fact that they achieved not a real, but an imaginary explanation of their identity. In the absence of uniformity of the gene mechanism, there would be no identity of individuals. The specificity of biology is what it is. We are only able to fix that it was the result of a sharp superfluous jump from inanimate nature to living. It led to the emergence and individuals, and species, and those forms of identity that are inherent in them. Biological identity in any form is a continuation of the nature of biological principles. It follows that non-cohesion determines the identity of biological entities. However, this circumstance does not negate the possibility of considering the relationship between individuals and species.

Here two ways of reasoning are possible. In the first case, the species are considered as the result of the interaction of individuals. In the second case, individuals are considered representatives of the species. In the first case, the generic principles, laws, and variables express the similarity of those principles, laws, and variables that are manifested to individuals. This means that the species is a formal community of its individuals. In the second case, the individual acts as a representative of the species, under the pressure of the members of which he is. Thus, individuals and species are related to each other in the same way as the specific and the formal are related. This ratio is their most important feature.

References

1. Barker, M., Wilson, R. (2010) Cohesion, gene flow and the nature of species. Journal of Philosophy 107(2), 61-79.
2. Hull, D. (1978) A matter of individuality. In Sober, E. (Ed.). Conceptual Issues in Evolutionary Biology. Third ed. Cambridge: MIT Press, 363-386.
3. Hull, D. (1992) Individual. In Keller, E.F., Lloyd, E.A. (Eds.) Keywords in Evolutionary Biology. Cambridge: Harvard University Press, 181-187.
4. McLaughlin, B., Bennett, K. (2018) Supervenience. The Stanford Encyclopedia of Philosophy. Available at: https://plato.stanford.edu/archives/spr2018/entries/super venience/
5. Neto, C. (2016) Rethinking cohesion and species individuality. Biological Theory 11(3), 138-149.
6. Pradeu, T. (2016) The many faces of biological individuality. Biology and Philosophy 31(6), 761-763.
7. Quine, W.O. (1961) Theories and Things. Cambridge, MA: Harvard University Press.
8. Quine, W.O. (1968) *Ontological relativity.* Journal of Philosophy 65(7), 185-212.
9. Sterelny, K. (2007) Dawkins vs. Gould: Survival of the Fittest. Cambridge, U.K.: Icon Books.

10.6. Biological information

In the modern philosophy of biology, the concept of information occupies a prominent place [3; 4]. Information comes up when we have to consider an organization that is presented in various forms. Latin 'informare' literally means that it is presented in various forms, which can be quite a lot. Great difficulties begin with the understanding of the multi-tier processes of the organization, which, as is often considered, are imbued with the flow of information. In physics and chemistry, the processes of transferring energy, momentum, angular momentum, and charges are well known. All attempts to present information as some property, like energy or charge, ended in failure.

A noteworthy attempt to express the nature of information was done by W. Gitt, R. Compton, and J. Fernandez. Summarizing the data of many sciences, they first produce a universal definition of information, and then show that it is applicable to the characterization of biology. Universal information is «a symbolically encoded, abstractly represented message conveying the expected action and the intended purpose» [2, 16]. The biological code, both in the case of DNA and RNA, is represented by four nitrogenous bases. The biological syntax is defined by codons, combinations of three nucleotides. Between codons and the amino acids, is no distinct physical and chemical bond. Therefore, codons for these amino acids are abstractions. Expected actions are represented by replication, transcription and translation processes. «The ultimate physical purpose for the DNA/RNA protein synthesizing system is for the initial creation of organisms, and for their operations, maintenance and reproduction» [2, 20]. Thus, biological information has four characteristic features: code plus syntax, abstract meaning, expected actions, and intended, including the ultimate purpose.

In my opinion, Gitt, Compton, and Fernandez gave the characteristic not so much information as an information process. In their concept, the notion of 'abstract meaning' seems to be the most controversial. Under the abstract is usually understood, something depleted, considered without some of its features or parts. It is clear that codons are not truncated amino acids. From this point of view, they should not be considered abstractions. The unusual moment in this situation, in my opinion, is that the information process includes a number of superventive jumps, in particular, from codons to amino acids and from proteins to phenotypic behavior. The information process acts as the union of a series of superventive leaps as a whole, which has a beginning and an end. Of course, the ability of nature, manifested by it in the design of biological information processes, is amazing. In this regard, it is striking that biology differs largely from physics, chemistry, and geology. They contain separate quality transformations but they do not bind into rigid networks of a clutch and do not form a system with feedback.

Below I will continue the analysis of the concept of biological information. In this connection, the position of Eugene Koonin seems to me extremely relevant.

> Biological information encoded in genomes is fundamentally different from and effectively orthogonal to Shannon entropy. The biologically relevant concept of information has to do with 'meaning', i.e. encoding various biological functions with various degree of evolutionary conservation. Apart from direct experimentation, the meaning, or biological information content, can be extracted and quantified from alignments of homologous nucleotide or amino acid sequences but generally not from a single sequence, using appropriately modified information theoretical formulae. For short, information encoded in genomes is defined vertically but not horizontally. Informally but substantially, biological information density seems to be equivalent to 'meaning' of genomic

sequences that spans the entire range from sharply defined, universal meaning to effective meaninglessness. [7, 1]

In my opinion, the relevance of the analysis of Koonin is determined by two circumstances. First, he proposes to highlight the meaning of biological information. Obviously, without highlighting such a meaning, the very concept of biological information turns out to be untenable. Secondly, Koonin organically connects the selection of the meaning of biological information with the process of evolution. Biological information is evolutionary in its essence. It is determined qualitatively and quantitatively in accordance with a certain line of biological evolution.

In connection with the analysis of E. Koonin, it seems to be relevant to pay attention to the significance of the principles of biological theory in defining the concept of biological information. These principles can supposedly be subordinated to each other in different ways. Both the metabolic principle of Crick and the phenotypic principle of Johannsen can be recognized as the initial principle in this sense. It immediately catches the eye that it is not the Crick principle that has a distinct biological meaning, but the Johansen principle. Starting from it, you can calculate the evolutionary value of biological information. The amount of information encoded in the genome, or in any part of it, is determined by the extent to which it determines a particular phenotypic trait or behavior of an organism or population.

The line of biological determinism is defined by a direct sequence of biological principles: the Crick principle → the Mendel principle → the Darwin principle → the Johansen principle. The line of biological significance goes in the opposite direction: Johannes's principle → Darwin's principle → of Mendel's principle → Crick's principle. As it turns out, the biological theory involves not only the direct but also the reverse order of the subordination of the principles of the theory. In this respect, biological theories differ sharply from physical, chemical, and geological theories.

It should be noted that the theory of information in its current form does not take into account the actual features of many sciences, including biology. Primary attention is paid to syntactic and semantic information, especially in the context of the classical information theory [8], algorithmic information theory [6] and complex specified information [1]. William Dembski, correctly noting that information processes emit specific qualities that cannot be reduced to their material bases, decided that they are indicative of intelligent design. He clearly underestimated the versatility of biological processes. Their features receive full expression neither in syntactics, nor in semantics, nor in pragmatics. Unlike people, organisms adapt to the environment due not to the initial goal setting, but to biological determinism. The state of affairs in biology can be expressed by the following aphorism: genetic causation has meaning. In physics and chemistry, there is causation, but it has no meaning. In the axiological sciences, in particular, in technical disciplines, there are meanings, but they are concluded in the processes not of causing, but of achieving the goals set. Biological information is not a certain substance; it acts as a characteristic of advancing towards phenotypic traits, which, by the way, are many. This means that biological information appears, as a rule, in the form of several sequences of processes.

Various objections were made against the concept of biological information, mainly on behalf of the general theory of developing systems [3]. The absolute majority of biologists object to the excessive convergence of the characteristics of organisms with the characteristics of people. This position is obviously correct. Nevertheless, as I see it, another circumstance should be taken into account. The transition from inanimate nature to organisms is realized in the form of a clearly expressed innovation of information content. At its expense, biology precedes the emergence of axiological systems.

Reference

1. Dembski, W.A. (1998) The Design Inference: Eliminating Chance through Small Probabilities. Cambridge: Cambridge University Press.
2. Gitt, W., Compton, R., and Fernandez, J. (2013) Biological Information – What is It? Biological Information. New Perspectives. Proceedings of the Symposium. New Jersey et al.: World Scientific, 11-25.
3. Godfrey-Smith, P. (2007) Information in biology. In Hull D., Ruse M. (Eds.). The Cambridge Companion to the Philosophy of Biology. Cambridge: Cambridge University Press, 103-119.
4. Godfrey-Smith, P., Sterelny, K. (2016) Biological information. The Stanford Encyclopedia of Philosophy. Available at: https://plato.stanford.edu/archives/sum2016/entries/information-biological/
5. Griffiths, P.E. (2001) Genetic information: a metaphor in search of a theory. Philosophy of Science 68(3), 394-412.
6. Kolmogorov, A.N. (1965) Three approaches to the quantitative definition of information. Problems of

Information Transmission 1(1), 1-7.

7. Koonin, E.V. (2016) The meaning of biological information. Philosophical Transactions of the Royal Society A: Mathematical, Physical and Engineering Sciences, 1-11.

8. Shannon, C.E., Weaver, W. (1949) The mathematical theory of communication. Champaign IL: University of Illinois Press.

10.7. The problem of reduction in biology

The problem of reducing some theories to others is prominent in biology [1; 4]. No wonder. The abundance of theories compels to look for connections between them. It is precisely in this connection that the thought is born that the abundance mentioned above can be reduced by reducing some theories to others. However, such a search can be conducted in at least two directions. In the first case, seek to highlight the foundation of scientific knowledge. Such a foundation is often attributed to physics. In this case, other branches of science, in particular chemistry, geology and biology, as a rule, come down to physics. The leaders of neopositivism of the 1929-1930s tried to determine foundation of science most energetically. Rudolf Carnap and Otto Neurath are known as ideologues of physicalism. Its traces are visible in chemistry and geology much clearer than in biology.

In biology, the second type of reductionism is of primary importance, namely, the reduction of a less developed theory to a more developed one. For example, they seek to reduce classical genetics to molecular genetics. The considered type of reductionism is based on the principle of the relevance of mature knowledge. By definition, more developed knowledge is the key to understanding less developed knowledge. Let me call this type of reductionism relevant. The content of knowledge is estimated differently, but most often, it is equated with theories. This approach is typical for Ernest Nagel, who, considering the possibility of reducing one theory to another, was guided by the deductive-nomological method of scientific explanation [3]. The theory of T_1 can be reduced to the theory of T_2 if the principles and laws of T_2 are derived from the principles and laws of the theory of T_1 by deduction. The insufficiency of this position is that deduction is recognized as the only scientific method. Induction and especially adduction and abduction are not even mentioned as theoretical methods.

An important milestone in the development of current reductionism was the article Kenneth Schaffner [6]. In the distant 1960s, he was well aware that any scientific and philosophical paradigm somehow illuminates the problem of reductionism. He examined the four paradigms of current reductionism, Nagel-Woodger-Quine, Kemeny-Oppenheim-Suppes, and Popper-Feyerabend-Kuhn. Schaffner favored the paradigm of Popper-Feyerabend-Kuhn. However, the position of these three authors is very peculiar. They recognize that there are more and less relevant theories, that they can be compared with each other, but exclude the direct reduction of one theory to another. It is at this point Schaffner took a rather principled stand, insisting, even in the face of pluralism of theories, that the one theory could be fully reduced to another. Unfortunately, he did not distinguish strictly current and fundamental reductionism, believing that molecular genetics speaks on behalf of physics and chemistry.

The conception of K.F. Schaffner faced severe criticism. Michael Ruse and David Hull argued that he failed to prove the reducibility of classical genetics to molecular [2; 5]. Hull not without irony remarked: «Biologists are working out the molecular makeup and functioning of living organisms, but no one to my knowledge is attempting to correlate systematically the terms of Mendelian and molecular genetics. Nor can I see why anyone other than a philosopher interested in fulfilling the requirements of formal theory reduction would be interested in doing so. If the genetic facts of life set out in this paper accurately reflect the empirical situation, there is good reason to suppose that no such relation could be established between molecular genetics and anything that might be termed Mendelian genetics» [2, 499]. In my opinion, this remark is not quite correct. The fact is that the uncritical use of an outdated theory contradicts the criterion of truth. Its concepts in their further use should be rethought. Otherwise, they are approved as unconscious delusions. If they are rethought, then obviously it can be done only by referring to a related theory. In relation to classical genetics, such theory is molecular genetics.

The past half a century after Schaffner-Hull controversy has been marked by numerous innovations [1]. All this time, K.F. Schaffner refined his theory. The conclusions, to which he came, in my opinion, are of particular interest. Schaffner defends two points. «The first thesis is that what have traditionally been seen as robust, reductions of one theory or one branch of science by another more fundamental one are largely a myth. Although there are such reductions in the physical sciences, they are quite rare and depend on special requirements. In the biological sciences, these prima facie sweeping reductions fade away, like the body of the famous Cheshire cat, leaving only a smile. . . . The second thesis is that the "smiles" are fragmentary patchy explanations, and though patchy and fragmentary, they are very important, potentially Nobel-prize winning advances. To get the best grasp of these "smiles," I want to argue that, we need to return to the roots of discussions and analyses of scientific explanation more generally, and not focus mainly on reduction models, though three conditions based on earlier reduction models are retained in the present analysis» [7, 377]. Explanation on behalf of molecular biology «is both reductive and non-reductive» [7, 397]. The reductive explanation is implemented mainly through the chosen causation model (micro-phenomena explain macro-phenomena). Thus, K.F. Schaffner contrasts global reductionism with partial.

Assessing the drawbacks and advantages of the reduction approach, most modern authors believe that it has faced insurmountable difficulties presented by the pluralism of knowledge, its systemic nature, complexity, self-organization processes, and interdisciplinary integration. Ingo Brigandt and Alan Love end their review article with a very entertaining conclusion: «It seems clear that debates about reductionism in biology have not reached a denouement but rather portend vigorous philosophical discussion as the heterogeneity of issues related to its ontological, epistemological, and methodological types are brought to bear on perennial biological topics. The task of philosophers focused on reductionism in biology will be to analyze these promiscuities of reasoning and seek to develop accounts of reduction that capture what scientists actually do and contribute to more general perspectives on biological knowledge and scientific inquiry». [1]

Let me express my attitude to the long history of the idea of reductionism. First, I note the relevance of the concept of theory. A long tradition of reductionism, presented, for example, E. Nagel, linked his fate with the phenomenon of theory. However, this phenomenon itself was understood in an extremely simplistic way, in particular, it was opposed to the practice. Instead of improving the concept of the theory, many researchers in one degree or another abandoned it. This failure led to the widespread fragmentation of scientific knowledge. The fact is that it is the concept of theory, together with the system of intertheoretical relations, which gives unity to knowledge, not allowing it to break up into separate fragments.

The failures of the reductionism program were also largely due to the neglect of intertheoretical transduction. A reductionist, considering two theories, as a rule, does not pay due attention to the history of the latter. There is no such scientific theory that would not have arisen by overcoming the difficulties of its predecessor. In this regard, it always explains these difficulties. The simplest league-theory can be written as follows: $T_2 \rightarrow T_1 \{T_2\}$. The partially outdated T_1 theory is updated from the standpoint of the T_2 theory. This means that the T_1 theory is reduced to the T_2 theory. An endless series of scientific discoveries leads to a chain of reductionism operations. From this point of view, reductionism is highly relevant.

Of course, the value of reductionism should not be overestimated. Scientific activity is the steady improvement of theories through intertheoretical transduction. Within its borders, reductionism acts as an update of partially outdated theories. Without reductionism, intertheoretical transduction cycles are impossible. The modern understanding of reductionism, in my opinion, should be based on intertheoretical transduction. It is here that its limits are revealed. Reduction takes place within the boundaries of league-theories, but not between them.

Using theories, most researchers present them as the result of many years of effort by a great number of authors. The large-scale structure of knowledge does not reveal the reductive and other connections between theories. Classical genetics and molecular genetics are large-scale units. They are united by a huge network of intertheoretical relationships that are beyond the power of individual researchers. However, they become obvious if the fine-grained structure of theories, the contribution of individual scientists is considered. If a scientist does not present his theory in a distinct form, then he is unable to single out its reductive conceptual force.

Thus, reductionism as a research program is important only in the framework of the theory of inter-theoretical transduction. The subject of special interest of the leading philosophers of biology has long been not so much reductionism, as the ratio of various biological theories. The program of naive reductionism now attracts very few people. On the other hand, the problem of intertheoretical relations acquired paramount relevance. In this regard, it is imperative to use the concept of reduction. Complete rejection of it contradicts the device of scientific theories. The concept of reduction is a paraphrase of the principle of the relevance of mature knowledge: a developed theory is the key to understanding its predecessor.

References

1. Brigandt, I., Love, A. (2017) Reductionism in biology. The Stanford Encyclopedia of Philosophy. Available at: https://plato.stanford.edu/archives/spr2017/entries/reduction-biology/
2. Hull, D. (1972) Reductionism in genetics – biology or philosophy? Philosophy of Science 39(4), 491-499.

3. Nagel, E. (1961) The Structure of Science: Problems in the Logic of Scientific Explanation. New York: Harcourt, Brace, and World.

4. Ney, A. Reductionism. Internet Encyclopedia of Philosophy. Available at: https://www.iep.utm.edu/red-ism/

5. Ruse, M. (1971) Reduction, replacement, and molecular biology. Dialectica, 25(1): 39-72.

6. Schaffner, K.F. (1967) Approaches to reduction. Philosophy of Science 34(2), 137-147.

7. Schaffner, K. F. (2006). Reduction: the Cheshire cat problem and a return to roots. Synthese, 151(3), 377-402.

10.8. Biological time

In biology, time is one of the central concepts, for it is obvious that evolution as a process is inseparable with time [11; 10; 1; 8; 5]. Despite the obvious connection between evolution and time, the nature of biological time remains largely unexplained. Scientists who attempt to express the specifics of biological time, in many respects, try to take into account the achievements of physics. Physicists have achieved remarkable success in understanding the nature of physical time, which really deserves attention. In the relativistic mechanics of A. Einstein it was shown that there is no single world time, the duration of the processes, viewed from different exact points of view, are not the same, i.e. they are not invariants. In quantum mechanics, the refinement of the nature of physical time continued. The Bohr-Heisenberg ratio expresses the complementarity of energy and time. This means that time as a physical parameter is most closely associated with energy characteristics. In addition, it turned out that quantum time is discrete and subject to probabilistic processes [6]. Physical time is not the same in different types of interactions, in gravitational interactions it is another one than, for example, in strong interactions. Proceeding from the conceptual structure of physical theories it is obvious that the nature of physical time is the seal of all their basic principles, first, the principle of least action. Given this circumstance, it is legitimate to assume that the durations are integral characteristics of the processes as having a certain beginning and a definite end [7]. Physicists mainly operate with one-dimensional irreversible time. Many attempts were made to identify the cause of the irreversibility of time, but they did not lead to the agreement of scientists [3]. In my opinion, the concept of a physical process already implies the irreversibility of time. Movement is possible from point A to point B and then in the opposite direction, but this does not mean that the duration of the process first increases and then decreases. It invariably increases. The concept of a reversible process, and then a reversible time is unsatisfactory. Time is a characteristic of any measurement process.

Turning to the nature of biological time, we have the right to preserve the methodological impulse that has been so meaningfully developed in physics. Of course, we are talking only about the epistemological analogy, which for a second should not go beyond criticism. Above, I noted that the nature of physical time is the seal of the principles of physical theories. Accordingly, the nature of biological time is determined by the principles of Crick, Mendel, Darwin, and Johansen. My recipe for analyzing the nature of biological time is this: first, interpret biological processes as manifestations of the principles of biological theories; secondly, consider them from beginning to end; third, express their integral characteristic, which, fourthly, will be just biological duration. Biological time is the set of biological durations.

Biological duration characterizes that part of the life path that is traveled by the body in the process of its evolution. It must necessarily take into account the degree of approximation to the endpoint of the process, which may be the death of the organism. The method of determining the biological duration shows that this duration does not coincide with the physical duration. The same physical durations, as a rule, are not adequate characteristics of biological processes. This means, by the way, that they must have different time units. Following physics, it is unacceptable to consider second as the unit of biological time. By definition, every second of physical time is congruent with any other. This congruence is defined by the principles of physical theory. Nevertheless, seconds are not congruent from the standpoint of biology, because they are completely indifferent to its principles and laws. That is why seconds are not adequate units of biological duration.

Along with the irreversibility of the most important feature of many processes and time is their cyclical nature. This circumstance in relation to geological processes in a bright rhetorical manner expressed Stephen Gould. «Time's arrow is the intelligibility of distinct and irreversible events, while time's cycle is the intelligibility of timeless order and law like structure» [4, 15-16]. Book of S.J. Gould found a wide resonance among biologists. Indeed, in biology, as in geology, the irreversibility of time is combined with cyclicality. Not only cycles but also rhythms permeate all life processes [2]. Unlike Gould, I do not believe that there is tension between the irreversibility and the cyclical nature of the processes. The fact is that irreversibility is realized through cycles and rhythms if any. There is a reason to believe that they always accompany biological processes. However, if they did not exist, then, nevertheless, there would be irreversibility.

I also note that cycles are not adequate units of measurement of biological time. In quantitative standings, they are not congruent, not equivalent to each other.

Biologically, it is also extremely important to take into account the systemic nature of biology [12]. The most important feature of the joint functioning of systems is their compatibility [9, 18]. A complex organism consists of many systems, each of which has a specific time. They must be compatible with each other. If one of the systems has exhausted its time resource, then it causes damage to the body, which is often irreplaceable. In this case, the death of the organism is inevitable.

Of particular note is the biological relativity of physical time. The biologist is interested in physical time only to the extent that it has a certain value for the course of biological processes. This circumstance is taken into account in biophysics, in which physics acts as a donor science.

Thus, biological time is a complex systemic formation, consisting of various forms of biological time. Biological durations are adequate characteristics of the course of biological processes, their progress through the stages of their life paths. Biological time is not reducible to physical time. Physical durations are not adequate characteristics of biological processes.

References

1. Backman, G. (1943) Wachstum und organische Zeit [Growth and organic time]. Leipzig: J.A. Barth. [In German].
2. DeCoursey, P.J., Dunlap J.C., Loros, J.J. (2009) Chronobiology. Massachusets: Sinauer Associates Inc.
3. Coveney, P., Highfield, R. (1990) The Arrow of Time: A Voyage through Science to Solve Time's Greatest Mystery. London: W. H. Allen
4. Gould, S.J. (1987) Time's Arrow, Time's Cycle: Myth and Metaphor in the Discovery of Geological Time. Cambridge (Mass.), London: Harvard University Press.
5. Gunther, B., Morgado, E. (2004) Time in physics and biology. Biological Research 37(4S), 759-765.
6. Hilgevoord, J. (2002) Time in quantum mechanics. American Journal of Physics 70(3), 301-306.
7. Kanke, V.A. (1984) Formy vremeni [Forms of Time]. Tomsk: Tomskiy gosudarstvennyy universitet. [In Russian].
8. Sabater, B. (2009) Time arrows and determinism in biology. Biological Theory 4(2), 174-182.
9. Setrov, M.I. (1971) Obshchiye printsipy organizatsii sistem i ikh metodologicheskoye znacheniye. [General principles of the organization of systems and their methodological significance]. Leningrad: Nauka. [In Russian].
10. Vernadsky, V.I. (1975) Razmyshleniya naturalista. Kn. 1. Prostranstvo i vremya v zhivoy i nezhivoy prirode. [Reflections of a Naturalist. Vol. 1. Space and Time in Animate and Inanimate Nature]. Moskva: Nauka. [In Russian].
11. von Baer, K.E. (1861) Kakoy vzglyad na zhivuyu prirodu pravil'nyy i kak primenit' etot vzglyad k entomologii? [Which view of wildlife is correct and how to apply this view to entomology?] Zapiski Russkogo entomologicheskogo obshchestva (1), 16–17. [In Russian].

12. von Bertalanffy, L. (1968) General System Theory: Foundations, Development, Applications. New York: George Braziller.

10.9. Biological experiment

Understanding the problems of the experiment is one of the central places in biology, however, it is not without difficulty [1; 9]. My position is that the experiment does not oppose the theory, but is its organic part. Below I will show that it does not contradict the trends that are characteristic of the modern philosophy of biology. In this connection, the article by Kenneth Waters [7] is very indicative. He rightly points out that «the explanatory and investigative practices of classical genetics were interwoven. Neither can be properly understood separately from the other. Explanatory reasoning depended on practical knowledge because the explanations appealed to causal regularities that were understood in light of knowledge about the procedures used to observe them. Without this practical knowledge, the scope of the regularities, even as applied to a single species, would have been unknown» [7, 718].

Thomas Morgan conducted his fames experiments with the Drosophila melanogaster. It was the main experimental object, which he reconstructed in such a way that the detected biological patterns were observed in the most distinct form. It is easy to see that Morgan as an experimenter acted purposefully so as the physicist G. Galileo did. Galileo, studying the free-fall phenomenon of bodies, rolled heavy metal balls along inclined planes so that the friction forces were the smallest. The studied phenomenon must be isolated in its pure form. Having found a pattern, he extended it to the bodies, which, in their motion, overcome the resistance of the medium. Acting in his chosen way, Galileo had to be guided by certain knowledge, i.e. be guided by some theory. An experiment is inseparable from theory.

Morgan chose such an experimental object, namely, Drosophila melanogaster, the observations of which made it possible to obtain important information with the maximum degree of confidence in their relevance. As you know, Drosophila every two weeks at a temperature of 25 °C gives numerous offspring. The male and female are clearly distinguishable in appearance – the male's abdomen is smaller and darker. The flies have only 8 chromosomes in the diploid set, they multiply quite easily in test tubes on an inexpensive nutrient medium. The reconstruction of the experimental flies made it possible to identify the features inherited by their offspring in the most distinct form. This reconstruction itself involved the use of theory, in this case, classical genetics.

In fact, Galileo and Morgan, being representatives of two sciences, physics and biology, significantly different from each other, used the same method, namely, the method of adduction. By the way, I note that with the method of adduction, physicists and chemists have developed much knowledge, concentrating their efforts on studying the properties of the simplest element, hydrogen.

Waters in relation to classical genetics T. Morgana emphasizes the unity of biological theory and experiment. Supporting the position of C.K. Waters, I have to clarify my position. Strictly speaking, in my opinion, it is not enough to mention only the unity of theory and experiment, the experiment is part of the theory. The theory should not be reduced only to the deductive method.

Significant attempts to comprehend the problems of a biological experiment have been undertaken repeatedly by Hans-Jörg Rheinberger [6]. With reference to the American art historian G. Kubler, he notes that, like an artist, an experimental scientist, hoping to discover a gold mine, works in the dark, guided by the tunnels and mines of earlier works [6, 2]. He is also very close to the idea of T. Kuhn that a scientific study is "a process driven from behind"; it is not determined by the already known goal [6, 4]. Nevertheless, at the same time, he, following G. Bachelar, believes, experimental work opens up new perspectives. «Experimental systems narrow the view, but they expand it in the same breath» [6, 7]. Experimental research is on the border of knowledge and ignorance. With the experiment, the researcher creates an empirical structure, an environment that it allowed, in this state of ignorance about ignorance to become able to act» [6, 8-9].

One proposition of Rheinberger seems to me be clearly controversial. This is a reference to T. Kuhn's statement. He is known to draw a direct analogy between empirical research and biological evolution [3, 237]. This evolution as a biological process knows no future. I belives, scientists, unlike animals, are initially focused on the future. They predict the future based on existing theories. The future is here connected with the desire to improve the theory freeing it from difficulties. True, of course, that the future is presented in a blurred form. Nevertheless, the experimenter does not act in total theoretical darkness. Certain landmarks are at his disposal and he obviously acts in accordance with them. Ultimately, Rheinberger recognizes that experimental research in biology binds together the past and future. However, this and the other, he does not represent in a sufficiently distinct form. They can hardly be distinguished without recourse to the ratio of partially outdated and new theories.

Perhaps the most detailed project of understanding a biological experiment was proposed by Marcel Weber [8; 9]. He is guided by the ideal of vera causa. «Recent scholarship has defended the traditional ideal of vera causa both as a normatively adequate methodological standard for experimental biology as well as a standard that biologists are actually committed to. The ideal requires that scientific explanations of a phenomenon cite true causes or verae causae» [9, subsection 5.2]. He extends this idea to the recognition of the paramount importance of the philosophy of mechanisms, which act as ramified chains of causal relationships. In accordance with the chosen ideal, the appropriately generalized Mill's method which he outlined in his system of inductive logic acquires paramount importance to identify the causes, [9, section 1].

Of course, the question arises about the legitimacy of the chosen approach, in particular, both the method of causation and the philosophy of the mechanisms. According to Lenny Moss, the mechanism philosophy is insufficient as a reliable basis, a kind of gold standard of the philosophy of biology. It was a reaction to a deductive-nomological model explanation, but at the same time, it blocked the philosophical recognition of the best conceptual, empirical and reflexive efforts that scientists demonstrate in their progress [5, 172]. Moss believes that the philosophy of the mechanisms is insufficient to explain the functioning of 'pleiomorphic ensembles' and 'intrinsically unstructured proteins' [5].

In my opinion, the philosophy of mechanisms, presented in a very favorable light in the review article by S. Craver and J.

Tabery [2], deserves high praise. Contrary to Moss, I do not think that the logic of the mechanisms fails to explain the pleomorphic ensembles and intrinsically unstructured proteins. The mechanisms of their functioning are not well understood, but there is no reason to doubt their presence. Nevertheless, I agree with L. Moss, the advocates of the philosophy of mechanisms really lose sight of many relevant aspects of modern scientific methods. What exactly? The answer to this question follows from consideration of the nature of intratheoretical transduction.

Intratheoretical transduction contains four stages, namely, prediction, experiment (including practice), processing of experimental data and updating of deductive principles. Each of these stages is characterized by special methods, collected under four names, deduction, adduction, induction and abduction. The deductive model of Hempel-Oppenheim explanations is characteristic only for the prediction stage, but not for the experimental stage. Experimental biologists rightly seek to find an alternative to the deductive model of explanation. The specified alternative, i.e. the method of the experiment is not a causal explanation, but the adduction method.

Why the ideal of vera causa is not a method? Because it is a form of manifestation of theory, all its stages, not just of the experiment. Causal relationships can be considered at the stages of prediction, factualization (experiment), data processing and updating of deductive principles. There is a fundamental difference between the methods and forms of manifestation of the theory. Methods of intratheoretical transduction vary from one stage of theory development to another. The forms of the manifestation of theory, be it an object, mental, linguistic, activity or causal presentation, permeate the entire process of conceptual transduction. The experimental method, or the method of adduction, consists in isolating the studied characteristics and measuring them. By itself, the experiment does not reveal the causes. To isolate them you have to use the full potential of the theory. From this point of view, the methods of inductive logic J.S. Mill are clearly insufficient.

An experiment is a stage of development of a certain whole and not an isolated event. The division of scientific labor leads to the formation of experts in the experiment. This separation is not a justification for independence from the above-mentioned whole, which is the theory. Unfortunately, some experimenters, striving for scientific independence, oppose experiment to theory. Such scientific separatism invariably narrows scientific horizons. M. Weber did not avoid opposing theory and experiment. «...The development of any discipline in experimental biology cannot be understood by focusing on theories and attempts to confirm or refute these theories. Experimental practice is simply not organized around theories, particularly not in biology. If this is so, we must ask in what other terms this practice can be explained or reconstructed. Recent scholarship has focused in particular on two kinds of entities: *model organisms* and *experimental systems*». [9, section 3]

Model organisms and experimental systems are true of paramount importance in a biological experiment. However, the interests of experimental biologists are not locked in them. Model organisms and experimental systems are needed for something, namely, to improve biological knowledge, i.e. the diversity of biological theories. To contrapose the experiment and the theory is counterproductive. An experiment is not a prediction, but together with it, it is a part of a single whole, which is precisely the theory in its most complete understanding. Of course, I do not equate theory with only deductive constructions.

Thus, in my opinion, it is inexpedient to develop a special philosophy of a biological experiment, isolating it from the philosophy of biology. The method of biological experimentation is not causation, but the method of adduction. The key to understanding biological experiments is the concept of intratheoretical transduction. It protects against the isolation of a biological experiment from a biological theory.

References

1. Brigandt, I. (2006) Philosophical issues in experimental biology. Biology and Philosophy 21(3), 423-435.
2. Craver, C., Tabery, J. (2017) Mechanisms in science. The Stanford Encyclopedia of Philosophy. Available at: https://plato.stanford.edu/archives/spr2017/entries/scienc e-mechanisms/
3. Kuhn, T. (1997) The road since structure. In Tauber, A.I. (Ed.) Science and the Quest for Reality. New York: New York University Press, 231-245.
4. Machamer, P., Darden, L, Craver, C. F. (2000) Thinking about mechanisms. Philosophy of Science 67(1), 1-25.
5. Moss, L. (2012) Is the philosophy of mechanism philosophy enough? Studies in History and Philosophy of Biological and Biomedical Sciences 43, 164-172.
6. Rheinberger, H.-J. (2012) Experiment, Forschung, Kunst [Experiment, research, art]. Available at: https://dg.websyntax.de/assets/Uploads/ContentElements

/Attachments/Hans-Joerg-Rheinberger-Experiment-
Forschung-Kunst.pdf/ [In German].
7. Waters, C. K. (2008). How practical know-how
   contextualizes theoretical knowledge: exporting causal
   knowledge from laboratory to nature. Philosophy of
   Science, 75(5), 707-719.
8. Weber, M. (2005) The Philosophy of Experimental Biology.
   Cambridge: Cambridge University Press.
9. Weber, M. (2018) Experiment in Biology. The Stanford
   Encyclopedia   of   Philosophy. Available   at:
   https://plato.stanford.edu/archives/sum2018/entries/biolo
   gy-experiment/

10.10. Biology and ethics

Anything that falls within the scope of a person is somehow evaluated in an ethical context. This rule fully applies to biology [2; 3; 4]. In this regard, it is necessary to consider the relationship between biology and ethics. As noted earlier, the ethical principle is inherent directly in all axiological theories. A properly understood structure of their principles should include the principle of maximizing the prosperity of all subjects of the theory and the principle of responsibility. These principles are organic, for example, for the social and human sciences. If it is possible to prove their relevance in relation to biological theories, researchers will have to admit the ethical content of these conceptions. In my opinion, there is no way to incorporate the above principles directly into biological theories.

All organisms behave in a selective way, but none of them cares about all organisms. As you know, animals in the population often care about each other. However, there are no such organisms, which take care of all biological subjects.

Nevertheless, the ethical project involves precisely all-inclusiveness cooperation. Of course, in biological theories, there is no principle of responsibility, which makes sense only in the continuation of the first ethical principle. Since biology is devoid of ethical principles, there are no proper grounds for recognizing biological ethics. It is not there, but undoubtedly another, there is ethical relativity of biology. This means that in the process of implementing an ethical project, people have an urgent need to use the achievements of the biological sciences. In the absence of such a need, they would not cultivate the biological sciences at all.

The provision of ethical relativity, if not biology, then, at least, of organisms were first expressed quite clearly by Immanuel Kant, who noted that «beings whose existence depends not on our will but on nature have, nevertheless, if they are not rational beings, only a relative value as means and are therefore called things» [5, 428]. He proceeded from the ethics of duty, according to which a person must be a worthy representative of humanity and not the whole kingdom of the living. The weakness of I. Kant's position is determined by the lack of analysis of the content of biological theories. He limited himself to references to metaphysics. The same is true for those researchers who seek to determine the status of biological ethics, based on utilitarian attitudes. Utilitarianists believe that the presence of suffering in animals is sufficient reason to recognize their moral status [12; 13]. The utilitarian ethics of compassion remains within the bounds of metaphysics, for the phenomenon of suffering itself does not receive a scientific-theoretical explanation. An attempt to achieve it would have forced the utilitarianists to consider the phenomenon of suffering in the context of various theories, in particular, social and biological. Then they would have to note the difference in the principles of these theories, which are not amenable to unification.

Defending the ethical relativity of biology seems to fall under the rubric of anthropocentrism, with its primary attention to people to the detriment of other beings. However, this opinion does not hold water. Due attention to the device of scientific theories is not anthropocentrism, which speaks on behalf of metaphysics. Ignoring the device of scientific theories, in principle it is impossible to establish the status of humans and animals. Their status is indeed different. Metaphysical ethical systems, in particular, deontological and utilitarian ethics, do not allow to express this circumstance.

Another metaphysical position is that the fact of the life of organisms is recognized as the basis for awarding them moral status [8; 10, 11]. Authors who adhere to such a point act as follows. They are initially guided by some ethical impulse, which, in fact, borrowed from the sciences of man. Then it is uncritically transferred to the whole field of biology. Ethical knowledge is not derived from theories but is prescribed to them. Such actions are scientifically wrong.

Of course, some researchers attempted to come to ethical conclusions directly from the content of biology, in particular, from Charles Darwin's theory. Remarkable in this regard is the argument of Ernst Mayr. «Man is the result of millions of years of evolution, and our most basic ethical principle should be to do everything toward the maintenance and future of mankind. All other ethical norms can be derived from this baseline... Any generation of mankind is the current caretaker not only of the human gene pool but indeed of all of nature on our fragile globe. » [9, 45-46]. Strictly speaking, Mayr seeks to stay on the scientific soil, but he fails. In the end, it all ends in metaphysical appeals. Humanity is really the result of a centuries-old process of evolution and jumps. Humanity truly seeks to secure its future. Nevertheless, people can do it only by developing their best theories, taking into account the uniqueness of biological concepts.

Humanity is at a certain stage of its development. In this position, it sets certain goals for itself, calculated not on a utopian future, but on goals achievable for quite definite periods. In this regard, taking into account the ethical relativity of biology, great anxieties are associated primarily with the use of animal meat [6], with experiments on them [7], genetic engineering not causing damage to the environment, including its biota. In all these cases, science, if it actually implements an ethical project, has great potential for improving the present state of affairs. If people do not deviate from a scientific project, then they are interested in the full development of ethical relativity of biology. It is my deep conviction that there are no such forms of ethical relativity of biology, which people could neglect without negative consequences for themselves. The genuinely relevant task is not to supplement science with metaphysical moral maxims, but to translate all axiological sciences onto ethical rails, invariably accompanied by the development of ethical relativity of biology.

References

1. Bentham, J. (1982) [1780/1789] Introduction to the Principles of Morals and Legislation. Ed. by J.H. Burns and H.L.A. Hart. London: Methuen.
2. Cochrane, A. (2020) Environmental Ethics. Internet Encyclopedia of Philosophy. Available at: https://www.iep.utm.edu/envi-eth/

3. Gordon, J-S. (2020) Bioethics. Internet Encyclopedia of Philosophy. Available at: https://www.iep.utm.edu/bioethic/

4. Gruen, L. (2017) The moral status of animals. The Stanford Encyclopedia of Philosophy. Available at: https://plato.stanford.edu/archives/fall2017/entries/moral -animal/.

5. Kant, I. (1998) [1785] Groundwork of the Metaphysics of Morals (Grundlegung zur Metaphysik der Sitten). Transl. by M.J. Gregor. Cambridge: Cambridge University Press.

6. Kaplan, D.M. (Ed.). (2012) The Philosophy of Food. Berkeley, CA: University of California Press.

7. Khoo, S. (2018) Justifiability and animal research in health: can democratization help resolve difficulties? Animals 8(2), 28.

8. Mautner, M.N. (2009) Life-centered ethics, and the human future in space. Bioethics 23(8), 433-440.

9. Mayr, E. (1984) Darwinism and ethics: a response to Antony Flew. In Caplan, A.L., Jennings, B. (Eds.). Darwin, Marx, and Freud. Their Influence on Moral Theory. New York and London: Plenum Press, 35-46.

10. Regan, T. (2004) The Case for Animal Rights. Second ed. Berkeley: University of California Press.

11. Schweitzer, A. (1990) Out of My Life and Thought. New York: Holt.

12. Singer, P. (1990) Animal Liberation. Second ed. New York: New York Review of Books.

Chapter 11. The nature of technology

11.1. Technology is a branch of science

The Greek word τεχνολογία literally means the theory of craft art. This word has become increasingly popular in developed European languages since the seventeenth century. Its value varies widely. In this book, technology is understood as a special branch of science, consisting of a huge number of theories that are grouped into separate disciplines, for example, such as electrical engineering, radio engineering, energy, and transport. By the number of individual theories, technology has no equal among other branches of science.

Defining technology as a branch of science, I quite consciously undertake an obligation to prove really that technology is nothing but a branch of science. This obligation goes against the tradition that has developed in the philosophy of technology. The second number of the fourth volume of the electronic journal "Techné" in 1998 was entirely devoted to the question of the relationship between science and technology.[12] All the authors of the articles were guided by the seemingly obvious position on the illegality of the inclusion of technology in the structure of science. They argued that the ties between science and technology were becoming ever closer. Nevertheless, no one has concluded that technology itself is a branch of science.

The arguments in support of the provisions on the inadmissibility of transferring technology to the category of branches of scientific knowledge are as follows. First, the specificity of the technology lies in the fact that it deals not with what is, but with what should be [4; 10]. Secondly, scientists know that and technologists how [9]. Thirdly, technology is an applied, practice-oriented science [3]. Fourth, engineers use knowledge primarily to develop, produce and operate artifacts. Scientists, on the contrary, use knowledge primarily to generate more knowledge [13, p. 226]. Numerous references to authors who disagree with the enrollment of technology in the branches of science are cited by Mieke Boon in an article with the remarkable title «In Defense of engineering sciences: on the epistemological relations between science and technology» [2]. The exception of technology and/or engineering sciences from science is indeed a strange decision. In this connection, the desire to question this ex-communication is fully justified. Boon defines its main meaning in the following way: «In the traditional view, science was scientific, not-useful, and intellectually high-standing, whereas technology was not-scientific, useful, and intellectually low-standing. The ideological battle, therefore, is about being recognized as scientific, useful and having high intellectual quality». [2, 63]. Clearly mistaken to consider technology as applied science.

To substantiate the scientific status of the technology, some arguments that I put forward earlier by me are necessary [7]. All branches of science are similar in that they are guided by concepts of principles, laws, and variables that are controlled by means of conceptual transduction methods, namely, deduction, adduction, induction, abduction, problematization, discovery, interpretation, and ordering of theories. All of these concepts and methods are characteristic of technological theories. By virtue of this circumstance, technology must be considered a branch of science on the same grounds as, for example, physics and economics. The similarity of concepts and methods is a prerequisite for the inclusion of theories into science. By virtue of what has been said, there is no reason for weaning technology from science. Of course, the arguments against the recognition of technology as science should also be considered.

The main argument is that science deals with what is, and not with what should be because of its usefulness. As is well known, this issue has been acquired фт acute form due to the position of David Hume regarding the problem of is-ought [6, 335]. He believed that scientifically justified knowledge should be based on logic and observation. What should be in accordance with the criterion of utility is not observable; therefore, moral knowledge is unscientific. After Hume, his argument was extended to all theories that operate on values, in particular, to economics and technology. Upon closer examination, it turns out that Hume's argument does not take into account the rich content of modern scientific methods, which are not reduced to observations or logic.

Unfortunately, historically it happened that Hume's argument was perceived by many positivist-minded philosophers, who were generally well versed in matters of natural science. Following Hume, it seemed to them that all the axiological sciences were unscientific. Advances in axiological sciences refute the thesis of the inaccessibility of the science for axiological knowledge. It is a mistake to suggest the ideals of science on behalf of purely natural science, and then, based on them, to assess the status of axiological theories, including technological concepts. Of course, axiological theories are different from natural ones; however, they are similar in conceptual and methodological terms. This circumstance allows uniting them as branches of science.

The is-ought problem is largely contrived by metaphysically oriented thinkers. This circumstance becomes clear, in particular, when considering it in the context of the concept of time. Natural science is not limited to fixing only the present. The experiment directly captures the present, but at the same time predicts the future. The predicted future is then compared to what has really come. Something similar occurs in the case of axiological sciences. Here, too, the future is predicted from the present. The onset of the future is analyzed in the natural and axiological sciences.

Many authors refer to the distinction of *knowing how* and *knowing that* in characterizing the uniqueness of technological knowledge. Per Norström did not agree with the authors, who believe that *knowing how* is a practical demonstration of *knowing that* [11], and with those researchers who reduce *knowing that* to *knowing how* [5]. «Technological *knowing how* is not *knowing that*. Neglect of these facts impoverishes our understanding of technological activities, by obscuring the way in which they are informed by» [8, 564]. It is significant that Norström, describing *knowing that* and *knowing how* distinguishes between intelligence and experience.

Authors who are considering *knowing that* and *knowing how*, as a rule, substantiate their position with concrete examples. Amelia has knowledge of operation P, such as cycling, but cannot perform it. Oliver rides a bicycle, not having developed knowledge of this operation. In my opinion, the authors, ignoring the theoretical nature of any knowledge, make a significant mistake. In fact, any characteristic of a given situation is carried out from the standpoint of a certain theory, but this circumstance is not always realized to the proper degree.

In my opinion, the meaning of *knowing that* and *knowing how* should be evaluated according to the theory of conceptual transduction. In this regard, let us turn to intratheoretical transduction and attempt to discover in its composition *knowing that* and *knowing how*. Let me remind the reader that intratheoretical transduction involves four steps: prediction, factualization, data processing, and updating of deductive principles. *Knowing how* is clearly a factualization that, as applied to technology, is most often called either experiment or practice. Status of *knowing that* is determined by the stages of prediction, data processing and updating principles. Therefore, there is a certain correspondence between, on the one hand, the stages of intratheoretical transduction, on the other hand, *knowing that* and *knowing how*. However, this correspondence is rather superficial.

The essential difference between the two methods of conceptual analysis from each other is striking. In all analyzes of *knowing that* and *knowing how* they cannot be separated from each other. It always turns out that *knowing that* implies *knowing how*; accordingly, *knowing how* involves *knowing that*. The stages of intratheoretical conceptual transduction are clearly separated from each other. Together they represent the content of the theory. In this regard, it is essential to emphasize that when analyzing the status of technology, the degree of manifestation of the theory should be taken into account. If someone badly owns the stage, either *knowing how* or *knowing that*, then this means that he is not at odds with the technological theory. This circumstance is essential for understanding the often-considered ratio of knowledge, abilities, and skills.

It seems that *knowing how* in contrast to *knowing that* is provided with abilities and skills. Say, a person who does not possess the appropriate abilities and skills is not able to realize *knowing how*. It is hard not to agree with this statement.

However, what is the meaning of the statement about the lack of abilities and skills? Obviously, a person is not able to successfully to complete the factualization stage. Learning abilities and skills means fully mastering the theory of conceptual transduction. The reader obviously understands that when characterizing the phenomena of abilities and skills one should take into account the content of not only intratheoretical but also intertheoretical transduction. For the sake of brevity of the analysis, in this case, I limit myself to considering only intratheoretical transduction.

It is extremely important to understand that, both in natural science and in axiology, the main purpose of human activity is the steady improvement of theories. Without theories, there is no point. Both scientists and ordinary people deal with physical phenomena, but the meaning of what they do is determined by physical theories. The situation is similar in technology. Whatever the technological phenomena their meaning will certainly become clear only by direct reference to the relevant technological theories. In this connection, the article by Sabine Ammon [1] is very indicative.

She emphasizes the difference in design and, accordingly, testing from the experiment: «... we find a deductive-nomological inference in the case of the experiment and a practical syllogism in the case of the test. Or, to put it more bluntly: we are dealing with laws when we experiment, and we are dealing with rules when we test. In contrast to an experiment, a test does not explore whether a certain effect can be subsumed under a law but rather explores whether a rule is effective» [1, 505]. In my opinion, an attempt to oppose design to experiment is unsuccessful, for it inevitably leads to the removal of design beyond the bounds of science. The essence of the situation under consideration is that using technological theory, one can make various accents, focusing one's attention, for example, on the development of a theory or on the production of one or another artifact. With the same theory, different semantic accents are possible. They do not lead beyond the limits of technological theory and its improvement. It is quite possible to distinguish between the forms of factualization, including, for example, an experiment conducted to clarify a certain position of the theory and its status as a whole, and the design of a product. Nevertheless, in both cases, factualization and inference take place in accordance with the content of conceptual transduction.

As already noted, according to Walter Vincenti engineers and scientists use knowledge in different ways [13, 226]. According to him, scientists go from less developed knowledge to more developed, and engineers from knowledge to artifacts. In this case, it is clearly misunderstood the fact that artifacts are of a theoretical nature because their construction is also a construction of a theory that is not allowed to freeze at the deduction stage with its deductive-nomological method. Both scientists and engineers do the same thing in the end, namely, they refine technological theories. They do not use theories but develop them. As for the widely used expression 'to use knowledge', it is not clear. Knowledge is contrasted, as a rule, with abilities and skills. The content of all three concepts of knowledge, abilities, and skills is considered intuitively clear. Their true content can be clarified by referring to the theory of conceptual transduction. In this case, it should be borne in mind that it is unacceptable to equate knowledge with theories.

Thus, I see no reason to consider technology as something other than a branch of science.

References

1. Ammon, S. (2017) Why designing is not experimenting: design methods, epistemic praxis and strategies of knowledge acquisition in architecture. Philosophy and Technology 30(4), 495-520.
2. Boon, M. (2011) In defense of engineering sciences: on the epistemological relations between science and technology. Techné 15(1), 49-71.
3. Bunge, M. (1966) Technology as applied science. Technology and Culture 7(3), 329-347.
4. Franssen, M., Lokhorst, G.-J., de Poel, I. van. (2015) Philosophy of technology. The Stanford Encyclopedia of Philosophy. Available at: https://plato.stanford.edu/archives/fall2015/entries/technology/
5. Hetherington, S.C. (2011) How to Know. United Kingdom: Wiley InterScience.
6. Hume, D. (1739).A Treatise of Human Nature. London: John Noon.
7. Kanke, V.A. (2017) Metascientific foundations of understanding of status of technology. Nuclear Energy and Technology 3(4), 243-248.
8. Norström, P. (2015) Knowing how, knowing that, knowing technology. Philosophy and Technology 28(4), 553-565.
9. Ryle, G. (1949) The Concept of Mind. London: Hutchinson.
10. Simon, H.A. (1996) The Sciences of the Artificial.Third ed. Cambridge, Massachusetts, London: MIT Press.
11. Stanley, J., Williamson, T. (2001) Knowing how. Journal of Philosophy, 98(8), 411–444.

12. Techné: Society for Philosophy and Technology (1998) 4(2). Available at: http://scholar.lib.vt.edu/ejournals/SPT/v4n2/

13. Vincenti, W.G. (1990) What Engineers Know and How They Know It: Analytical Studies from Aeronautical History. Baltimore (MD): Johns Hopkins University Press.

11.2. Principles of technological theories

The conceptual content of technology is rarely discussed, and yet it deserves full attention. In my book [8, 13-125] section by section, the conceptual content of the technology is considered. In this place, I will confine myself to concise remarks.

First, it should be noted that the definition of technology as a science of technical artifacts is misleading. In technology, decisive importance possesses not technical artifacts, but people, technologists. Not otherwise, but thanks to people, technologists, technical objects are produced and used. In the world of physics, there are no persons, but technology is a science about them.

The most capacious concepts of any scientific theory are principles. In an effort to determine the features of technical theories, the characteristic of the relevant principles is of primary importance. If they did not exist, then technical theories would not have to be recognized as scientific. In my opinion, they really are. I mean that the design of any technical device is preceded by some utility factor, whether it is the production of useful electricity by a nuclear power plant or the carriage of goods by car. Any technical theory starts with a specific utility principle or efficacy principle. It is impossible to deduce it. Therefore, it is a principle.

Watching the flight of birds, people concluded that it would be useful for them to fly. This is a conclusion by analogy, but not a consistent scientific conclusion, starting with a certain principle. The possibility of technological conclusions arises only corresponding to the efficacy principle. This definition is accompanied by an indication of the principles of the second level, among which the most famous are the principles of efficiency, reliability, safety, speed of operations, and ease of management, durability, and maintainability. The quantitative expression of the principles of the second kind is the corresponding criteria. Based on them, taking into account the successes and failures in the design and use of a technical device, the integral efficacy criterion is determined. It can be specified, for example, in the form of a desirability function [6; 2].

Based on the integral efficacy principle, individual efficacy criteria are defined. In turn, based on them, the integral efficacy criterion is produced. There is no logical circle error in this mutual definition of criteria. Technological processes are implemented through cycles. The initial integral efficacy criteria initiate the appearance of individual criteria, the evaluation of which after the next cognitive cycle leads to the improvement of the integral criterion itself.

Many individual criteria, as a rule, correspond to one integral criterion. All of them can hardly be considered. It is enough to consider only those individual criteria that are relevant for a given function of desirability, which corresponds to a certain interval of confidence. In the case of a racecar, other criteria are actual that in the case of a car as a means of luxury. Each integral criterion corresponds to a well-defined theory. If there are several integral criteria, then it is necessary to consider the ratio of theories. All principles of technological theories are optimized in a certain way.

The peculiarity of the principles of technological theory is the best evidence of the fallacy of understanding it as applied knowledge, for example, physical or chemical. By definition, applied knowledge must be derived from fundamental knowledge. However, as part of physics and chemistry, there are no technological efficacy principles. They are not deducible and, therefore, technology is not an applied science.

Understanding technology as an applied science is extremely popular not by chance. [5; 4] The reason for this phenomenon lies in the misunderstanding of the phenomenon of interdisciplinary relation, especially the relativity of donor theories. Consider two related theories of T_A and T_B. T_A - acceptor, T_B - donor theory. In this connection, the theory of T_B has a subordinate value, which is considered only with respect to the theory of T_A. This circumstance can be expressed by the symbol $T_B[a]$. Add two more donor theories to T_A, namely, T_C and T_D; similar to the theory of T_B, they also have in relation to the theory T_A the relative value of $T_C[a]$ and $T_D[a]$. We now consider a multi-stage process for the production of some technical artifact A, which by definition is the object of the theory of T_A: $T_A \Rightarrow T_B[a] \rightarrow T_C[a] \rightarrow T_D[a]$. $T_B[a] \rightarrow T_C[a] \rightarrow T_D[a]$ is a superventive process, accompanied by qualitative leaps. Theories of T_B, T_C and T_D are incommensurable with each other. The piquancy of the situation is that their primary level of incommensurability is superimposed by the general correlation [a], which is determined by the theory of T_A. Supervention is accompanied by a connection that emanates from the theory of

T_A. In this sense, the theory of T_B, T_C, and T_D acquire relativity, fixing their connection with the theory of T_A.

Understanding technology as an applied science means that the ratio $T_A \Rightarrow T_B[a] \rightarrow T_C[a] \rightarrow T_D[a]$ is replaced by equality $T_A = T_B \rightarrow T_C \rightarrow T_D$. There is a clear simplification, namely, the reduction of technology to the natural sciences. The technological theory of T_A and, consequently, the process of endowing donor theories with technological sense, which is determined primarily by the content of the T_A theory's efficacy principle, is beyond the attention of researchers. In the article [4] an attempt was made to reveal the origins of understanding technology as an applied science. However, its authors do not consider the phenomenon of relativity of donor theories in relation to technological theories. In my opinion, this forgetfulness leads to the understanding of technology as an applied science.

In this place, it is reasonable to recall the system analysis widely used in technology [7; 9; 3]. Many technical devices are system-organized objects. For example, in relation to a nuclear power plant, more than twenty system levels are distinguished [5, 147]. The systems approach allows a certain degree of comprehension of the complexity of the system. The hierarchy is divided into its levels. Each of them is characterized by special theories. The system approach clearly expresses the superventive variety. Unfortunately, as a rule, the systems approach is not accompanied by careful use of intratheoretical and intertheoretical conceptual transitions, as well as by taking into account the significance of the phenomenon relativity of donor conceptions to technology theories. Intratheoretical transitions are necessary to understand what is happening inside the system. Intertheoretical transitions make it possible to take into account the connections between systems. The phenomenon of the relativity of donor theories allows us to understand the originality of the technical device. The systems approach complements the theory of conceptual transduction. It does not have an independent meaning.

References

1. Bunge, M. (1972) Toward a philosophy of technology. In Mitcham, C., Mackey, R. (Eds.). Philosophy and Technology. New York: Free Press, 62-76.
2. Derringer, G., Suich, R. (1980) Simultaneous optimization of several response variables. Journal of Quality Technology 12(4), 214-219.
3. Eder, W.E. (2016) Theory of technical systems – educational tool for engineering. Universal Journal of Educational Research 4(6), 1395-1405.
4. Gil-Pérez, D., Vilches, A., Fernández, I., Cachapuz, A., Praia, J., Valdés, P., and Salinas, J. (2005) Technology as 'applied science.' Science & Education, 14(3-5), 309–320.
5. Gordon, B.G. (2006) Ideologiya bezopasnosti / Trudy NTTS YARB [The ideology of safety / Proceedings of NTC JaRB]. Moskva: NTTS YARB publ. [In Russian].
6. Harrington, E.C, Jr. (1965) The desirability function. Industrial Quality Control 21(10), 494-498.
7. Hubka, V. (1984) Theorie Technischer Systeme [Theory of technical systems]. Berlin: Springer-Verlag. [In German].
8. Kanke, V.A. (2013) Istoriya, filosofiya i metodologiya tekhniki i informatiki [History, Philosophy and Methodology of Technology and Computer science]. Moskva: Yurayt. [In Russian].
9. Ropohl, G. (2009). Allgemeine Technologie: eine Systemtheorie der Technik. 3 Aufg. [General Technology: a

Systems Theory of Technology. Third Edition]. Karlsruhe: Universitätsverlag Karlsruhe, 2009. [In German].

11.3. Finding ways to understand the technology

This section could be called «A Bird's Eye View of Technology". For many decades, researchers have persistently sought to find such an angle of view on technology that would ensure its most adequate understanding. In this regard, it is reasonable to consider, firstly, my own position. Secondly, the so-called general technology, and thirdly, the philosophy of technology.

My concept is presented in the book [7]. I believe that technology consists of a huge number of theories that are combined in league-theories. All arguments about technology, that ignore this circumstance are significantly losing in scientific power and should ultimately be credited to metaphysics.

People manage technological concepts and theories through conceptual transduction methods. From this point of view, technology is no different from other axiological branches of science, as well as from the natural sciences. In connection with the above, let us consider the relevance of intratheoretical transduction methods for technology, that is, deduction, adduction, induction, and abduction.

Deduction regulates the process of prediction, the transition from principles to laws and from them to variables. Such a transition is found in any technical theory. Unfortunately, it often does not do without costs. Principles are not always given in mathematical form. As a rule, their full list is not given; their subordination is not considered in detail.

Of course, any technical theory is not without laws. They are usually represented by numerous equations and inequalities expressing the relationships between variables, for example, the characteristics of the mixture in an internal combustion engine or the parameters of the coolant used in the nuclear cycle. In technology, unlike physics, the idea of universal laws is not held in high esteem. Here it is well recognized that the laws vary from one situation to another. There is no hint of rejection of the concept of scientific law. As for variables, they are mainly used in the intuitive shell, i.e. without special consideration of their technological relativity.

All technological measurements are made under the auspices of the method of adduction. This means that special efforts are being made to ensure that a particular parameter is measured in a clean, uncluttered form. If, for example, the temperature of a graphite stack of a nuclear reactor is measured using a thermocouple, then the effect of radioactive radiation on it is taken into account. The concept of non-destructive testing is widespread in technology. It is meant that measurement should not disturb in any significant way the course of the investigated processes. Strictly speaking, they are at least to some extent necessarily violated. However, the concept of non-destructive testing is relevant as a desire to highlight the parameter being studied in a 'pure' form.

In the vast majority of technological theories, the factualization process is conducted very carefully. Such an example is quite indicative. The control system of the upper block level of the automated process control system for Bushehr NPP is designed to receive 8 thousand analog, 100 thousand discrete and 360 thousand diagnostic signals [8, p. 34]. To receive and process such a multitude of signals, a wide range of instrumentation is needed, the number of which on a single NPP unit reaches several thousand.

Processing of diagnostic signals, including measurement results, is carried out in accordance with the method of induction. In this case, as a rule, regression analysis and computer visualization of its results are decisive. A rare driver, tracking indicators of speed, the efficiency of components, cooling system temperature, fuel level, and engine speed, on the dashboard of a car, understands that these indicators are the result of the targeted use of the induction method.

As is well known, after induction, the turn comes to the method of adduction. Its purpose is to update the principles of the theory. Unlike scientists, people controlling the technical device usually do not consider this circumstance. They, for example, many NPP operators, believe that factualization is necessary only in order to track the deviation of a technical device from its normal state, which must be restored in one way or another. The scientist understands the relevance of data processing more thoroughly. He understands that they, strictly speaking, should be used to update the formulation of the normal state, which should not be considered finally given. The results of technological abduction are usually used in the production of a new technical device of the same type.

Thus, all methods of intratheoretical transduction are relevant for technology. However, what about the methods of intertheoretical transduction, that is, the methods of problematization, discovery, interpretation, and construction of league-theories? In fact, they are widely used, but here it is not without a certain kind of difficulty. In technology, the concept of the theory is far from being as popular as, for example, in physics. Apparently, this circumstance should be explained by widespread neopositivist attitudes among technologists and with their insufficient attention to the concept of the theory.

Technologists do not get tired to talk about inventions that allowed overcoming some difficulties (problems). Let me give an appropriate example. The single-cylinder internal combustion engine has an uneven course and is completely unbalanced. The uneven course is overcome in a four-cylinder engine; the balance is achieved in a six-cylinder engine. There are obvious transitions from less developed theories to more developed ones. Moreover, each transition is accompanied by the overcoming of some problems.

The given example shows that the theories of single-cylinder (T_{L1}), four-cylinder (T_{L4}) and six-cylinder (T_{L6}) internal combustion engines form in historical terms the problematic, and in the sense of interpretation the interpretational (league-theoretical) series.

Problematic series: $T_{L1} \rightarrow T_{L4} \rightarrow T_{L6}$.

Interpretational series: $T_{L6} \rightarrow T_{L4}\{T_{L6}\} \rightarrow T_{L1}\{T_{L6}\}$.

It is enough to refer to the history of the creation of typical technical artifacts, for example, wheels, guns, bicycles, cars, computers, as their long evolutionary series is immediately revealed. This circumstance was already noticed by the founders of evolutionary anthropology and archeology E.B. Tylor [12] and A.P. Rivers [4]. The question is how to understand them. In this connection famous Russian linguist, Yuri Stepanov operates with the concept of an evolutionary semiotic series [11, 605]. He means that there is a definite sign (semiotic) connection between the members of the series. In addition, there is also a certain mutual influence of the evolutionary series on each other. In my opinion, Stepanov explains the structure of the evolutionary series of technical artifacts in insufficient detail. Desirable conceptual clarity can be achieved by considering the league-theories, whose objects are artifacts and interdisciplinary connections between them. In this case, it is necessary to take into account the theory of conceptual transduction.

I mean that advanced technological theory is the key to understanding a less advanced technological concept. Before the creation of a single-row four-cylinder internal combustion engine, the unevenness of the stroke of a single-cylinder engine was only stated, but not explained. Only after the creation of the four-cylinder engine, it became clear what exactly its predecessor lacked. It is significant that people did not abandon the single-cylinder engines. Under certain conditions, their use, for example, on motorcycles is quite acceptable.

Thus, my position in the understanding of technology involves the paramount attention to conceptual transduction. Technology acts as the management of technological concepts and theories through conceptual transduction methods. Technological discipline, for example, energy or transport is a set of related league-theories according to some efficacy principle.

Let me move on to general technology.

First attempts to create a general technology. The first systematic manual on technology was written by the German J. Beckman, whose book «A Guide to Technological Science» [3], first published in 1877, was then reprinted several times. As a student of the famous systematizer of biology C. Linnaeus, Beckmann sought to present the technology in a holistic way. However, in his work are not found generalizing ideas. He limited himself to essays on the history of the development of crafts and inventions, paying particular attention to their economic value. Unlike Beckman F. Reuleaux attempted to present the general kinematics of machines [9]. Prior to the allocation of the nature of technological systems, it did not come. The technology is not reducible to kinematics.

General technology from the standpoint of the general theory of systems and cybernetics. In search of general technology, many researchers place special hopes on cybernetics and the general theory of systems. In this connection, the studies of V. Hubka [6] and G. Ropohl [10] drew particular attention. Both developed the concept of a sociotechnical system. This meant that the technology acquired a subordinate position in relation to the social sciences. In my opinion, the correct position is to take into account the interdisciplinary connections of technology and social sciences; technology should certainly be considered as an independent branch of science. Both V. Hubka and G. Ropohl passed this circumstance. Thus, this time the general technology, in fact, again did not take place.

General technology as a theory for solving inventive problems (TRIZ). This program has a pronounced metascientific orientation. It was developed by the Russian inventor and patent specialist Genrich Altshuller [2; 1]. After analyzing the fate of more than 40,000 patents, he summarized it in the form of eight laws [2, 122-127].

Static laws

1. *The law of completeness of parts of the system.* In each technical system, all four parts of it must be represented: engine, transmission, working body, and control body. Each of these parts must be workable.

2. *The law of «energy conductivity» of the system.* Through the passage of energy in all parts of the system is a necessary condition for the viability of the technical system.

3. *The law of harmonization of the rhythms of parts of the system.*

Kinematic laws

4. *The law of increasing the degree of the ideality of the system.* The development of all systems goes towards increasing the degree of ideality. An ideal technical system is a system whose weight, volume and area tend to zero, although its ability to perform work does not diminish.

5. *The law of uneven development of parts of the system.* Because of this, there is an urgent need to modify certain parts of the system.

6. *The law of transition to the super-system.* Having exhausted the possibilities of development, the system is included in the super-system as one of the parts; at the same time, further development goes at the super-system level.

Dynamic laws

7. *The law of transition from the macro level to the micro level.*

8. *The law of increasing degree of combination of substance and field.*

Crucial in TRIZ is the identification of contradictions and then overcoming them through some rules, which number four dozen. It is proposed, for example, to divide an object into its separate parts and separate the 'interfering part' from it. G. Altshuller was an adherent of dialectical materialism, according to which development consists in the transition from one contradiction to another, more developed. He did not use this dialectical law in a systematic manner, limiting himself to the statement about the necessity of isolating contradictions and overcoming them. What G. Altshuller called contradictions in the philosophy of science are called problems. In fact, his efforts were focused on two methods of intertheoretical transduction, problematization, and discovery. However, the trouble was that the TRIZ methods were considered irrespective of the methods of intratheoretical transduction. This is the major weakness of the TRIZ.

Another disadvantage of TRIZ is that it weakly expresses the features of technical objects. It is not difficult to verify that, in fact, all the laws of TRIZ are quite suitable for characterizing not only technical systems but also various organisms, in particular, humans. It seems that supporters of TRIZ developing theories to be based solely on the features of technical systems, ultimately, deviate significantly from them. This is a kind of payment for not considering technological theories as such. Without taking into account the specifics of these theories, TRIZ becomes highly speculative.

When searching for the English-language analog of TRIZ, the theory of constraints (TOC) of Eliyahu Goldratt attracts attention [5]. In contrast to Altshuller, Goldratt argues about overcoming, not contradictions, but constraints. He is not guided by the dialectic of contradictions, but by an understanding of the chains of causation. Actual examples relate mainly to economic management. Ultimately, he, like G. Altshuller, comes in a belief system in which the specificity of the analyzed systems is not properly visible. Both TRIZ and TOC are formal theories. In this their quality they do not deserve disapproval. The trouble is that they have largely lost touch with their scientific, informal basis. A formal theory should not be speculative.

It is time to consider *metaphysical generalizations of technology*. Representatives, and sometimes very prominent, of the main philosophical directions, in particular, positivism, Marxism, pragmatism, phenomenology, hermeneutics, and poststructuralism, often seek to give a comprehensive description of the phenomenon of the technique. As a rule, all of them, for example, K. Jaspers, E. Husserl, M. Heidegger, and H. Jonas, have rather vague ideas about the content of technological theories. Nevertheless, they are confident that the conceptual strength of their favorite philosophical trends is sufficient to characterize the technology. Meanwhile, these philosophical directions were formed without regard to technology. As a result, their potential is insufficient for the content characteristics of the technology. The considered generalizations are metaphysical in nature. In this quality, they, in my opinion, do not deserve high praise. Nevertheless, it does not follow from this that it is necessary to abandon the considered philosophical characteristics.

Philosophical and metaphysical generalizations of technology should be accompanied by their significant updating due to metascientifical research, implemented directly in the field of technology. In my opinion, the currents of knowledge must continuously circulate between technology, meta-technology and the philosophy of technology. In this case, metatechnology is understood as the comprehension of the nature of technological concepts and methods of their management. These methods are methods of conceptual transduction. The technological theory based on conceptual transduction is a general technology. As shown in this section, all attempts to develop a general technology without studying the conceptual and methodological content of technological theories end in failure.

References

1. Altshuller, G. (1999) The Innovation Algorithm. Transl. by L. Shulyak, and S. Rodman. Worcester, MA: Technical Innovation Centre Inc.
2. Altshuller, G.S. (1979) Tvorchestvo kak tochnaya nauka [Creativity as an Exact Science]. Moskva: Sovetskoye radio. [In Russian].
3. Beckman, J. (1990) [1877] Anleitung zur Technologie oder zur Kenntnis der Handwerke, Fabriken und Manufacturen. 2. Aufl. Basel: Basler Papiermühle. [In German].
4. Bowden, M.C. (1984) General Pitt-Rivers: The Father of Scientific Archaeology. Salisbury: Salisbury and South Wiltshire Museum.
5. Goldratt, E.M. (1987-1990) Essays on the Theory of Constraints. Great Barrington, MA: North River Press.
6. Hubka, V. (1984) Theorie Technischer Systeme [Theory of technical systems]. Berlin: Springer-Verlag. [In German].
7. Kanke, V.A. (2013) Istoriya, filosofiya i metodologiya tekhniki i informatiki [History, Philosophy and Methodology of Technology and Computer science]. Moskva: Yurayt. [In Russian].
8. Mengazetdinov, N.E., et. al. (2013) Kompleks rabot po sozdaniyu pervoy upravlyayushchey sistemy verkhnego blochnogo urovnya ASU TP dlya AES «Busher» na osnove otechestvennykh informatsionnykh tekhnologiy [The complex of works on the creation of the first control system of the upper block level of the automated process control

system for Bushehr NPP based on domestic information technologies]. Moskva IPU RAN. [In Russian].

9. Reuleaux, F. (1876) The Kinematics of Machinery. London: Macmillan and Co.

10. Ropohl, G. (2009) Allgemeine Technologie: eine Systemtheorie der Technik. 3 Aufg. [General Technology: a Systems Theory of Technology. Third ed.]. Karlsruhe: Universitätsverlag Karlsruhe, 2009. [In German].

11. Stepanov, Y.S. (2001) Semiotika kontseptov [Semiotics of Concepts]. In Stepanov, Y.S. (Ed.) Semiotika: Antologiya [Semiotics: Anthology]. Moskva: Akademicheskiy proyekt; Yekaterinburg: Delovaya kniga, 603-612. [In Russian].

12. Tylor, E.B. (1871) Primitive Culture. Vol. 1. London: John Murray.

11.4. Philosophy of technology: Marxist variants

The philosophy of technology is inevitably interpreted by certain philosophical positions. From this point of view, philosophers formulated interesting positions from antiquity; in particular, we can recall the characteristic of technology by Aristotle. However, it took many centuries before systematic studies of the nature of technology appeared. It was in this connection that the book «The Foundations of the Philosophy of Technique» from the distant 1877 attracted attention [7]. Ernst. Kapp was a Hegelian. G. Hegel believed that the world spirit returns to itself, passing through the stages of nature and man and society. Thus, the following philosophical cycle takes place: world spirit → otherness of spirit in nature → otherness of spirit in man and society → world spirit. Kapp inserted the technique into this cycle as a person's otherness. In fact, he proposed the Hegelian philosophical cycle in a new form: the world spirit → otherness of spirit in nature → the otherness of spirit in man and society → the otherness of man in technology → the world spirit. Kapp believed that a person unconsciously transfers his functional relationships to a technique [7, V]. This is the essence of his «organ-design principle».

As a supporter of the philosophy of G. Hegel, Kapp is quite consistent. However, he would be even more consistent if considered the technique not only as of the creature of the man but also of society. This was done 33 years earlier by Karl Marx in his "Economic and Philosophical Manuscripts" [11]. The approach proposed by Marx was much more important for the fate of the philosophy of technology than the approach of Kapp.

The main feature of Marx's philosophy was that, following Hegel, he replaced the scientific method with the dialectical method, according to which in science the ascent from less developed contradictions to more developed ones is realized. At first glance, it seems that Marx moves from one problem to another and, in fact, implements the problematic method. Nevertheless, this impression is misleading. The fact is that the movement of contradictions does not express the mechanism of scientific thought, which in its true foundations is realized by the methods of deduction, adduction, induction, and abduction. Realizing the conceptual transduction, the researcher is aware of the movement of contradictions. If this movement replaces intratheoretical transduction, then the scientific method simply disappears, it is replaced by speculation. The work of Karl Marx is a good illustration of this rule.

Marx made selfless attempts to understand the relationship between nature and society, individual and social, technical and social. Arguing consistently, he had to consider the features of natural, technological and social theories and interdisciplinary connections between them. Unfortunately, K. Marx did not own the described approach. As a result, he came to many striking metaphysical (speculative) conclusions.

As K. Marx explains in the fifth chapter of his main book «Capital», the labor process unites man with nature. Labor from the form of activity passes into the form of being and in this form freezes in the products of labor. Labor concluded in goods, in particular, in all technical artifacts, is dual; it is, on the one hand, an individual, and, on the other hand, social, abstract labor. Machines are the means of producing surplus value. Economic epochs differ not by what is produced, but by how it is produced, by what means of labor. [10, 128] As a result, technology turns out to be a concentration of a huge mass of abstract labor, in which the workers alienate themselves from themselves. The capitalists skillfully use this fact for mercenary purposes. Ultimately, it is technology, which embodies social substance, abstract labor. Ultimately, the basis of the development of society is not the mind, not the theory, but the material. It is possible to overcome the exploitation of the capitalists of the workers by means of a socialist revolution, not theory According to K. Marx in his famous 11 theses about Feuerbach's philosophy, it is not enough just to explain the world, it should be changed [9]. In this thesis, Marx proclaims the primacy of revolutionary practice over theory. A theory is powerless in the face of revolutionary practice.

The correct line of reasoning consisted of defining economic collisions through economic theories with the indispensable consideration of the interdisciplinary connections of economics and technology. In this case, no social conflicts would lead beyond the theories and, therefore, the principle of theoretical representation. Marx, however, acts in a fundamentally different way: he introduces economic content directly into the sphere of technology. The technique is an economic phenomenon. In reality, technology is an object representation of technical theory. Therefore, it is not a technical factor. K. Marx proclaimed the technique as an economic factor. Its content is determined by the capitalist mode of production. Strictly speaking, K. Marx does not need technological theories.

An actual variation of Marxist ideas about the nature of technology was the attempt by Max Horkheimer to develop a critical theory as opposed to the traditional one [6]. «It is obvious that man may be materially, emotionally, and intellectually impoverished at decisive points despite the progress of science and industry. Science and technology are only elements in an existing social totality, and it is quite possible that, despite all their achievements, other factors, even the totality itself, could be moving backwards, that man could become increasingly stunted and unhappy, that the individual could be ruined and nations headed toward disaster» [6, 259].

In this regard, Horkheimer criticized the reduction of reason to empirical, instrumental and technological rationality. Theodor Adorno adhered to the same position: «technology is neither a primary social entity, nor humanity, but only something derivative, a form of organization of human labor» [2, 368]. The critical theory puts under critical fire, among other things, also science and technology. M. Horkheimer and T. Adorno, dissatisfied with the fact that metaphysics was replaced by instrumental rationality, intended to replace it with critical theory. The good desire to develop a new philosophical and theoretical paradigm faced with indefinable difficulties, because it was not possible to present it in detail.

An attempt by T. Adorno to link the fate of the critical theory with negative dialectics [1] ended in an embarrassment, because, like the Hegelian and Marxist dialectic, it did not go beyond metaphysics. The desire to create a new image of social theory based on aesthetics [3] also did not lead to success. The content of his aesthetic theory was not so weighty that from his position it would be fruitful to criticize the science, accepted in modern society.

Herbert Marcuse gave new impulses to the position of the influence of historical practice on the status of technology. He insisted on the possibility of «translation of values into technical tasks – the materialization of values» [8, 234]. Just as capitalism gave rise to technological rationality, topical protest movements, for example, of gender or environmental order, can counterpose to it more viable technological theories that are not limited to any single form of rationality and irrationality. Technological reality will not stand under the pressure of the creative imagination of active subjects.

The views of H. Marcuse had a significant influence on the formation of the position of, perhaps, the most prominent representative of the modern neo-Marxist understanding of the Andrew Feenberg technology phenomenon [5, 128]. Unlike his predecessors from Marx to Marcuse, he seeks to pay due attention not only to the social significance of technology but also to its own content. In this regard, he considers the primary instrumentalization as functionalization, which characterizes the technique itself, and the secondary instrumentalization integration, which characterizes the place of technology in its interaction with nature and society [4, 305-310].

Primary instrumentalization implies decontextualization (isolation of material from its natural abode), reductionism (liberation of things from their useless in technical terms parts), autonomization of the artifact produced, and positioning (regulation of technical actions). Secondary instrumentalization contains systematization operations (inclusion of a technical object into a natural or social system), mediation (endowing the object with ethical and aesthetic properties), vocation (the influence of a technical object on who uses it) and initiative (forms of actions not defined directly by positioning). Thus, according to A. Feenberg, it is necessary to clearly distinguish between the techniques itself and its significance in the composition of non-technical systems. The phenomenon of technological rationality does not frighten A. Feenberg, for it is amenable to democratization. In my opinion, A. Feenberg presented the movement of neo-Marxist thought in understanding the phenomenon of technology in a very consistent way. It is time critically evaluate this movement.

First, I note that researchers who follow the line of Marxism do not consider technological theories as such, in particular, their principles. Even A. Feenberg is limited to general considerations, in particular, on decontextualization, reductionism, autonomization and positioning, without detailed consideration of the conceptual and methodological nature of technological theories. Secondly, no neo-Marxist authors consider sufficiently thoroughly interdisciplinary connections between technological theories and other conceptions. Third, they belittle the value of the theory, opposing practice to it. As a result, they find themselves in the thrall of dualism: theory – practice. Fourth, they do not fully abandon the condescending attitude toward the merits of technological theories. All of them have bright axiological content. There is absolutely no reason to either exaggerate or belittle their importance. Fifth, the authors in question are unconvincingly using the achievements of the modern philosophy of science, including the philosophy of axiological sciences. Sixthly, a critical review of K. Marx's metaphysics leaves much to be desired. In many ways, this metaphysics cannot be reconciled with the modern philosophy of science.

References

1. Adorno, T. (1973) [1966]. Negative Dialectics. Trans. by E.B. Ashton. New York: Seabury Press.
2. Adorno, T. (1989) O tekhnike i gumanizme [On technology and humanism]. In Filosofiya tekhniki v FRG [Philosophy of Technology in Germany]. Moskva: Progress, 364-371. [In Russian].
3. *Adorno, T. (1997) [1970]* Aesthetic Theory. Minneapolis: University of Minnesota Press, 1997.
4. Feenberg, A. (2000) From essentialism to constructivism: Philosophy of technology at the crossroads. In Higgs, E., Light, A.W., and Strong, D. (Eds.) Technology and the Good Life? Chicago and London: The University of Chicago Press.
5. Feenberg, A. (2016) Realizing philosophy: Marx, Lukács and the Frankfurt School. In Critical Theory and the Challenge of Praxis: Beyond Reification. New York: Routledge, 117-130.
6. Horkheimer, M. (2002) Critical Theory. Selected Essays. Transl. by M.J. O'Connell and others. New York: Continuum.
7. Kapp, E. (1877) Grundlinien einer Philosophie der Technik [Basics of a Philosophy of Technology]. Braunschweig: Verlag von G. Westermann. [In German].
8. Marcuse, H. (1964) One-Dimensional Man. Boston, MA: Beacon Press.
9. Marx, K. (1845) Theses on Feuerbach. Transl. by C. Smith and D. Cuckson. Marxists Internet Archive, 2002. Available at: www.marxists.org/
10. Marx, K. (1954) [1887] Capital. A Critique of Political Economy Volume I. Book One: The Process of Production of Capital. Ed. by F. Engels. Moscow: Progress Publishers.

11. Marx, K. (2007). Economic and Philosophic Manuscripts of 1844. New York: Dover Publications.

11.5. The philosophy of technology: questions to pragmatism

Classical American pragmatism was formed not long after Marxism, by the end of the XIX century. Then its value steadily increased. However, only a century later its exceptional importance to the philosophy of technology was realized. This was largely due to Larry Hickman, who was far from trivial to assess the value of John Dewey's philosophy precisely in connection with the demands of the philosophy of technology [1; 2]. One of his key articles begins by stating, «The pragmatism was strongly committed to the sciences». [5, 175]. This is a relevant and very strong argument in an attempt to prove the primary relevance of the pragmatic and not any other, version of the philosophy of technology. Indeed, the authors of the first versions of the philosophy of technology, including Karl Marx and Martin Heidegger, did not possess the scientific method to the extent that it was available by John Dewey. He did not oppose natural and axiological sciences, did not see the evil fate of man in technology. He strove consistently, using, above all, the achievements of science to present the ways of democratic improvement of human society. In this way, a worthy place was given to technology.

The central idea of Dewey was «to naturalize technology by locating inquiry into tools and techniques within an evolutionary account of human development» [5, 176]. This aspiration is the main leitmotif of Hickman's developed philosophy of technology. The point is that it is not enough just to proclaim the relevance of the scientific method, but it is necessary to identify the mechanisms, methods, and tools of scientific progress. According to Hickman, technology is «the invention, development, and cognitive deployment of tools and other artifacts, brought to bear on raw materials and intermediate stock parts, with a view to the resolution of perceived problems» [3, 26]. And this is where a certain conflict arises, noticed by Robert Innis «Dewey's pragmatism is, more generally, a productive (or even instrumental) pragmatism, not a technological one» [7, 52]. Hickman brings under the rubric of technology not only technical but also all other sciences. However, traditionally, the philosophy of technology refers to a specific discipline that deals with the elected namely technical entities, of mental, linguistic or object nature. In other words, the instrumentalism of J. Dewey has not been brought to the necessary degree of specification, which is necessary for establishing direct contact with the technical sciences. In his absence, the desire for a consistent implementation of the scientific method remains largely a good wish. Pragmatism Dewey opens the way to the scientific method, but it still needs to be realized. The question of how to implement it remains in the work of Hickman open.

Hickman's response to Innis's criticism is quite indicative. He noted, firstly, that the understanding of technology as a separate thing with an essence should be rejected. Secondly, it is a natural activity. Thirdly, by treating technology as a query, he overcomes the dissociation of the arts/humanities and the technosciences. Fourth, his understanding of technology opens the way for technodiversity [4, 74-75]. No arguments do in any way override the need for an adequate understanding of the philosophy of technology. The technosciences do not possess the essence that is often proclaimed on behalf of metaphysics. They really are not alien to human nature. There is no need to separate them from other sciences with which they are in interdisciplinary relationships. There is technodiversity if the latter is understood as a variety of technical theories and their interpretations. None of the above negates the distinctiveness of technosciences and the need for their comprehension by means of the philosophy of technology.

Hickman is far from alone in bringing technology beyond the limits of technoscience. In the same vein, Paul Durbin argues. Following the covenants of the democratically oriented pragmatic thinkers J. Dewey [1] and especially G.H. Mead [8], he encourages philosophers to maximize ethical activity, calling his philosophy activism [2].

Theories of L. Hickman and P.T. Durbin is two different variations of the heritage of the classic American pragmatism. In this connection, in my opinion, it is quite legitimate to distinguish two league-theories, namely, Hickman-Dewey and Durbin-Mead. A significant drawback of these theories is, in my opinion, that the essence of the scientific method is not realized in a distinct form. Article by Joseph Pitt 'Technological Explanation' [9] deserves special attention against this background.

Speaking on behalf of pragmatism, he seeks to reveal the peculiarities of technological, and not physical, social, or any other explanation. The third section of the article has the remarkable name 'Technological Versus Scientific Explanation'. Pitt believes that a scientific explanation is deductive-nomological, i.e. it is governed by scientific laws that are not characteristic of technology [9, 864]. In his opinion, the deductive-nomological explanation is characteristic exclusively for physics and chemistry, but not for technology, which is the creation of people. In my opinion, J.C. Pitt is clearly mistaken. The deductive-nomological explanation captures the deductive derivation of laws from principles. This takes place both in physics and in any technological theory. Principles of technological theories are invented by people, but as such, they determine the connection of variables, which is the law.

Having rejected deduction, J.C. Pitt does not even mention adduction, induction, and abduction. This omission, in my opinion, blocks the presentation of an adequate conception of scientific explanation. In his search, Pitt notes failure in technology teleological, social and psychological explanations [9, 864-865]. As for the social and psychological explanations, they really are not technological explanations, because they do not take into account the specifics of the technological sciences. The situation is different with a teleological explanation. J.C. Pitt rejects it so far as it is silent about design. In fact, the teleological explanation is characteristic of all axiological theories, including technological conceptions. This is obvious because the setting and achieving goals is crucial. The teleological explanation acts as consistent use of the methods of deduction, adduction, induction, and abduction.

Ultimately, J.C. Pitt addresses an explanation that goes back to systems theory. He examines the relationship of the system, its structure and the functions of its individual components. Nevertheless, such an explanation, as noted in section 10.3, in the case of ignoring the methods of conceptual transduction is not consistent.

Another feature of the conception of J.C. Pitt is that the technical explanation is understood as a successful contact with the audience, the answers to its questions «Why?» and «How?» [9, 866-867]. In essence, it is a question of the relationship between theories of the one who explains and the members of the audience. In this regard, there are relevant pedagogical and hermeneutic moments. They remain unanswered if, following J.C. Pitt not to consider the ratio of theories of individuals, who ask questions and answer them.

I adhere to the belief that classical pragmatism is focused on the consistent use of the scientific method. At the same time, I have to admit that even outstanding representatives of the pragmatic philosophy of technology, in particular, L. Hickman, P.T. Durbin, and J.C. Pitt is mainly limited to declaring its commitment to the scientific method. Its potential largely remains unfulfilled. As the reader knows, I associate this potential with the theory of intratheoretical and intertheoretical transduction.

In conclusion, I will consider the question of the influence of the pragmatic version of the philosophy of technology on its other interpretations. Considering the positions of the phenomenologist D. Ihde, neo-Marxist A. Feenberg and the fundamental ontologist M. Heidegger, L. Hickman states that «each of these positions was both anticipated and developed in detail as a part of John Dewey's pragmatic technology» [5, 178]. In my opinion, L. Hickman clearly hurried with the admission of D. Ihde, A. Feenberg and M. Heidegger to the pragmatist camp.

The fact is that each original conception of the philosophy of technology begins with a certain basic principle, the content of which imposes its stamp on all other concepts of the theory. The pragmatist L. Hickman is guided by the principle of instrumentalism; D. Ihde – by the principle of variation; A. Feenberg – by the principle of generation of critical theory through protests; the fundamental ontologist M. Heidegger – by poetic principle. Different principles correspond to different theories. They contain similar linguistic expressions, but they are interpreted in fundamentally different ways. Pragmatically interpreted practice differs significantly from phenomenological, neo-Marxist and fundamental ontological practice. The so-called pragmatic turn indicates the influence of pragmatism on other philosophical directions. This influence, of course, exists, but it does not lead either to the replacement of philosophical trends by pragmatism or to the introduction of its individual parts into it. Interdisciplinary communication may be more or less close, but they never cancel the peculiarity of the disciplines. This rule also applies to the ratio of various interpretations of the philosophy of technology.

References

1. Dewey, J. (1935) Liberalism and Social Action. New York; Putnam.
2. Durbin, P.T. (2010) Philosophy, activism, and computer and information specialists revisited. AI and Society 25(1), 119-122.
3. Hickman, L. (2001) Philosophical Tools for Technological Culture: Putting Pragmatism to Work. Bloomington: Indiana University Press.
4. Hickman, L. (2003) Revisiting philosophical tools for technological culture. Techné: Research in Philosophy and Technology 7(1), 64-81.
5. Hickman, L. (2009) Technological pragmatism. In J.K.B. Olsen, J.K.B., Pedersen, S.A. and Hendricks, V.F. (Eds.). A Companion to the Philosophy of Technology. Malden, MA: Wiley-Blackwell, 175-179.
6. Hickman, L. (1990) John Dewey's Pragmatic Technology. Bloomington: Indiana University Press.
7. Innis, R.E. (2003) The meanings of technology. Techné: Research in Philosophy and Technology 7(1), 49-58.

8. Mead, G.H. (1964) The moral philosopher and the moral life. In Selected writings: George Herbert Mead. Ed. by A. Reck. Indianapolis, IN: Bobbs-Merrill, 6-24.
9. Pitt, J. C. (2009) Technological explanation. In Meierse A. (Ed.). Philosophy of Technology and Engineering Sciences. Handbook of the Philosophy of Science. Amsterdam at el.: North Holland, 861–879.

11.6. Postphenomenological philosophy of technology: vague method

The postphenomenological philosophy of technology is a rather interesting project [4; 7; 12; 12; 14], gaining an increasing number of supporters. The basics of this interpretation of the philosophy of technology were developed by Don Ihde. They deserve paramount attention. In the shortest possible terms, D. Ihde himself expressed them.

Postphenomenology is a modified, hybrid phenomenology. On the one side, it recognizes the role of pragmatism in the overcoming of early modern epistemology and metaphysics. It sees in classical pragmatism a way to avoid the problems and misunderstandings of phenomenology as a subjectivist philosophy, sometimes taken as antiscientific, locked into idealism or solipsism. Pragmatism has never been thought of this way, and I regard this as a positive feature. On the other side, it sees in the history of phenomenology a development of a rigorous style of analysis through the use of variational theory, the deeper phenomenological understanding of embodiment and human active bodily perception, and a dynamic understanding of a lifeworld as a fruitful enrichment of pragmatism. And, finally, with the emergence of the philosophy of technology, it finds a way to probe and analyze the role of technologies in social, personal, and cultural life that it undertakes by concrete – empirical – studies of technologies in the plural. This, then, is a minimal outline of what constitutes postphenomenology. [8, 23]

Classical pragmatism is used by D. Ihde for leveling shortcomings of classical phenomenology, the three principles of which remain unshakable, namely, understanding of embodiment, the method of variation, and lifeworld. Of these three concepts, of course, the method of variation is central. Without it, all arguments about the embodiment and lifeworld lose their power, because the mechanism for their realization is not clear. Methodologically, D. Ihde focuses on phenomenology, not pragmatism. The scientific and methodological side of classical pragmatism was developed in the most presentable form by Charles Peirce and John Dewey. Peirce was guided by three-tier conceptual transduction: abduction - deduction - induction [13, vol. 5]. Dewey supplemented it with arguments about the instrumental value of theories in solving problems. There is every reason to assert that he did not reject intratheoretical transduction and was also close to comprehending the correlation of theories and problems [3], which is part of the intertheoretical transduction.

Don Ihde, with all his attention to classical pragmatism, essentially ignores its methodological basis, which is Peirce's three-tier transduction. In essence, abandoning it, he made the main methodological emphasis on the method of variations. To show its strength, he considers various geometric shapes, which, depending on the point of view, look different and, therefore, they are multistable. [8, 12-16] His other examples show that, depending on the situations, various properties and functions of technical artifacts, such as throwing tools, are used.

Trying to appreciate the status of the variation method, let me turn to scientific theories with high authority, including physics and economics. Thanks to A. Einstein, it was realized that many parameters are relative because they depend on reference systems. The length of the object in different reference systems is not the same. The price of goods depends on the market. The relevant vehicle speed depends on the traffic situation. All this is well known to scientists without the help of phenomenologists. But in order to arrive at final conclusions regarding the pluralism of objects and their properties, they certainly use, more or less successfully, all the methods of conceptual transduction. Arguing about objects, scientists use very advanced theories. However, they do not refuse the wealth of sensory perceptions. Against the background of scientific methods, the proposed method of variations looks like an event extremely depleted in scientific and theoretical terms. Scientists have no sense to adopt it. Without it, they demonstrate numerous and highly remarkable examples of pluralism.

The method of variation by E. Husserl [6, sec. 87] involves the use of a number of concepts, such as eidetic variation, free imaginary variation, and essence. I have read many philosophical works in which the phenomenology of E. Husserl was enthusiastically commented. Nevertheless, I do not know of a single example of the consistent and successful use of the phenomenological theory of variations in any science.

The method of variations of Husserl as a whole is not an equivalent replacement for conceptual transduction methods. Moreover, the Ihde method, which is a simplification of the Husserl method, is not such a substitute. The incompatibility, on the one hand, of the method of variation, on the other hand, of pragmatic methods of conceptual transduction, shows that the inoculation of pragmatism to phenomenology, in fact, did not take place. Scott Aikin arrived at a similar conclusion: «Pragmatism's naturalism is inconsistent with the phenomenological tradition's anti-naturalism» [1, 317]. At the same time, he adheres to the position traditional for American philosophers that naturalism is oriented toward the natural sciences and causal explanation. Phenomenologists, unlike pragmatists, do not side with this position. In my opinion, the conceptual content of naturalism is not enough to characterize strictly the fundamental incompatibility of phenomenology and pragmatism. We should talk about the scientific method in its modern sense, i.e. about the methods of intratheoretical and intertheoretical transduction taking into account the whole spectrum of interdisciplinary relations.

It is significant that pragmatism was originally distinguished by its pronounced orientation not on natural, but on axiological sciences, in particular, on economics and political science, but also on technology. Throughout the 20th century, pragmatists demonstrated their ability to be guided by scientific methods applied to axiological theories with their value principles, such as maximizing the profit rate in the economy and maximizing democracy in political science. Such principles are completely absent in the natural sciences. Therefore, one should not liken axiological sciences to a natural one. Another thing is that their methods are similar to each other.

In my opinion, the decisive error of D. Ihde is that he estimated the variation method as the pinnacle of scientific methodology. He believes that the postphenomenological technology has become the pinnacle of the following metamorphoses of science [8, 7]. The 1930s through the 1950s – domination of logical positivism; by the 1950s to the 1960s – adding histories and revolutions to the notion of science practice; the 1970s – is seen as a particular social practice; the 1980s – recognition that science itself is also technologically embodied; in the late 1980s and 1990s – science was seen frequently as gender phenomenon in cultural practice.

The considered line of reasoning is that the assessment of the status of science is proposed without analyzing the conceptual and methodological structure of theories of two dozen branches of science. The absence of such an analysis leads directly to metaphysics, so alien to naturalism. If we turn directly to the conceptual structure of scientific theories, then there is no room for metaphysics. In neopositivism, critical rationalism and analytical philosophy, the structure, and history of scientific theories were productively clarified. In a fundamentally different way, phenomenology, hermeneutics, and poststructuralism developed. In these philosophical directions, with their particular attention to mental processes (phenomenology), to achieving agreement in controversial situations (hermeneutics) and pluralism of points of view (poststructuralism), problems relevant to science were revealed. Nevertheless, they were offered in metaphysical packaging, without clearly representing the relevant methods. From this point of view, it is obvious that the phenomenology not only of Husserl but also of D. Ihde, being metaphysically oriented, is not the scale of science. This circumstance appears most clearly when comparing the methods used in science with the method of variations proposed on behalf of phenomenology.

The fundamental ontology of M. Heidegger also belongs to the metaphysically oriented philosophical directions. I am forced to pay attention to this circumstance since very often phenomenology is evaluated from the standpoint of a fundamental ontology, which is considered the only true one. This line of thought is characteristic of the authors of the article [15]. They propose to rehabilitate the ontological dimension in the postphenomenological philosophy of technology. In my opinion, this appeal is insignificant. First, phenomenology is not without an ontological dimension. This is clear to the extent that the intentional acts considered in phenomenology, by definition, refer to ontology. Secondly, M. Heidegger's fundamental ontology itself must be considered critically, and on behalf of the modern philosophy of science, which it avoids. Then it turns out that in terms of methodology, ontology following phenomenology does not stand up to the competition with scientific theories, in particular, technological ones. The proposed by M. Heidegger poetic method [5] does not meet the criteria of clarity that are accepted in science. Based on the content of scientific theories, one can imagine the meaning of exact words and adequate practical actions. Otherwise, they remain largely unclear in their content. Consistently implement in scientific theories the methods of variation and poetic method so far no one has succeeded. Matters here are not in the shortcomings of scientific theories but in the methodological inconsistency of phenomenology and fundamental ontology with the vital needs of the most advanced, i.e. scientific knowledge.

At this point, it is reasonable to assess the relevance of the post prefix in the word postphenomenology (compare: [2]). Any philosophical direction is subject to numerous modifications. Displaying their diversity by prefixes is hardly possible. However, as a rule, researchers most often use two prefixes neo and post. The prefix neo indicates the inviolability of basic principles. Neopositivism is with all its innovations positivism. The prefix post indicates a cardinal transformation. Poststructuralism is no longer structuralism. D. Ihde noted that the graft of pragmatism to phenomenology makes the content of the latter «more phenomenological» [9, 19]. Thus, if we follow the tradition dominant in philosophy, then the phenomenology of D. Ihde should be considered as neophenomenology. Breaking this tradition, D. Ihde calls his theory postphenomenology. That is his unconventional choice.

Following the variation method, the central place in the concept of D. Ihde occupies implementation and lifeworld concepts. The concept of an embodiment is that «we are Homo faber not just because we make things but also because we are made by them» [12, 15]. D. Ihde considers the embodiment as the interaction between people and things [12; 10]. Essentially, interdisciplinary relations are not considered as such. Consideration of these relationships is also highly desirable when characterizing lifeworld. If they are not considered, then, in essence, lifeworld emerges as everyday life. This trend is clearly visible in the works of D. Ihde.

In my opinion, the main way to improve the phenomenological interpretation of the philosophy of technology is its transfer to a clear scientific track.

References

1. Aikin, S. F. (2006) Pragmatism, naturalism, and phenomenology. Human Studies, 29(3), 317-340.
2. De Preester, H. (2010) Postphenomenology, embodiment and technics. Human Studies, 33(2-3), 339–345.
3. Dewey, J. (1910) How we Think. New York: Dover Publications
4. Friis, J., Crease, R. (Eds.). (2015) Technoscience and Postphenomenology; The Manhattan Papers. New York, London: Lexington Books.
5. Heidegger, M. (2008) Being and Time. Transl. by J. Macquarrie and E. Robinson. New York: Harper and Row.
6. Husserl, E. (1973) [1939] Experience and Judgement. Trans. By J.S. Churchill and K. Ameriks, London: Routledge.
7. Ihde, D. (1990) Technology and the Lifeworld: from Garden to Earth. Bloomington: Indiana University Press.
8. Ihde, D. (2009) Postphenomenology and Technoscience: The Peking University Lectures. Albany: State University of New York Press.
9. Ihde, D. (2010) Heidegger's Technologies: Postphenomenological Perspectives. New York: Fordham University Press.
10. Ihde, D. (2011) Postphenomenological re-embodiment. Foundations of Science, 17(4), 373-377.
11. Ihde, D. (2016) Husserl's Missing Technologies. New York: Fordham University Press.
12. Ihde, D., Malafouris, M. Homo faber Revisited: Postphenomenology and Material Engagement Theory. Available at: https://link.springer.com/article/10.1007/s13347-018-0321-7/
13. Peirce, C. S. (1931-1958) Collected Papers of Charles Sanders Peirce. 8 vols. Ed. by C. Hartshorne, P. Weiss, and A. Burks. Cambridge MA: Harvard University Press.

14. Rosenberger, R., Verbeek, P.P. (2015) Postphenomenologicl Investigations: Essays on Human-Technology Relations. New York, London: Lexington Books.
15. Zwier1, J., Blok, V., Lemmens, P. (2016) Phenomenology and the empirical turn: a phenomenological analysis of postphenomenology. Philosophy and Technology 29(4), 313-333.

11.7. Poetic conception of technology: unmanifested authenticity

The author of the influential conception of technology is Martin Heidegger. Before addressing it directly, I will review the main points of the scientific understanding of technology. They will allow treating the conception of M. Heidegger critically. In the shortest terms, the scientific understanding of technology comes down to the following points.

(1) It is recognized the usefulness of technological theories that are self-sufficient, not less than other scientific conceptions, for example, physical and economic.

(2) Technological theories are axiological conceptions, their principles, laws, and variables have a value character.

(3) The technique as a set of technical artifacts and actions is an object representation of technological theories.

(4) The nature of technology as such is determined by its own content, and not by an external, no matter how it is understood.

(5) Technological theories, along with numerous other scientific conceptions, are full participants in a vast network of interdisciplinary relationships.

(6) Technological theories themselves have some ethical content. It is positive if ethical principles are incorporated directly into technological theories.

(7) The integral ethical significance of technology is determined by maximizing its contribution to interdisciplinary relationships with all other axiological theories.

M. Heidegger presented his understanding of technology in expanded form in an extensive article «The Question concerning technology». It, first published in 1954, is a peculiar result of his many years of effort to present the philosophy of technology in the clearest and detailed form. Initially, M. Heidegger set the task «to open our human existence to the essence of technology» [8, 3]. With such a statement, obviously, we should agree. Any science is the result of people's creativity, technology, too. In this sense, it has a human dimension.

Further M. Heidegger states «technology is not equivalent to the essence of technology. [...] Likewise, the essence of technology is by no means anything technological» [8, 4]. From a scientific point of view, these statements are not true. The fact is that in scientific theory with its principles, laws, and variables there is no essence. By virtue of this and for a number of other reasons, essentialism is now not held in high esteem. There is no need to criticize essentialism once again. However, another circumstance deserves to be noted. The nature of technology, its specificity is entirely determined by its own content. The specifics of the technology is not somewhere outside of it, it is determined primarily by its principles. Compare: the specifics of the economy lies in itself.

Heidegger notes, «the current conception of technology, according to which it is a means and a human activity, can therefore be called the instrumental and anthropological definition of technology» [8, 5]. Quite justifiably, both these concepts are recognized as untenable to the extent that the nature of people is expressed in a clearly insufficient form. As already noted, technology, as a branch of science is self-sufficient, no less than any other field of science. From this point of view, it is not enough to consider technology only a means subordinate to other sciences. It is also not enough to consider technology as just a form of activity of people represented in a poor form, for example, not defined ethically. One should not attribute the criticism of M. Heidegger of instrumentalism and activism to the pragmatic conception of the philosophy of technology. Prominent representatives of pragmatism, in particular, L. Hickman and P. Durbin, understand instrumentalism and activism differently than M. Heidegger. Nevertheless, his desire to go beyond the limits of instrumentalism and activism, as it promises something new, is quite acceptable.

This new is as follows: «Technology is a way of revealing. If we give heed to this, then another whole realm for the essence of technology will open itself up to us. It is the realm of revealing, i.e., of truth» [8, 12]. This translation of the original German text «Die Technik ist eine Weise des Entbergens. Achten wir darauf, dann öffnet sich uns ein ganz anderer Bereich für das Wesen der Technik. Es ist der Bereich der Entbergung, d.h. der Wahrheit» [9, 13] leaves much to be desired. Entbergung is the production of something that is not given in the present. These include e.g. cognition, experiment as well as the treatment of nature, the production of products, the development of theories, the collection of new ideas, etc.

Genuine, and undistorted, is poetic (from Greek ἀλήθεια = truth) production. Poetic production is revealing of anything. What exactly is this sublime thing? Maybe God, some kind of ethical principle or something else very majestic? M. Heidegger does not answer this question. In this case, his contact with science is interrupted.

The scientist, not without pleasure, accepting M. Heidegger's aspiration to develop an idea of poetic technology, insists on a certain characteristic of what should be manifested by it. However, M. Heidegger is not his assistant in this matter. Nevertheless, the scientist to a certain extent agrees with M. Heidegger. Together with him, he believes that technology is not devoid of any significant flaws that must be overcome. In this regard, he again listens attentively to M. Heidegger, who uses the term 'Ge-stell' [Enframing] to characterize the current state of technology. «Enframing means the gathering together of that setting-upon which sets upon man, i.e., challenges him forth, to reveal the real, in the mode of ordering, as standing-reserve. Enframing means that way of revealing which holds sway in the essence of modern technology and which is itself nothing technological» [8, 20].

According to M. Heidegger, standing in reserve is a sphere of science, as well of Enframing, under the influence of which a person himself is captured in reserve. This means that the true escapes from science, from technology, and from man. The task is to enable people to return to the path of truth.

It should be noted that the concept of standing in reserve, which is guided by M. Heidegger, is ат idea fixe. All sciences manifest their mental, linguistic and real representation. In the case of a real presentation, attention is focused on the relevant objects and subjects. Nevertheless, science, including technology, is not limited to a real view. Not only objects, in particular, technical artifacts but also people, including their mental and language representations, practical actions, diverse concepts, for example, principles and laws, are in the field of vision of technology.

M. Heidegger, without any justification, blames science and technology, which he distinguishes from science, for absolutizing of the standing in reserve. However, he is right in the other; technology really needs an adequate understanding and improvement. How to achieve this? Again, there is a reason to listen to M. Heidegger. He compares technology with art, which managed to follow the path of poetic revealing. The technique must follow this path; otherwise, humanity is doomed to wither in a frantic technical race [8, 35].

How can we estimate the hopes of M. Heidegger from a scientific point of view? Technology, on the one hand, and art, on the other hand, are fundamentally different axiological concepts. One can hope for their fruitful interdisciplinary cooperation, but no more. From a scientific point of view, the favorable future of technology is determined by the improvement of the whole complex of technological sciences and their comprehensive inclusion in the interdisciplinary whole with the necessary emphasis on ethics. Instead of the mysterious references to poetic revealing, science puts in focus the constantly improved principles of the axiological sciences, including technology, and ethics. Science does not need saving props from the side, only it can help itself get out of difficult situations.

Albert Borgmann notes four flaws in M. Heidegger's technology philosophy [1, 430-431]. 1) Deviation from the standards of consistent thinking. 2) Lack of clear ways to involve humanity in the implementation of his project. 3) Inability, with the chosen structure of thinking, to justify the attractiveness of technology. 4) The way of giving his ideas a fruitful political and social character remains unexplained. However, A. Borgmann notes «the profundity Heidegger's thoughts on the thing and technology» [1, 431]. What is this depth of thought? First, the reference to the foundations of theories. Secondly, the formulation of acute problems. Thirdly, the criticism of the dominant opinions. Fourthly, the mastery of the rhetoric of metaphysics.

Nevertheless, M. Heidegger's thinking has an organic disadvantage. He gives obviously superficial characteristics of modern scientific theories. In fact, he does not consider their conceptual nature. He believes that metaphysics is the key to understanding science. This is a solid misconception.

M. Heidegger laid the foundations of the poetic paradigm of understanding technology. It was most vigorously supported by A. Borgmann [2-5]. Both thinkers, relying on Greek philosophy, propose to develop a true understanding of technology, which should warn against the destruction of the Western world. Both Heidegger and A. Borgmann are critical of technology if it does not meet the criteria of environmental prudence and social justice.

Of course, in a number of respects, A. Borgmann substantially modifies Heidegger's theory. In this connection, the decisive transition of A. Borgmann to the ethics is especially significant, particularly in connection with the ideas of Aristotle and John Rawls. However, unlike these two authors, A. Borgmann considers ethical guides in the context of technology, without which talking about things, including goods, is meaningless. The mainline of reasoning A. Borgmann is presented in the most distinct form in the article [4]. Let me list the names of its sections: Critiques of consumption – Paradigmatic consumption – An alternative critique – The principle of symmetry – Focal things and practices.

Paradigmatic consumption consists of the consumption of goods, but instead of achieving prosperity and freedom, it led to a loss of the identity of individuals and their self-awareness. Case in point: computer users are usually guided by some patterns that suppress individuality.

The device paradigm consists in combining the consumption of goods using complex technical devices. This use has changed the nature of consumption, but not canceled, but, on the contrary, aggravated its shortcomings, noted in the previous paragraph.

The trouble with paradigmatic consumption and its modern form as a device paradigm is that the symmetry between people and the environment, reality, is broken. Meanwhile, they must be in harmony with each other. It is not difficult to see that, using the paradigmatic consumption and device paradigm concepts, A. Borgmann rethinks M. Heidegger's concept of Enframing.

«What paradigmatic consumption displaces on the real side of the original symmetry are things that have a life and dignity of their own-mountains, works of art, playing fields, and sacred places. We can call such things focal and the devotion to them a focal practice» [4, 421]. Is that technology appropriate for the life forms of focal things and practices? They contribute to the formation and support of the identity of social groups of people. They are typical of everyday life. Focal things and practices are opposed to forms of moral and cultural decay.

Heidegger saw the path of salvation from technological absolutism in likening technology to art. A. Borgmann sees a way out of a difficult situation in the development of focal things and practices.

Bergmann's theory does not remain without critics. P. Durbin urges him on behalf of American pragmatism to greater social and political activity [7]. H.L. Dreyus and C. Spinosa, also adhering to the line of M. Heidegger, believe that A. Borgmann, concentrating on things, overlooks large-scale technical systems, for example, bridges [6].

In my opinion, the main drawback of the A. Borgmann theory is clearly insufficient attention to the institute of science. He focuses on the possibility of upgrading technology, but not on technological science. All concepts used by him are scientifically substantiated insufficiently. The desire to do without science ends for the most part with metaphysical appeals of not quite clear content.

References

1. Borgmann, A. (2005) Technology. In Dreyfus, H.L., Wrathall, M.A. (Eds.). A Companion to Heidegger. Oxford: Blackwell, 420-432.
2. Borgmann, A. (1983) Technology and the Character of Contemporary Life. Chicago: University of Chicago Press.
3. Borgmann, A. (1999) Holding On to Reality: The Nature of Information at the Turn of the Millennium. Chicago: University of Chicago Press.
4. Borgmann, A. (2000) The moral complexion of consumption. The Journal of Consumer Research 26(4), 418-422.

5. Borgmann, A. (2006) Real American Ethics. Chicago: University of Chicago Press.

6. Dreyus, H.L., Spinosa, C. (1997) Highway bridges and feasts: Heidegger and Borgmann on how to affirm technology. Man and World 30(2), 159-177.

7. Durbin, P.T. (2015) Albert Borgmann: Real American Ethics: taking responsibility for our country. AI and Society, 32(2), 289-291.

8. Heidegger, M. (1977) The Question Concerning Technology and Other Essays. Transl. by W. Lovitt. New York: Harper.

9. Heidegger, M. (2000) Gesamtausgabe. I Abteilung: Veröffentlichte schriften 1910-1976. Band 7. Vorträge und Aufsätze [Full composition of writings. I Part: Publications 1910-1976. Volume 7. Lectures and essays]. Frankfurt am Main: Vittorio Klostermann GmbH. [In German].

11.8. Hermeneutic and poststructuralist searches

In this section, I will discuss two interpretations of the philosophy of technology, which, unlike their more successful rivals, so far, in my opinion, have not acquired the status of sustainable conceptual paradigms. This is hermeneutic and poststructuralist philosophy of technology. D. Ihde explained the relevance of hermeneutics to the technology as follows: «in so far as all technologies as used by humans are ascribed with ranges of often complex meanings, so also are texts, so that at a deeper level hermeneutics and technologies potentially exhibit considerable interrelations...». [6, 180] He called W. Dilthey and M. Heidegger the largest representatives of hermeneutics. Let me return to the question of the need for hermeneutics for technology.

In philosophy, the greatest hopes were pinned on hermeneutics in connection with the need to develop a method for the axiological sciences. Wilhelm Dilthey was especially energetically searching for it. He did not achieve the desired success. Martin Heidegger also did not particularly successful in developing this method. His hermeneutic ideas were systematized by Hans-Georg Gadamer [4]. Again, the matter did not reach the development of a full-fledged method for axiological sciences. Moreover, it is clear why. In the field of axiological sciences, scientists, for example, psychologists and economists, use the same methods as representatives of natural science, namely, methods of deduction, adduction, induction, and abduction. Of course, the concepts of the axiological sciences, in contrast to the concepts of the natural sciences, are values, but the above-mentioned methods are perfectly coordinated with this circumstance.

The assertion that hermeneutics provides the key to understanding texts is not confirmed. For example, the absolute majority of physicists and economists are well aware of the content of the texts of their articles and books, without resorting to the services of hermeneutics. There is no reason to compare technical artifacts with texts. Texts are the language manifestation of a theory. Technical artifacts are not the language, but the object representation of the theory.

What is the main advantage of hermeneutics? Judging by the history of its development, it consists of the study of dialogues or discourses. However, not only hermeneutists study discourses. The peculiarity of the position of the hermeneutists is that they consider ways of reaching an agreement, consensus. In this regard, poststructuralism with its emphasis on dissensus is an alternative to hermeneutics. Indicative in this connection is the opposite of the discursive ethics of Jürgen

Habermas and the conception of agonistic language games of Jean-François Lyotard [5; 9; 10]. Thus, if one wishes to use, as applied to the technology, the achievements of modern hermeneutics and poststructuralism he should, first, pay attention to the nature of discourses, to the agreement and disagreement of their participants. In this case, the achieved consensus or dissensus appears as a certain ratio of theories.

It is essential to emphasize that the hermeneutic or poststructuralist aspect is added to one or another interpretation, for example, neo-Marxist or phenomenological, but does not oppose it. It is substantive hardly to assert that, along with the phenomenological, there is also a hermeneutical interpretation of the philosophy of technology. In this regard, I cannot agree with Bernhard Irrgang, who attaches an independent meaning to the hermeneutics of technology [7].

In my opinion, in the works devoted to the hermeneutics of technology [4; 6; 7; 11; 13], due attention is not paid to the concept of the hermeneutic method. If this method is not explained then hermeneutic enthusiasm degenerates into frank metaphysics. Robert Rosenberger insists on the hermeneutic character of the 'variational cross-examination' used by him [11]. This choice is quite remarkable because the variational cross-examination is nothing more than an extended version of the phenomenological method of variation. Arun Tripathi considers hermeneutics as applied to technological culture [13]. In this case, the fate of hermeneutics is associated with culture. This is also a demonstration move. The fact is that often when considering cultural phenomena, hermeneutics is given preference, not to science. Such a step would be justified if, in relation to the sphere of culture, hermeneutics was really more advanced than science. Such evidence is missing. Ultimately, all cultural phenomena are most productively studied through scientific methods.

The inclusion of prominent representatives of poststructuralism in the ranks of technology philosophers, as a rule, is explained rather by the relevance of their theories, be it Michel Foucault's archeology or deconstruction of Jacques Derrida, than their direct analysis of the phenomenon of technology [1; 3; 8; 12]. In my opinion, in this regard, the status of the corresponding view must be taken into account. It should play the role of a certain generalization, which by definition contains impulses emanating from a wide range of heterogeneous knowledge, including technology. The teaching of Foucault on the mechanisms of political power relates mainly to the political sphere. It is hardly permissible to transfer it uncritically to the sphere of technology. The concept of deconstruction by Derrida, by definition, is of a generalized nature. In this regard, we can hope that it is productive in the field of technology. Only a thorough analysis can determine the degree of its productivity.

In my opinion, not yet succeeded the presentation of a poststructuralist version of the philosophy of technology in an impressive way. Bearing in mind the archeology of Foucault, one can insist on considering the genesis of technological knowledge, identifying problems through solving them in such a way as to ensure a variety of technological discourses. It is possible to insist on deconstruction, the method of which has never been presented in a distinct form by Derrida. One can pin great hopes on the paralogical agonistic language games of Lyotard, whose methods he did not present in a clear form. The basic attitude of the poststructuralists are well known: pluralism and dynamism, overcoming any terror and opening the way for the development of each person. Nevertheless, for now, this program is not developed impressively because of the vague methodology. That is why I believe that it is too early to put the poststructuralist interpretation of the philosophy of technology on a par with the Marxist, pragmatic, phenomenological, and poetic interpretations. The same applies to the hermeneutic interpretation of the philosophy of technology.

Each of the previously considered interpretations of the philosophy of technology has certain strengths. However, they all share the same flaw. They are not sufficiently substantiated scientifically. In this regard, one should refer to those philosophical directions that stand out for their distinct not metaphysical, but scientific orientation. Such is, above all, analytical philosophy. However, I will not take it upon myself to assert that the analytical philosophy of technology has taken place. I consider my version of the philosophy of technology to be metascientific. It involves a thorough analysis of the content of technological theories and their interdisciplinary relationships with non-technical conceptions.

References

1. Dorrestijn, S. (2012) Technical mediation and subjectivation: tracingand extending Foucault's philosophy of technology. Philosophy and Technology 25(2), 221-241.
2. Gadamer, H.-G. (1960) Wahrheit und Methode. Grundzüge einer philosophischen Hermeneutik [Truth and method. Fundamentals of a Philosophical Hermeneutics]. Tübingen: Mohr. [In German].

3. Gerrie, J. (2003) Was Foucault a philosopher of technology? Techné: Research in Philosophy and Technology, 7(2), 14–26.

4. Gill, K.S. (2017) Hermeneutic of performing knowledge. AI and Society 32(2), 149–156.

5. Habermas, J. (1990) Moral Consciousness and Communicative Action. Transl. by C. Lenhatdt and S.W. Nichoisen. Cambridge, MA: MIT Press.

6. Ihde, D. (2009) Hermeneutics and technologies. In Olsen, J.K.B., Pedersen, S.A. and Hendricks, V.F. (Eds.). A Companion to the Philosophy of Technology. Oxford: Blackwell, 180-183.

7. Irrgang, B. (2014) Handling Technical Power: Philosophy of Technology. Stuttgart: Franz Steiner Verlag.

8. Kuiken, K. (2006) Between Heidegger and Derrida: on the impossible futures of techne. Canadian Review of Comparative Literature / Revue Canadienne de Littérature Comparée 33(3-4), 293-310.

9. Lyotard, J.-F. (1984) The Postmodern Condition: A Report on Cognition. Manchester: Manchester University Press.

10. Lyotard, J.-F. (1988) The Differend: Phrases in Dispute. Transl. by G.V.D. Abbeele. Minneapolis: University of Minnesota Press.

11. Rosenberger, R. (2016) On the hermeneutics of everyday things: or, the philosophy of fire hydrants. AI and Society 32(2), 233-241.

12. Stiegler, B. (2001) Derrida and technology: fidelity at the limits of deconstruction and the prosthesis of faith. In Jacques Derrida and the Humanities: A Critical Reader. Ed. by T. Cohen. Cambridge: Cambridge University Press, 238-270.

13. Tripathi, A.K. (2017) Hermeneutics of technological culture. AI and Society 32(2), 137-148.

11.9. Technological ethics: metaphysical colonialism

Hans Lenk and Günter Ropohl once prophetically remarked, «[t]he problem of technical progress is still in incongruence with technical and ethical competence. To overcome this lack of congruence, a new ethic is needed. People should not do everything they can, they must first learn what they can and should do». [7, 20] This incongruence is still not overcome, despite the efforts of a large group philosopher of technology. Perhaps we do not sufficiently understand the essence of the moral situation in which technologists are involved. Moreover, this is despite the fact that ethics has established its citizenship in technology much more thoroughly than in other areas of human activity. In connection with the noted, let me dwell, above all, based on technological ethics.

Hans Jonas justified the need for technological ethics by a large-scale ambivalent influence of technology on all aspects of modern human culture [4]. He was convinced that modern civilization is technological, and not, for example, economic. His reasoning is clearly metaphysical, including an analysis of the state of modern scientific knowledge. However, I am convinced that genuine technological ethics can take place only if its foundations are distinguished scientifically. With this in mind, I turn to the conclusions of Mario Bunge and Evandro Agazzi, famous connoisseurs of the philosophy of science. According to their reflections, the fate of technological ethics is closely linked with an understanding of the content of science.

The main conclusion of Bunge reads as follows, «[u]nlike pure science, which is intrinsically valuable or at worst and on occasion worthless, technology can be valuable, worthless or evil, according to the ends it is made to serve. Consequently, technology must be subjected to moral and social control» [2,

78]. Further, M. Bunge insists on the individual responsibility of each technologist and proposes a way to calculate value preferences, sufficient "to construct a technoethics" [2, 79]. As for the calculation of values, on this account, a huge amount of knowledge has been accumulated in the theory of decision-making [10]. The problem of separation of individual and collective responsibility is well known from jurisprudence [3].

M. Bunge considers technology as an applied science in relation to natural science. Objectives, for example, economic, political and environmental, which technology pursues, are formed outside of it. This means that the technology itself is devoid of value content, comparable in scale with the humanities and the socio-political sciences. Continuing this line of argumentation, it is necessary to recognize that technoethics is formed outside of technology. In contrast to M. Bunge, I believe that the technology itself has a distinct and bright value content, concluded primarily in its principles. Therefore, the formation of technoethics should take place directly in technological theories.

The M. Bunge article reviewed above was written more than half a century ago, but it has not lost its meaning. I now turn to the latest literature on the same problem of substantiating the scientific nature of technological ethics by the example of the article by E. Agazzi [1]. He defines his position as follows, «If one conceives philosophy of science simply as an epistemology of science consisting in a logical-methodological investigation about the language of scientific theories, this broadening would appear spurious. This view, however, is too narrow and dated: a fully-fledged philosophical investigation on the complex phenomenon of science cannot prevent important outlooks and instruments of the philosophical inquiry (in particular ethics) from legitimately pertaining to the philosophy of science» [1,

587]. Agazzi considers the epistemological approach to be correct, but only as long as it becomes necessary to take into account value orientations. However, how does this accounting relate to the device of individual sciences and, above all, the technology that interests us? This question remains unanswered. I, therefore, believe that his 'axiological view of scientific activity' [1, 593] does not receive a scientific explanation. Nevertheless, the need for technological ethics can be justified in a scientific way. For this purpose, need to turn to the content of technological theories.

In my opinion, their principles should be headed by the principles of maximizing the prosperity of all stakeholders and of responsibility to them. [5, 94] In this case, the technology itself receives ethical significance in accordance with its nature. If these principles are not included in the composition of the technological theory, the sources of technological ethics are incomprehensible. Ethics must be congruent with the composition of individual sciences. Ethics is extracted directly from them, and then in a generalized (formal) form is returned to them. In contrast to E. Agazzi, I consider that the methodology of the axiological sciences, which does not deal with ethical principles, is simply erroneous because the content of these sciences themselves is misunderstood. Scientists do not need an axiological view of scientific activity, but a proper understanding of the conceptual and methodological content of the sciences.

E. Agazzi correctly notes that the value criteria complement each other. He proposes to consider this complementation through the system-theoretic model [1, 595]. In this regard, I believe that technological ethics should be considered not only by itself but also in relationships with all other varieties of ethics, the number of which equals the number of axiological branches of science. Depending on the specific situation, the relative relevance of regional ethics changes, in particular, political, economic or technological.

After considering the foundations of technological ethics, I turn to researchers who develop it directly on behalf of the philosophy of technology. In this connection, a review article by Carl Mitcham and Katinka Waelbers [8] is indicative. They define the most urgent problem plan of technological ethics as a quadrant, whose four vertices are substantivism (technologies shape society), determinism (technological development is determined by an inner logic), instrumentalism (technological artifacts are neutral tools, passively to be used by humans) and voluntarism (humans develop technology at own free will). All four ethical extremes are inappropriate [8, 371-374]. In this regard, attempts to overcome these extremes through actor-network theory. [6] In this case, special attention is paid to the nature of technical artifacts.

The main drawback of this review is that no attention is paid directly to technological theories. Of course, many authors are guided by the concepts of technological substantivism, determinism, instrumentalism, and voluntarism. Noting this fact, it should be borne in mind that they are all unacceptable absolutizing. Technological substantivism absolutizes the significance of technological theories. Technological determinism greatly simplifies the understanding of the methodological content of technological theories. Technological instrumentalism does not take into account the form of self-sufficiency that is characteristic of technological theories. Technological voluntarism ignores the historical sequence of technological theories. A more developed theory does not arise by itself or because of the free will of the inventor, but as an overcoming of the difficulties of the previous theory. All these shortcomings are not overcome either in the framework of actor-network theory or through neo-Marxist, neopragmatic, postphenomenological or neopoetic technology. The fact is that in all these conceptions not enough attention is paid to the content of technological theories. I have to point once again out this paramount circumstance.

In my opinion, the state of modern technological ethics leaves much to be desired. First, there is a lack of attention to technological theories. Philosophical ethics, including its deontological, utilitarian, and pragmatic variants are considered as not scientific, but metaphysical conceptions. They are used to understand technological problems, and this is done on behalf of Marxism, pragmatism, phenomenology, fundamental ontology, and existentialism.

Joseph Pitt, participating in the discussion about the possible ways of the development of pragmatic technological ethics, spoke out against ethical colonialism. "What do I mean by ethical colonialism? It is an attempt to endow everything in the world as an actor with moral value. It is to deny that there are other types of values, such as epistemic values, which have their own integrity and can operate in an ethical neutral framework "[9, 32]. He noted that "the two basic pragmatic maxims can serve as a basis for an evolving ethical system. 1. Consider the consequences 2. The community is the ultimate arbiter"[9, 38]. Both of these provisions, presented in a formal form, are quite relevant. However, it should be borne in mind that during their implementation, firstly, to handle carefully technological theories with all their concepts and methods. Secondly, just as carefully it is necessary to implement the network of those ethical interdisciplinary relations, one side of which is technological ethics. Neither the first nor the second is usually performed. Another important circumstance is that, as I noted earlier, technological theories should be headed by ethical principles. This leads to the fact that indeed all concepts of technological theory, including technical artifacts, acquire ethical significance. The physical object is marked by the stamp of the principle of least action; this is not surprising. The economic object is marked by the stamp of the principle of profit maximization. It is also not surprising that any technological artifact is marked by the stamp of the principle of maximizing the technological prosperity of all stakeholders. With due attention to the conceptual and methodological structure of technological theories, there is no reason to fear the trap of ethical colonialism. One should be afraid not of scientific reasoning, but metaphysical, in other words, metaphysical technological ethical colonialism.

References

1. Agazzi, E. (2018) Philosophy of science and ethics. Axiomathes 28(6), 587-602.
2. Bunge, M. (1975) Towards a technoethics. Philosophic Exchange 6(1), 69-79
3. French, P.A. (Ed.). (1972) Individual and Collective Responsibility. Cambridge, Mass: Schenkman.
4. Jonas, H. (1979) Das Prinzip Verantwortung: Versuch einer Ethik für die technologische Zivilisation [The Principle of Responsibility: Trying an Ethics for Technological Civilization]. Frankfurt am Main: Insel-Verlag, 1979. [In German]

5. Kanke, V.A. (2018) Metodologiya i etika yadernoy energetiki [Methodology and Ethics of Nuclear Power Engineering]. Moskva: Yurayt. [In Russian].
6. Latour, B. (2005). Reassembling the Social: An Introduction to Actor-Network Theory. Oxford: Oxford University Pres
7. Lenk, H., Ropohl, G. (1993). Technik zwischen können und sollen [Technology Between Can and Should]. In Lenk, H., Ropohl, G. (Hrgs.). Technik und Ethik [Technology and Ethics]. Stuttgart: Philipp Reclam, 5-21.
8. Mitcham, C., Waelbers, K. (2009) Technology and Ethics: Overview. In A Companion to the Philosophy of Technology. Ed. by J.K.B. Olsen, S.A. Pedersen, and V.F. Hendricks. Oxford: Blackwell, 367-383.
9. Pitt, J.C. (2004) Ethical colonialism. Techné: Research in Philosophy and Technology 7(3), 32-38.
10. Steele, K., Stefánsson, H. O. (2016) Decision theory. The Stanford Encyclopedia of Philosophy. Available at: https://plato.stanford.edu/archives/win2016/entries/decisi on-theory/

Chapter 12. The nature of agricultural sciences

12.1. Agricultural sciences and agricultural theories

People, providing their existence, are forced in one way or another to use plants, animals and other organisms. In this regard, they are inevitably the creators of agriculture, the most solid judgments about which are formed within the framework of agricultural science. The composition of agricultural science includes a huge amount of uncounted agricultural theories. Grouping them according to the degree of similarity, they talk about individual agricultural sciences, such as, for example, plant and animal sciences. Every single agricultural science consists of disciplines, the exact number of which is not defined. Disciplines, in turn, consist of subdisciplines. Thus, there is every reason to assert that agricultural science is a huge variety of agricultural theories. In this regard, priority must naturally be given to the concept of agricultural theory. However, strangely, this circumstance is poorly understood by scientists. The fact is that in the modern philosophy of science there is a widespread anti-theoretical syndrome. Under the influence of it, scientists prefer to reason about experiments, which is tacitly recognized as a more rigorous scientific form than theory. This is a serious conceptual mistake because substantive content of experiments can be judged only within the framework of certain scientific theories.

One of the most concise and at the same time meaningful definitions of the agricultural science states: «Agricultural Sciences is the study of the relationship between soils, plants and animals to produce and process food, fiber, fuel, and any other agricultural commodities that have an economic, aesthetic and cultural value»[1, 7]. The above definition seems to be quite acceptable, and yet it should hardly be considered correct. First, I note that the relationship between soils, plants, and animals is carried out by people, and not by the previously listed objects themselves. The relationship between soils, atmosphere, hydrosphere, plants, and animals existed in that era when there were no people on planet Earth. The above relations were in the absence of agriculture. This argument shows that plants and animals are objects of agricultural science, but not subjects. The subjects of agricultural science are people, not plants and animals. As for the soils, the atmosphere, and the hydrosphere, in agriculture, they act as mediums.

Let me return directly to the definition of agricultural science in question. It argues that this branch of science is necessary for the production of commodities with an economic, aesthetic and cultural value. The commodity is an economic concept. Should agricultural science be reducible to economics or to aesthetics and culture, which are mentioned in the definition under consideration? In my opinion, the very understanding of agricultural science as a special branch of science indicates the inadmissibility of its reduction to any other branches of science. The fact is that in the process of the formation of agricultural science, a special block of specific values was formed. To show this circumstance, consider the transition *biology – agricultural science – economics*. Those values that appear in agricultural science are absent in biology. For example, in biology, there is no principle of maximizing the productivity of grain crops, in particular, wheat. The same principle does not exist in economics, where the principle of profit maximization is guided. Scientific thought can move from biology to agricultural science and from it to economics, medicine, technology, sociology and other branches of science. On this path, jumps of concepts and theories will certainly occur. It is in this connection that it is necessary to single out special branches of science, one of which is precisely agricultural science. Agricultural science is a collection of theories whose principles are to maximize and optimize traits of organisms, plants, animals, fungi, and bacteria, which are useful for people. Agricultural science is an equal participant in the wide network of interdisciplinary relations between different branches of science that is realized by people. It is not reducible to any other branch of science.

Thus, the first attention should be paid to the nature of agricultural theories. As I have repeatedly stressed earlier, the most capacious concepts of the theory are principles. What are the principles of axiological theories? These are the goals, which scientists are striving to achieve in the next cycle of knowledge. These goals are to maximize certain characteristics of the objects of agricultural theories, above all, animals and plants. The unity of these characteristics forms the quality of the object as its integral index. For example, the quality of staple foods (of maize, rice, wheat, potatoes, etc.) is determined primarily by their content of amino acids, fatty acids, vitamins, and minerals. Smell, color, size, the presence of harmful impurities are also taken into account. The desired qualities act as a set of individual useful indicators. They are precisely the principles of plant agricultural theories. The principles of animal agricultural theories are defined in a similar manner. This time, the set of features determines the desired quality of the animals. Thus, the principles of agricultural theories are those goals that agrarian set for themselves. These principles are not given finally they are constantly revised. Depending on the goals substituted, the ways of their achievement are worked out. They usually act as the implementation of certain mechanisms, the connection of variables, i.e. laws. The content of the laws and variables included in their composition is determined by the principles. Each principle does not arise by chance, but because of the evaluation of the preceding realized agrarian cycles.

After determining the nature of agricultural theory, which, as a rule, is not given due attention, it is advisable to consider its methods. On this account, there is a variety of literature with a special focus on the relevance of agricultural experiments [2-7]. The content of these works shows that the agricultural science firmly established the relevance of the consistent use of the following actions: 1) designing the experiment, 2) conducting the experiment, 3) statistical data processing by means of dispersion, correlation, regression, and covariance analysis, 4) hypothesis. If we present the methodological content of these four actions, we get the following series of methods: 1) deduction (for design), 2) adduction (for experiments), 3) induction (for statistical data processing), and 4) abduction (for hypothesizing). All four methods of intratheoretical transduction are given. This suggests that agricultural science took place. All the basic conditions necessary for the approval of the scientific status of agricultural theories are met.

Above, I have listed the methods of intratheoretical transduction. However, often they are not even mentioned. This does not mean that they are not. For example, the emphasized features of laboratory and field experiments, respectively, are clearly related to the method of adduction. It is significant that most researchers prefer to talk about experiments, and not about theories. In fact, experiments are not considered in the context of theories. At best, researchers talk about the formulation of hypotheses [6, 131]. It is important to understand that the main purpose of conducting experiments is to ensure the development of theories. Each cycle of knowledge leads to a new theory. Agricultural cognition is done by cycles. In these cycles, experiments occupy a worthy place, but they are not exhausted by them.

Jonathan Harwood, believing that experiments are necessary mainly for testing theories, also draws attention to the unusual consequences of experiments, in particular, disputes about their usefulness and persuasiveness for a particular audience [3]. It is hard not to agree with these conclusions. Nevertheless, it is obvious that in all cases the final clarity occurs only when the experiment is considered as an organic part of the theory.

In the context of issues of interest to us, Thomas Wieland considers «the transformation of plant breeding from an agricultural practice into an applied academic science in the late 19th and early 20th centuries Germany. [...] In order to better understand the transformation of plant breeding into an applied academic science we have to take different levels into account, i.e. the levels of organizations, individuals and objects, at which science and technology interact» [7, 309]. However, he notes, «there is no hierarchy between theoretical and practical knowledge» [7, 339]. I completely agree with the last remark of T. Wieland. However, unlike him, I do not think that it is necessary to oppose theoretical and practical knowledge in the least degree. The fact is that practical knowledge is also theoretical. It cannot be transformed into a science. The transformation about which T. Wieland argues is the development of science in the historical period under consideration. T. Wieland perfectly showed that, first, scientists, agronomists, and breeders differently represented scientific theory, and second, they were forced to combine their theories for the sake of mutual success. The combination of various forms of representation of agricultural theories is one of the urgent problems of agricultural science. In my opinion, agricultural science is not a form of applied science. This circumstance was emphasized at the beginning of the section.

Thus, in my opinion, in the methodology of agricultural science, the weakest link is insufficient attention to the concepts of theory and principles.

References

1. Department of Education. (2007) Learning Programme Guidelines: Agricultural Sciences. Pretoria: Department of Education.
2. Gupta, V.K., Parsad, R., Mandal, B.N. (2015) Significance of Experimental Designs in Agricultural Research. New Delhi: ICAR-Indian Agricultural Statistics Research Institute.
3. Harwood, J. (2015) Comments on experimentation in twentieth-century agricultural science. History and Philosophy of the Life Sciences, 37(3), 326-330.
4. Maat, H. (2011) The history and future of agricultural experiments. NJAS - Wageningen Journal of Life Sciences 57(3-4), 187-195.
5. Parolini, G. (2015) In pursuit of a science of agriculture: the role of statistics in field experiments. History & Philosophy of the Life Sciences 37(3), 261-281.
6. Sahu, P.K. (2013) Research Methodology: A Guide for Researchers in Agricultural Science, Social Science and Other Related Fields. New Delhi; New York: Springer India.
7. Wieland, T. (2006) Scientific theory and agricultural practice: plant breeding in Germany from the late 19th to the early

20th century. Journal of the History of Biology, 39(2), 309-343.

12.2. Agricultural science and ecology

Agriculture, on the one hand, and the environment, on the other hand, intensively interact with each other. This interaction is so strong that, as a rule, it is unacceptable to abstract from it. In this regard, we have to give the right to vote ecology. Ernst Haeckel defined the ecology as follows: «By ecology we understand the whole science of the relations of the organism to the surrounding external world, to which we can calculate in a broader sense all "existential conditions". These are partly organic, inorganic; both these and those are, as we have previously shown, of the greatest importance to the form of organisms because they compel them to conform to them». [4, 286] The most important concepts of ecology are the concepts of biome and ecosystem. «The whole complex of organisms present in an ecological unit may be called the biome. [...] The fundamental concept appropriate to the biome considered together with all the effective inorganic factors of its environment is the *ecosystem*, which is a particular category among the physical systems that make up the universe. In an ecosystem, the organisms and the inorganic factors alike are *components*, which are in relatively stable dynamic equilibrium. Succession and development are instances of the universal processes tending towards the creation of such equilibrated systems». [13, 306].

In its original form, ecology was a biological theory. This meant that it was guided by the concept of a biological-ecological system (bioecosystem). Its main factors recognized plants and animals. With regard to agricultural science, this approach is insufficient, because ecology is not biological science. The necessary change in the understanding of ecology is achieved by the notion of the agricultural ecological system (agroecosystem). In accordance with it, the main environmental factor is recognized by people who influence the external environment through the agriculture they develop. Along with bio and agroecosystem, one can also use the concepts techno-ecosystem and socio-ecosystem. Ecology in its most general sense is a formal science that studies similar features of various systems. Therefore, it is illegal to consider ecology as biological conception, as E. Haeckel did, or as agricultural science. The concept of agroecosystem is an organic part of agricultural science.

The apple of contention for scientists is the question of a conceptual understanding of the interaction between agriculture and the environment. In this regard, we often refer to the concepts of reductionism and holism. «Reductionism encompasses a set of ontological, epistemological, and methodological claims about the relations between different scientific domains. The basic question of reduction is whether the properties, concepts, explanations, or methods from one scientific domain (typically at higher levels of the organization) can be deduced from or explained by the properties, concepts, explanations, or methods from another domain of science (typically at lower levels of the organization).» [3, 1]. Holism «is the idea that all the properties of a given system (biological, chemical, social, economic, mental, linguistic, etc.) cannot be determined or explained by the sum of its component parts alone. Instead, the system as a whole determines in an important way how the parts behave. » [5, 1]. Both reductionism and holism meet with significant difficulties [1; 2; 6; 7; 9; 11; 12]. I will consider the foundations of these difficulties from the perspective of the theory of conceptual transduction.

The well-known fact is that on the way physics – chemistry – geology – biology – agricultural science there is a huge variety of theories. All attempts to reduce them to physics invariably end in failure. Principles of theories, in particular, agricultural and biological concepts, are very different from each other. This indicates the impossibility of reducing the agricultural theories to biological conceptions. The program of reductionism, in fact, failed. It cannot be reconciled with a variety of modern theories. The collapse of reductionism testifies, first, to the presence of emergent leaps in the evolution of phenomena. Secondly, their presence does not negate the existence of a connection between the theories of the upper and lower levels, for example, between agricultural and biological conceptions. The bottom-up transition is often referred to as supervenience [10]. Supervenience is not causal, but an emergent determination.

Of course, there must be top-down determination. It is called downward causation. Nevertheless, in reality, a top-down determination is not a causal link. Top-level theories are not the causes of lower-level theories. What is the nature of top-down determination? In my opinion, this determination is not causal, but symbolic. This means that the top-level theory imputes its nature to the low-level concept. For example, biological theory (T_{bio}) is symbolic being (S) of agricultural conception (T_{agro}). The effect of T_{agro} on T_{bio} is that T_{bio} acquires a symbolic (S) meaning: $T_{agro} \rightarrow ST_{bio}$. The agricultural theory attaches symbolic meaning also to physical, chemical, and geological conceptions:

$$T_{agro} \rightarrow ST_{bio} \rightarrow ST_{geo} \rightarrow ST_{chem} \rightarrow ST_{phys}. \qquad (11.1)$$

Physical, chemical, geological and biological factors are used in such a way that they ensure the success of the agricultural business. If there are causal relationships, for example, of a physical or chemical nature, then they are given a special, namely, agricultural meaning. Superventive leaps provide the existence of biological and agricultural phenomena.

At first glance, the explanation of symbolic relations I proposed is not scientific, but mythological. Nevertheless, this is a deceptive impression. I remain on the solid ground of science, without making any step towards mythology. My reasoning is based on firmly established scientific facts, according to which, first, people are able to bring about phenomena that go beyond the conceptual boundaries of natural science. Secondly, their theories are not reducible to concepts from the field of natural science. So downward determination has a symbolic nature in the sense explained above.

For a long time, it seemed that the general theory of systems [14] gives the required scientific brilliance to the holism program. These hopes were not justified. The general theory of systems argues in favor of the conclusion that causal relationships can exist between parts of the whole, but not between a part of the whole and the whole itself, as advocates of the holism program insist on. If we try to give a consistent explanation of the foundations of the general theory of systems, we will have to turn to the concepts of bottom-up supervenience and downward symbolization.

Due to the general theory of systems, paramount attention was paid to the concept of a system as a balanced whole. System objects are characteristic of all areas of natural science. This circumstance has to be taken into account in agricultural science. The banal truth is that people, striving to ensure the success of agriculture, are capable of destroying its natural basis, which is often biosystems. Often, but not always, people are interested in the preservation of biosystems as the natural basis of agriculture. In this case, the biosystem turns into an agrosystem. People are forced to take into account the inadmissibility of the destruction of agricultural systems. If the destruction of the agrosystem is permissible, then the consequences of this event should be carefully considered.

References

1. Abächerli, A. (2016) Holism and reductionism: how to get the balance right. Open Access Library Journal 3, e2628.

2. Bechtel, W., Hamilton A. (2007) Reduction, integration, and the unity of science: natural, behavioral, and social sciences and the humanities. In Kuipers T.A.F. (Ed.). General Philosophy of Science: Focal Issues. New York: Elsevier, 377-430.

3. Brigandt, I., Love, A. (2017) Reductionism in biology. The Stanford Encyclopedia of Philosophy. Available at: https://plato.stanford.edu/archives/spr2017/entries/reduction-biology/

4. Haeckel, E. (1866) Generelle Morphologie der Organismen. Allgemeine Grundzüge der organischen Formen-Wissenschaft, mechanisch begründet durch die von Charles Darwin reformirte Descendenz-Theorie. Band 2 [General morphology of organisms. General principles of the science of organic forms, mechanically founded on the theory of descendancy reformed by

Charles Darwin. Volume 2]. Berlin: G. Reimer. [In German].

5. Holism. New World Encyclopedia. Available at: http://www.newworldencyclopedia.org/entry/Holism#cite_ref-5/

6. Kaiser, M.I. (2011) The limits of reductionism in the life sciences. History and Philosophy of the Life Sciences 33(4), 453-476.

7. Kevin, S. (2005) The end of "naive reductionism": rise of systems biology or renaissance of physiology? American Journal of Physiology. Cell Physiology 288, C968–C974.

8. Kim, J. (1992) Downward causation in emergentism and non-reductive physicalism. In Beckermann, A., Flohr, H., and Kim, J. (Eds.). Emergence or Reduction? Essays on the Prospects of Nonreductive Physicalism. Berlin: Walter de Gruyter, 119-138.

9. Mazzocchi, F. (2012) Complexity and the reductionism-holism debate in systems biology. Wiley Interdisciplinary Reviews: Systems Biology and Medicine 4(5), 413-427.

10. McLaughlin, B., Karen, B. (2014) Supervenience. The Stanford Encyclopedia of Philosophy. Available at: http://plato.stanford.edu/archives/spr2014/entries/supervenience/

11. Mittelstrass, J. (2015) Complexity, Reductionism, and Holism in Science and Philosophy of Science. The Pontifical Academy of Sciences: Plenary Session 5. Nov 2012 - 7. Nov 2012. Vatican City, Rome, 45-53.

12. O'Neill, R.V. (2001) Is it time to bury the ecosystem concept? (With full military honors, of course!). Ecology 82(12), 3275–3284.

13. Tansley, A.G. (1935) The use and abuse of vegetational concepts and terms. Ecology 16(3), 284-307.

14. Von Bertalanffy, L. (1968) General System Theory Foundations, Development. New York: George Braziller.

12.3. Agricultural ethics as the pinnacle of agricultural science

Each axiological theory in its sequential development inevitably culminates in ethics. In this regard, the situation in agricultural science is similar to the situation in technology. Technology culminates in technological ethics, agricultural sciences in agricultural ethics. Agricultural ethics has significantly progressed over the last 10-15 years [1-7]. Its path of development has been marked by certain successes, but also by significant difficulties. As noted earlier, for the development of some kind of special ethics, it is necessary to introduce the principles of maximizing the prosperity of all stakeholders and the principle of responsibility directly into theories (see sections 6.10, 9.10, 10.9). So, let me turn to the foundations of agricultural ethics, which, in my opinion, were considered most thoroughly within the framework of the Council for Agricultural Science and Technology (CAST). [4]

The first section of the four authors' article, titled "Ethics", states that it deals with standards of correct and incorrect behavior that cannot be learned from the law, culture, religion, science [4, 2]. In my opinion, this statement is far from the truth. First, the very idea of right and wrong behavior, ascending, as is well known, to the views of Aristotle, is regarded as something intuitively given. On such a basis, it is hardly possible to develop a coherent theory of ethics. Its beginning is the scientific principle of maximizing the prosperity of all stakeholders. Secondly, ethics really cannot be extracted from the law. Unlike ethics, it deals with the permissible and the unacceptable. However, it should also be borne in mind that there are legal ethics. Third, the authors correctly assert that agricultural ethics are not found in the culture. With cultural theories, the situation is the same as with jurisprudence. It is quite legitimate to consider various types of cultural ethics, but none of them is the basis for agricultural ethics. Fourth, the authors are right that the foundations of ethics cannot be extracted from religion. The fact is that it initially has not an ethical, but an eschatological character. Eschatology does not tolerate the primacy of ethics in any way.

Fifth, and most importantly, the authors of the article in question mistakenly claim that ethics cannot be developed on a scientific basis. They come from the opposition of *is*-sentences and *ought*-sentences. Sometimes it is argued that the *ought*-sentences are alien to science. This fallacy goes back to the long-obsolete views of David Hume. Both natural and axiological sciences represent past, present, and future events. It is not true that natural sciences, for example, physics, deal exclusively with *is*-sentences. However, they really do not operate with *ought*-sentences. As for axiological theories, they operate with is-sentences, and with *ought*-sentences. Economists, political scientists, technologists, physicians, and psychologists quite skillfully are guided by *ought*-sentences. If, for example, the physician recommends that the patient refrains from smoking, then he is guided by the idea of what ought to be. The denial of the scientific nature of ethics asserts its not scientific, but metaphysical character.

The second section of the article in question discusses the method for addressing ethical issues. In this regard, the relevance of the three main secular ethical traditions, namely, the conception of rights and utilitarian and virtue theories, is emphasized. The authors of the article are critical of these three traditions. «Ethical theorists differ about which of these three theories provides the best standard or criterion for judging right and wrong. […].More often than not, however, the three theories yield conflicting conclusions. » [4, 3]. However, they do not see a way of abandoning the traditions under consideration, believing that it is these traditions that provide the methodological key to resolving ethical problems typical of agricultural science. In fact, this key is directly the methods of agricultural science, i.e. methods of intratheoretical and intertheoretical transduction. They are sufficient to determine ways to maximize the prosperity of all stakeholders in the agricultural business. As for the conception of rights and utilitarian and virtue theories, their methodological content itself must be clarified in the light of the theory of conceptual transduction. Only after that, they are scientifically sound. Otherwise, considered theories do not contribute to the development of agricultural ethics in a scientific way. Moreover, they push it to metaphysics.

Having decided on the methods of agricultural ethics, the authors of the article under discussion consider its key topics and issues, namely, farm structure, animal ethics, food safety, environmental influences, international trade, food security, agricultural biotechnology, research ethics, trust in science [4, 4-8]. All these topics and issues, as well as many others, are relevant. However, in this regard, it is important to emphasize that agricultural ethics is involved in all aspects of agricultural science. It deals not only with selected questions. The degree of universality, respectively, of agricultural science and agricultural ethics, is the same.

In the conclusion of the article, the authors note that the institutionalization of agricultural ethics implies «the responsibility of each of us». [4, 10] However, the nature of responsibility is not clarified.

This article is accompanied by a glossary, which is preceded by a warning «ethics is not science». [4, 10] This conclusion regarding the status of agricultural ethics seems to be clearly erroneous. It is not the case that something unscientific through agricultural ethics is joined to agricultural science. Quite the contrary, through agricultural ethics agricultural science, reaches its peak development.

Agricultural ethics are in the making. This stage of it will end only when it is transferred to the scientific track.

References

1. Thompson, P.B. (2013) Agricultural ethics. In LaFollette, H. (Ed.). The International Encyclopedia of Ethics. Malden, MA: Wiley-Blackwell, 171-177.
2. Kaplan, D.M. (2009) Agriculture ethics. In A Companion to the Philosophy of Technology Ed. by J.K.B. Olsen, S.A. Pedersen and V.F. Hendricks. Malden, MA: Wiley-Blackwell, 384–386.
3. Grimm, H. (2010) Ethical issues in agriculture. In Christen, O., Squires, V., Lal, R., and Hudson, R.J. (Eds.). Interdisciplinary and Sustainability Issues in Food and Agriculture. Oxford: EOLSS Publishers / UNESCO, I, 97-109.
4. Burkhardt, J., Comstock, G., Hartel, P.G. and Thompson, P.B. (2005) Agricultural Ethics. Issues Paper. CAST 29. Ames, Iowa, USA.

5. Thompson, P.B. (2012) The agricultural ethics of biofuels: the food vs. fuel debate. Agriculture 2(4), 339-358.
6. Anthony, R. (2012) Building a sustainable future for animal agriculture: and environmental virtue ethic of care approach within the philosophy of technology. Journal of Agricultural and Environmental Ethics 25(2), 123–144.
7. Yeates, J.W. (2017) How good? Ethical criteria for a 'good life' for farm animals. Journal of Agricultural and Environmental Ethics 30(1), 23-35.

12.4. Ethical relativity of ecology and earth sciences

Along with agricultural ethics, environmental ethics are usually considered [2-6]. Normally no distinction is made between environmental and ecological ethics. James Nash defines them uniformly: «Ecological (or environmental) ethics is the study of what humans, individually and corporately, ought to value, ought to be, and ought to do in relationships with all other beings and elements in the biosphere. As in normative ethics generally, ecological ethics involves evaluating, justifying (or not), and prescribing values, norms, and standards of character and conduct in view of the ecological conditions that contribute to the well-being of humans and other life forms.» [5, 237]. In the conclusion of the article, he makes a somewhat unexpected conclusion: «From the perspective of ecological ethicists, their discipline is not another branch or subdiscipline of ethics, such as medical or business ethics. It is rather the expansion of every branch of ethics, the wider context for every ethical focus. Business ethics, for example, must now think not only socially and economically, but also ecologically – considering moral responsibilities to other life forms and their habitats, present and future, in economic planning. Henceforth, all ethics must be done in the context of ecological ethics – or else they will be distorted and constricted ethics. » [5, 239]. It remains unclear whether environmental ethics is an ethic. If not, then there is no reason to call it ethics.

In my opinion, considering the correlation between agricultural science and ecology, one should clearly distinguish their status. Axiological science is only agricultural science, but not ecology as part of biology and not earth sciences with their interest in the atmosphere, hydrosphere, lithosphere, and pedosphere. Ecology and earth sciences have ethical relativity (for the concept of ethical relativity, see 6.10), but no more. From this point of view, the introduction of concepts of ecological and environmental ethics is illegal.

Determining the status of agricultural ethics and ethical relativity of ecology and earth sciences, one should proceed from the nature of the relevant theories. However, as a rule, this is not done. In this case, metaphysics cannot be avoided, in particular, by criticizing anthropocentrism [2; 3] and considering the nature of life's intrinsic values [1]. In the case of interest to us, anthropocentrism occurs if the interdisciplinary links of agricultural science with ecology and earth sciences are ignored. Attention to intrinsic properties is justified insofar as the peculiarity of ecology and earth sciences should be taken into account. However, they are not dealing with values, but with specific, inherent to them features of natural phenomena.

For me, of paramount interest is the introduction of the concept of ethical relativity of the ecology on a scientific base. The article by Kristin Shrader-Frechette [6] is of considerable interest in this respect. She came to the following conclusions.

«Ecology, more empirically and theoretically underdetermined than many other sciences, cannot provide clear, precise directives for environmental ethics» [6, 314].

«Ecological theory provides necessary, but not sufficient, scientific grounds for environmental ethics and policy» [6, 317].

«Three solutions come to mind: 1. ethical default rules to use in situations of ecological uncertainty, 2. scientific-case-study environmental ethics, and 3. recognizing human rights against life-threatening pollution» [6, 322].

«Traditional ethics can give us powerful weapons for defending the environment. » [6, 328].

Claiming that «ecology, more empirically and theoretically underdetermined than many other sciences», Shrader-Frechette is certainly right. Nevertheless, the conclusion that the ecology does not give «precise directives for environmental ethics», seems to me extremely controversial insofar as it leads beyond the bounds of science. Of course, ecology needs to be improved. Nevertheless, if we want to consistently characterize the ethical relativity of ecology, and then there is no other way then to consider interdisciplinary relations of agricultural science and ecology.

The same argument I put forward against the claim that environmental theory does not provide conditions for environmental ethics and policy. Science is self-sufficient; it cannot be supplemented by something unscientific.

Shrader-Frechette would be right if the three solutions she proposed would lead outside of science. However, this is not. The second solution, which deals with the scientific-case-study, is initially scientific. The first decision, according to which one should prepare ahead for possible troubles, is also scientific. It is thanks to science that we know that various kinds of surprises await us at every step, in particular, because of the probabilistic nature of knowledge. Outside of science, this circumstance is taken into account far less thoroughly. The third decision concerns human rights, which are substantiated in jurisprudence, i.e. again in the field of science. Since all three solutions proposed by K. Shrader-Frechette do not derive in the field of traditional ethics, which itself is in urgent need of scientific clarification, the conclusion that it gives us «powerful weapons for defending the environment» seems to me unreasonable.

The main disadvantage of the existing theories of agricultural ethics and of ethical relativity of ecology and earth sciences is that the achievements of science are underused.

References

1. Agar, N. (2001) Life's Intrinsic Value. New York: Columbia University Press.
2. Brennan, A., Yeuk-Sze, L. (2016) Environmental Ethics. The Stanford Encyclopedia of Philosophy. Available at: https://plato.stanford.edu/archives/win2016/entries/ethics -environmental/Callicott, J.B. (2018) Environmental Ethics. In Dellasala, D.A., Goldstein. M.I. (Eds.). Encyclopedia of the Anthropocene. Vol.4. Ethics. Oxford; Waltham, MA: Elsevier, 1-10.
3. Cochrane, A. (2020) Environmental Ethics. International Encyclopedia of Philosophy. Available at: https://www.iep.utm.edu/envi-eth/
4. Nash, J.A. (2003) Ecology, ethics of. In Huyssteen, J.W.V, van and McCord, J.I. (Eds.). Encyclopedia of Science and Religion. Second ed. New York: Macmillan Reference USA, 237-239.

5. Shrader-Frechette, K. (2011) Ecology and environmental ethics. Values and Ethics for the 21st Century. Madrid: BBVA. 309-333.

12.5. Political science and agricultural ethics

In agricultural ethics, the principles best known from political science are widely used, namely, the principles of freedom [2; 6; 19], equality [4; 8; 11] and justice [1; 5; 9]. In the libertarian approach, the interpretation of agrarian processes is carried out from the standpoint of the principle of freedom, according to which everyone is free in his actions as long as he does not violate the rights and freedoms of other people. The right to freedom is considered natural. In relation to agriculture, attention to the libertarian approach was attracted by Garret Harden [6]. Criticizing the doctrine of the public domain, he refers to the principle of freedom. On the other hand, if everyone pursues his own goals, then he will certainly harm other people. In this regard, he considers a common pasture, divided into several plots, the owners of which, increasing the livestock, damage the pasture as a whole. Freedom should be limited. However, how to achieve this without giving up the very principle of freedom? G. Hardin refers to the statement of Frederic Engels that freedom is an awareness of necessity. Necessity is realized in education. This statement ends his article. In my opinion, G. Harden does not notice that he imposes the principle of freedom on agronomy. First, he asserts the relevance of the principle of freedom and then refers to education and science. The correct course of reasoning presupposes an inverse sequence: the agrarian science is taken as the initial one, and then, within its boundaries, determine the legitimacy of the appeal to the principle of freedom.

With an egalitarian approach, the principle of freedom is limited by the principle of justice, according to which additional assistance is provided, as claimed by John Rawls, to those who are in a losing position. In this regard, equalizing trends inevitably manifest themselves, in particular, in the allocation of resources [12].

The principles of freedom, equality, and justice belong to the field of political science. Taking into account this circumstance, the libertarian, egalitarian and justice approaches should be recognized by means of agrarian-political modeling. The applicability to the understanding of agricultural science of the above approaches indicates its axiological nature. These approaches in understanding the natural sciences are completely out of business.

Understanding of the nature of agricultural science may be carried out from various ethical positions. In English-speaking countries in this regard, most often refer to utilitarianism and pragmatism. The fact is that utilitarianism that has matured on the English soil is still popular in England. In the United States, it was abandoned at the beginning of the 20th century. Pragmatism was opposed to utilitarianism. Utilitarianism is famous for its fundamental principle: the maximum utility for the greatest number of people. Any action is evaluated by the degree of its utility. The most prominent representative of both philosophical and agrarian utilitarianism is Peter Singer [10]. He recognizes the need to modify classical utilitarianism. In particular, he opposes anthropocentrism: the utility must be assessed not only for people but also for animals.

The main difficulty of utilitarianism consists in the choice of value reference points. In the classical utilitarianism of Jeremy Bentham and John Stuart Mill, the happiness of people and the absence of pain and suffering were recognized as main value landmarks. These values were not extracted from any science but simply declared. With the scientific approach, utilities should not be introduced into agricultural science from the outside, they, by definition, are contained in it itself. In my opinion, the problem of choosing value orientations is solved as follows. All concepts of the agricultural sciences recognized as values. The principles are objectives that are weighed in accordance with the procedures of the theory of decision-making. The history of practical decisions allows refining the assessment of values. However, it does not negate moral collisions associated, for example, with the consumption of animal meat. In the case of moral collisions, the lesser of the evils is elected.

English-speaking researchers who are dissatisfied with the utilitarian approach tend to turn to pragmatism. This is especially true for American authors. Indicative in this sense is the position of Paul Thompson [13, 541-542]. He believes that utilitarianism, with its emphasis on people's interests, lacks attention to the values of ecosystems as such. They are better than in utilitarianism, taken into account in the framework of deontological ethics. Nevertheless, this ethics is alien to the history of the development of agricultural thinking with its practical character. Thompson sees a way out in an attempt to combine value ethics with pragmatism.

American pragmatism has long been the authoritative philosophical system. Of course, it can be used, not without success, in clarifying the interrelationships of agricultural science with philosophy [3; 7]. It is even somewhat surprising that, when interpreting agricultural science, American researchers do not often turn to pragmatism. In the philosophy of science, American authors tend to adhere to a pragmatic line.

However, pragmatism, like utilitarianism, sometimes lacks a metascientific justification. The virtues of pragmatism should not be taken for granted, they should be checked by the material of the agrarian sciences themselves.

References

1. Benton, T. (1993) Natural Relations: Ecology, Animal Rights and Social Justice. London: Verso.
2. Bookchin, M. (1982) The Ecology of Freedom: The Emergence and Dissolution of Hierarchy. Palo Alto, CA: Cheshire Books.
3. Bromley, D. (2006) Sufficient Reason: Volitional Pragmatism and the Meaning of Economic Institutions. Princeton, NG: Princeton University Press.
4. Clark, J., Martin, C. (1996) Liberty, Equality, Geography: The Social Thought of Elisée Reclus. Littleton, CO: Aigis Publications.
5. Dobson, A. (ed.) (1999) Fairness and Futurity: Essays on Environmental Sustainability and Social Justice. Oxford: Oxford University Press.
6. Harden, G. (1968) The tragedy of the commons. Science 162(3859), 1243–1248.
7. Lynne, G. (2002) Agricultural industrialization: a metaeconomics look at the metaphors by which we live. Review of Agricultural Economics 24(2), 410-427.
8. Naess, A. (1973) The shallow and the deep, long-range ecology movement. *Inquiry* 16 (1-4), 95-100.
9. Shrader-Frechette, K. (2002) Environmental Justice: Creating Equality, Reclaiming Democracy. Oxford: Oxford University Press.

10. Singer, P. (1975) Animal Liberation: A New Ethics for our Treatment of Animals. New York: New York Review / Random House.
11. Taylor, P. (1986) Respect for Nature. Princeton: Princeton University Press.
12. Thompson P.B. (2010) Land. In Comstock, G.L. (Ed.). Life Science Ethics. Raleigh: Springer Publishing, 123-144.
13. Thompson, P.V. (2008) Agrarian philosophy and ecological ethics. Science and Engineering Ethics 14(4), 527-544.

12.6. In search of the principles of agricultural sciences

The most capacious concepts of any scientific theory are principles. Usually, it is advisable to give them paramount attention, seeking to improve them. In agricultural science, the search for the most relevant principles resulted in the controversy of supporters of conventional, organic and sustainable agriculture, respectively [3; 4]. The most common positions of conventional agriculture are attacked by the positions of organic or sustainable agriculture. The principles of organic agriculture are vigorously popularized by the International Federation of Organic Agriculture Movements (IFOAM). This refers to the following four principles. 1) The principle of the health of the soil, plant, animal, human and planet as one and indivisible whole. 2) The principle of emulating and helping to sustain ecological systems. 3) The principle of ensuring fairness with regard to the common environment and life opportunities. 4) The principle of protecting the health and well-being of current and future generations and the environment [1].

The modern draft of sustainable agriculture was formulated by the United Nations General Assembly in 1987 [5]. Since then, numerous attempts have been made to present the principles of sustainable agriculture in a distinct form. Unfortunately, the formulations of principles of both organic and sustainable agriculture suffer from vagueness. In this regard, there is a need for special philosophical studies. An interesting attempt in this direction is the article by Clark Wolf [4].

The section «Agriculture and the Environment: Nature versus Culture? » ends with the following statement: «Any effort to distinguish nature and culture (thereby implying that culture is unnatural) will be unavoidably controversial». [4, 34] C. Wolf is right in criticizing the opposition of nature and culture. However, they should certainly be distinguished. In relation to agricultural science, there are special theories that express its originality.

To characterize the views of supporters of conventional and sustainable agriculture C. Wolf uses the concepts of worldview and ideology, which «are constituted by a complex of beliefs and values that inform the choices people make» [4, 34]. The terminology chosen by him to a certain extent leads away from the philosophy of science, in which researchers operate with the concept of theory, which contains in the case of axiological conception values, but not simultaneously values and beliefs. Based on scientific theories, one can interpret the content of worldviews and ideologies. If one starts from worldviews and ideologies, avoiding talk of scientific theories, then one cannot evade metaphysics.

According to C. Wolf, there are two ideological perspectives, conventional and sustainable. In the first case, agriculture should be maximally productive, in the second, the most sustainable. These two requirements do not completely contradict each other. «Since we have no ideology-free platform from which to view them, our critical evaluation will no doubt carry some of our own unexamined commitments.» [4, 38] Wolf rightly seeks to uncover these unexamined commitments. In this regard, he considers various interpretations of the concept of sustainability.

Following C. Wolf, I list of different understandings of the concept of sustainability [4, 40-42]. 1) Sustainability is a development that meets the needs not only of the present generation but also of future generations (G.H. Brundtland). 2) Sustainability is the leave to the future the option or the capacity to be as well-off as we are (R.M. Solow); 3) Sustainability is focused on opportunities, capabilities, or freedoms of future generations (B. Barry, R. Howarth, A. Sen). 4) Sustainability is focused on resources (B. Norton). 5) According to the 'Triple Bottom Line', sustainability expresses the unity of the three types of sustainability, namely, environmental, social and economic.

The conclusion of C. Wolf reads as follows «Sustainable agriculture embodies an ideal of agricultural production that expresses values of environmental responsibility, intergenerational fairness, and the integrity of human communities» [4, 51]. However, all three concepts, namely, responsibility, fairness, and integrity, are not considered by him in any detail.

The article by C. Wolf makes a dual impression. On the one hand, it refers to extremely urgent issues. On the other hand, the final statements cannot be called well-founded. In essence, C. Wolf assesses the concept of conventional agriculture in terms of sustainable agriculture. This is the correct method of matching rival theories. However, it must be interpreted truly scientifically, not metaphysically.

In my opinion, the main achievement of the theory of sustainable agriculture is to take into account the interdisciplinary links of agricultural science. Such accounting is not typical for conceptions of conventional and organic agriculture. Of course, interdisciplinary links cannot be limited only to the ecology, the economy, and some social sciences. Ultimately, it is necessary to take into account the interdisciplinary relation of agricultural science with all other sciences. In agricultural science, the principle of maximizing productivity remains in force, but it is partly limited by the need to observe the principles of other sciences. In the absolute majority of cases, it is not the principles of one science that are of decisive importance, but their actual optimum. Maximization takes place in separate axiological theories. If they are considered in interdisciplinary relations, then comes the turn of optimization.

Since all sciences are relevant, together with them their principles deserve support. The principle of productivity of agricultural objects should not be realized to the detriment of the medical principle of health, the economic principle of maximizing business profits, the political science principle of maximizing justice and freedoms. Nevertheless, this does not mean that the principles of health, profits, justice, and freedom become the principles of agricultural science directly.

Everything valuable that is offered on behalf of development projects of conventional, organic and sustainable agriculture, receives its adequate assessment directly in agricultural sciences. An implemented new cycle of knowledge and, therefore, practice, always allows you to compare the benefits and omissions, for example, from the use of herbicides or the implementation of a new technology of feeding livestock. On this path, there are always some difficulties, but they are somehow overcome. Science is always a way to overcome difficulties. This is its nature. It does not tolerate any dictates on itself, including on behalf of morality. Robert Solow ended his famous article with the statement that sustainability as a moral general obligation «is a vague concept. It is intrinsically inexact. It is not something that can be measured out in coffee spoons. It is not something that you could be numerically about. It is, at best, a general guide to policies that have to do with investment, conservation, and resource use. And we shouldn't pretend that it is anything other than that. » [2, 187] In my opinion, in science, everything is measurable, however, not always by coffee spoons. Any portion of interdisciplinary relation can be assessed no worse than various kinds of agricultural or economic effects.

References

1. IFOAM. (2005) Principles of Organic Agriculture. Bonn: IFOAM.
2. Solow, R. M. (1991) Sustainability: an economist's perspective. In Dorfman, R. and Dorfman, N. (Eds.). Economics of the Environment: Selected Readings. New York: W. W. Norton, 179-187.
3. Tal, A. (2018) Making conventional agriculture environmentally friendly: moving beyond the glorification of organic agriculture and the demonization of conventional agriculture. Sustainability 10(4), 1-17.

4. Wolf, C. (2018) Sustainable Agriculture, Environmental Philosophy, and the Ethics of Food. Oxford Handbooks Online. doi: 10.1093/oxfordhb/9780199372263.013.35/
5. World Commission on Environment and Development (WCED). (1987) Our Common Future. United Nations General Assembly, Report of the World Commission on Environment and Development.

Chapter 13. The nature of medicine

13.1. What is medicine?

Medicine is one of the branches of science; it consists of disciplines and subdisciplines. For example, internal medicine is a discipline, and cardiology and endocrinology are subdisciplines of internal medicine. Subdisciplines and disciplines, and, consequently, medicine in general, consist of theories. Their exact number is not known. Nevertheless, since the number of diseases in nosology is estimated at tens of thousands, there are no fewer medical theories. The most relevant taxon of medicine as a branch of science is the concept of scientific medical theory. Medicine consists of theories. The nature of medicine is determined by the nature of medical theories.

A very comprehensive literature on the philosophy of medicine [2-4; 7; 8; 10-12] testifies that it took place as a theory about the conceptual and methodological nature of medical theories. Moreover, I will dare to assert that its content as a whole confirms the relevance of the theory of conceptual transduction. Like all other branches of science, medicine is guided by methods of conceptual transduction, in particular, by methods of deduction, adduction, induction, and abduction, as well as by four methods of inter-theoretical transduction. It is about achieving the medical scientific community as a whole, which, unfortunately, by its individual representatives is not always fully understood. I will consider, in this regard, the controversy of several authors, which was initiated by the article Alex Broadbent [1].

«I suggest, in this article, that the core medical competence is neither to cure, nor to prevent, disease, but to understand

and to predict it. » [1, 289]. «I have argued that understanding is the core intellectual competence of medicine» and «I argue that the core practical competence of medicine is the ability to make predictions about health and disease. » [1, 301]. The mainline of reasoning A. Broadbent is that many doctors treat their patients poorly. In his opinion, this is the consequence of their misunderstanding of the basic medical competencies, in which the treatment is being put. Partly A. Broadbent is right - the one who treats patients poorly is at odds with medical competence. However, it does not follow from this that the inept doctor replaced the right competencies with the wrong ones. He misunderstands all medical competencies. If relatively speaking, they are treatment, understanding and predicting, and then he misinterprets the content of all three competencies.

The questions posed by A. Broadbent are explained without any difficulty from the standpoint of the theory of conceptual transduction. The intratheoretical transduction cycle contains four stages, namely, prediction, factualization, data processing, obtained at the factualization stage, and updating of the initial deductive principles. Together, they provide understanding. Broadbent paid tribute to one of these stages, namely, prediction. The value of the other three stages of intratheoretical conceptual transduction including treatment, which is a type of factualization he clearly underestimated. His other mistake is that he misinterprets the content of understanding. It is not a separate stage of conceptual transduction. If one wants to use the concept of understanding without fail, it should be interpreted as an awareness of the significance of all four stages of intratheoretical conceptual transduction. A doctor, who poorly anticipates the course of events or treats poorly, ineptly handles the results of treatment, clearly misunderstands the nature of medicine.

A. Broadbent argues, «medicine provides an understanding even when it cannot cure» [9, 296]. He does not give due attention to the fact that it is unacceptable to oppose each other stages of the holistic cycle. Understanding is a holistic process. Who is not able to act correctly, he does not understand.

According to the theory of intratheoretical transduction, factualization, and it appears in three forms, of an experiment, observation (passive experiment) and practice, is part of the theory. Factualization is always an intervention in the course of certain events, which is not the case with a prediction. Therefore, contrary to A. Broadbent, a prediction is not practical competence. There is no reason also in naming understanding intellectual competence. Intellect is implemented in a cyclic process. Therefore, intellectual competences are all abilities realized by people in science.

Strictly speaking, the stages of conceptual transduction do not need additional characteristics. Based on conceptual transduction, the content of such terms as 'theoretical', 'practical', 'understanding' is explained.

The responses to A. Broadbent's article are also interesting from a methodological point of view. Chadwin Harris called his article "The continuing allure of cure" [5]. To cure is, of course, relevant. Nevertheless, the cure is just one of the stages of intratheoretical conceptual transduction. Without the other three, it is untenable. Genuine allure deserves the whole cycle of intratheoretical transduction and not its chosen part. The cure is a type of factualization. Its other varieties are observation, experiment, and prevention.

Thaddeus Metz objects A. Broadbent «medicine's nature might be such as not to have an essence, in the sense of a set of necessary and sufficient conditions, but rather to be a practice characterized by a cluster of particular practices, no single one of which is necessary for it to count as "medicine". [9, 307]. In this case, two terms should be distinguished: 'the essence of medicine' and 'the essential nature of medicine'. From the standpoint of conceptual transduction the essence of medicine does not exist. However, supporters of the thesis consider differently, because they have the essence of medicine is a cure. T. Metz did not deviate significantly from this line. His 'cluster of particular practices' is the same essence of medicine, but not in one, but in several individuals of the same type. As for the "of a set of necessary and sufficient conditions", they, of course, are and determine the essential nature of medicine. This, as applied to intratheoretical transduction, is nothing but prediction, factualization, data processing and updating of deductive principles. Of course, we should not forget about the stages and, accordingly, the methods of intertheoretical transduction. Without intratheoretical and intertheoretical conceptual transduction, there is no essential nature of medicine. Another thing is that for its characteristics it is necessary to indicate the peculiarity of medicine. A recent attempt in this direction was made by Peter [12].

He believes that the «disease entity» is the key theoretical concept of medicine [12]. Hucklenbroich compares the concept of 'disease entity' with the concept of 'chemical element'; chemists have built a periodic system of chemical elements, respectively, doctors will create a system of diseases. «A main task of medical research consists in the discovery, definition, and characterization of all disease entities that occur in empirical reality, and to build a comprehensive system reflecting all their similarities and differences» [6, 612]. This curious parallel proves little. In determining the true nature of medicine, it must be borne in mind that any axiological scientific theory deals with subjects. Medicine is an axiological science because values appear in it; therefore, it is not a natural science. The subjects of medicine are patients, not only sick, but also healthy (in the case of prophylaxis or proactive control).

The next step in determining the nature of medicine involves finding out its main principle. In any axiological theory, some positive quality of subjects is maximized. In medicine, it is reasonable to consider the quality of the medical condition of patients, which should be steadily increased in the process of medical treatment. The main principle of medicine is the principle of sustained improvement in the medical conditions of patients. For any person, sick or healthy, this or that medical condition is characteristic. It is always amenable to improvement. To achieve it is a joint task of physicians and their patients. The quality of the medical condition is determined by medical indicators (variables). The relations between them are medical laws.

Thus, the medical theory is the management of medical concepts that represent the dynamics of patients' medical conditions. The principle of sustained improvement of the medical conditions of patients is crucial.

In axiological theories, their principles necessarily are specialized in relation to the goal. It is precisely the basis of medical theory. The status of principles in axiological and natural theories is fundamentally different, but not in all. In both cases, the principles bear the stamp of the specifics of a particular situation. Only in axiological theories do people themselves determine the way to the achievement of their desired goal. Regulating the course of physical processes, people set some goals, the achievement of which occurs in accord with the principle of least action, the status of which is determined not by people, but by nature. In medicine, people are responsible for both principles and goals. Nevertheless, they are not free to ignore completely natural phenomena, for they are the medium of actions taken. With regard to medicine, natural phenomena, i.e. physical, chemical, and biological processes are symbols of medical concepts, most notably, of patients. Medicine as created science is not limited to natural sciences. The above-considered attempt by Peter Hucklenbroich to express the conceptual uniqueness of medicine is interesting, but the status of axiological scientific theory he has clearly not sufficiently taken into account.

References

1. Broadbent, A. (2018) Prediction, understanding, and medicine. Journal of Medicine and Philosophy 43(3), 289-305.
2. Bunge, M. (2013) Medical Philosophy: Conceptual Issues in Medicine. Singapore: World Scientific.
3. Caplan, A. (1992) Does the philosophy of medicine exist? Theoretical Medicine and Bioethics 13(1), 67-77.
4. Gifford, F. (Ed.). (2011) Philosophy of Medicine. Amsterdam, The Netherlands: Elsevier.
5. Harris, C. (2018) The continuing allure of cure: a response to Alex Broadbent's «Prediction, understanding, and medicine». Journal of Medicine and Philosophy 43(3), 313-324.

6. Hucklenbroich, P. (2014) «Disease entity» as the key theoretical concept of medicine. Journal of Medicine and Philosophy 39(6), 609–633.
7. Marcum, J. (2020) Philosophy of medicine. The Internet Encyclopedia of Philosophy [On-line]. Available at: http://www.iep.utm.edu/medicine/
8. Marcum, J. (Ed.). (2016) The Bloomsbury Companion to Contemporary Philosophy of Medicine. New York: Bloomsbury.
9. Metz, T. (2018) Medicine without cure?: a cluster analysis of the nature of medicine. Journal of Medicine and Philosophy 43(3), 306-312.
10. Reiss, J., and Ankeny, R. (2016) Philosophy of medicine. Stanford Encyclopedia of Philosophy Available at: : https://plato.stanford.edu/archives/sum2016/entries/medicine/
11. Schramme, T. and Edwards, S. (Eds.). (2017) Handbook of the Philosophy of Medicine. Dordrecht: Springer.
12. Solomon, M., Simon, J.R., and Kincaid, H. (Eds.). (2017) The Routledge Companion to Philosophy of Medicine. New York: Routledge.

13.2. Medical theory and science

In my opinion, the most problematic issue of the philosophy of medicine is the question of the true nature of medical theory. As a rule, it is discussed in passing. The nature of medical epistemology is much more readable. In this case, the discussion is not specifically related to current issues of medicine.

The relatively old article by P. Thagard sets a certain tone in the discussion of the nature of medical theory. He identifies five philosophical approaches in understanding theories [12, 49]. Syntactic – a theory is a collection of universal generalizations in a formal language. Model-theoretic – a theory is a set-theoretic structure. Paradigm –– a theory is a worldview based on exemplars. The third world – a theory is an abstract entity in an autonomous, nonphysical, non-mental world. Cognitive –– a theory is a mental representation of mechanisms. The authors of these concepts are respectively C.G. Hempel [5], F. Suppe [11], T.S. Kuhn [6], K. Popper [10], and P. Thagard [13]. P. Thagard rightly highlights the weaknesses of the syntactic, model-theoretic, paradigm and third world approaches. In the approaches of T.S. Kuhn and K. Popper, the structure of the scientific theory is not presented in any detailed form. Without its indication, the characteristic of the theory is not sufficiently detailed. From the works of F. Suppe, you can learn a lot about mathematical models of theories, but not about their structure. It is not clear how his theory with an emphasis on set theory can be used to characterize the nature of medical science. C.G. Hempel is known to be the author of the deductive-nomological model of explanation. In this regard, the deduction is of paramount importance. However, the theory does not boil down to the deduction. It, as repeatedly emphasized earlier, also includes adduction, induction, and abduction. Feature position C.G. Hempel is that as a follower of logical positivism, he characterized the nature of all scientific theories from the standpoint of logic. Unfortunately, at the same time, he did not consider in any detail the specifics of the correlation of logic as a formal science with the natural and axiological concepts of the sciences, in particular, with medicine.

The peculiarity of the position of P. Thagard lies in the fact that he declares himself a supporter of cognitive science and after it also a cognitive account of medical theory. In this regard, the understanding of the nature of cognitive science is crucial. «Cognitive science is the interdisciplinary investigation of mind and intelligence, embracing the fields of psychology, neuroscience, linguistics, philosophy, and artificial intelligence. » [12, 51] Thagard wrongfully considers interdisciplinary investigation a science. His position is that the nature of medical theory should be determined from the position of psychology, neuroscience, linguistics, philosophy, and artificial intelligence. In my opinion, this project can be implemented only after determining the specifics of the medical theory itself. It, according to P. Thagard, consists of the representation of mechanisms in which proper and improper functioning generates the states and symptoms of a disease. [12, 59] The mechanisms themselves are implemented due to the causes [4; 1]. Causality comes to the fore.

Aristotle distinguished four causes, material, formal, efficient and final cause.[2] In modern science, there was no reason for the preservation and development of the concepts of material and formal cause. However, the relevance of the concepts of efficient and final cause remains. Efficient cause acts as a source of those changes that are considered in the natural sciences. The final cause is the source of change leading to the achievement of some goals. Final causes are relevant to any axiological theory, including medical theory. Thus, it is correct to assert that medical theory is the management of final causes. In this regard, a very topical question arises about the structure of this management process itself, the presence of relatively independent parts in it. In my opinion, there are at least four of them, because it is necessary to distinguish between prediction (including the planning of actions), factualization (including treatment), data processing and updating of outdated deductive principles (including the principle of sustained improvement of conditions of patients).

In all these four cases, causal mechanisms are implemented differently. Their conceptual content is also different. Thus, it turns out that the definition of medical theory, as a presentation of the mechanisms that generate the states and symptoms of a disease is not enough, because the stages of the implementation of medical theory and their conceptual content are not highlighted.

The fate of medical theory is often associated not only with the deductive-nomological and causal explanation but also with inference to the best explanation [7, section 2.d.]. Inference to the best explanation and abduction is relevant to understanding the nature of any theory. Abduction as a method follows immediately after induction and consists of updating outdated deductive principles. The inference to the best explanation is usually considered an operation independent of induction [3]. It is not part of the theory. The ordering of competing theories takes place in the framework of not intratheoretical but intertheoretical transduction. Moreover, it is not the case that theories are simply compared. A more developed theory is seen as a way to overcome the problems of its predecessor.

The question of the nature of medical theory is relevant to ascertaining the status of medicine as a whole, whether or not it is a science. In this regard, Ronald Munson puts forward interesting arguments. «The first difficulty that faces anyone who addresses the question of whether medicine can be a science is the fact that we have no generally accepted analysis of what it is for a discipline or an enterprise to be a science. Thus, it is not possible to solve the problem of medicine by consulting a set of explicit criteria and then making a decision. Furthermore, I think it is pointless to step into this darkness and declare more or less by fiat that certain conditions are necessary or sufficient for being a science. Science is simply too diverse, various, and changeable to be summed up by a few rules of language use» [9, 189]. There is a rather curious situation – philosophers having a very preliminary idea about both science and art fiercely argue whether medicine is a science or an art. Unlike R. Munson, I believe that it is possible to distinguish strictly the criteria of science. They, in particular, are methods of intratheoretical and intertheoretical transduction. If they are implemented quite consistently and purposefully, then there is science.

Not having the criteria of science, R. Munson, nevertheless, believes that medicine and science differ in their internal aims, criteria of success and principles regulating the conduct of the discipline's activities [9, 189]. «I began by showing that an argument to the effect that medicine (or part of it) is already a science is unsuccessful in its own terms. Next, I argued that medicine and science differ both in their aims and their criteria for success: the aim of medicine is to promote health through the prevention and treatment of disease, while the aim of science is to acquire knowledge; medicine judges its cognitive formulations by their practical results in promoting health, while science evaluates its theories by the criterion of truth. I then demonstrated that medicine (as medical practice) has a moral aspect that is not present in science. » [9, 204]

Only at first glance, the argument of R. Munson seems to be flawless. Suppose that medicine really differs from the sciences, for example, physics: physicists acquire knowledge about nature, physician promotes health of patients. How do they achieve success? It turns out an unexpected circumstance, namely, physicists and physicians act uniformly. They plan some actions and predict their results, carry out these actions, evaluate their results and, finally, change the initial bases (principles of theories). In both cases, the truth criterion is assigned to the most advanced theories. As for the ethical component, it does not go beyond the principles of medicine. In both physics and medicine, success comes to those who are guided by the concepts of principles, laws, and variables and control them through the methods of deduction, adduction, induction, and abduction. Guided by the same methods, physicists improve physical theories and physician medical theories. Quite a clear similarity of medicine and physics forces us to consider them consisting of scientific theories. Physical and medical theories are different. Nevertheless, not by scientific criteria. The internal goals and success criteria of all scientific theories are the same; this is the improvement of theories, which in the case of practicing physicians translates into a promotion of health of patients. The frequent opposition of knowledge and practice, which R. Munson did not avoid, only seems to be obvious at first glance. The conceptual analysis reveals similar grounds of physics and medicine.

O.S. Miettinen takes a rather peculiar position on the problems discussed in this section. Medicine is «[t]he art of preventing or curing disease; the science concerned with disease in all its relations. » [8, 56] In this regard, medicine can be a scholarly field, using, for example, the evidence-based medicine movement. «Today's medicine still is, in all essence, nonscientific» [8, 63]. It is only partly scientific, not fully.

The corresponding conceptual analysis shows that there are no obstacles to the realization of the scientific path of preventing or curing disease. Proponents of attributing medicine to the field of art sincerely believe that it has such features that are not subject to science, in particular, actions, inaccuracy, intuition, emotion, communication, uncertain therapeutic decisions. Science, on the contrary, is attributed to knowledge, a mechanistic understanding, predictability, contrast, precise justifications for actions, and algorithmic, reproducibility [14].

Fixing this opposite, U. Wiesing is convinced that «the prediction for medicine to develop from an 'empirical healing art' to a 'rational, molecular science' is nonsensical from an epistemological point of view.» [14, 457] My position is that in medicine nonsensical is not guided by the concepts of principle, law, variable, does not to take into account the factualization lessons, does not improve all the concepts used. In essence, there is no alternative to these actions, which constitute the true nature of scientific theories, and not ignoring actions, emotion, communication, uncertain therapeutic decisions. Otherwise, irreparable damage is done to scientific medicine. I add to this that it is inappropriate to oppose science and art. The above stages characteristic of a scientific theory are inherent in art as well.

The medical theory is the management of notions of medical principles, laws, and variables, implemented through the methods of deduction, adduction, induction, and abduction, representing, among other things, causal mechanisms, as well as actions, language, thinking, and emotions.

References

1. Cheng, P.W. (1997) From covariation to causation: a causal power theory. Psychological Review 104(2), 367–405.
2. Falcon, A. (2015) Aristotle on causality. The Stanford Encyclopedia of Philosophy. Available at:

https://plato.stanford.edu/archives/spr2015/entries/aristot
le-causality/

3. Harman, G.H. (1965) The inference to the best explanation. Philosophical Review 74(1), 88-95.

4. Harré, R., Madden, E. H. (1975) Causalpowers: A Theory of Natural Necessity. Totowa, NJ: Rowman and Littlefleld.

5. Hempel, C.G. (1965) Aspects of Scientific Explanation. New York: The Free Press.

6. Kuhn, T.S. (1970) The Structure of Scientific Revolutions. Second Ed. Chicago: University of Chicago Press.

7. Marcum, J. (2020) Philosophy of medicine. The Internet Encyclopedia of Philosophy. Available at: http://www.iep.utm.edu/medicine/

8. Miettinen, O.S. (2015) Medicine as a Scholarly Field: An Introduction. Dordrecht, Heidelberg, New York: Springer International Publishing.

9. Munson, R. (1981) Why medicine cannot be a science. Journal of Medicine and Philosophy 6(2), 183-208.

10. Popper, K. (1972) Objective Knowledge. Oxford: Oxford University Press.

11. Suppe, F. (1977) The Structure of Scientific Theories. Second ed. Urbana: University of Illinois Press.

12. Thagard P. (2005) What is a medical theory? In McNamara, L. (Ed.). Multidisciplinary Approaches to Theory in Medicine. Vol. 3. Amsterdam: Elsevier, 47-62.

13. Thagard, P. (2012)The Cognitive Science of Science: Explanation, Discovery, and Conceptual Change. Cambridge, Massachusetts: The MIT Press.

14. Wiesing, U. (2018) From art to science: a new epistemological status for medicine? On expectations regarding personalized medicine. Medicine, Health Care and Philosophy 21(4), 457-466.

13.3. Framework and patterns of medical epistemology

George Khushf quite pertinently notes that «a host of different kinds of knowledge claims have been identified, each with different uses and logics of justification. A general framework is needed to situate these diverse contributions in medical epistemology, so we can see how they fit together. But developing such a framework turns out to be quite tricky. » [7, 461]. Whenever the views of any researcher are considered, one has to evaluate his theory as a whole, about which he, as a rule, does not report anything. Khushf himself was also in a very difficult position, as there is an obvious flaw in the theories of the framework of understanding medical epistemologies. He considered four possible approximations in the characteristics of medical epistemologies, which, in his opinion, culminate in their generalized characteristics: 1) first approximation: descriptive, normative, and meta-epistemologies; 2) second approximation: pure versus applied epistemologies; 3) third approximation: individual versus social epistemology; 4) a fourth framework: epistemologies as compensations for heightened risks of error. Highlighting these four approaches is far from obvious. In this regard, I will note some of their controversial or clearly debatable points.

Medicine is an axiological science, i.e. it deals with values and, therefore, norms. It is impossible in principle to assert something about medicine without focusing on the normative approach. Therefore, the opposition of descriptive and normative epistemology as applied to medicine is an erroneous action. As for medical meta-epistemology, it deserves special attention.

G. Khushf understands the medical metaepistemological approach as characteristic of the philosophy of medicine [1,

463]. Kazem Sadegh-Zadeh was the first to use the term 'metamedicine' «The term 'metamedicine' is coined as an abbreviation for 'philosophy and methodology of medicine'. The prefix 'meta' indicates what we are doing: we are not doing medicine but we are talking about medicine, i.e., we are investigating medicine as practice and as research». [12, 3] Considering that methodology along with conceptology is part of the philosophy of medicine, one can say that metamedicine is equal to the philosophy of medicine. Is it reasonable to replace the philosophy of medicine with metamedicine? In my opinion, it is reasonable. The fact is that the consideration of epistemological issues in medicine is the business of physicians, not philosophers. If the term 'philosophy of medicine' is used, it seems that physicians are entitled to place the burden of addressing epistemological questions on philosophers. It does not take into account that the hour of philosophy comes when the similar features of special metatheories, such as metamedicine, metamathematics, and metaeconomics, are considered. The vocation of philosophers is to develop not metamedicine, but the philosophy of science.

After clarifying the term 'metamedicine', it immediately becomes clear that the opposition between the normative and metaepistemology does not make sense. In essence, we are trying to figure out the nature of nothing else but metamedicine. It makes no sense to say that metamedicine has a metaepistemology approach or approximation.

Let me turn to the consideration of the opposition of pure versus applied epistemologies. G. Khushf believes that there is an antithesis between pure, theoretical and applied practical knowledge [7, 468]. The first knowledge appears in the form of propositional sentences that fix the truth but do not imply direct practical action. It is understood that the distinction between theoretical and practical knowledge is quite relevant for understanding the true nature of medical epistemology.

Physicians are guided consciously or unconsciously by the principle of sustained improvement of the medical conditions of patients. This means that all their actions, affirmations, feelings and emotions acquire genuine medical meaning only when their content is understood as the realization of this principle. The diagnosis of a disease that is not accompanied by some practical action is not a genuine medical diagnosis. Suppose patient A has consulted doctor B, who has diagnosed him accordingly. At this, their contacts were interrupted. Patient A avoids any course of treatment. At first glance, it seems that the patient and the doctor are limited solely to the theoretical position because it did not come to practice. This opinion is superficial. The fact is that the theory of both the doctor and the patient was not realized. These two theories are not genuine theories. With regard to medicine, the opposite of theoretical and practical arises only when the true theory is compared with its unfinished version. We are interested in precisely the full-weighted theory, and not its parts. Medical practice is part of any medical theory. It is illegal to oppose part of the theory of the whole theory.

It is time to look at the relationship between individual and social epistemology. The point is that every participant in a medical case is it a scientist, attending physician or patient, has an individual theory. At the same time, he is involved in a system of complex social mechanisms, which are «often incoherent and opaque», and «at least partly incoherent and insufficiently justified. » [7, 480] Medical epistemology, of course, must consider this circumstance. However, how? In my opinion, by considering a wide network of intertheoretical relations. Each participant in medical interventions has to take into account the correlation of his individual medical theories with group medical theories, as well as with non-medical theories.

Concerned about the pluralism of medical social mechanisms, G. Khushf, nevertheless, seeks to reveal their general orientation. He concludes, «[e]pistemologies are better understood as strategies for overcoming the error, rather than as comprehensive accounts of how we attain justified, true beliefs.» [7, 482] The pluralism of social practices does not weaken but strengthens the understanding of epistemologies as compensations for heightened risks of error. In my opinion, the development of medicine indicates its steady improvement. Of course, it does not do without correcting previously made mistakes. Is it possible to equate, on the one hand, the need to eliminate errors and, on the other hand, the need to develop medical theories? In my opinion, this should not be done.

What is a mistake? The one who makes a mistake is guided by outdated theory. The developed theory is the key to understanding mistakes. In the absence of developed theories, we simply do not understand the nature of the mistakes made. We are not going from overcoming mistakes to advanced theories, but from developing theories to overcoming mistakes. Medicine strategy is a development strategy.

Above, I criticized some of the statements of G. Khushf. Nevertheless, his article makes me a sincere sense of admiration. He demonstrated exceptional attention to such topical issues of medical epistemology that other researchers, as a rule, do not consider. Few people dare to characterize medical epistemology as a whole. He gave such a characteristic. Below I will try to repeat his feat.

I argue that the theory of conceptual transduction is the desired framework for understanding medical epistemology. It is characterized by certain patterns, i.e. conceptual formations that give a regular intelligible form to epistemology. These units are stages and methods of intratheoretical and intertheoretical transduction, as well as interdisciplinary relations. To verify this, it suffices to consider the main trends in the development of scientific medicine.

Randomized controlled trial (RCT) can be carried out in a positivist manner. Nevertheless, induction is understood as statistical analysis. Even more relevant and at the same time a difficult project is evidenced based medicine (EBM). «Evidence based medicine is the conscientious, explicit, and judicious use of current best evidence in making decisions about the care of individual patients. The practice of evidence based medicine means integrating individual clinical expertise with the best available external clinical evidence from systematic research. » [11, 71] EBM is clearly beyond the scope of the positivist project. Research emphasis is not so much on the experiment but on the evidence. EBM has such high requirements [1-5; 8; 13], which inevitably has to consider the sequence of certain research patterns. Often an even broader concept than proof comes to the fore, the concept of meta-analysis [6; 9]. Meta-analysis is the integration of a number of studies into a coherent whole. «We want to stress that meta-analyses should be performed in the framework of systematic reviews ensuring standardized assessment of the methodological quality of included studies, the appropriate examination of heterogeneity across studies, and investigations about the completeness of the identified evidence. » [9, 6-7]

The concept of meta-analysis was originally understood as all-out empowerment of statistical analysis [10]. With the development of medicine, it became more comprehensive. Nowadays, in my opinion, it has acquired a truly metascientific value. Statistical analysis, including RCTs, is preceded by the design of the experiment, the implementation of the experiment, which, as a rule, is saturated with measurements, the comprehension of statistics, leading to a new solution. In essence, the researcher goes through all four stages of intratheoretical transduction: prediction (design of the experiment, observation or practical actions), factualization (obtaining qualitatively and quantitatively determined facts), data processing, allowing extracting new effects, and, finally, updating of the original ideas. In the case of RCTs, the result obtained has the character of a group law, for it is obtained by studying a group of people. If the doctor prescribes treatment for his patients, then each of them passes through a new transduction cycle. If desired, the doctor can summarize his experience with patients in the form of a statistical study.

Thus, the stages and methods of conceptual transduction determine the frameworks and patterns of medical epistemology. I showed this determination in relation to intratheoretical transduction. Of course, it is accompanied by intertheoretical transduction.

References

1. Blumenthal-Barby, J.S. (2013) «Choosing wisely» to reduce low value care: a conceptual and ethical analysis. Journal of Medicine and Philosophy 38(5), 559-580.
2. Blumenthal-Barby, J.S., Ubel, P.A. (2018) In defense of «denial»: difficulty knowing when beliefs are unrealistic and

whether unrealistic beliefs are bad. The American Journal of Bioethics 18(9), 4-15,

3. Cartwright, N. (2007) Are RCTs the gold standard? BioSocieties 2(1), 11-20.

4. Cartwright, N. (2011) A philosopher's view of the long road from RCTs to effectiveness. The Lancet 377(9775), 1400-1401.

5. Faust, H. S. (2013) A cause without an effect? Primary prevention and causation. Journal of Medicine and Philosophy 38(5), 539–558.

6. Foroutan, F., Guyatt, G., Alba, A.C., and Ross, H. (2018) Meta-analysis: mistake or milestone in medicine? Heart 104(19), 1559-1561.

7. Khushf, G. (2013) A framework for understanding medical epistemologies. Journal of Medicine and Philosophy 38(5), 461-486.

8. Marcum, J.A. (2013) The role of emotions in clinical reasoning and decision making. Journal of Medicine and Philosophy 38 (5), 501–519.S

9. Nordmann, A.J., Kasenda, B., Briel, M. (2012) Meta-analyses: what they can and cannot do. Swiss Med Wkly 142(w13518).

10. Pearson, K. (1904) Report on certain enteric fever inoculation statistics. British Medical Journal 2(2288), 1243–1246.

11. Sackett, D.L., Rosenberg, W.M.C., Gray J.A.M,, Haynes, R.B., and Richardson, W.S. (1996) Evidence based medicine: what it is and what it isn't. British Medical Journal 312(7023), 71-72.

12. Sadegh-Zadeh, K. (1980). Toward metamedicine. Metamedicine 1(1), 3-10.

13. Worrall, J. (2007) Evidence in medicine and evidence-based medicine. Philosophy Compass 2(6), 981-1022.K

13.4. Principles and principlism

In clarifying the nature of medical theory, the four principles approach, implemented with undoubted mastery by Tom Beauchamp and James Childress in their theory of biomedical ethics [2; 3], is of current importance. «Beauchamp and Childress identify four primary principles –respect for autonomy, non-maleficence, beneficence (including utility), and justice – and several derivative rules – veracity, fidelity, privacy, and confidentiality – along with various other rules, such as informed consent». [4, 22] The approach they implemented, despite frequent criticism of it, acquired the character of the paradigm of medical ethics. It is supported even by those authors who are prone to critical of the four principles approach [compare 7; 8]. Their criticisms of the Beauchamp and Childress theory do not extend beyond the paradigm of this concept. In a somewhat ironic manner, the strategy of developing ethical concepts with principles that do not ensure their unity is often referred to as principlism [5].

We must pay tribute to Beauchamp and Childress, who carefully thought out the content of their theory [3; 4]. Their theory is structured as follows. Genuine principles are chosen that have more general content than the rules. Depending on the specific situations, the content of the principles and rules, especially the principles, is clarified. This is done by specifying and balancing principles. «Specifying principles is a way to try to reduce or eliminate the conflict; balancing principles is an effort to resolve the conflict through determining which principle outweighs the other in the circumstances». [4, 25] The theory culminates in the achievement of reflective equilibrium, the coherent state of all seemingly incompatible principles, rules, and judgments. On the concept of reflective equilibrium, see [1; 6; 9, 507].

Danner Clouser and Bernard Gert most sharply criticized the theory of Beauchamp and Childress. «The points we want to raise are rarely if ever addressed in the literature. Therefore it is important that we make clear what our focus is. It is that principlism lacks systematic unity, and thus creates both practical and theoretical problems. Since there is no moral theory that ties the "principles" together, there is no unified guide to action which generates clear, coherent, comprehensive, and specific rules for action nor any justification of those rules. » [5, 227]

Clouser and Gert are right; all parts of the theory must be consistent with each other. The question is how to understand this consistency. Beauchamp and Childress believe that everything is consistent in their theory. The trouble with Clouser and Gert is that they proclaim the need for a consistent moral theory, but do not offer a variant of it. They believe that a consistent moral theory should explain the need for the well-known moral rules «Don't kill», «Don't deceive», «Keep your promise», and «Do your duty» [5, 234]. This remark, as well as the entire content of their article, shows that, in fact, they consider all medical ethics in isolation from basic medical theories. The same is true of the position of Beauchamp and Childress, namely, the alienation of medical ethics from medical theories.

In my opinion, medical ethics is contained in the medical theory itself in the event that it is introduced, firstly, the principle of maximizing the prosperity of all stakeholders, secondly, the principle of responsibility [sections 6.10, 9.10]. One should worry about not the unity of medical ethics, taken in isolation from medical theories, but about the ethical completeness of these theories. Immediately it turns out that with the principle of maximizing the prosperity of all stakeholders, there is no need for principles of respect for the autonomy of a person, as well as in principle of justice. All stakeholders include both individual patients and other stakeholders. In the presence of the principle of sustained improvement of the medical conditions of patients, there is no need for the principles of non-maleficence, beneficence (including utility). The patient eliminates any harm and at the same time involves beneficence, doing good deeds. Of course, the ethically oriented medical theory also contains the potential of properly understanding of the specification, balancing and reflective equilibrium.

The specification is that all principles are understood in relation to certain patients. The main goal is to improve the medical condition, first, those patients who turned to doctors for help. Nevertheless, doctors do not forget, in particular, in connection with the public status of medical care, other patients, real and possible.

Balancing consists of comparing medical values. All medical actions are evaluated quantitatively according to their contribution to the achievement of the goal. For example, a painful procedure is contraindicated in children more than adults are. Representatives of any axiological science mostly perfectly compare and then combine the values with which they have to meet. In difficult cases, resort to the relevant consultations. In our case, there is no need for a special analysis of difficult medical situations. There is no doubt that physicians, and only they, are able to resolve them in the best possible way.

As for the reflexive equilibrium, then, in my opinion, its scientific content is doubtful. The fact is that the principles of medical theory, namely, firstly, the principle of maximizing the prosperity of all stakeholders, secondly, the principle of responsibility, thirdly, the principle of sustained improvement of the medical conditions of patients do not conflict with each other. Therefore, there is no need for balancing of principles. Another thing is that their subordination should be clearly established. The first principle of medical theories is the principle of maximizing the prosperity of all stakeholders. Conflict situations are characteristic not so much for principles as for theories. The conflict of theories is overcome through intertheoretical transduction.

Thus, scientific medical theory culminates in the ethical principles of maximizing the prosperity of all stakeholders and responsibility. At the same time, medical ethics are not formalized outside medical theory, but directly within its boundaries. The true principles of scientific theories are those from which laws are derived. The substitution of genuine principles by their surrogates is unacceptable.

References

1. Arras, J. (2007) The way we reason now: reflective equilibrium in bioethics. In The Oxford Handbook of Bioethics. Ed. by B. Steinbock. Oxford, New York: Oxford University Press.46-71.
2. Beauchamp, T.L. and Childress J.F. (2008) Principles of Biomedical Ethics, Sixep ed. Oxford: Oxford University Press.
3. Beauchamp, T. L. and DeGrazia, D. (2004) Principles and principlism. In Khushf G. (Ed.). Handbook of Bioethics. Taking Stock of the Field from a Philosophical Perspective.

New York, Boston, Dordrecht, London, Moscow: Kluwer Academic Publishers, 55-74.

4. Childress, J.F. (2007) Methods in bioethics. In The Oxford Handbook of Bioethics. Ed. by B. Steinbock. Oxford New York: Oxford University Press, 15-45.
5. Clouser, K. D. and Gert, B. (1990) A critique of principlism. Journal of Medicine and Philosophy, 15(2), 219–236.
6. de Maagt, S. (2017) Reflective equilibrium and moral objectivity. Inquiry 60(5), 443-465.
7. Hine, K. (2011) What is the outcome of applying principlism? Theoretical Medicine and Bioethics 32(6), 375–388.
8. Keeling, M. and Bellefleur, O. (2016). 'Principlism' and Frameworks in Public Health Ethics. Montréal, Québec: National Collaborating Centre for Healthy Public Policy.
9. Rawls, J. (1999) A Theory of Justice. Revised ed. Cambridge: Belknap Press.

13.5. Diagnostics: dual-processing theory vs conceptual transduction

The problem content of the diagnosis is one of the central topics in medicine. This circumstance is recognized by all. However, its understanding is rarely accompanied by proper metascientific analysis. Diagnosis is the recognition of a genuine medical condition of a patient, i.e. defined in the context of the most developed theory. The stages of medical diagnosis were described more or less in detail, in particular, the selection of a set of symptoms reported by the patient to the doctor, the development of the working hypothesis, the decision on the patient's illness or his health. Based on the decision made, a forecast is made of the change in the patient's medical condition in the future and some procedures are appointed.

In my opinion, an understanding of those concepts that allow for diagnosis is crucial in diagnosis. The diagnosis is the word of the Greek roots; literally, it means that having passed through knowledge, i.e. guided by him, it is necessary to determine the patient's condition. A mature dialogue between the doctor and the patient is desirable because in his process the true features of the disease are found out. Of course, the conceptual position, on the one hand, of the patient, on the other hand, of the doctor, is different. The patient does not possess the medical theories to the proper degree. Otherwise, he would have diagnosed himself. The patient's knowledge is generally not sufficiently articulated. That is why the doctor does not expect any special revelations from him but mainly draws attention to the symptoms of the patient's illness. Responsibility for making a final decision he imposes on himself, even if the patient has a medical education.

What does the doctor have as an analyst? A network of interrelated theories that are subordinated to each other in a certain way. He is guided by this conceptual framework. The information that the patient tells him, the doctor embeds into these theories. Moreover, this integration is carried out at three addresses, which are: a) league-theories, b) separate theories within these league-theories, c) stages characteristic of the chosen theory. The most difficult situation occurs when firstly the symptoms called the patient or observed in his appearance and line of conduct, cannot be identified as scientific and medical concepts, namely, variables. Secondly, because of their fragmentary nature, they do not fit into the chains of inference that are characteristic of a particular medical theory. In this case, the doctor seeks to clarify the situation with additional questions or clinical analyzes until, finally, he is able to determine the desired theory. The first stage of the diagnosis ends with the choice of some working theory. Guided by it the doctor recreates the medical condition of the patient. How it is done? By conceptual transduction.

Thus, the stages of conceptual transduction are preceded by an introductory part, consisting of the recognition of some initial theory. This recognition is based on known theories. In connection with this recognition, in a strange way, a fundamentally different understanding of the style of thinking prevails in diagnostics than in evidenced based medicine. Its origin is not analytical philosophy, as is the case in evidenced based medicine, but cognitive psychology. This is a dual-processing theory [1-6], which is considered either heuristic-analytic [3] or intuitive-analytic conception [1; 4]. This means that the analytical stage is preceded by a fundamentally different stage of thinking, the heuristic (intuitive). In my opinion, the foundations of the dual-processing theory were considered in most detail by Jonathan Evans [3] and Pat Croskerry [1].

Evans believes that heuristic thinking is hypothetical or suppositional, implicit, automatic, preconscious and pragmatic; analytical thinking is slow and sequential in nature, controlled rather than automatic, explicit, logic responsive to verbal instructions [3, 382]. «In general thinking, the two systems are interdependent, since preconscious heuristic (or pragmatic) processes supply content continuously to consciousness for analytic processing. » [3, 82] Croskerry believes that in contrast to the analytical approach to decision making the intuitive approach is experiential-inductive (not hypothetical-deductive), of bounded rationality (not unbounded rationality), heuristic (not normative reasoning), gestalt effect and pattern recognition (not robust decision making), modular responsivity (not critical, logical thought), unconscious thinking theory (not deliberate, purposeful thinking) [1, 1023].

Evans and Croskerry enumerate concepts without giving any of them any distinct characteristics. In the kaleidoscope of concepts, it is extremely difficult to impose the order required by scientific methodology. Therefore, in criticizing their position, I will limit myself to a concise reference to the conceptual transduction methodology, in which, as the reader knows, it is necessary to distinguish eight stages of cognition. Above, at the beginning of the section, I presented the structure of the diagnosis from the standpoint of conceptual transduction. There is nothing in this view that is implicit, automatic, intuitive, or implicitly creative.

Consider a specific situation. The patient complains to the doctor for pain in the right side of the body. The doctor knows that such a symptom may indicate many diseases. It needs to correlate the pain symptom with one or, possibly, several diseases. He makes a choice between theories, sifting out, based on the information available to him, one opportunity after another, until he is able to present a diagnosis and outline a way to treat a patient with the necessary, greater or lesser degree of confidence. The doctor usually relies on appropriate clinical tests. This means that when making a diagnosis, he does not reinvent the wheel; he once again performs intratheoretical transduction cycles. The repetition of transduction cycles is accompanied by the refinement of medical theories as applied to a particular patient. The diagnosis is the initial conceptual transduction, less accurate than its subsequent variants. This means that there is no need to contrast the diagnosis and treatment because they have a methodological unity. The untenable opposition of diagnosis and treatment is the basis of a dual-processing theory.

Evans in an attempt to present hypothetical thinking in a systematic way considers three principles [3, 379]. The singularity principle – people consider a single hypothetical possibility, or mental model, at one time. The relevance principle – people consider the model which is most relevant (generally the most plausible or probable) in the current context. The satisficing principle – models are evaluated with reference to the current goals and accepted if satisfactory.

The content of these principles is largely trivial. Of course, the researcher begins with individual theories and then improves them. How exactly the theories should be managed is explained through intertheoretical transduction. It is the process of managing theories, which is accomplished through the methods of problematization, discovery, interpretation, and ordering. It is with these methods that the researcher is guided if he succeeds in the management of theories. Thus, there is no need for the principles of singularity, relevance and satisficing. Strictly speaking, they are not principles, because laws are not derived from them.

In my opinion, the dual-processing theory is the result of hasty epistemological conclusions, originally made by representatives of cognitive psychology, and then uncritically transferred to medicine.

References

1. Croskerry, P. (2009) A universal model of diagnostic reasoning. Academic Medicine 84(8), 1022-1028.
2. Croskerry, P. (2013) From mindless to mindful practice – cognitive bias and clinical decision making. The New England Journal of Medicine 368(26), 2445-2448.

3. Evans, J.S.B.T. (2006) The heuristic-analytic theory of reasoning: extension and evaluation. Psychonomic Bulletin and Review 13(3), 378-395.
4. Hammond, K.R. (1990) Intuitive and analytic cognition: information models. In Sage, A. (Ed.). Concise Encyclopedia of Information Processing in Systems and Organizations. Oxford, UK: Pergamon Press, 306 -312.
5. Mamede, S. and Schmidt H.G. (2017) Reflection in medical diagnosis: a literature review. Health Professions Education 3(1), 15-25.
6. Miller, R.A. and Masarie, F.E. Jr. (1989) Use of the quick medical reference (QMR) program as a tool for medical education. Methods of Information in Medicine 28(4), 340-345.

13.6. Medical truth

Medical truth is a concept necessary for rejecting medicine provisions that do not correspond to its scientific status. Unfortunately, the problem of medical truth is rarely discussed thoroughly. I will note a number of provisions that seem to me to be fundamental in characterizing medical truth.

First, medical truth belongs to the class of axiological truths. We recognize as true those actions that lead to the most effective result. Secondly, medical truth is always relative. In accordance with the growth of scientific knowledge, what was considered true yesterday is not recognized as such today. Thirdly, there are many quantitative gradations of truth, which are not limited to the estimates of 0 (misconception) and 1 (true). Yesterday's truths are not completely denied. Some position is recognized as true in a certain respect. Fourth, the truth cannot be formulated without reference to theory. Fifth, the provisions of the most developed theory are recognized as trust. Sixthly, along with the relevance of the most developed theories, the viability of other theories is also recognized. Given this circumstance, the truth is understood in the context of the theory of conceptual transduction. A true position is one that organically integrates into the medical league-theories. Seventh, the status of truth is determined by the success of the entire medical scientific community. It is not solely determined by the opinion of one person.

The problem of pluralism of truth in medicine is full of many problematic aspects. According to the reasoning of Gerd Achenbach, the complexity of the problem under discussion is determined largely by three circumstances [1]. Successes in one field of medicine are set off by failures in another area that was previously in the shadows. One should consider medicine as a whole, but it is not clear how to do this, especially in the light of J. Goethe's statement that every age has its own philosophy. On the question of medical truth, there is also a shortage of time for doctors and patients. Finally, it should be remembered that, despite all the successes of medicine, the result of a person's life is his death.

B.G. Achenbach raised more questions than answered. This is not surprising, since, judging by his article, there is no theory at his disposal that allows him to work out these answers. In my opinion, these answers could be so. Medical truth does not exist in a single form for whole medicine. Since medicine consists of many separate sciences, the truth is own in each of them. There is nothing surprising. Medicine is a branch of science, not a separate theory. Of course, all medical truths can be brought together. In this case, they should be given a uniform assessment, namely, how much they slow down the aging of the patient, which will certainly end in death. This circumstance does not limit medical truth; truth does not guarantee the deliverance of the patient from death. Its purpose is different – to prolong life. As for the lack of time, it does not cancel the concept of truth. It should simply be understood that the concept of truth has a temporal dimension because it is not absolute, but relative. The pluralism of philosophical interpretations of truth also does not negate its status. All their achievements and shortcomings should be critically evaluated, carefully carrying out something like medical-philosophical modeling.

Surprised by the multidimensionality of the concept of truth in medicine, B.G. Achenbach tends to fix the existence of its many faces. In this regard, he even recalls the famous philosophical relativist Paul Feyerabend, who considered all theories equally relevant. In my opinion, Feyerabend did not take into account that the most developed theories, which head the corresponding league-theories, have priority importance in any science, including medicine. This circumstance puts obstacles to impetuous relativism, which Achenbach could not avoid following Feyerabend.

Unfortunately, it is necessary to note that in the philosophy of medicine the problem of truth is given little attention. In medical ethics, considerable attention is paid to the problem of 'truth-telling', but not to the problem of truth itself. This remark does not apply to Grant Gillett, who seeks to fit the understanding of medical truth into the context of culture. He summarized his long-term efforts in an abstract of the article [3] as follows.

Truth and knowledge are conceptually related and there is a way of construing both that implies that they cannot be solely derived from a description that restricts itself to a set of scientific facts. In the first section of this essay, I analyze truth as a relation between a praxis, ways of knowing, and the world. In the second section, I invoke the third thing – the objective reality on which we triangulate as knowing subjects for the purpose of complex scientific endeavors like medical science and clinical care. Such praxes develop robust methods of «keeping in touch» with disease and illness (like biomarkers). An analysis drawing on philosophical semantics motivates the needed (anti-scientistic) account of meaning and truth (and therefore knowledge) and underpins the following argument: (i) the formulation and dissemination of knowledge rests on language; (ii) language is selective in what it represents in any given situation; (iii) the praxes of a given (sub)culture are based on this selectivity; but (iv) human health and illness involve whole human beings in a human lifeworld; therefore, (v) medical knowledge should reflectively transcend, where required, biomedical science towards a more inclusive view. Parts three and four argue that a post-structuralist (Lacanian) account of the human subject can avoid both scientism and idealism or unconstrained relativism. [3, 633].

Gillett begins his study with the semantic concept of truth, and then complements it on behalf of language, inter subjectivity, practice, culture, and some projects of major philosophical directions, giving decisive preference to Lacan's poststructuralism. Such a project is based on metaphysics and not on medicine as a branch of science and its interdisciplinary connections with other branches of science. It is not surprising, therefore, that the scientific position seems to him insufficient. My position is the opposite of what Gillett suggests. I do not think that metaphysics, in particular, of Wittgenstein, Heidegger, and Lacan, is the key to understanding the nature of science, including medicine. Their metaphysical views themselves need to be understood from the standpoint of various branches of science. In this case, it turns out that a correctly understood science does not need to be supplemented, including on behalf of practice and culture. They themselves appear in their most developed form as manifestations of certain scientific theories, in particular, social and art. Scientism, of course, is destructive, if, as is usually done, it is understood as a disregard for the achievements of knowledge that is not properly documented scientifically. In contrast to scientism, the scientific position is completely consistent and does not need to be supplemented with non-scientific bloopers.

As for the semantic concept of truth, it is, of course, outdated. Its disadvantage is that it not only absolutizes the object representation of the theory but also, most importantly, does not take into account the development of scientific knowledge. However, true is only the knowledge that is represented by the most advanced theories.

As I noted earlier, the problem of medical truth remains within the framework of the philosophy of medicine in oblivion. This fact suggests that many researchers believe the concept of medical truth is not relevant. It is a clear misconception. If there is no proper understanding of the nature of medical truth, the ways of overcoming medical errors that lead to numerous detrimental consequences are not clear [4]. The more fully a physician realizes the potential of medical truth, the less he is mistaken. This potential is realized only when the physician is guided by the most developed medical theories. He always faces the need to answer the most urgent question for him: "Do I really, by making a diagnosis, controlling the course of treatment I prescribed and informing the patient about the nature of his illness, act in accordance with the most developed medical theories?"

References

1. Achenbach, B.G. (2011) Pluralismus in der Medizin: Wahrheit als Verschiedenheit [Pluralism in medicine: truth as diversity]. Deutsche Ärzteblatt 108(3), A 98-101. [In German].
2. Gillett, G. (2006) Medical science, culture, and truth. Philosophy, Ethics, and Humanities in Medicine 1, 13.
3. Gillett, G. (2015) Culture, truth, and science after Lacan. Bioethical Inquiry 12(4), 633-644.
4. Mamede, S., Schmidt, H.G., and Rikers, R. (2007) Diagnostic errors and reflective practice in medicine. Journal of Evaluation in Clinical Practice 13(1), 138-145.

13.7. Informed consent as group theory

Knowing the truth, the doctor must effectively dispose of it. In this regard, there is an urgent question about the appropriateness of telling the patient the truth. Is the patient able to understand the doctor? The ratio of truth and truth-telling is saturated with numerous problems [1-7; 9; 10]. For the last four decades, they have been discussed, as a rule, with the firm conviction that there is no return from the partnership's medical ethics to the policy of paternalism, in which patients' rights to participate in making decisions related to their treatment were not recognized [10].

Strengthening the partnership strategy could not do without the development of certain concepts, among which the most important was the concept of informed consent. As often happens in science, researchers gradually increase the attention to a certain concept, and only then, it turns out that its nature is in a certain fog. A similar story happened with the concept of informed consent. As a result, various ways of finding out the true nature of this concept have been proposed. In this regard, John Kleinig notes «that there is always an expressive dimension to consent – that consent must be signified – and that only if consent takes the form of a communicative act can the moral relations between A and B be transformed. Absent such communication, B has no business doing that for which A's consent is needed even if A condones or would acquiesce to it. Consent is a social act in which A conveys something to B – something that, once communicated [...] now gives B a moral right or entitlement that B previously lacked. » [5, 10]

The true nature of informed consent cannot be elucidated without paying special attention to the status of the doctor and patient, especially the latter due to his usually insufficient medical competence. The patient may become a full creator of informed consent if he understands the content of medical actions, but which, as a rule, is not [2]. This means that it is not enough to be satisfied with just a superficial understanding of the nature of informed consent. According to a number of authors, «the ideal informed consent process involves an ongoing, interactive conversation between the participant and knowledgeable, responsive research staff who were trained in best practices. » [6, 65] Bert Heinrichs seeks to clarify the very content of the process of developing informed consent. In this regard, he refers to the theory of speech acts of John Searle and concludes, «That we should think of "to consent" in the special meaning it has in the concept of informed consent as a declarative speech act. » [4, 39] Informed consent acts as declarative, and not assertions, commission, directives or expressive speech act. (compare: [8, 205-210])

Thus, much about the nature of informed consent has been clarified; nevertheless, controversial issues remain. They are so acute that informed consent over the course of six decades is now and again compared with the myth [1; 3; 4]. In my opinion, the theory of conceptual transduction allows clarifying the nature of the phenomenon of informed consent.

One way or another, but in medicine, it is impossible to do without special consideration of the doctor-patient relationship. What are the exact consequences of their contacts? In searching for an answer to this question, it is necessary first to take into account that they are guided by various theories, the manifestation of which takes place through actions, conversations, and publicized and not publicized reflections. The contact the doctor and patient lead to the meeting of their individual theories, T_{doc} and T_{pat}. Each of these medical theories consists of many parts, namely, principles, laws, variables, actions, speech and mental acts. Are theories comparable with each other? As a rule, they are comparable.

Two obvious extremes, namely, complete commensurability or equally complete incommensurability of theories are hardly ever encountered. As a rule, there is a partial commensurability of theories. Theories intersect with each other. These points of intersection express the formal unity of the two theories. Let me demonstrate this unity with a geometric example. Imagine crossing a straight line and a parabola. The point of intersection exists in two dimensions, and not in one. One point belongs to the parabola, and the other to the straight line. Only formally, they merge into one point. All points of intersection of two theories form a group theory. It expresses the mutual understanding of the contacting subjects, which in our case are the patient and the doctor. Outside the points of intersection, they disagree with each other.

Thus, we have to deal with three theories, two individual conceptions and one of group. Each of the persons is guided not by group, but by individual theory. Why? Because the true theory has a well-defined conceptual nature, in particular, the correlation of principles, laws, and variables. The points of intersection of theories do not reproduce this nature, because they are woven from pieces torn from individual theories. Group theory is quasi-theory. It expresses the agreement of people with each other. This circumstance is usually misunderstood, believing that the theories of people can completely coincide with each other. Such a complete coincidence of theories has never been observed by anyone. Thus, a partial, formal agreement between people is quite possible.

The second circumstance, which should also be noted, is that the theory of the doctor in conceptual terms, as a rule, exceeds the theory of the patient. This means that he understands the shortcomings of the patient's theory and, therefore, has the potential to overcome them. The patient is in most cases not able to understand the shortcomings of the theory of the doctor. In the relationship between the doctor and the patient, the decisive role belongs to the doctor, but not because he is a supporter of paternalism, but solely because of the merits of his theory. The doctor has the ability to contribute to the development of the patient's medical theory. The higher the patient's competence, the more informed his consent. There is no informed consent as such. It is justified to one degree or another.

The awareness of the doctor is also not absolute. If he is not in trouble with the ethics of responsibility, then he is constantly improving his theories. By virtue of this very reason, he will contribute to the development of the patient's medical competence. Thus, there is no doubt about the relevance of the concept of informed consent. It is equally obvious that its epistemological content has not yet been sufficiently studied. Realizing this, I offer as a basis for thinking through the content of informed consent the theory of conceptual transduction. I see no alternative to it as far as all other ways of developing the concept of informed consent I know lack an organic connection with the philosophy of science.

References

1. Boyd, K. (2015) The impossibility of informed consent? Journal of Medical Ethics 41(1), 44-47.
2. Dawson, A. (2004) What should we do about it? Implications of the empirical evidence in relation to comprehension and acceptability and randomization. In Holm, S. and Jonas, M.F. (Eds.). Engaging the World: The Use of Empirical Research in Bioethics. Amsterdam, The Netherlands: IOM Press, 41-52.
3. Fellner, C. H. and Marshall, J.R. (1970) Kidney donors. The myth of informed consent. American Journal of Psychiatry 126(9), 1245-1251.

4. Heinrichs, B. (2019) Myth or magic? Towards a revised theory of informed consent in medical research. Journal of Medicine and Philosophy 44(1), 33-49.

5. Kleinig, J. (2009) The nature of consent. In Miller, F. and Wertheimer, A. (Eds.). Ethics of Consent: Theory and Practice. Oxford: Oxford University Press, 3-24.

6. Lentz, J., Kennett, M., Perlmutter, J., and Forrest, A. (2016) Paving the way to a more effective informed consent process: recommendations from the Clinical Trials Transformation Initiative. Contemporary Clinical Trials 49, 65-69.

7. Manson, N. C. and O'Neill, O. (2007) Rethinking Informed Consent in Bioethics. Cambridge, United Kingdom: Cambridge University Press.

8. Searle, J. R. and Vanderveken, D. (1985) Foundations of Illocutionary Logic. Cambridge, United Kingdom: Cambridge University Press.

9. Singh, M.M. (2017) Breaking bad news in clinical setting: a systematic review. Indian Journal of Applied Research 7(12), 29-32.

10. Sisk, B., Frankel, R., Kodish, E., and Isaacson, J.H. (2016) The truth about truth-telling in American medicine: A brief history. The Permanente Journal 20(3), 74-77.

13.8. Methodology for the definition of the concepts of disease and health

There is no doubt that the concepts 'disease' and 'health' occupy one of the central places in medicine. Nevertheless, there are great differences regarding the ways of determining their nature. The most frequently discussed way of defining the concepts of disease and health was presented by Christopher Boorse:

1. The *reference class* is a natural class of organisms of uniform functional design; specifically, an age group of a sex of a species.

2. A *normal function* of a part or process within members of the reference class is a statistically typical contribution by it to their individual survival [or] reproduction.

3. *Health* in a member of the reference class is *normal functional ability*: the readiness of each internal part to perform all its normal functions on typical occasions with at least typical efficiency.

4. A *disease* [later, *pathological condition*] is a type of internal state which impairs health, *i.e.*, reduces one or more functional abilities below typical efficiency. [1, 562; 2, 684]

This and similar ways of defining the concepts of health and disease claim to be universal. In this regard, Halvor Nordby formulated the following position on behalf of the philosophy of language: «if a common understanding of disease can be analyzed into a definition, then this is a non-trivial definition. But any nontrivial analysis must be viciously circular: the analysis must presuppose that disease can be defined, but this is what the analysis is supposed to yield as a result. This means [...], that disease and other controversial health concepts do not have analyses grounded in a common language. Stipulative and contextual definitions can have local significance, but the normative roles of such definitions are at the same time limited. » [3, 169]. For all the legitimacy of this position, it is not sufficiently scientifically substantiated. The physicians who characterize the phenomena of disease and health do not operate on common, but the scientific language and they speak on behalf of not the philosophy of language, but the philosophy of science, namely, the philosophy of medicine as a science. Of course, the general definitions in science are quite legitimate, but their status must be stipulated. In this connection, the statement of Mary Walker and Wendy Rogers «*that we do not need to reject the possibility of defining the general concept "disease"*» [4, 402] deserves to be supported. In this regard, they propose «a new approach to defining disease» [4].

Their proposed approach to the definition of the concept of the disease consists in indicating a cluster of signs, which are then given a contextual definition depending on the nature of the disease, for example, cancer or measles.«[...] X is a disease if X meets some combination of the following criteria:

1. involves dysfunction;

2. is harmful, causing suffering or incapacitation;

3. is in principle explainable in terms of facts about human biology

and psychology; and

4. is beyond the direct conscious control of the individual». [4, 412]

According to Walker and Rogers, a disjunctive, prototype, and cluster definition of the disease should be distinguished. In the case of a disjunctive definition, the necessary and sufficient conditions of a certain disease are indicated, but there is no selection of their common or similar features. With the prototype definition, prototypes of diseases are distinguished. Nevertheless, at the same time criterion adequacy is not achieved. «We want to be able to count a state as a disease in virtue of the features it has, not in virtue of these features being similar to those of a prototype.» [4, 411] The cluster definition of disease expresses strengths of the disjunctive and the prototype definition of a disease, without being burdened by their weaknesses. It identifies similar features and at the same time gives them a criterion justification. Walker and Rogers believe that, as applied to the definition of the disease, they realize the innovative potential of the teaching of Ludwig Wittgenstein on the family similarity of language games [5, sections 65-71].

In my opinion, difficulties in defining the concepts of disease and health are mainly associated with a lack of understanding of the true nature of scientific medical theories.

As noted earlier, the basic principle of medicine is the principle of sustained improvement of the medical conditions of patients. Add to this that improvement is always achieved in the way of the patient from birth to death. Physician, obviously, must somehow take into account the many links of this process. Each link combines two events. Its most important characteristics are the likelihood of a new event and event time. [6] The event can be not just death. It can be the relapse, receiving an organ transplant, pregnancy, failure of treatment, recovery, etc. Like physicists, the physician predicts the onset of certain events, each of which implies, firstly, the fixation of certain patient states, and secondly, the characterization of the process of changes in his condition.

Adequate scientific characterization of conditions and processes involves the measurement of quantitative values of some medical parameters, in particular, body temperature, blood pressure, the value of the rheumatoid factor, and many others. There are many quantitative data. In their characterization, scientists prefer to name a parameter and its quantitative value. Nevertheless, they also use linguistic variables that relate to a certain set of parameters, for example, they talk about afebrile, subfebrile, febrile temperature. Each of these three concepts has scientific significance only if the quantitative boundaries of the parameter are specified. For example, subfebrile temperature is from 37.3 °C to 38.0 °C. The grossest characteristics are dichotomous characteristics, for example, good / bad, beautiful / ugly.

Disease and health are obviously dichotomous concepts. Their scientific characteristic is impossible without specifying the appropriate quantitative values. The situation is complicated by the fact that illness and health are integral parameters. For example, patient's condition for rheumatoid arthritis is determined by the significance and ratio of several parameters, in particular, rheumatoid factor (RF), anti-citrullinated protein antibody (ACPA), the erythrocyte sedimentation rate (ESR) and C-reactive protein (CRP), each with some relative weight. Rheumatoid arthritis disease and rheumatoid arthritis health are two integral values, one of which is negative and the other is positive. What is their fundamental difference from each other? In case of the painful condition of the patient the likelihood of an undesirable event, eventually, death increases significantly more than in his health conditions. How many times more? If necessary, the physician in all possible details using quantitative data will describe the process of changing, for example, the conditions of the joints of healthy and sick patients. Nevertheless, he would hardly call one quantitative characteristic that would distinguish the disease from health.

Thus, illness and health are two (relatively rough) correlative characteristics of patients' conditions in the composition of a well-defined medical theory, for example, cardiology or rheumatology. They indicate different rates of increase in the likelihood of undesirable patient states. Physicians are designed to maximize the reduction in the growth of these probabilities in the case of both sick and healthy patients.

So far, I have characterized disease and health as concepts of separate medical theories. Can they be generalized to the level of disciplines and subdisciplines? Of course, it is possible to the extent that all medical theories are guided by a similar principle of sustained improvement of the medical conditions of patients. However, it must be borne in mind that, ultimately, the basis of the concepts of illness and health are medical theories that are combined in league-theories. Medical subdisciplines and disciplines and, finally, medicine as a branch of science consist of league-theories. Disease and health as basic concepts refer to medical league-theories. Others, in particular, disciplinary and subdisciplinary concepts of disease and health, must be reduced to the concepts of league-theories.

If medical theories did not have similarity, then it would be impossible to relate the concepts of disease and health with medical disciplines and medicine as a branch of science. Does this similarity confirm the medical relevance of Wittgenstein's view of the family similarity of language games? Only to a small extent. The concept of Wittgenstein's language games is not the key to understanding the philosophy of science, including the philosophy of medicine. Quite the contrary, the philosophy of science is the key to understanding the actual aspects of the Wittgenstein conception. The fact that medical theories are similar to each other was known long before Wittgenstein. The question is what this similarity is. On this account, he essentially did not say anything.

Returning to the article by Mary Walker and Wendy Rogers, I note that they only slightly concerned the nature of medical theories. The meaning of their supposedly relevant cluster criteria can be understood solely based on medical theories. For example, dysfunction is that the disease increases the likelihood of unwanted events. The belief that the disease «is in principle explainable in terms of facts about human biology and psychology», in my opinion, erroneous. The disease is explained solely by medical theory, and not by biology or psychology, which are in interdisciplinary relations with it.

Is it legitimate to use disjunctive definitions in determining decease and health? Of course, it is. The introduction of the concepts of illness and health is a disjunctive operation. The criticism of Walker and Rogers of disjunctive definitions is only legitimate at first glance. The fact is that they compare them with the criteria for diseases that are not properly explained through medical theories. If you go down to them, then all doubts about the relevance of the disjunctive definitions disappear.

Is it advisable to use the definitions of prototypes in defining decease and health? In my opinion, it is advisable. The results of statistical studies are always prototypes. Without reliance on them, it is impossible to develop a theory of treatment for a particular patient. However, it should be borne in mind that an individual theory is always different from the prototypical one. Individual and prototypical theories complement each other.

References

1. Boorse, C. (1977) Health as a theoretical concept. Philosophy of Science 44(4), 542–573.

2. Boorse, C. (2014) A second rebuttal on health. Journal of Medicine and Philosophy, 39(6), 683–724.

3. Nordby, H. (2006) The analytic–synthetic distinction and conceptual analyses of basic health concepts. Medicine, Health Care and Philosophy 9(2), 169-180.

4. Walker, M.J. and Rogers, W.A. (2018) A new approach to defining disease. Journal of Medicine and Philosophy, 43(4), 402-420.

5. Wittgenstein, L. (1953) Philosophical Investigations. Transl. by G.E.M. Anscombe. Oxford, United Kingdom: Blackwell.

6. *Kaplan, E.L. and Meier, P. (1958) Nonparametric estimation from incomplete observations. Journal of the American Statistical Association 53(282), 457-481.*

7. Aletaha, D. et al. (2010) Rheumatoid Arthritis Classification Criteria. Arthritis & Rheumatism 62(9), 2569-2581.

13.9. The concept of health in the context of medical theory

In this section, I will consider more closely the most relevant aspects of the content of the concept of health. In this regard, I decided to focus on the article Beatrijs Haverkamp, Bernice Bovenkerk, and Marcel Verweij [1]. After reviewing the concepts of health, they presented five key definitions of the concept of health. 1) Health as absence of disease (Boorse), 2) Health as the ability to achieve vital goals (Nordenfelt), 3) Health as (meta-)capability (Venkatapuram), 4) health as complete physical, mental, and social well-being (WHO), and 5) health as an ability to adapt and self-manage (Huber et al.). (See the original sources in the article [1]).Then they had to comprehend the pluralism of definitions of the concept of health. In this regard, three authors reviewed these concepts in the context of five pairs of conceptual distinctions: Naturalism vs. Normativism, Reductionism vs. Holism, Internalism vs. "Circumstantialism", Universalism vs. Relativism, and Subjectivism vs. Objectivism. After that, they presented a way of thinking about both the diversity and the unity of the various concepts of health, and not opposing one to the other. Their decisive choice was that they presented health as a Wittgensteinian family of thick concepts (the aspect of diversity together with unity - V.K.), and the whole review as a practice-oriented (aspect of unity together with diversity - V.K.).

The considered concept of three authors (HBV-conception) combines many problematic aspects of the philosophy of medicine. In this, I see it undoubted dignity. At the same time, I evaluate these aspects from a fundamentally different point of view, namely, from the standpoint of the theory of conceptual transduction. HBV-conception gives me an excellent opportunity to present my understanding of the philosophy of medicine in a more detailed form than was done in the previous section.

Regarding the five definitions of the concept of health

All five definitions of the concept of health seem to me to be insufficient to the extent that they appear as some generalizations, the addressee of which is not given quite clearly. In my opinion, this addressee should be medical theories. The authors of the definitions in question indirectly recognize this fact, however, the path that leads from medical theories directly to the definitions of the concept of health is not considered with a sufficient degree of rigor. The emphasis is not on the content of medical theories but on their formal characterization. I do not doubt the pluralism of medical theories, but I do not think that it is adequately conveyed by the five health definitions discussed.

Regarding conceptual dichotomous distinctions

It is clear why the authors of HBV-conception turned to the consideration of conceptual dichotomous distinctions. They appear in the vast majority of works devoted to the problems of disease and health, and, therefore, need special consideration. The question is exactly how to consider them. In my opinion, all these distinctions should be considered solely in the context of the content of medical theories.

Naturalism vs. normativism

Certainly, many authors adhere to the line of either naturalism or normativism. Those authors have mistaken who in their preference ignore the status of medical theories, and it, as explained earlier, is axiological. Only normativism, which is often identified with constructivism, agrees with the axiological nature of medical theories. Naturalism contradicts the status of medical theories. Of course, in this case, naturalism is understood as a natural science position, and not as a methodological direction, according to which medicine should be understood as a science. Medicine is consistent with methodological naturalism, but not with the recognition of it as natural science. In contrast, for example, from biology, medicine is not a natural science.

The authors of HBV-conception believe that health is naturalistic, i.e. descriptive and regulatory concept [1, 390]. In my opinion, this is an erroneous position. In medicine, of course, descriptions are used as denoting phrases. Nevertheless, medical descriptions in contrast to natural science descriptions represent what should be. Normativism is opposed to natural-science descriptivism, which coincides with naturalism.

Reductionism vs. holism

This means that health is simultaneously a characteristic of both the organism as a whole and the organism as being combined from its parts [1, 390]. When characterizing health, it is quite legitimate to use a system analysis, within which the ratio of part and whole is considered. This relationship is not a contradiction; its parts are not opposites. For its characteristics, it is illegal to use Latin word versus with the meaning 'against'.

Internalism vs. «circumstantialism»

According to internalism, health is an internal property of the organism. According to «circumstantialism», it is necessarily connected with external circumstances for the patient. The word versus is inadequate to describe the external and the internal. In medical theory, both the external and internal characteristics of the patient are expressed.

Universalism vs. relativism

This time it is meant that the health standards are recognized either universal for all patients, or relative, taking into account their specifics [1, 392]. These standards are relative. At the same time, it is possible to single out their similarities, coming to formal definitions. Special and formal do not oppose each other.

Subjectivism vs. objectivism

The point is about «whether and to what extent the perspective of the health subject determines the health judgment». [1, 393] Some authors in the understanding of health give paramount importance to subjective factors; others do not consider them relevant. To determine which of them is mistaken, it is necessary to turn directly to medical theories. Immediately it turns out that, the value of subjective factors is sometimes greater sometimes less. To characterize these values, there is no need to oppose subjectivism and objectivism.

Healthy is not a thick concept

The authors of HBV-conception believe that «different concepts thus appear to describe different conditions as healthy and thus as valuable. » [1, 595] The concept of health, they say, resists splitting into facts and values. In this regard, health is recognized as a thick concept. In my opinion, an attempt to interpret health as a thick concept does not clarify, but, on the contrary, confuses the situation. In axiological theories, which are, in particular, medical conceptions, all concepts, including facts, are values. There is no need to distinguish between facts and values. Differentiation of facts vs. values takes the minds of those philosophers who relate the facts to natural theories, and values, to axiological conceptions. They do this contrary to the true nature of scientific theories. Facts exist in physics and medicine. In the second case, they are values. As such, they differ from the facts of physics, which are not values.

The authors of HBV-conception have identified such conceptual distinctions that do not have sufficiently distinct content. They are indeed present in the works of some authors. Nevertheless, it does not follow from this that they should be considered true. As a rule, these authors do not reveal a connection between conceptual distinctions and basic medical theories. If we turn to theories, and this must be done in order to ensure the proper scientific level of the research being conducted, then it turns out that medical conceptions as axiological theories are no more peculiar than, for example, technological theories. There is no mystery in medical theories that would force us to consider its concepts, including the concept of health, as something extraordinary.

In the previous section, I was critical of the orientation of the philosophers of medicine on the concept of family similarity of the language games of Ludwig Wittgenstein. He did not give this conception a distinct scientific meaning, leaving it in the original metaphysical shell. The imposition of any metaphysical conception to science, in our case, to medicine, certainly ends with confusion. This rule remains in force in case of uncritical use of the concept of family similarity of language games. Of course, the concept of language games is of considerable interest to medicine. This is a special topic. It, I believe, does not lead to the need to revise ways to determine the content of the health concept.

It remains for me to consider the commitment of the authors of HBV-conception to the practice-oriented review of health concepts. This orientation prevails in the modern philosophy of science, it acquired the character of a certain methodological paradigm, which became largely due to the influence of the principles of classical pragmatism, within which the theory was moved to the shadow of practice. In fact, medical practice is not an intuitive act; it is always a manifestation of medical theory. Ignoring this circumstance does not allow providing developed theories with a proper conceptual level. In my opinion, the authors of HBV-conception could not avoid this rule.

In my opinion, the main achievement of the authors of HBV-conception is that they have demonstrated the need to create a multilink theory of health, one that unites multiple points of view into a single whole. In modern philosophy of medicine, there is an acute need for such holistic theories. The more of them, the better. I contrasted HBV-conception to theory, the methodological basis of which is conceptual transduction. According to this theory, all conclusions must be properly based on medical theories. Any hasty metaphysical intuitions and jumps are denied.

Reference

1. Haverkamp, B., Bovenkerk, B., and Verweij, M.F. (2018) A practice-oriented review of health concepts. Journal of Medicine and Philosophy 43 (4), 381-401.

13.10. Medical ethics

Medical ethics is often and without justification, understood as an integral part of bioethics. However, strictly speaking, bioethics refers to biology, not medicine. Biology has ethical relativity (6.9). This means that there is no biological ethics per se. The history of the term 'bioethics' deserves mention. It was first used in 1927 by a German biologist Fritz Jahr [8]. Following I. Kant's philosophy with its concept of a categorical imperative and speaking out against positivism, he formulated a bioethical imperative: treat every living being as a goal of yourself and treat it as such. In the 1970s, the term 'bioethics' has gained wide popularity due to the American biochemist Van Rensselaer Potter [12]. It was about the discipline that was supposed to ensure the integration of biology, ecology, medicine under the auspices of human values. If such a discipline could really exist, then medical ethics would be its integral part. This is how many modern researchers believe, understanding by medical ethics the compassionate attitude of doctors towards their patients. Nevertheless, the fact is that interdisciplinary research, expressing connections between the sciences, does not form an independent science. From this point of view, medical ethics cannot be a part of bioethics.

Understanding the true nature of medical ethics is not easy [1; 6; 7]. In this regard, it is reasonable to refer to the works of John Arras [1; 2]. He should be given his due: many problematic issues of understanding the status of medical ethics have come into his field of vision. It is especially valuable that he considered the theoretical aspects of medical ethics. The study of its foundations necessarily leads to an analysis of the status of some theories.

Arras emphasizes ethical theories of high, low and middle levels. Concepts of the high level are guided by ethical principles that are developed by philosophers, in particular, Kantians and utilitarians. With this approach, medical ethics becomes an applied branch of philosophical ethics. However, as it turns out, this approach is not enough to express the specifics of the relevant medical situations. In this regard, in an effort to ensure the scientific level of medical ethics, they switch to the concepts of the low level, a vivid example of which is the casuistic approach, limited to factual information, which prevents scholastic conclusions. Nevertheless, as applied to the concepts of the low level, there is a lack of ethical provisions of a generalizing nature. From here comes the idea of a transition to theories of the middle level, which signify a moderate approach to medical ethics. This is the approach Arras considers the most relevant.

> [O]nce we realize (1) that high theory, especially in its non-pluralistic forms, is a spectacularly ill-suited medium for bioethical

reflection in the clinic and policy circles, and (2) that ideal political theory, while providing us perhaps with a description of Paradise Island, doesn't provide us with a map telling us how to get there under nonideal conditions, then it becomes clear that nonideal, mid-level theorizing is the site of the philosophical action in bioethics and related fields. Understood in this more modest sense, "theory" is a completely natural and should be an entirely uncontroversial element of bioethics or of any practical ethical reflection. Indeed, it's hard to imagine what the field would look like without it. »
[1, 7. Conclusion]

Arras refers to the concepts of mid-level principlism [3], improved casuistry [4], narrative ethics [5], value ethics [11], pragmatism [10] and feminism [13]. However, what to do with this pile of conceptions? The way out is in the theory of contractualism of John Rawls, according to which, in the search for justice, the parties to the contract seek equilibrium in their claims [2]. The claims of all parties involved in the discourse are recognized, but each of them seeks to avoid the extremes of the concepts of both the high and low levels. Thus, the most common modern concept of understanding medical ethics is reduced to the concept of reflective equilibrium of ethical theories of the mid-level. In my works, a fundamentally different approach is implemented [9].

First, I introduce the concept of the substantial ethics developed by philosophers in the framework of Kantianism, utilitarianism, hermeneutics, and pragmatism. It is developed far from science and therefore subject to scientific testing through medical theories. J. Arras is right in asserting the insufficiency of these concepts, but he does not mention the relationship of ethics with medical theories. From substantial ethics, he, like many other authors, moves to the level of case analysis. Of course, medical facts deserve full consideration. However, in my opinion, it is inappropriate in this regard to question the phenomenon of medical theory.

My focus is, secondly, to understand the medical theories as a source of medical ethics. Ethics does not join them from the outside but acts as their comprehension. Medical ethics is a side of medical theories in the context of determining the most effective ways of dealing with patients. In this regard, the principle of maximizing the prosperity of all stakeholders is included directly in medical theories. At the same time, prosperity is understood as the improvement of the medical conditions of patients. A second ethical principle is also introduced into medical theories, namely, the principle of responsibility, understood as a duty to be guided by the most developed medical theories.

Thus, medical ethics is not constituted outside of medical theories, but directly within them. From this point of view, the illusiveness of ethical theories of not only the high but also the mid-level becomes immediately apparent.

Above, I pointed out the position of John Arras, who believes that medical ethics is unthinkable without mid-level theorizing. The trouble of not only mid-level but also high-level and low-level theorizing is that the true nature of medical theory is not properly taken into account. As a result, it is not possible to free medical ethics from a metaphysical ballast alien to it.

Medical ethics encompasses a wide range of issues related to all aspects of medical practice. When it comes to complex issues, such as reproductive and thanatological medicine, or laboratory research, or the moral codes of doctors, you should always focus on basic medical theories and their development through the methods of conceptual transduction. Medical ethics cannot take place without careful attention to issues of medical epistemology.

References

1. Arras, J. (2016) Theory and bioethics. The Stanford Encyclopedia of Philosophy. Available at: https://plato.stanford.edu/archives/win2016/entries/theory-bioethics/
2. Arras, J. (2007) The way we reason now: reflective equilibrium in bioethics. In Steinbock B. (Ed). Oxford Handbook of Bioethics. New York: Oxford University Press, 46-47.
3. Beauchamp, T. and Childress, J.F. (2009) Principles of Biomedical Ethics. Sixth ed. New York: Oxford University Press.
4. Brody, B. (2002) Stories of Sickness. New York: Oxford University Press.
5. Charon, R. (2006) Narrative Medicine: Honoring the Stories of Illness. New York: Oxford University Press.
6. Gordon, J.-S. (2020) Bioethics. Internet Encyclopedia of Philosophy. Available at: https://www.iep.utm.edu/bioethic/#H5/
7. Gordon, J.-S. (2011) Global ethics and principlism. Kennedy Institute of Ethics Journal 21(3), 251-276.
8. Jahr, F. (1927) Bio-Ethik. Eine Umschau über die ethischen Beziehungen des Menschen zu Tier und Pflanze [Bio-ethics. A look around the ethical relationships of humans to

animals and plants]. Kosmos. Handweiser für Naturfreunde 24(1), 2-4. [In German].

9. Kanke, V.A. (2010) Sovremennaya etika [Modern Ethics]. Moskva: OMEGA-L. [In Russian].

10. Miller, F., Fins, J., and Bacchetta, M. (1996) Clinical pragmatism: John Dewey and clinical ethics. Journal of Contemporary Health Law and Policy 13(1), 27-51

11. Pellegrino, E. (1993) The Virtues in Medical Practice. New York: Oxford University Press.

12. Potter, V. R. (1971) Bioethics: Bridge to the Future. New Jersey: Prentice Hall.

13. Sherwin, S. (2008). Whither bioethics? How feminism can help reorient bioethics. International Journal of Feminist Approaches to Bioethics 1(1), 8-27.

Chapter 14. The nature of pedagogy

14.1. Pedagogy, metapedagogy, philosophy of pedagogy and philosophy of education

This chapter of the book is devoted to pedagogy (from the ancient Greek παιδαγωγική τέχνη paidagōgikḗ téchnē - the art of teaching and raising of children). Nowadays, pedagogy is understood as one of the branches of science, which is represented by the theories of training and education of any individuals and groups of people, not only children but also adults. All these theories are headed by the same principle, namely, the principle of maximizing the competence of students. Competence is understood in this case as the degree of comprehensive mastery of students by some scientific theory. The second crucial feature of pedagogy is that it is not represented by any theories, but exclusively by those that are adapted to the capabilities of students.

The reader knows that I proceed from a scientific imperative; there is no acceptable alternative to scientific theories. All that we are dealing with is a manifestation of some scientific theories. This means with regard to the problems, we are interested in, that education is a manifestation of pedagogical theories. It is illegal to talk about education regardless of pedagogical theories. This circumstance should be considered when determining the status of the philosophy of pedagogy and philosophy of education.

Few people, along with the philosophy of physics, also introduce the concept of the philosophy of physical processes. In this case, researchers clearly distinguish scientific theory from its manifestations. However, in the field of pedagogy, the situation is fundamentally different; here the absolute majority of authors proclaim the relevance not of the philosophy of pedagogy, but of the philosophy of education. In my opinion, it is a clear misconception. The concept of learning gets its meaning only through pedagogy. Accordingly, its philosophical meaning is rooted not in itself, but in the philosophy of pedagogy. The philosophy of education is a meaningless term. Considering the views of other authors, I have to use the term 'philosophy of education'. Nevertheless, this is only a manner of expression, nothing more. My true interest is metapedagogy and philosophy of pedagogy.

A pedagogical theory always accompanies some basic scientific theory, for example, physical or economic. In this regard, it is legitimate to characterize pedagogy as a superstructure theory. It acts as a unity of specific and formal pedagogical theories. For example, the methods of teaching physics in the 5th grade of secondary school is a specific pedagogical theory. The methods of teaching physics in school, without an emphasis on a particular class, is a formal pedagogical theory.

Metapedagogy is the conceptology and methodology of directly separate, specific and formal pedagogical theories. It does not extend beyond pedagogy and therefore is the lot of professional teachers, not philosophers. The hour of philosophers comes when the selection of similar features of various metapedagogical theories, in particular, of physical, biological, economic and any other kind is carried out. The philosophy of pedagogy is a formal metapedagogy. For it, the philosophy of science is crucial. The dynamics of theories that lead to metapedagogy can be presented, for example, as follows: physics – methods of teaching physics in the 7th grade (special pedagogical theory) – methods of teaching physics in school (formal pedagogical theory) – pedagogy of secondary education (formal pedagogical theory) – conceptology and methodology of secondary education (metapedagogical theory) – philosophy of secondary education (philosophical theory).

Philosophy of pedagogy is a scientific discipline. This means that the philosophy of pedagogy perceives from philosophy only its scientific and not metaphysical content. The latter is perceived only if it is interpreted productively in a scientific sense.

Having determined the status of the philosophy of pedagogy, I will address the current disputes regarding the nature of the philosophy of education. The two current and at the same time very different positions are particularly prominently represented by Harvey Siegel and Philip Kitcher, whose position is energetically supported by John White.

According to H. Siegel, «[p]hilosophy of education is that branch of philosophy that addresses philosophical questions concerning the nature, aims, and problems of education. As a branch of practical philosophy, its practitioners look both inward to the parent disciplines of philosophy and outward to educational practice, as well as to developmental psychology, cognitive science more generally, sociology, and other relevant disciplines». [10, 3] He insists on the return of the philosophy of education to the fold of the general philosophy. [10, 7]

P. Kitcher proceeds from the perspective not of philosophy as such, but of the Dewey project for the development of democratic communities. [3; 5] «Our most important tasks are to articulate further the Deweyan connection between democracy and education, to probe more accurately the economic preconditions of democratic education, to expose as precisely as possible the sources of conflict between capitalism, as we now have it, and Dewey's ambitious project, and, on that basis, to conceive of ways of modifying the economic constraints. To identify, or re-identify, the project of philosophy in this way is only to take a tiny step toward carrying out this task, but I believe that it is a step worth taking.» [6, 316] Unlike H. Siegel, P. Kitcher and J. White are skeptical about the pedagogical relevance of the potential of philosophy. That is why they seek to bring the philosophy of education from under the supervision of philosophy. In their understanding, the philosophy of education is an ethically oriented social practice provided by learning.

In my opinion, the weaknesses of the two concepts under consideration are determined primarily by the fact that their authors neglect the relationship between metapedagogy and philosophy of pedagogy. The views of H. Siegel are to the area of metapedagogy. However, his position is characterized by two main weaknesses. Firstly, in relation to philosophy, he does not distinguish between its metaphysical and scientific parts. The philosophical skepticism of P. Kitcher is partly justified, but only in relation to the metaphysical part of philosophy. It is unproductive in relation to pedagogy. Secondly, H. Siegel views the movement only from philosophy to pedagogy, ignoring the reverse movement. This leads to the absolutizing of philosophy in relation to pedagogy. In fact, the currents of knowledge go both from pedagogy to philosophy, and from philosophy to pedagogy.

In my opinion, the position of P. Kitcher is also not without significant weak points. He even more than H. Siegel neglects the relationship between metapedagogy and philosophy of pedagogy. Moreover, in his field of vision are mainly social disciplines. Meanwhile, pedagogy deals not only with social but also with numerous other disciplines, in particular, natural and formal ones. Another weakness of his position is that he does not distinguish between the ethics of the social sciences and the ethics of pedagogy. It is not clear what kind of ethics he considers. I also believe that P. Kitcher and J. White do not quite adequately set forth the pedagogical credo of J. Dewey. It includes democracy through education but does not come down to it. In particular, experiential learning and teaching are of independent importance. [4]

Thus, the sharp controversy between H. Siegel and J. White [9; 11] did not lead to a significant clarification of the nature of the philosophy of pedagogy. Nevertheless, it became apparent that the true nature of the philosophy of pedagogy needs clarification. Gert Biesta does not quite agree with this position. He notes that the connection between philosophy and education was implemented differently in the English-speaking and German-speaking world. In this regard, he concludes, «that the discussion about the proper location of philosophy of education cannot be resolved within the terms of the idea of philosophy of education». [1, 10] This strange conclusion is the result of the uncritical attitude of G. Biesta to the concepts of the philosophy of education under consideration. They are considered equally true, and therefore they cannot be combined with each other, determining the true nature of the philosophy of pedagogy.

A fundamentally different position than G. Biesta sticks to Stefan Cuypers. Acknowledging pluralism, he nevertheless insists on prioritizing the analytical approach of R.S. Peters, who substantiated the need for a conceptual analysis of the key problems of pedagogy and giving them a practical and ethical character. [2] Cuypers argues that « [i]n the light of the prestige of the scientific paradigm is taken as a whole», an analytical approach of the R.S. Peters for all its flaws, was a decisive turn in understanding the nature of the philosophy of education. [2, 59]. Such a characteristic of R.S. Peters is not accurate. It should be borne in mind that he identified the conceptual analysis with the linguistic one with its emphasis on ordinary, not scientific language. This means that he did not reach the clearly expressed philosophy of science. Without it, there is no prestige of the scientific paradigm. In my opinion, following it is crucial in understanding the status of the philosophy of pedagogy.

The scientific paradigm with an emphasis on the history and philosophy of science is consistently followed by Michael Matthews, who insists on the topicality of discipline-based philosophy of education. [7; 8] I am not ready fully agree with his position only insofar as it is not communicated to the theory of conceptual transduction and, accordingly, consideration of those connections that give vitality to the unity of metapedagogy and philosophy of pedagogy. Both of them should be completely transferred to the scientific ground. While this task is far from the resolution.

References

1. Biesta, G. (2014) Is philosophy of education a historical mistake? Connecting philosophy and education differently. Theory and Research in Education 12(1), 65–76.
2. Cuypers, S. (2014) The power and limits of philosophy of education. Theory and Research in Education 12(1), 54–64.
3. Dewey, J. (1944) Democracy and Education. New York: Free Press.
4. Dewey, J. (1910) How We Think. Boston: D. C. Heath and Co.

5. Dewey, J. (1975) Moral Principles in Education. Carbondale: Southern Illinois University Press.
6. Kitcher, P. (2009) Education, democracy, and capitalism. In Siegel, H. (Ed.) The Oxford Handbook of Philosophy of Education. New York: Oxford University Press, 300–318.
7. Matthews, M.R. (2014) Discipline-based philosophy of education and classroom teaching. Theory and Research in Education 12(1), 98–108.
8. Matthews, M.R. (2014) Science Teaching: The Role of History and Philosophy of Science. Second ed. New York: Routledge.
9. Siegel, H. (2014) John White on philosophy of education and philosophy. Theory and Research in Education 12(1), 120–127.
10. Siegel, H. (2009) Introduction: philosophy of education and philosophy. In Siegel, H. (Ed.) The Oxford Handbook of Philosophy of Education. Oxford: Oxford University Press, 3-8
11. White, J. (2013) Philosophy, philosophy of education and economic realities. Theory and Research in Education 11(3), 294–303.

14.2. From scientific to educational theory

In understanding the nature of education, I proceed from the scientific paradigm, according to which there is no worthy alternative to scientific theories. It follows that educational theory is a type of scientific theory. The scientific paradigm is rooted in modern education. However, it is now being questioned. In this respect, the position of Edgar Jenkins is very indicative. Based on the position of Henry Bauer and Morris Shamos, who allegedly proved that the scientific method is a myth [1; 5], Jenkins states: «There is thus a case for abandoning all reference in curriculum discussion to the term 'scientific method' or to any account that attempts to reduce a creative, flexible and diverse undertaking to a uniform and stepwise exercise in logic. This diversity of approach that characterizes the generation and validation of scientific knowledge about the natural world also necessarily means that 'scientific method' can no longer be used to underpin the notion of science as a common field of activity. Instead, the emphasis should be upon diversity, imagination, and creativity, both among the sciences and in the ways in which scientific research is conducted. It also means that teaching scientific method, understood as enabling pupils to think in the way practicing scientists think, is no longer a tenable curriculum goal. Such a goal has been a prominent feature of attempts to promote scientific literacy or provide the rationale for other programs directed towards science for all. Significantly, both scientific method and scientific literacy have been dismissed as a 'myth'». [3, 275–276] The decisive mistake of Edgar Jenkins is that criticism directed against outdated forms of science ends with the conclusion that science and its core a scientific method have of a worthy alternative, of which, however, is not given any definite characterization. Meanwhile, I showed that the methods of conceptual transduction are relevant to all branches of science, no matter how diverse they are. [4] These methods strictly correspond to all the innovations of modern sciences.

Based on my many years of research, I confidently return to the conclusion that in modern education there are no alternatives to science, its concepts, and methods. Adding to this conclusion the principle of theoretical representation, I conclude that the nature of pedagogy in all its parts is determined by the state of the corresponding pedagogical theories, including didactic ones. The decisive feature of the status of pedagogical theories is that, first, they must be accessible to students. This means that they are, as a rule, simpler than the scientific theories that are characteristic of their inventors. Secondly, the degree of availability of educational theories to students depends on their nearest development zones, which differ from one person to another.

So, what should be educational theory? In searching for an answer to this question, one should refer to the cycles of intratheoretical and intertheoretical conceptual transduction. How is it permissible to simplify a complex theory so that it is accessible to the student? Firstly, it is obvious that the cyclical nature of knowledge should be maintained. If we exclude some stages of conceptual transduction, the dynamics of the theories, their life cycle, are disturbed. It is unacceptable, for example, to exclude factualizing from the intratheoretical transduction cycle, and problematization from the intertheoretical transduction cycle. Secondly, it is advisable to thin out each stage of transduction, as well as its conceptual content. Suppose that some stage of transduction consists of six stages: $(1) \rightarrow (2) \rightarrow (3) \rightarrow (4) \rightarrow (5) \rightarrow (6)$. It can be simplified to the next row: $(1) \rightarrow (2) \rightarrow (4) \rightarrow (6)$. As a rule, it is undesirable to abandon the first and final stages of cognition, the content of which is especially significant. It is also possible thinning the conceptual content, some concepts are either not considered, or are analyzed in passing. I will give some examples of the above.

Example 1. Peano's axioms determine the content of formal arithmetic, which is studied by children. At first glance, it seems that they have no idea about these axioms. If this were so, then the arithmetic accessible to them would have to be recognized as unscientific. However, let us take a closer look at the situation under discussion. The first five Peano axioms have the following content:

1. 0 is a natural number.
2. For every natural number x, $x = x$.
3. For all natural numbers x and y, if $x = y$, then $y = x$.
4. For all natural numbers x, y and z, if $x = y$ and $y = z$, then $x = z$.
5. For all a and b, if b is a natural number and $a = b$, then a is also a natural number.

In my opinion, babies treat natural numbers as if they know Peano's axioms. Nevertheless, about the induction axiom, which is also part of Peano's axioms, they have no idea. There is no such educational theory, which in the case of its relative to the true content would not be reduced to a more developed theory known in science.

Example 2. The exposition of modern most developed physical theories in universities, as a rule, begins with the principle of least action. In secondary school, however, it is usually not studied because students do not know the calculus of variations, which makes it possible to move from the principle of least action to Newton's laws. There is a clear thinning of deduction. The transition from physical principles to laws is excluded, but there is a transition from laws to variables.

Example 3. The modern economic theory involves the use of a variety of mathematical theories, in particular, mathematical analysis and game theory. You can easily find textbooks that describe only one mathematical theory.

The pedagogical theory is always formed through the rarefaction of some initial theory of a higher level than it is. Of course, not every act of rarefaction deserves approval. The fact is that very often, the rarefaction is carried out thoughtlessly and as a result, it is erroneous. In this connection, it is significant, for example, that even in developed theories, the operation of abduction rarely receives proper coverage. For example, graduates of physical faculties of universities are usually best informed about physical deduction, and they know little about the abduction. The same applies to the methods of intertheoretical transduction, genuine Cinderella modern not only the school but also university pedagogy.

Above, noted the relative simplicity of any educational theory. In this regard, it is reasonable to recall the didactic principles of John Comenius. « (i.) Each language, science or art must be first taught in its most simple elements, that the student may obtain a general idea on it. (ii.) His knowledge may next be developed further by playing rules and examples before him. [2, 122] In essence, Comenius describes the deduction method, which implies a transition from principles to laws and variables. However, it seems that he talks about the method of ascent from simple to complex.

In teaching students, it is possible to go back from simple to complex, gradually supplementing theory with those elements from which the teacher has previously abstracted. The more rarefied is the theory, so it is simpler. The more the theory is saturated with concepts and transitions between them, the more difficult it is. Nevertheless, it should be borne in mind that the main path of knowledge development is realized through the transition not from simple to complex, but from less developed theory to more developed through conceptual transduction methods. The transition from simple to complex is realized not by the methods of conceptual transduction, but by the method of transition from the abstract (rarefied) to concrete (saturated).

It is well known that the teacher achieves the greatest success when he offers the student a theory that he can learn. In this connection, the notion of the nearest student development zone, developed by the Russian psychologist Lev Vygotsky, is relevant. « The difference between mental age, or the current level of development, and the level that the child reaches when solving problems not by himself, and in cooperation, defines the zone of proximal development. » [6, 247] Vygotsky meant that every person, including a child, firstly has a certain level of mental development. Secondly, he, cooperating with the teacher, is able for one or another period to raise his mental level. How successfully a student is able to progress is determined by the teacher through test tasks and communication with him. The levels of mental development of students Vygotsky measured in years. Suppose that student A is 9 years old. In terms of his mental development, he corresponds to an average student of 7 years. For a year of study, he is able to acquire the level of development of an average student of 11 years. Consequently, its zone of proximal development is equal to 4 years per year. Apprentice B is also 9 years old, and his level of development is age-appropriate. For the year, he is able to reach the level of a student of 10 years. Consequently, the zone of its closest development is 1 year in a year. Pupil A is clearly more talented than B, which is expressed by appropriate quantitative indicators.

In my opinion, Vygotsky's methodology should be summarized as follows. The teacher is a connoisseur of a number of educational theories in the same discipline, which he evaluates through local ratings indicated in parentheses: T1 (1), T2 (3), T3 (4), T5 (6), T7 (9), T8 (11), T9 (15), T10 (20). If, for example, a student owns T2 (3) theory and is able to master the T8 (11) theory for a year, then his zone of proximal development is equal to 8 conventional units per year. Of course, it is also possible to define development zones corresponding to other time intervals, calculated in semesters or years of study. A reader may object to me that teachers never carry out the operation of calculating theories that I have proposed. My objection is that they carry out this operation 'by eye', limited to linguistic variables. Nevertheless, teachers cannot avoid the need to determine the current and future levels of development of their pupils.

For the teacher, it is extremely important to understand the way in which actual educational theories are formed. If this path is misunderstood, then not to avoid blunders. One of them is that the connection between the educational theory and its scientific predecessor is not taken into account. In this case, the teacher does not understand exactly which concepts and transitions between them are beyond his attention. Another mistake is that the principles of theories are explained sloppy. Their list is not given and their subordination is not indicated. Another mistake is that in connection with the Bologna process, administrators continually reduce the contact work of teachers with students. These abbreviations are usually of a formal nature. On the one hand, administrators have very vague ideas about the nature of educational theories. On the other hand, teachers who once again rewrite the work programs of the disciplines also do not work properly. They do not take into account expedient ways of rarefaction of theories.

References

1. Bauer, H.H. (1992) Scientific Literacy and the Myth of the Scientific Method. Urbana, IL: University of Illinois Press.
2. Comenius, J.A. (1967) The Great Didactics. Transl. by M.W. Keatinge. New York: Russell and Russell.
3. Jenkins, E. (2007) School science: a questionable construct? Journal of Curriculum Studies, 39(3), 265-282.
4. Kanke, V.A. (2018) Spetsial'naya i obshchaya filosofiya nauki. Entsiklopedicheskiy slovar'
   [Special and general philosophy of science. Encyclopedic Dictionary]. Moskva: Infra-M. [In Russian].
5. Shamos, M.H. (1995) The Myth of Scientific Literacy. New Brunswick, NJ: Rutgers University Press.
6. Vygotsky, L.S. (1982) Thinking and Speaking. In Collected Works of L.S. Vygotsky. In 6 volumes. Volume 2. Problems of general psychology. Moscow: Pedagogy, 5–361.

14.3. Ways to solve epistemological problems

Epistemology is by definition the theory of knowledge. There is no doubt that it is closely correlated with the philosophy of education. However, how exactly should they correlate with each other? This question is very controversial. [1-3; 6-10] The absolute majority of authors, when considering epistemological problems, start from some popular versions of philosophy, for example, the philosophy of M. Heidegger [3], L. Wittgenstein and C.S. Peirce [1]. They trust philosophers most of all, believing that it is their innovations that are crucial for epistemology. Such an approach seems to me to be metaphysical to the extent that it does not involve the philosophy of science in any significant way. My approach is fundamentally different. I start from the achievements of the philosophy of science, and I check the conclusions of professional philosophers through science. Only science contains the potential to test the validity of any conclusions. The neglect of this potential turns philosophy into metaphysics with the arbitrariness of its statements. Another feature of my approach is that I represent science not in the form of statements of maximum generality, but in connection with its types of branches, i.e. taking into account the differences of natural, axiological and formal theories. Unfortunately, it must be stated that imaginary problems are often imposed on behalf of the epistemology of the philosophy of education. Once formulated, they do not take into account the achievements of science and, especially, the philosophy of science. Every now and then, the philosophers of education see epistemological problems where they really do not exist. These are the consequences of their uncritical perception of clearly obsolete varieties of the philosophy of science. In connection with the above, I will consider a number of actual epistemological problems, which are discussed most often.

Problem 1. The ratio of rationality, normativity and justification (compare: 3; 6–9).

Wishing to determine the status of concepts of rationality, normativity, and justification, one should refer to the content of sciences. Perhaps they can be interpreted very consistently and thereby clarify their status. Perhaps this will not succeed. In this case, these concepts should be considered as candidates for exclusion from the scientific, including pedagogical epistemology.

As is well known, rational is contrasted with the irrational. How exactly, based on the content of scientific theories, can we understand the ratio of the rational and the irrational? The rationale can be understood as a consistent implementation of conceptual transitions carried out in the processes of intratheoretical and intertheoretical transduction. From this point of view, there is no opposition between the rational and the irrational. The irrational is a departure from consistent thinking.

The rational and the irrational can be understood as respectively the mental (cogitative) and the sensual (emotional). Such two forms of manifestation of scientific theories really exist; they in no way contradict each other. The fact is that they express the same conceptual content, without conflicting with each other.

About normativity. Norms are values established by some authority. Considering that values are the basis of norms, it is advisable to turn to them. Values appear exclusively in axiological theories. They are not in natural and formal theories. There is no opposition between values and facts. In natural theories, facts like all their other concepts are not values. In axiological theories, all concepts, including facts, are values. The widespread assertion that values are inherent not only in axiological theories but also in the formal and natural conceptions, does not hold water. Completely unfoundedly features of axiological theories are attributed to natural and formal theories. Let me illustrate what has been marked with deduction and induction as an example. These operations are carried out both with values as part of axiological theories and with descriptions of natural conceptions. They assume the nature of relevant theories. This means that in the natural sciences deduction and induction are not values.

About the justification. It is realized through the methods of conceptual transduction. This is a very multilink process, each stage of which supports all the others. There is nothing like that in metaphysics. If a teacher seeks to adhere to the line of evidence-based pedagogy, then he has no choice but to implement conceptual transduction.

Problem 2. Accounting for social and historical aspects of knowledge.

Koichiro Misawa argues that these aspects of knowledge are best taken into account through the philosophy of Martin Heidegger, who considered the relationship between Earth and the World. [3] In fact, Heidegger confined himself to very vague reasoning about the many relationships that are inherent in human existence in the World. In science, historical aspects of knowledge are taken into account through league-theories. The social aspects of knowledge are also confidently taken into account. This is done through the implementation of interdisciplinary connections of social theories with other types of theories. It was not by chance that Martin Heidegger fell into the trap of fascism, his knowledge in the field of social sciences, in particular, political science, was very limited. It is doubtful that he is the main teacher in taking into account the social and historical aspects of being.

Problem 3. Personal epistemology.

Every person during his life learns a great many theories, ranks them in a certain way and optimizes their combination. The combination of individual and group theories is of paramount importance (see 8, section 12.7). It is obvious that in education teachers should purposefully regulate the process of personal development of students. Personal epistemology is expressed by the variety of individual theories of the student, of his desire to develop these theories. This is personal epistemology from the standpoint of the theory of conceptual transduction. If the researcher does not own this theory, he develops other concepts of personal epistemology. In this regard, the concept of Katarina Holma and Heidi Hyytinen is very indicative. In an effort to express the philosophical normative aspects of personal epistemology, they counter Peirce's fallibilism to naive realism and relativism. [1] From the standpoint of the theory of conceptual transduction, it is not difficult to understand the content of these three indicated directions.

Naive realism consists absolutizing of the object representation of theories. Other representations of theories, in particular, language and mental, are considered something of secondary importance. An attempt is made to reduce all representations of theories to object representation.

Relativism recognizes any knowledge as relative, without taking into account that there is a certain continuity between the conceptions, which make up the league-theories.

By fallibilism, Charles Peirce «meant the view that people cannot attain absolute certainty concerning questions of fact». [4, 59] Peirce used the concept of fallibilism to characterize the content of a separate theory. In contrast, Karl Popper expanded fallibilism to the recognition of the need to falsify theories. Both Peirce and Popper did not know the concept of league-theory.

The conceptions of realism, relativism, and fallibilism do not exhaust the possibilities of understanding personal epistemology. Here it is relevant to recall the paradigms of Thomas Kuhn and the thesis of Duhem-Quine about the possibility of preserving the loyalty of the chosen theory. It is important for us that all these conceptions in terms of content are significantly poorer than the theory of conceptual transduction.

Problem 4. Knowing-how and knowing-that.

Distinguishing knowingly-how and knowingly-that introduced Gilbert Ryle. [5, 28]. He used it to interpret the content of consciousness from the position of behaviorism. The piquancy of the situation lies in the fact that Ryle was an ardent opponent of all forms of philosophical dualism, but gave rise to the opposition of knowing-how and knowing-that, which in modern education is often regarded as the opposition of practice and of theory or knowledge and skills. In the light of widespread practice turn, priority is usually given to knowing-how. This is provided that educators have a vague idea of the true content of knowing-how and knowing-that. Quite justified, philosophers seek to come to their aid.

Gerard Lum seeks to free the view of Ryle from the layerings of positivism. He believes that our ability to create a picture of other people's minds is crucial. In this case, we use the judgments of identity and the judgments of significance. Therefore, we collect fragmented evidence. They, and after them the distinction of knowing-that and knowing-how, are nothing more than fragments of knowledge, and not actual epistemological distinctions. [2, 658-659]. Lum convincingly shows that isolation knowing-how from knowing-that leads to numerous epistemological costs, a clearly contraindicated to the field of education.

Christopher Winch also does not agree to consider knowing-how and knowing-that as epistemological oppositions. In his interpretation, they are parties of overall competence knowing 'wh'. Knowing-how and knowing-that «*are distinct but closely related epistemic abilities and that in assessing professional capacity we often find them together as part of an overall professional competence.*» [10, 351].

Certainly, the criticism of the naive contrast of knowing-how and knowing-that and its detrimental consequences in education is quite relevant. However, the way of analyzing these concepts chosen by Lum and Winch seems to me to be insufficient. In my opinion, an appeal to the theory of conceptual transduction makes it possible to clarify the status of knowing-how and knowing-that in the most comprehensive way. It should take into account the cyclical nature of the conceptual, in particular, intratheoretical transduction.

Knowing-how refers to the factualizing stage, realized through observations, experiments, and practices. Knowing-that refers to three other stages of intratheoretical transduction, i.e. to prediction and planning, data processing and updating the original principles. Due to the cyclical nature of scientific theories, the opposition of the various stages of conceptual transduction is untenable. That is why the contrast of knowing-how and knowing-that is also untenable. It is acceptable, following G. Lum, to consider knowing-how and knowing-that as some fragments of educational activity. However, they are related in their status to conceptual transduction (for the sake of brevity, I limited myself to considering intratheoretical transduction). Knowing-wh as overall competence is the theory in its entirety.

The history of non-critical use of concepts of knowing-how and knowing-that is very indicative of the correlation of pedagogy, metapedagogy, and philosophy of pedagogy. In the absence of adequate support from the side of metapedagogy and the philosophy of pedagogy, the myth of two crucial competencies, namely, knowledge (knowing-that) and skills (knowing-how), has become widespread. Overcoming this myth is an urgent task of metapedagogy.

References

1. Holma, K. and Hyytinen, H. (2015) The philosophy of personal epistemology. Theory and Research in Education 13(3), 334–350.
2. Lum, G. (2017) Making sense of knowing-how and knowing-that. Journal of Philosophy of Education 51(3), 655–672.
3. Misava, K. (2015) Harvey Siegel on epistemology and education: rationality, normativity and justification. Bulletin of Tokyo University and Graduate School of Social Welfare 10, 19-29.
4. Peirce, C.S. (1955) The scientific attitude and fallibilism. In Buchler, J. (Ed.). Philosophical Writings of Peirce. New York: Dover.
5. Ryle, G. (1949) The Concept of Mind. London, Hutchinson.
6. Siegel, H. (2004) Epistemology and education: an incomplete guide to the social-epistemological issues. Episteme 1(2), 129–137.
7. Siegel, H. (2008) Is "education" a thick epistemic concept? Philosophical Papers 37(3), 455–69.
8. Siegel, H., Phillips, D.C. and Callan, E. (2018) Philosophy of education. The Stanford Encyclopedia of Philosophy. Available at:

https://plato.stanford.edu/archives/win2018/entries/educ
ation-philosophy/
9. Watson, L. (2016) The epistemology of education.
    Philosophy Compass 11(3), 146–159.
10. Winch, C. (2017) Knowing 'Wh' and knowing How:
    Constructing professional curricula and Integrating
    Epistemic Fields. Journal of Philosophy of Education 51(2),
    351-369.

14.4. In search of the foundations of theories

In my opinion, the phenomenon of theory in the modern philosophy of science, including the philosophy of pedagogy, is not given due attention. In this regard, a large-scale discussion of the vicissitudes of the theory is a rather significant event. Researchers from the fields of sociology, medicine, pedagogy, the whole complex of cognitive sciences seek to redefine the status of scientific theories. It is quite revealing exactly how they are trying to do this.

For the fate of grounded theory, the monograph of two American medical sociologists Barney Glaser and Anselm Straus was of fundamental importance. [4] According to their opinion, theories used in the study of social problems often do not express the essence of events, they are imposed from outside, without taking into account the specifics of the evidence. Emphasis should be placed not so much on testing existing theories with their deductive structure as applied to new situations, on generating truly relevant theories through an inductive method based on available data. [4, 1] The adequacy of theories is determined primarily not by a deductive, but by an inductive method. The deductive method is not denied, but its relevance is determined not before but after the inductive method. The systematic processing of data is crucial; therefore, it is precisely the data that are the grounds of scientific theories.

The proposed approach is, of course, frankly positivist. However, it should be borne in mind that in the modern American philosophy of science, the positivist approach is constantly criticized. On the one hand, there is a dominant attitude towards data, which is so characteristic of positivism. On the other hand, positivism is recognized as insufficient, it does not take into account the post-positivist tendencies due to, in particular, the lessons of American pragmatism and the historical school in the philosophy of science. It is not surprising, therefore, that numerous supporters of grounded theory sought to avoid accusations of following outdated philosophical paradigms. [7] Only Barney Glaser was in no hurry to abandon positivism. Anselm Straus and Juliet Corbin began to interpret the status of grounded theory from the standpoint of American pragmatism and symbolic interactionism. [9, 10] Kathy Charmaz proposed a constructive version of grounded theory [1-3], supposedly the most decisively breaking with the positivist tradition. She expresses her position as follows.

• The grounded theory research process is fluid, interactive, and open-ended.

• The research problem informs initial methodological choices for data collection.

• Researchers are part of what they study, not separate from it.

• Grounded theory analysis shapes the conceptual content and direction of the study; the emerging analysis may lead to adopting multiple methods of data collection and to pursuing inquiry in several sites.

- Successive levels of abstraction through comparative analysis constitute the core of grounded theory analysis.

- Analytic directions arise from how researchers interact with and interpret their comparisons and emerging analyses rather than from external prescriptions. [1, 178].

According to Fiona James, Charmaz did not reach a decisive break with positivism, which can happen only by turning to the philosophy of L. Wittgenstein with his concept of language games. [5]

I will review the status of grounded theory from the standpoint of conceptual transduction. Just it allows you to clarify some controversial issues. Authors who write about grounded theory, as a rule, do not give a detailed description of the nature of the scientific theory. They are limited to its characteristics as a network of concepts that allow predicting new phenomena. Nevertheless, in the case under consideration, a more developed concept is in demand, including, in particular, consideration of the phases and methods of conceptual transduction.

The founders of grounded theory sought not to fall under the dictates of outdated theories that did not take into account the particularities of the situations studied. These fears are partly relevant, but they are unnecessary in the light of the fact that the researcher has a certain theoretical experience, and is not excessive in the claims. The researcher begins to explore new phenomena by comparing them with those that he studied earlier. There is nothing wrong with such a research course. The mistake of supporters of grounded theory is that they do not take due account of the cyclical nature of theoretical transduction, where the phases and methods of research follow each other. There is no once and for all established first and second, but there is a previous and subsequent. The deduction is replaced by adduction; it is by induction, which is replaced by abduction. The grounds replace each other. At the induction stage, considered in isolation from other methodological phases, the data are indeed primary, not secondary. However, at the deduction stage, data are predicted based on principles. In this case, the grounds are principles, not data (facts). There are no scientific theories with one type of grounds. Supporters of grounded theory, in fact, misunderstand the nature of the foundations of theories. The term 'grounded theory' is inconsistent.

I now turn to the central link of grounded theories, namely, to the coding of data. [6, 11] As is well known, the theory includes peoples and objects that are reproduced by means of principles, laws, and variables. Moreover, the variables are part of both laws and principles. Variables are data. Of course, they as constituents of theories must be genuine, not imaginary. Coding acts as a thinning of messages, in particular, received from interviewees. Inaccurate data are excluded from the theory. In pedagogical theories, only pedagogical concepts remain, in medical-only medical ones. All of them are relevant only if, in principle, are measurable, i.e. are features of entities.

In the classic versions of grounded theories, open, selective and theoretical coding are used; in Straussian variants, open, selective and axial coding are cultivated, which are summarized by the conditional matrix; finally, in constructive versions of grounded theories, open and refocused coding is used. [6, 7] The difference in coding types is that first, a full set of variables is provided (open coding), and then the most important concepts are selected from them (selective, axial and refocused coding), finally, they are included in the composition of laws and principles (theoretical coding and conditional matrix).

Coding is indeed an extremely important operation because it often allows you to select previously unused variables, for example, the alarming expectations of students on the eve of exams. In accordance with the results of coding, and it is part of the data processing, the researcher is steadily adjusting his position, taking into account the characteristics of individual theories, for example, students. In my opinion, the main merit of the supporters of grounded theories is that they presented the content of the inductive method, which lets open new concepts in the fullest possible form. This circumstance is most clearly manifested in axiological theories. Entering dialogues and discourses with each other, people formulate unexpected ideas, the status of which must be taken into account. This circumstance is especially evident in pedagogy when adults communicate with children. The so-called 'children's concepts' often have a solid pedagogical meaning.

Thus, the status of grounded theories is best assessed from the standpoint of conceptual transduction theory. It is clear why. In fact, supporters of grounded theories focused on data processing, i.e. at one stage of conceptual transduction. Its true meaning is revealed only when the conceptual transduction is considered in its entirety.

However, is the most productive way of assessing the status of grounded theories appeals to one or another of the main philosophical directions? Perhaps not. As I have already noted, the emphasis on data processing is the trademark of positivism. This means that all supporters of grounded theories without any exceptions should be assigned to the positivist camp. By the main criterion of their characteristics, they are positivists. Of course, there are secondary criteria. Nevertheless, they all make sense only after the first, most important criterion. Glaser, unlike its colleagues, has a special interest in the problem of reality. This preference is quite possible. Any theory somehow demonstrates the reality. Strauss prefers a pragmatic perspective in line with symbolic interactionism. This emphasis is quite legitimate. Charmaz emphasizes the active creative role of the researcher during coding. This aspect of the matter is also relevant. James sees the perspective of constructivist grounded theory only in the context of the philosophy of the language of the late Wittgenstein.

In my opinion, Glaser, Strauss, Charmaz, and James opposing their philosophical preferences to each other, make a significant mistake, which consists in ignoring the strengths of their opponents. Various philosophical interpretations of scientific theories do not destroy but complement each other. Their second mistake is that, considering the philosophical trends, in essence, they understand them in a metaphysical sense. Philosophical trends are not given scientific characterization. Indicative in this regard is the position of James, who believes that Wittgenstein is the most relevant author for understanding the nature of constructivist grounded theory. Wittgenstein formulated the conception of language games in the metaphysical distance from all sciences. It is extremely difficult to apply it directly to clarify the sciences, in particular, pedagogy. The conception of language games can be significantly clarified after a thorough study of pedagogical theories. Metaphysical constructions should not be taken for granted; they need scientific substantiation.

Thus, adherents of grounded theories managed significantly clarify the issue of the content of data processing through the method of induction. However, they did not notice that the theory of intratheoretical and intertheoretical transduction gives a much richer perspective.

References

1. Charmaz, K. (2006) Constructing Grounded Theory: A Practical Guide Through Qualitative Analysis. London: Sage.
2. Charmaz, K. (2009) Shifting the grounds: constructivist grounded theory methods. In Morse, J. M. (Ed.). Developing Grounded Theory: The Second Generation. California, CA: Left Coast Press, 127-194.
3. Charmaz, K. (2012) The power and potential of grounded theory. Medical Sociology Online 6(3), 1–15.
4. Glaser, B., and Strauss, A. (2006) [1967] The Discovery of Grounded Theory: Strategies for Qualitative Research. London, UK: Aldine Transaction.
5. James, F. (2018) Where are the grounds for grounded theory? A troubled empirical methodology meets Wittgenstein. Educational Philosophy and Theory 50(4), 369-379.
6. Kenny, M., and Fourie, R. (2014) Tracing the history of grounded theory methodology: from formation to fragmentation. The Qualitative Report 19(52), 1–9.
7. Kenny, M., and Fourie, R. (2015) Contrasting classic, Straussian, and constructivist grounded theory: methodological and philosophical conflicts. The Qualitative Report, 20(8), 1270-1289.

8. Mills, J., Bonner, A., and Francis, K. (2006) The development of constructivist grounded theory. International Journal of Qualitative Methods 5(1), 25–35.
9. Strauss, A., and Corbin, J. (1990) Basics of Qualitative Research: Grounded Theory Procedures and Techniques. First ed. Newbury Park, CA: Sage Publications.
10. Strauss, A., and Corbin, J. (1994) Grounded theory methodology: an overview. In Denzin, N., and Lincoln Y. (Eds.). The Handbook of Qualitative Research. Thousand Oaks, CA: Sage Publications, 273–285.
11. Tie, Y.C., Birks, M., and Francis, K. (2019) Grounded theory research: a design framework for novice researchers. SAGE Open Medicine 7, 1–8.

14.5. Measurement in pedagogy

The peculiarity of pedagogical theories depends largely on measurement processes. Their understanding meets certain difficulties. Joel Michell particularly vigorously attracted the attention to them. [5] He argued that in psychology and pedagogy, the very content of measurement is unscientific. «[M]easurement **is the numerical estimation of the ratio of a magnitude of a quantitative attribute to a unit of the same attribute.** » [5, 383] From this point of view, it is not enough, following Stanley Stevens, to define measurement as the «assignment of numerals to objects or events according to rules» [6, 1]. A scientific approach to measurement suggests, first, that the quantitative nature of an attribute is proved, and then the operation is determined, by which the parameter value is found. According to Michell, the described scientific approach is not implemented in psychometrics when measuring intense quantities, for example, the intensities of sensations.

Denny Borsboom, in his review of an extensive book on measurements in pedagogy [2], notes that «[i]n fact, although the word measurement figures as prominently in the book as the title suggests, there is no discussion of what it might mean; no discussion of the extant philosophy of science literature on the topic; no discussion of formal measurement theory; no discussion of how the activity of measurement relates to the activity of testing; and no discussion of the relevance of all these issues to the question of validity and the process of validation.» [1, 706] This remark, in my opinion, can be addressed to all the theories of testing, in particular, to the item response theory, including to the Rasch model. Their organic flaw is that the mechanism for quantifying individual tests is not properly defined. The absolute majority of researchers, without properly defining the basic concept of test theory, namely, the assessment of tests, hastily removed to the field of mathematics, which, in fact, does not take into account the peculiarities of pedagogy.

Bearing in mind the difficulties of pedagogical measurement theory, Ian Cantley argues that researchers should focus not on the Newtonian model, but on the aspects of Wittgenstein's later theory and Bohr's philosophy of quantum theory. [3, 405] Physics, quite definite, is proclaimed a model for pedagogy.

In my opinion, the problem of pedagogical measurements really needs careful reflection. The crucial issue is not the measurement of intensive quantities, which was successfully resolved in the representational theory of measurement [4; 7, section 3.4], but the place of measurement in pedagogical theories. The content of quantitative parameters can be judged only based on the relevant theories and, above all, their principles.

Pedagogical theories are axiological conceptions. They are led by the principle of maximizing student competence. It is precisely in accordance with this principle that their successes and failures are assessed. A typical situation is as follows. The teacher connects improving the competence of students with the assimilation of some theory. It is divided into sections. Suppose there are only three of them. In this case, Tst = Tst (1) + Tst (2) + Tst (3). Successful assimilation of the theory as a whole is estimated, for example, at 100 points. The student's mastery of each section advances it towards the same end goal. That is why it is permissible to summarize points related to different sections. Of course, the sections themselves, as a rule, are not equivalent. Therefore, each of them is evaluated in accordance with its contribution to the achievement of the ultimate goal. For example, the values of Tst (1), Tst (2), Tst (3), respectively, can be equal to 20, 30 and 50 points.

Each section, in turn, is divided into its parts, for which the corresponding number of points falls. For example, the scores of all subsections of the second section should add up to 30 points. Each part of the subsection is represented by some task (test), the successful implementation of which is estimated by a certain number of points. A more difficult task is assigned a higher mark. I would especially like to note that all the points, for example, the first, the second, etc. are congruent to each other insofar as they signify equivalent steps towards the goal.

Thus, the teacher's understanding of the content of the theory, the parts of which he assesses with the corresponding points, is crucial in assessing students' knowledge. Of course, the student understands the validity of certain assessments only if he owns the relevant theory. Understanding this, teachers, as a rule, painstakingly explain to students why certain grades are given for the successful implementation of these tasks. Otherwise, the assessment of students' knowledge is something mysterious.

The nature of the units of knowledge that I call points varies from one academic discipline to another. The points of knowledge in physics do not coincide with the points of knowledge in biology. You cannot get a high score in physics, responding to tests in biology. However, in certain cases it is permissible, to sum up, heterogeneous knowledge points. This is valid if, for example, in the university entrance exams, they are considered as necessary to achieve the same goal. If different academic disciplines lead to the achievement of the same goal, then their assessments are quite legitimately considered homogeneous with respect to this goal. The same estimates exist at different levels. They can be heterogeneous at one level and at the same time homogeneous at another level. Some subtleties of pedagogical measurements will become more apparent in connection with the discussion of the approach of Ian Cantley.

He believes that the Copenhagen interpretation of quantum mechanics, developed in the main features by Nils Bohr, and the late philosophy of Ludwig Wittgenstein with its emphasis on practical actions, sets the advanced paradigm of educational dimensions. This line of reasoning raises numerous questions. Is it legitimate to consider pedagogy in the context of physics, given that, unlike physics, it is not a descriptive, but axiological science? Is it right to focus on the Copenhagen interpretation of quantum mechanics while there are other relevant interpretations, for example, the many-worlds of Hugh Everett? It makes sense to turn directly to the arguments of Ian Cantley.

For the convenience of the reader, I will number the main arguments of Cantley.

Argument 1. Quantitative parameters do not exist before the process of their measurement; they are constituted precisely by it. [3, 7–8]

With regard to the pedagogical situation, this means that the level of knowledge of students is determined during their tests. This is of course correct. The fact is that within the framework of intratheoretical conceptual transduction, the measurement results are first predicted and then updated. The results depend on how the contact of the teacher and the student was realized. The teacher defines some reference system. He assesses in accordance with his views. At the same time, to a certain extent, one cannot avoid subjective arbitrariness. Trying to avoid it, teachers develop uniform criteria for assessing knowledge based on tests. The unification of tests is intended to a certain extent to exclude the subjective arbitrariness of teachers. The considered features of measurement processes are characteristic of all sciences. It is not necessary to connect their nature with quantum mechanics.

Emphasizing the uniqueness of each measurement process, Cantley makes a very binding conclusion: «The need to refer to the ability of an individual with respect to a particular question undermines the rationale for calculating total test scores (which are often purported to represent ability in a particular area) since the summing of item scores on a test is predicated on the notion that each item is measuring the same construct, e.g. 'mathematical ability'. It is meaningless to combine scores in this way because no single ability exists. » [3, 8] In my opinion, Cantley makes a significant mistake. The fact is that the peculiarity of individual acts of measurement does not cancel the reality of quantum theory as a whole. The Schrödinger equation expresses the evolution of a quantum system and makes it possible to calculate its duration. The case is not limited to a single duration, which is not interconnected with others durations.

Argument 2. The Analogue of Quantization.

«Since there are only two discrete possibilities for each question, correct or incorrect, the pupil's ability with respect to each test item is a quantized attribute». [3, 7–8] Cantley draws an analogy between pedagogy and quantum mechanics obviously hastily, without paying due attention to their various conceptual devices. In this connection, it suffices to note that if we remove the Planck constant from quantum mechanics, then there will be no quantum quantities in it. In pedagogy, no one has yet managed to find an analog of Planck's physical constant.

Argument 3. The Analogue of Heisenberg's Uncertainty Principle.

«[I]t is impossible for the individual to respond to two questions simultaneously and, therefore, it is only possible for the ability of the individual to be known with respect to a single question at any instant in time.» [3, 8]. The content of Heisenberg's Uncertainty Principle is that there are parameters that, due to their close relationship, limit the uncertainties of their measurements. Cantley does not name such parameters in relation to pedagogy. As for the answers to different questions at different times, they do not limit each other. They are perfectly combined in the same theory. Cantley did not prove that in pedagogical dimensions there is an analog of Heisenberg's Uncertainty Principle.

Argument 4. The Analogue of Wave Function Collapse. [3, 9–10]

This means that before the measurement process, the student's possible answers to a question can be described by a certain probability function of the corresponding expectations. Answering the question, the student realized one possibility, while others turned out to be erroneous and, therefore, there is no need to take them further into account. According to Cantley, there was a collapse of the probability function. Consequently, there is an analogy between quantum mechanics and pedagogy. Cantley does not take into account that the wave function in quantum mechanics gives an exhaustive interpretation of a quantum object. In pedagogy, things are different. Student theory is not limited to the expectations of his answers to selected questions. It involves the indication of its principles, laws, and variables, as well as their management methods. You can use probabilistic representations. However, not necessarily there is a need to refer to the wave function of quantum mechanics.

Argument 5. The Analogue of Complementarity. [3, 10–11]

It is understood that the behavioristic and introspective positions are complementary to each other. They cannot be combined into a single picture. Cognition is realized in such a way that researchers in psychology and pedagogy are moving from behavioristic to introspective patterns, considering them complementary to each other. Cantley does not take into account that the relevance of the principle of complementarity was mainly associated with an attempt to understand the duality of physical phenomena. After the creation of quantum mechanics, it turned out that, contrary to Bohr, it gives a unified picture of all quantum phenomena. Quantum phenomena are not dualistic. Accordingly, there is no need for the principle of complementarity.

The behavioristic and introspectivist representations of pedagogical theories also do not conflict with each other. These are different representations of theories, but their conceptual structure is the same. The two paintings in question do not limit each other, and therefore there is no need to consider them complementary in the sense of N. Bohr.

Thus, I have considered the main – not all – arguments of Ian Cantley, who consider the Copenhagen interpretation of quantum mechanics as an exemplary theory for assessing the nature of measurement in education. I am critical of this attempt because it seems to me that this is a set of exercises in metaphysics. Where the researcher should have referred directly to the scientific nature of pedagogical theories, he turned to metaphysics. In my opinion, the correct path of research should begin directly from the consideration of pedagogical theories and the definition of measurement processes in their composition. Unfortunately, this way of research is rarely used. Meanwhile, any deviation from it inevitably leads to metaphysics.

References

1. Borsboom, D. (2009) Book Review. Educational Measurement (Fourth ed.) R. L. Brennan (Ed.). Westport, CT: Praeger, 2006, 779. Pages. Structural Equation Modeling: A Multidisciplinary Journal 16(4), 702–711.
2. Brennan, R.L. (Ed.). (2006) Educational Measurement. Fourth ed. Westport, CT: Praeger.

3. Cantley, I. (2017) A quantum measurement paradigm for educational predicates: implications for validity in educational measurement. Educational Philosophy and Theory 49(4), 405-421.
4. Luce, R.D. and Suppes P. (2004) Representational measurement theory. In Wixted, J. and H. Pashler. (Eds.) Stevens' Handbook of Experimental Psychology, vol. 4: Methodology in Experimental Psychology. Third ed. New York: Wiley, pp. 1–41.
5. Michell, J. (1997) Quantitative science and the definition of measurement in psychology. British Journal of Psychology 88(3), 355–383.
6. Stevens, S. S. (1951) Mathematics, measurement, psychophysics. In Stevens, S.S. (Ed.). Handbook of Experimental Psychology. New York: Wiley and Sons, pp. 1–49.
7. Tal, E. (2017) Measurement in science. The Stanford Encyclopedia of Philosophy. Available at: https://plato.stanford.edu/archives/fall2017/entries/measurement-science/

14.6. Didactic principles as epiconcepts

As a science, pedagogy represents teachers and students through principles, laws, and variables, which are controlled by the methods of deduction, adduction, induction, abduction, problematization, discovery, interpretation and ordering of theories. Pedagogical specificity is expressed by the principles of maximizing the competencies of students. I presented in the shortest possible way the conceptual and methodological content of pedagogy as a whole, including individual pedagogical theories. In this regard, it is somewhat surprising that many researchers seek to clarify the true nature of pedagogy through didactic principles. [1-9] The list of didactic principles is quite arbitrary, and their exact number is unknown. Authors, who strive to be the most detailed, call at least 20 principles. [1; 3; 4; 6; 9] Michael van Wyk, who possesses the ability to give short names to didactic principles, gives the following list: principles of suitability, totality, motivation, assessment, socialization, activity, individuality, clarity, equity, creditability, adaptability, learner-centeredness, remedial, planning, mother-tongue instruction, relevance, differentiation, human-resource development, clear focus, integration, progression, nation-building, non-discrimination, critical thinking, and creativity. [9, 114]

According to my observations, the authors who give a list of didactic principles never justify its necessity. The principles are considered obvious; their relevance does not need to be proved. By definition, didactic principles are fundamental and, therefore, to characterize them, there is no need to refer to any other concepts that are more fundamental than the principles themselves. This position seems to me deeply erroneous. It is a consequence of a lack of understanding of the conceptual and methodological nature of pedagogy as a science. I will illustrate my position on the example of consideration of the principles of criticism and creativity.

The authors of the articles [2; 3] do not claim that they are guided by a special didactic principle of criticism. Nevertheless, the phenomenon of criticism itself has for them an undoubted initial apparent solidity. This just means that criticism is viewed as a didactic principle. With reference to the authority of Popper and Quine, it is argued that criticism is necessary as far as the theories are opposed to each other. [3, 1670-1671] Someone could argue that despite the differences in theories there is no need to criticize them: world of science, they say, should be taken without a murmur as it is. Let us take a closer look at the phenomenon of criticism, given the potential of conceptual transduction.

Intratheoretical transduction always ends with a revision of the principles of the theory. Intertheoretical transduction always leads to a more or less significant updating of obsolete theory. Scientific methods are such that, if they are implemented consistently, the entire content of the theory is necessarily updated. This means that there is no need for criticism as something external to conceptual transduction. Criticism is relevant not because of the opposition of theories, but in accordance with the nature of the methods of science. Wanting to understand the phenomenon of criticism, one should proceed from the nature of scientific theories. Otherwise, it is not possible to ascertain the actual potential of the phenomenon of criticism. Criticism makes sense only as a consistent implementation of the potential of scientific theories themselves. Nevertheless, unfortunately, as a rule, it is not understood in this way. Concepts, which are alienated from their fundamentals and therefore having lost contact with it, I call epiconcepts (from the Greek. Ἐπι - above). The validity of epiconcepts, including didactic principles, must be proved.

Let me now turn to the phenomenon of creativity, the invention of the new. Vikki Pollard et al celebrate: «We found that creative teaching requires determination, an openness to the unexpectedand curious, confident risk taking. We have suggested that to foster these characteristics, the university provide professional development opportunities which focus on the element of surprise in learning activities highlight the fulfilment that can be achieved and that are supported through institutional rewards. » [7, 191] About the mysteriousness of creativity written hundreds of books. However, when referring to conceptual transduction, it immediately turns out that creativity is realized in full accordance with its dynamics. You wish to be a creative person - strictly follow the canons of conceptual transduction. You will obviously meet with surprises, and with successes and failures. Nevertheless, you will avoid the fate of a layperson who is trying to accomplish scientific exploits, having scant knowledge of the nature of science.

In the course of my professional activity as a scientist and teacher, I repeatedly turned to didactic principles and invariably convinced of their conceptual superficiality. They are filled with genuine pedagogical power only when their content is revealed through conceptual transduction. Otherwise, they are a form of not reinforcement, but on the contrary, of weakening of the scientific potential of pedagogy.

References

1. American Psychological Association, Center for Psychology in Schools and Education. (2017) Top 20 principles from psychology for prek–12 creative, talented, and gifted students' teaching and learning. Available at: www.apa.org/ed/schools/teaching-learning/top-twenty-principles.aspx/

2. Gardner, P., and Johnson, S. (2015) Teaching the pursuit of assumptions. Journal of Philosophy of Education 49(4), 557-570.

3. Henderson, J.B., MacPherson, A., Osborne, J., and Wild, A. (2015) Beyond construction: five arguments for the role and value of critique in learning science. International Journal of Science Education, 3(10), 1668-1697.

4. Law, E.H.-F., Joughin, G., Kennedy, K.J., Tse, H., and Yu, W.M (2007) Teacher educators' pedagogical principles and practices: Hong Kong perspectives. Teaching in Higher Education 12(2), 247-261.
5. Marius-Costel, E. (2010) The didactic principles and their applications in the didactic activity. Sino-US English Teaching 7(9), 24-34.
6. Nasser, F.M. (2017) Teaching in higher education: good teaching through students' lens. Studies in Education Evaluation 54(1), 4-12.
7. Pollard, V., Hains-Wesson, R., and Young, K. (2018) Creative teaching in STEM. Teaching in Higher Education 23(2), 178-193.
8. The Learner-Centered Principles Work Group of the American Psychological Association's Board of Educational Affairs (BEA). (1997) Learner-centered psychological principles: A framework for school reform & redesign. Available at: https://www.apa.org/ed/governance/bea/learner-centered.pdf/
9. Van Wyk, M.M. (2010) The selection of didactic principles by teachers in the field of economics: an exploratory factor analysis. Journal of Social Sciences 24(2), 111-117.

14.7. Strategy 20-D: goals and quality of education

The question of how to ensure high-quality education in the near future is causing heated debates. [2-9] This is largely due to the lack of the theoretical basis that is necessary for the productive discussion of the most pressing issues of pedagogy. In this regard, I will present a conceptual framework that will be used to evaluate critically a number of approaches to assessing present and future education.

I proceed from the scientific imperative, according to which science, in the unity of all its organic parts, is called upon and is indeed capable ensure a favorable future for humankind. In this capacity, it has no alternative. Science achieves this success only in the case, as it has been repeatedly stressed earlier, if all its axiological branches are headed by two ethical principles, namely, the principle of maximizing the prosperity of all people and the principle of responsibility. Undoubtedly, the present and future of the human community are determined primarily by the content of axiological branches of science. Nevertheless, they cannot realize their potential in the absence of support from the natural and formal branches of science. In this regard, it is extremely important to understand that the project for the successful development of humankind is not based on individually selected branches of science, for example, on economics and computer science, but on all two dozen branches of science. That is why I insist on the 20-D (D – dimensions) strategy, which takes into account all branches of science, the number of which is equated exclusively for methodological purposes 20.

From the above follows the requirement of ensuring the completeness of knowledge. People are designed to maximize the fullness of knowledge; otherwise, they mistakenly lend their capabilities, being ultimately unable to realize the principle of integrity. They often talk about integrity, but the significance of this actual ethical principle is rarely revealed. This is the principle of maximizing the completeness of scientific knowledge. If desired, this principle can be called the principle of integrity. So, the favorable future of humankind is determined by science, headed by three ethical principles, the principles of maximizing the prosperity of all stakeholders, the principle of responsibility and the principle of integrity.

As for education, it is a continuation of the scientific and ethical project. It is designed to ensure its absorption by students. A very important conclusion follows from this – the scale of assessment of the level of development of pedagogy, and, consequently, of education, is the degree of expression of actual scientific achievements. They, in turn, are determined by the level of development of the philosophy of science. A person who wants to have a scale of education evaluation should, firstly, start from science, secondly, follow the paths of the philosophy of science, and only then formulate decisive conclusions. Unfortunately, this circumstance extremely rarely gets its correct expression in the pedagogical literature.

The German term Halbbildung (half education) [3] is often used to characterize impaired education. [1] Theodor Adorno believed that Halbbildung is a fragmentary superficial education that is acquired solely as an end in itself or for adapting to existing social conditions. [1, 121] Halbbildung is the alienation of education from culture as a whole. According to Adorno, the key to understanding the phenomenon of actual education is not science, but humanitarian culture. This approach is insufficient to the extent that it does not receive the proper characteristics of the field of science. As a result, it is impossible to understand the very possibility of the formation of various forms of underdeveloped education. How and why does the opposition of a developed and underdeveloped education arise? Is not the thesis about the possibility of a developed education a utopia?

Developed education is realized as the unity of all branches of science, culminating in ethics. It should be borne in mind that, firstly, due to the scientific division of labor, science as a whole is divided into separate branches of science, discipline, and subdiscipline. Let us call this division horizontal. Secondly, in accordance with the various abilities of people in the field of science, disciplines, and subdisciplines are divided into different levels of education (vertical separation: compare, for example, primary, secondary and tertiary education). Both horizontal and vertical separation of science leads to the disappearance of holistic science. This disappearance is not mandatory, but in fact, it takes place very often. My conclusion is – any separation of science into its parts with the loss of its integrity is flawed. This separation is necessary, but it must necessarily be combined with the integrity of science. It is about the unity of integration and differentiation of scientific knowledge. The guarantee of preserving the integrity of science is the purposeful use of the potential of the theory of conceptual transduction realized in education in the form of a 20D-strategy.

A natural question arises: which educational theory is an alternative to the conceptual transduction and, accordingly, a 20D-strategy? In search of an answer to this question, it is reasonable to pay attention to the competency-based education that has acquired broad, in essence, planetary scope. Many authors believe that the competence approach has become an alternative to the humanistic one. [7] However, according to my observations, they all meet with significant difficulties in characterizing the bases of not only humanistic but also competency-based approaches.

An impressive attempt to identify the grounds, and this, above all, some of the principles of competency education, was made by Pavel Zgaga. [8] There is a rather curious situation - gigantic efforts are being made to develop competence education with a poor understanding of its grounds. Mobility, autonomous universities, student participation, community education are often referred to as principles of competency education. [8, 4]. It is not difficult to see that none of them is brought to the consideration of the true content of scientific knowledge. However, without this, the foundations of education cannot be reached. Not surprisingly, Zgaga came to a rather strange conclusion.

> The Bologna Process has provided an *agora* – not a 'philosophy', in particular not an all-round 'philosophical school'. [...] Our investigation proves that the basic principles should not be taken for granted. First, there is no final list of 'the EHEA (the *European Higher Education Area – V.K.)* principles' and, second, even if there were one the principles should not be regarded simply as action lines – readymade for an immediate useful application. In the same way as sailors do not navigate to the Northern Star but only use it to help them define their position and their course at sea, the EHEA*)* principles are not here to make them "fully implemented" (thus declaring the "end of history"?). The development of principles is necessarily done by way of hypothesis, "as something to be tested and debated". Therefore, instead of fixing a "final list" of principles and their "full implementation" our findings suggest the launching of a new discussion: a discussion on the reality and new challenges of higher education *beyond 2010,* including testing and debating its foundations, its principles. When discussing principles, the real point is to search, not to find; it is more important to travel than to arrive. [8, 15]

In my opinion, Pavel Zgaga is mistaken. Without offering his own concept of education and not finding it in the competency movement, he decides that it is possible to do without it; it is enough to search for something that, ultimately, cannot be found. In fact, any area of scientific knowledge, be it math, physics, economics or pedagogy, cannot do without principles. They, of course, are in pedagogy. Another thing is that this circumstance not considered by many researchers, including those who are optimistic about competency-based education. Zgaga's arguments about the 'final list of H the EHEA principles' and 'end of history' do not pertain to the substance of the question under consideration. The question of the existence of principles for building progressive pedagogy is discussed, and not the possible shortcomings of those authors who incorrectly assess the importance of pedagogical principles.

Another assessment of the Bologna process is that its content is associated mainly with the neoliberal understanding of economic and political entities. [3] Of course, the adaptation of education to a superficial understanding of the essence of economic and political processes leads to negative consequences. However, it is not enough just to criticize the concept under consideration; a developed concept of education certainly should be opposed to it. Nevertheless, this is usually not done.

Without a developed scientific-pedagogical concept, it is impossible to assess the quality of teaching, including the content of the activities of leading professors. My position, in this case, is determined by the 20D-strategy. The quality of teaching is the higher, the more fully the teacher realizes the potential of conceptual transduction and, ultimately, 20D-strategy. The researchers cite various criteria for successful educational activities, in particular, fostering student interest, developing their creative and critical thinking. [4; 7] However, these criteria are rarely linked together. In this case, it does not do without unimportant rhetoric. In my opinion, it is successfully overcome by the theory of conceptual transduction.

References

1. Adorno, T. W. (1959) Theorie der Halbbildung. Gesammelte Schriften, Band 8: Soziologische Schriften I. [Theory of half-education. Collected Writings, Volume 8: Sociological Writings I.] Frankfurt am Main: Suhrkamp, 93–121. [In German].
2. Bahia, S., Freire, I. P., Estrela, M.T., Amaral, A., and Santo, J.A.E. (2017) The Bologna process and the search for excellence: between rhetoric and reality, the emotional reactions of teachers. Teaching in Higher Education 22(4), 467-482.
3. Cone, L.L. (2017) Towards a university of Halbbildung: how the neoliberal mode of higher education governance in Europe is half-educating students for a misleading future. Educational Philosophy and Theory 50(2), 1-11.
4. Gourlay, L., and Stevenson, J. (2017) Teaching excellence in higher education: critical perspectives. Teaching in Higher Education 22(4), 391-395.
5. O'Brien, D. (2017) Inequality of opportunity: some lessons from the case of highly selective universities. Theory and Research in Education 15(1), 53–70.
6. Peters, M.A. (2019) Global university rankings: metrics, performance, governance. Educational Philosophy and Theory 51(10), 5-13.
7. Wood, M., and Su, F. (2017) What makes an excellent lecturer? Academics' perspectives on the discourse of

'teaching excellence' in higher education. Teaching in Higher Education 22(4), 1-16.

8. Zgaga, P. (2012) Reconsidering the EHEA principles: Is there a "Bologna Philosophy"? In: Curaj A., Scott P., Vlasceanu L., Wilson L. (Eds.). European Higher Education at the Crossroads. Dordrecht: Springer, 1–20.

9. Zovko, M.-É., and Dillon, J. (2018) Humanism vs. competency: traditional and contemporary models of education. Educational Philosophy and Theory 50(6-7), 554-564.

14.8. Pedagogy in era of pluralism

One of the issues of the journal «Teaching in Higher Education» is entirely devoted to the discussion of the problematic aspects of education in the modern era, which the authors call the post-truth era or the era of alternative facts. [1-4; 5-10; 12, 13] There are many factors that support the flow of misinformation, which include, in particular, the protection of obsolete values by the authorities, the dissemination of superficial knowledge on the Internet, mass media, far from the standards of scientific knowledge. The search for their bases most often leads to postmodernism. Therefore, its installations should be given primary attention.

The authors of the texts under consideration are certainly right in the fact that modern education, having fallen into a difficult situation, cannot shy away from resisting negative trends.

In this post-truth context, higher education, with its pivotal role as knowledge producer (research) and reproducer (teaching), is key. It is higher education that generates both expertise (through research) and the next generation of experts (through teaching), as well preparing its graduates to engage critically with an information-complex world. The question is: what is the role of higher education in a post-truth age, how should it be reconfigured and what does this mean for the relationship between (a) research and teaching; (b) academics and students; and (c) the academy and the wider public? We believe that higher education must be responsive to the challenges of the post-truth era and join the 'fight back' against 'the war on truth' (D'Ancona 2017) – indeed, it is this idea that inspired this special issue. [7, 280]

This opposition can be successful only if there is a clear program for the development of scientific knowledge that is not visible in a distinct form in texts under consideration. My immediate goal is to present its main landmarks.

First, it should be noted that the concepts of 'post-truth era' and 'alternative facts' are untenable. Philosophical postmodernism, i.e. poststructuralism was not able to debunk the concept of scientific truth. In science, the most developed theories are considered true and, therefore, all their content is also true. There is no reason for abandoning this position under the pressure of poststructuralism.

Under the alternative facts are the facts that refute any, including the most developed theories. However, there are no such facts. All significant facts are certainly included in the theory. They are not allowed to be outside of them.

The difficulties faced by scientists and teachers are not connected with the concepts of truth or facts, but with the understanding of the pluralism of theories. It was precisely in this connection that a certain breakdown occurred, which is negatively manifested in the whole of modern education. The comprehension of scientific theories, of their conceptual content, and methods, is accomplished in their metaconceptions and in a generalized form in the philosophy of science. It is enough to turn to individual branches of science to make sure that this process requires considerable and extraordinary efforts from researchers. As a result, the main pain syndrome of modern science turned out to be concentrated in metascience and philosophy of science. The lack of metascientific and philosophical-scientific knowledge significantly weakened the immune system of scientists. In upholding the ideals of scientific knowledge, the absolute majority of scientists began to behave rather uncertainly. In addition, they did not receive adequate support from philosophers.

Philosophers divided into two camps, those who spoke on behalf of metascience and the philosophy of science and those who opposed the metaphysics to the philosophy of science. The philosophers of science rightly include positivists, neopositivists, critical rationalists and most analytical philosophers. The camp of metaphysicists of science includes many phenomenologists, hermeneutists, poststructuralists, and some analytical philosophers. The main characteristic feature of metaphysicists of science is that they do not pay due attention to science and as a result, they misunderstand scientific methods. Scientific methods are replaced by metaphysical surrogates, be it the synthesis of impressions of E. Husserl, the dialectic of questions and answers of H.-G. Gadamer, deconstructivism of J. Derrida, the incommensurability of related theories of T. Kuhn and P. Feyerabend. In this place, perhaps, it is appropriate to note that many ideas of the metaphysicists of science are of considerable interest, in particular, poststructuralists contributed to the rise of interest in the pluralism of knowledge. Nevertheless, metaphysicists never reach a consistent metascience and philosophy of science.

As already noted, scientists have encountered particularly difficult problems in interpreting the pluralism of theories. For such an understanding, it is sufficient to follow the theory of inter-theoretical conceptual transduction and the consideration of interdisciplinary connections. Unfortunately, I have to admit that the theory of intertheoretical conceptual transduction is poorly known to the absolute majority of scientists.

Many people due to various circumstances are not able to assimilate scientific theories. They have no choice but to operate with underdeveloped concepts. The result is a clash of two theoretical fronts, the scientific and the unscientific. If scientists refuse to participate in this collision, then they themselves contribute to the decline of the prestige of science. The vocation of scientists requires courage from them! The same applies to educators. This is a special kind of courage, coupled with the presence of solid scientific, metascientific and scientific-philosophical knowledge. I would especially note that it is impossible to resist superficial knowledge, including post-truth fabrications without an adequate level of metascientific and scientific-philosophical training.

Referring to the texts specified in the references, I find that all their authors completely ignore science and metascience. Bruno Latour, who himself made a considerable contribution to the development of not so much the philosophy of science as the metaphysics of science, sets the task of updating empiricism as a theory of facts. [11, 231]. Nevertheless, at the same time, he does without those scientific methods by which facts are comprehended in science. Considering the facts outside of intratheoretical conceptual transduction, he finds himself outside the philosophy of science.

Robert Farrow and Rolin Moe urge academic authorities to be more open, truthful and transparent, to attach greater importance to questions of knowledge. [6] This recipe, in insufficient philosophical training of academic authorities, acquires the character of a good wish. Many researchers seek to overcome post-truth projects at the expense of special attention to computer science. [1; 4] In this case, there is also a sharp sense in metascientifical and scientific-philosophical work. Significant hopes are pinned on student research as an antidote to superficial views. [3; 10] Nevertheless, we must not forget that research work should be properly comprehended. Once again, we have to come back to the questions of metascience and the philosophy of science. Jake Wright seems to recognize this. He proposes to combat naive views through a focused discussion of the metadisciplinary goals of a particular training course. [13, 370] I am not ready to agree with him just because he describes these goals in a very general way. It is not clear what scientific methods and to what extent he is guided.

Thus, widespread pluralism poses new challenges for teachers. My main conclusion is that they cannot be resolved without directly addressing the potential of conceptual transduction.

References

1. Bhatt, I., and MacKenzie, A. (2019) Just google it: digital literacy and the epistemology of ignorance. Teaching in Higher Education 24(3), 302–317.

2. Brooke, M., Monbec, L., and Tilakaratna, N. (2019) The analytical lens: developing undergraduate students' critical dispositions in undergraduate EAP writing courses. Teaching in Higher Education 24(3), 428–443.

3. Clark, T., and Hordósy, R. (2019) Undergraduate experiences of the research/teaching nexus across the whole student lifecycle. Teaching in Higher Education 24(3), 412–427.

4. Cooper, T. (2019) Calling out 'alternative facts': curriculum to develop students' capacity to engage critically with contradictory sources. Teaching in Higher Education 24(3), 444–459.

5. D'Ancona, M. (2017) Post Truth: The New War on Truth and How to Fight Back. London: Ebury Press.

6. Farrow, R., and Moe, R. (2019) Rethinking the role of the academy: cognitive authority in the age of post-truth. Teaching in Higher Education 24(3), 272–287.

7. Harrison, N., and Luckett, K. (2019) Experts, knowledge and criticality in the age of 'alternative facts': re-examining the contribution of higher education, Teaching in Higher Education 24(3), 259-271.

8. Hauke, E. (2019) Understanding the world today: the roles of knowledge and knowing in higher education. Teaching in Higher Education 24(3), 378–393.

9. Hordern, J. (2019) Higher expertise, pedagogic rights and the post-truth society. Teaching in Higher Education 24(3), 288–301.

10. Hughes, G. (2019) Developing student research capability for a 'post-truth' world: three challenges for integrating research across taught programmes. Teaching in Higher Education 24(3), 394–411.

11. Latour, B. (2004) Why has critique run out of steam? From matters of fact to matters of concern. Critical Inquiry 30(2), 225–248.

12. McGregor, R., and Park, M. (2019) Towards a deconstructed curriculum: rethinking higher education in the global North. Teaching in Higher Education 24(3), 332–345.

13. Wright, J. (2019) The truth, but not yet: avoiding naïve skepticism via explicit communication of metadisciplinary aims. Teaching in Higher Education 24(3), 361–377.

Chapter 15. The nature of psychology

15.1. Psychology as a set of individual theories

The meaning of the term 'Psychology', invented by the Croat Marko Marulic [5], has many interpretations. In one place, I brought them more than 20. [4, 169–171] According to the American Psychological Association, «[P]sychology is the study of the mind and behavior. The discipline embraces all aspects of the human experience — from the functions of the brain to the actions of nations, from child development to care for the aged. In every conceivable setting from scientific research centers to mental healthcare services, "the understanding of behavior" is the enterprise of psychologists». [2] Keith Holyoak believes that «[P]sychology is the science that investigates the representation and processing of information by complex organisms. [3, xl] Prominent Russian psychologists Vladimir Shadrikov and Vladimir Mazilov believe that the subject of psychology is the inner life of man. [6; 7] All the definitions of the subject of psychology known to me have a significant drawback, which is discussed below.

Psychology is in demand when individuals are found in their activities with significant shortcomings. The nuclear power plant operator is not stress-resistant enough in critical situations, a woman has difficulty in communicating with men, adolescents demonstrate various forms of deviant behavior, and work colleagues do not get along well with each other. Psychology comes to the fore when the personal factor acquires increased relevance. In the language of science, this means that in determining the subject of psychology, one has to take into account the peculiarity of individual theories, their difference from group theories.

Theories that guide people in their communication differ from each other. This is common knowledge. If anomalies do not arise in this communication, the theories of communicants do not differ significantly from each other. It even seems that all communicants are guided by the same theory. At the occurrence of anomalies in the communication of people, it is necessary to pay attention to that circumstance which was not noticed earlier. It turns out that an extensive network of relations between the group and individual theories is realized in the world of the joint activity of people. By opening any university textbook, you can easily see that students are primarily studying group theories. Nobody learns theories of Oliver, Amelia, and Jack. Meanwhile, each of them has its own theory. Trying to reveal their content, one has to turn to psychology. Psychology is a collection of individual theories. It testifies to the characteristics of either individual people or individual groups of people.

Of fundamental importance in determining the status of psychology, is the ratio of individual and group theories. The fact is that they are closely related to each other. It is illegal to regard them as formations isolated from each other. Medicine and economics are different branches of science. The only thing that binds them together is interdisciplinary relations. A fundamentally different situation occurs if the relationship between medicine and medical psychology or economics and economic psychology is considered. In these two cases, it is not the ratio of two different branches of science that is considered, but the ratio of the group and individual theories that is realized within the same branch of science, medicine, or economics.

A widespread erroneous interpretation of the status of psychology is that it is understood as a special branch of science with a conceptual content that does not depend on other branches of science. Psychology as a separate branch of science, they say, deals with the mentality, language, and behavior. However, it is obvious that these phenomena are studied not only by psychologists but also by representatives of all branches of science, in particular, physicists, mathematicians, and economists.

If psychology were an independent branch of science in the above sense, then it would be characterized only by its inherent principles. For physics, the principle of least action is characteristic, for the economy - the principle of maximizing the profits of entrepreneurs. What principle is characteristic of psychology? I have not found the answer to this question from any author. In my opinion, researchers are not able to name the principles of psychology insofar as they do not reflect on the principles of those branches of science that include psychology. The principle of economic psychology is the principle of profit maximization.

An interesting attempt to define the mission of psychologists was undertaken by members of the American Psychological Association: «**Our mission is to promote the advancement, communication, and application of psychological science and knowledge to benefit society and improve lives**». [1] The definition under consideration is not fully satisfactory because the principles of psychology are not named. In my opinion, the mission of psychologists consists of the full assistance of development of all branches of science in accordance with their conceptual content, including the principles of these branches of science. If you wish, you can list these principles.

Another widespread mistake in determining the status of psychology is that its subject is associated only either with mentality [6; 7] either with mentality and behavior. [2] The authors of these definitions do not take into account the principle of theoretical representation, according to which any theory, including psychological, has many representations with the same conceptual content. That is why isolating some representations from others is untenable. Any science, not just psychology, deals with the mentality, language, and behavior. As for the form of presentation of information, they vary from one science to another. Holyoak did not specify what kind of information is psychological.

Thus, psychology is the totality of all individual scientific theories. In this capacity, it forms the foundation of all branches of science, formal, natural, and axiological. That is why it is wrong to consider psychology either a natural or axiological discipline.

References

1. American Psychological Association (2019) About APA. Available at: https://www.apa.org/about/index/
2. American Psychological Association (2019) How does the APA define "psychology"? Available at: https://www.apa.org/support/about-apa/
3. Holyoak, K. J. (2009) Psychology. In Wilson, R.A., and Keil, F.C. (Eds.). The MIT Encyclopedia of the Cognitive Sciences. Cambridge, Massachusetts, London, England: The MIT Press, xl – xlix.
4. Kanke, V.A. (2014) Istoriya, filosofiya i metodologiya pedagogiki i psikhologii [History, philosophy and

methodology of pedagogy and psychology]. Moskva: Infra-M. [In Russian].

5. Krstic, K. (1964) Marko Marulic – The author of the term "psychology". Acta Instituti Psychologici Universitatis Zagrabiensi 36, 7–13.

6. Mazilov, V.A. (2018) Psikhologiya v XXI stoletii: problema predmeta nauki [Psychology in the XXI century: the problem of the subject of science]. Metodologiya i istoriyapsikhologii (1), 108–123. [In Russian].

7. Shadrikov, V. D. (2004) O predmete psikhologii (mir vnutrenney zhizni cheloveka) [On the subject of psychology (the world of the inner life of man)]. Psikhologiya. Zhurnal Vysshey shkoly ekonomiki (1), 5-19. [In Russian].

15.2. Transduction mechanism of psychological theories

The nature of any scientific theory, including the psychological conceptions, is determined primarily by its conceptual content and methodological structure. From this point of view, the controversy of the well-known Russian psychologist Andrei Yurevich and philosopher Vladimir Porus is of considerable interest. Both of them in their research pays special attention to the methodology of scientific research.

In his reflections, Yurevich proceeds from the position of sociologist and psychologist Robert Brown, who believed that the social sciences use seven types of explanations: (i) genetic, or historical explanations, (2) explanations of actions in terms of intentions; (3) explaining particular instances of behavior in terms of the dispositions or tendencies of persons to act in certain ways; (4) explaining in terms of reasons; (5) functional explanations; (6) empirical generalizations, (7) explanations in terms of general laws. [3] It is not difficult to notice that the pluralism of psychological explanations goes beyond the type of explanation that is characteristic of the natural sciences, and which is often identified with the covering-law explanations of Carl Hempel. [6] Covering-law explanations correspond to the sixth and seventh types of explanations from the list of Brown, but not the first five from the same list. Hence the conclusion that the psychological explanation goes beyond the limits of covering-law explanations. As for the types of explanations (1) - (5), they do not correspond to the ideal of a scientific explanation, which Yurevich interprets as explaining a phenomenon by general law or theory. [13, 79] Moreover, Yurevich believes that empirical generalizations are rather banal. [13, 79]

At this point, I consider myself obliged to somewhat explain the situation about the empirical generalizations. They, what Yurevich does not take into account, are part of intratheoretical transduction. The deductive part of the theory does not come down to summarizing the particular under the general. It consists in the transition from principles to laws and individual variables. In the language of mathematics, this is a transition from functionals to functions and from them to individual variables. Empirical generalizations are relevant not by themselves, but as part of intratheoretical transduction. With scientific methods, the situation is far from being as simple as it seems to Yurevich. No wonder he faced insurmountable difficulties.

Yurevich does not consider covering-law explanations as a scientific method of psychology. However, he is not able to find him an alternative. He sees a way out of a difficult situation in the process of explanation that goes beyond the limits of the system being explained. «*Reductionism, i.e. going beyond the limits of the system under study, while explaining it, is not only inevitable but also necessary in science, being the basis for deepening explanations and reaching them at the level that is considered to be scientific.* » [13, 82]. Of course, the connection of psychology with other sciences, in particular, with biology and neurophysiology, which, by the way, does not necessarily be focused on reductionism, should be taken into account, but such an account does not clarify the nature of the scientific method of psychology, as well as of those sciences with which it is united by interdisciplinary relations.

It is interesting to compare the position of Yurevich with the point of view of Vladimir Mazilov, another prominent Russian methodologist of psychology. Mazilov insists on the need for a plurality of types of psychological explanation that cannot be reduced to one of them. In addition, a psychological explanation is contained in psychology, justifying its status; there is no need to go beyond it. [8] The weakness of this position is that the variety of psychological explanations is not accompanied by the recognition of their unity. This circumstance suggests that Mazilov was not able to identify the true methodological foundations of psychology.

Philosopher Vladimir Porus, realizing that psychologists, including experts in methodology, cannot identify the unity of various types of explanations, hurries to their aid. According to his conception, the following two points are crucial. First, one or another kind of psychological explanation is recognized as relevant only if it contributes to the development of psychology, as it turns out in the process of empirical research. Secondly, the types of explanations should be regarded as reciprocal transcriptions: the meaning of one type of explanation can be read in the language of another type of explanation. Mutual transcription indicates the unity of meaning of all kinds of scientific psychological explanations. [10, 95] Porus claims that he put forward a certain hypothesis, hoping for the possibility of its successful implementation. From his article, the reader will not know what exactly the method of scientific psychology is.

Continuing the search for a scientific method of psychology, it is reasonable to turn to the program of the mechanism. [1; 2; 4; 5;] Its main meaning is that the mechanism defines the integral method of the social sciences and psychology. «Mechanism is «a unifying framework for understanding psychological explanation». [2, 195] Not all researchers agree with this conclusion, in particular, adherents of the functional approach [12], however, it is most frequently seen as the alternative to the covering-law explanations. «A mechanism for a phenomenon consists of entities and activities organized in such a way that they are responsible for the phenomenon. » [7, 132] To understand something psychologically means to understand how it does work. [4] The basic concepts of the theory are not principles and laws, but entities and activities. In relation to people, these activities are desires, beliefs, and opportunities.

The mechanism as a program is rarely viewed critically with the necessary degree of thoroughness. However, in my opinion, Karl-Dieter Opp was able to do it not without brilliance. [9] He showed that, contrary to popular belief, the methodological content of mechanistic theories does not conflict with covering-law explanations and the theory of rational choice. Without repeating Opp's extensive argumentation, I present it in the simplest possible way.

Often, the methodological status of mechanistic theories is associated with a causal explanation. In this case, the theory appears as a certain causal chain, for example, such:

$$U \rightarrow V \rightarrow W \rightarrow X \rightarrow Y.$$

How to understand the relationship of two neighboring causal factors, for example, $U \rightarrow V$? Obviously, in the form of a statement: if U, then V. This is the wording of the law. A causal explanation, which does not seem to contain a law, in fact, cannot do without it. Either the necessity of the law is recognized, or the ratio of two causal factors turns out to be arbitrary, which is inconsistent with the status of a scientific explanation.

I now turn to the theory of rational choice with its principle of maximizing one or other chosen preferences. The choice suggests that the explanation ties together desires, beliefs, and opportunities. All this happens under the auspices of the principle of maximizing the chosen factor.

According to Opp, supporters of the mechanism program should clearly express the conceptual content of the theories by implementing the program of empirical theory comparison. [9, 352–353] It will allow, without giving up the pluralism of theories, to improve them.

Sam Racover is also concerned about the methodological status of psychology. Its unusual special status is determined by the absence of well-defined measurement units. On this basis, he proposes to consider psychology as an associational science. [11] Regarding the difficulties of measuring in psychological research, Racover is largely correct. In my opinion, they are complicated by the continuing process of the revision of values by the participants in the psychological process. Under these conditions, it is extremely difficult to present laws and principles in the form of stable quantitative relations. Hence, the desire to be satisfied with qualitative reasoning. However, their quantitative design is quite possible. A characteristic feature of the Racover position is that he avoids absolutization of the originality of psychology, which differs from physics, but not so sharply as to not consider it a science. Everything that is characteristic of scientific theories, including observation and experiment, analysis of the results and formulation of new hypotheses is possible in psychology [11, 147] Continuing this line of reasoning, I am inclined to believe that all methods of intratheoretical and intertheoretical transduction are typical for psychology no less than for all other sciences. This is my main conclusion, largely inspired by the failure of the search for the psychology of some special methods. However, is this conclusion compatible with the kinds of explanations that were discussed at the beginning of this section?

Historical explanations are implemented through intertheoretical transduction. The intentions and dispositions of participants in psychological processes are determined by their experience, which they have accumulated, repeatedly carrying out cycles of conceptual transduction. Causal factors are identified in the process of analyzing the results of observations, experiments, and practices. The functions of the subjects are clarified in the process of identifying the mechanisms that lead to the achievement of the goal. Empirical generalizations are typical moments of intratheoretical transduction. They open the way to the laws and principles of the phenomena under study.

Psychological explanation methods are intratheoretical and intertheoretical conceptual transduction methods. The types of explanations that Robert Brown highlighted are nothing more than moments of conceptual transduction. Strictly speaking, they should not be considered as types of explanations. Their status is significantly less weighty than it appears to researchers who trusted Brown. It is not surprising that all of them fail to identify the methodological basis of psychological theories. Surprisingly another, oblivion by them of theories, followed by attempts to put entities and their activities in the place of principles and laws. I am inclined to believe that such attempts are relapses of not completely overcome positivism. As for the mechanisms of psychological theories, they are represented by a sequence of conceptual transduction stages and methods, and not by causative factors. Causing, not enriched with the notional content of the principles of theories, distorts these theories themselves. Finally, I note that, in my opinion, it was not by chance that Porus, Opp, and Racover unanimously recommended a program to improve psychological theories with regard to their empirical credentials. In fact, they were close to the theory of intratheoretical and intertheoretical conceptual transduction. But they did not get this theory directly expressed.

References

1. Bechtel, W. (2009) Looking down, around, and up: mechanistic explanation in psychology. Philosophical Psychology 22(5), 543-564.
2. Bechtel, W., and Wright, C.D. (2011) What is psychological explanation? In Symons, J. and Calvo, P. (Eds.). The Routledge companion to philosophy of psychology. New York, NY, US: Routledge,Taylor & Francis Group, 113-130.
3. Brown, R. (1963) Explanation in Social Science. Chicago, Aldine Publishing Company.

4. Cummins, R. (2000) 'How Does It Work?' Vs. 'What Are The Laws?' Two conceptions of psychological explanation. In Keil, F. and Wilson, R. (Eds.). Explanation and Cognition. Cambridge, MA: MIT Press, 117-144.

5. Hedström, P. (2005) Dissecting the Social: On the Principles of Analytical Sociology. Cambridge: Cambridge University Press.

6. Hempel, C.G. (1942) The function of general laws in history. The Journal of Philosophy 39(2), 35-48.

7. Illari, P.M., and Williamson, J. (2012) What is a mechanism? Thinking about mechanisms across the sciences. European Journal for Philosophy of Science 2(1), 119-135.

8. Mazilov, V.A. (2008) Nauchnaya psikhologiya: problema ob"yasneniya [Scientific psychology: the problem of explanation]. Istoriya i metodologiya ob"yasneniya 3(1), 58-73. [In Russian].

9. Opp, K.-D. (2013) What is analytical sociology? Strengths and weaknesses of a new sociological research program. Social Science Information 52(3), 329–360.

10. Porus, V.N. (2008) Kak ob"yasnyat'? Znak razvilki na puti psikhologii [How to explain? Sign of a fork in the path of psychology]. Istoriya i metodologiya ob"yasneniya 3(1), 88-97. [In Russian].

11. Racover, S.S. (2012) Psychology as an associational science: a methodological viewpoint. Open Journal of Philosophy 2(2), 143-152.

12. Shapiro, L.A. (2017) Mechanism or bust? Explanation in psychology. Britisn Journal for the Philosophy of Science 68 (4),1037-1059.

13. Yurevich, A.V. (2008) Problema ob"yasneniya v psikhologii [Problem of explanation in psychology]. Istoriya i metodologiya ob"yasneniya 3(1), 74-87. [In Russian].

15.3. Forms of representations of psychological theories and mind-body problem

In my initial plans, I intended in the section to discuss questions related to the mind-body problem. After reviewing the vast array of literature on this issue, I was convinced that in its context it is extremely difficult to free oneself from metaphysics, in my opinion, in no way consistent with the principle of theoretical presentation. Meanwhile, it is precisely this principle that opens the gate to scientific methodology. René Descartes postulated the existence and difference of mind and body because he personally has clear ideas of them. [1, 54] He did not proceed from the scientific formulation of the question according to which to exist is to be a representation (manifestation) of a scientific theory. The statement that we know something without reference to scientific theory is the mark of metaphysics.

As soon as we turn to the principle of scientific representation, it immediately becomes clear that the representations of a scientific theory are not limited to only two forms, body, and mind, or, to put it more generally, matter and mentality. Behavior, activity as abstract labor, cognition, and language are the forms of representation of psychological theories that were used primarily by behaviorists, Marxists, and cognitivist, respectively. One or another psychological direction, as a rule, absolutizes one of the forms of representations of psychological theories. The scientific character of a certain form of presentation of psychological theory is recognized by the scientific community only if it is productively used in scientific research. So, not two, but many more forms of representations of psychological theories should be considered.

The next important circumstance is that all representations of psychological theories are specific. Language-, mind- and body-representation are used in all sciences, not only in psychology. This means that psychology deals not with the mind and body, but with psychological mind and psychological body. Not only psychology deals with the mind. The absolute majority of authors considering a mind-body problem do not pay any attention to this circumstance. They clearly and erroneously consider psychology as the science of all sciences.

What are the representations of theories? In airless space, they cannot take place; they must always have some kind of medium. The situation with language-representation is extremely clear, the medium of which is most often sound waves in the range of certain frequencies. In much, the analogic is the situation with mind-representation. This time the main medium is the neocortex. The nature of mind-representation is no more mysterious than the nature of language-representation.

It is extremely important to bear in mind that the content of all forms of representations of a scientific theory is the same and it acts as a mechanism realized by conceptual transduction. The representations of scientific theories are different in form, but not in content. This circumstance is of paramount importance for understanding the possibility of interaction, namely, the causation. The causes are clarified in the course of intratheoretical transduction, especially during the induction phase. Factor A is the cause of effect B if the variations of signs B cannot be obtained otherwise than by varying signs A. The causation is an integral part of conceptual transduction.

As regards the correlation of different forms of representations of the same theory, they are completely isomorphic to each other in conceptual and methodological terms. Isomorphic entities are not causally related to each other. Otherwise, they would not be identical in conceptual and methodological terms. Thus, there is not and cannot be any causal relationship between mind-representation and body-representation. This conclusion seems does not to correspond to the fact that people often think first, then speak, and act. In this case, is the mind not the cause of language, behavior, and actions? No, it is not. A certain part of the conceptual transduction was carried out first through mind-representation and then were continued in other representations. There is a switch from one form of representation to another, but not causation. Switching between presentations is necessary so far as the conceptual transduction is realized only when all the representations really took place. If, for example, mind-representation and body-representation are not accompanied by action-representation, so desired by a pragmatist, full-fledged conceptual transduction did not take place.

Considering the representations of psychological theories, of course, it is necessary to take into account their interdisciplinary connections with other scientific theories. Each type of psychological theory has originality, by virtue of which it cannot be reduced to a different theory. Economic psychology cannot be reduced to political psychology. If the psychological theory is in contact with any other, non-psychological theory, then there is a certain correlation between the processes within the competence of these theories, but no more. For example, physical and physiological processes may be symbols of certain psychological processes.

From positions above developed theory, I will consider the mind-body problem. In this regard, I will focus on an interesting review article by Shulamith Kreitler. [2] «The paper traces the changes in the conceptualization of body-mind relations in psychology in terms of five sequential phases. The first phase is characterized by the view that there is nothing but the body. The second phase is marked by the conception that the mind is the only relevant agent. The third phase is based on the view that both body and mind exist but are on parallel tracks. The main assumption in the fourth phase is that both body and mind exist and function in interaction. Finally, the major tenet of the fifth phase is that body and mind are identical. » [2, 60]

The first phase of the conceptualization of body-mind relations Kreitler connects with behaviorism. She correctly notes that behaviorists are too straightforwardly oriented towards physiology. Strictly speaking, they used not body-interpretation, but behavior-interpretation.

The second phase led, according to Kreitler, to a better understanding of the specifics of psychological processes. [2, 63] However, in my opinion, this specificity is connected with body interpretation no less than with mind interpretation.

The third phase functioned as a double monism: mind-interpretation focused on psychology and body-interpretation on physiology and physics. [2, 64] The absolute majority of psychologists underestimate the relevance of body-interpretation. They tend to believe that the concept body is characteristic of physics largely than psychology. This is certainly not the case. This erroneous interpretation is largely a consequence of the understanding of the body as a corporeal being. In psychology, the body is a psychological subject as a unity of signs that form a separate personality.

The fourth phase, described favorably by Kreitler, mainly represents interdisciplinary relations of psychology and physiology. Contrary to Kreitler, I do not think that there is an interaction between the body and mind.

With the fifth phase, Kreitler has certain hopes for the future. In my opinion, it is erroneous insofar as it is wrong to identify the body-interpretation and mind-interpretation. These are fundamentally different interpretations.

In my opinion, the centuries-old controversy around the mind-body problem did not lead to a significant renewal of its foundations. My proposal consists in its conceptual enrichment due to the theory of conceptual transduction, in particular, the vigorous use of the concept of 'a form of representation of psychological theory'.

References

1. Descartes, R. (1984) The Philosophical Writings of Descartes, 3 vols. Vol. 2. Trans. by J. Cottingham, R. Stoothoff, and D. Murdoch, Cambridge: Cambridge University Press.
2. Kreitler, S. (2018) The mind-body problem: the perspective of psychology. Open Journal of Philosophy 8(1), 60-75.

15.4. Some lessons of emotion trend in philosophy of psychology

Andrea Scarantino and Ronald de Sousa rightly point out that «it is surprising that throughout much of the twentieth century, scientists and philosophers of mind tended to neglect the emotions – in part because of behaviorism's allergy to inner mental states and in part because the variety of phenomena covered by the word "emotion" discourages tidy theorizing. » [11] For the sake of justice, it should be noted that philosophers who are far from behaviorism have also not achieved significant success in understanding emotions. The philosophy of science has always focused on the process of thinking, which did not include emotions. In my opinion, this situation persists in our days, despite a comprehensive study of the world of emotions. In my view, the doctrine of emotions is still not included in the structure of any developed concept of the philosophy of science. I see my task in an attempt to present ideas about emotions as an organic part of the philosophy of science.

There are many theories of emotions that are difficult to systematize. [6; 7; 11] Nevertheless, it is obvious that those authors who are striving to find such grounds for theories of emotions that allow expressing them unity are doing the right thing. Scarantino and de Sousa see these bases in characterizing emotions as feelings, evaluations, and motivations, respectively. [11] G. Johnson prefers to consider the three contexts of the theories of emotions, namely, evolutionary, social and internal. [7] In the future, I will take into account these two classifications of foundations of theories of emotions.

When analyzing the content of theories of emotions, some paradoxical moments are striking. One of them concerns the relationship of feelings and emotions with evaluations as cognitive formations. Feelings and emotions are variations of affects. Evaluations are usually identified only with emotions, but not with feelings. Moreover, often it is evaluations that are considered the main characteristic of emotions. This is contrary to the installation that emotions according to their nature belong to affects. The main symptom of affects is not called at all. Whenever emotions are characterized as evaluations, they are credited to the field of thinking, which, in my opinion, is wrong. Anja Berninger argues, «we should understand emotions as a manners of thinking». [3, 198] In my opinion, there is no reason to transfer emotions from affects to thinking. Emotions are manners of affecting. Thinking and affecting are two equally independent branches of mentality. It is not surprising, therefore, that they have different mediums. Mediums of affecting are studied in affective neuroscience. [1; 5] We need to know the content of affecting because it expands our capabilities.

Another topical issue concerns the understanding of emotions as evaluations and motivations. In the absolute majority of works, when characterizing emotions as evaluations, the evaluation process is understood as something simple, self-evident. In fact, this is a rather complicated process. [10] In my opinion, it necessarily implies a comparison of theories. Without consideration of theories, the comparison of any phenomena loses all meaning. This means that the nature of emotions should be tied to the principle of theoretical representation. How to do it? I see the only acceptable answer to this question, we have to recognize that emotions are theories. Along with language, object and intellective representations of theories, there is also their affective representation. That it opens the way to understand the process of evaluation in the world of affects.

Affective representation of theories also allows you to put on a scientific basis understanding of evolution as motivation. Motives are principles of axiological theories. If these principles are presented as emotions, then the emotions themselves are motives. Not all emotions are motives. Emotional motives should be determined not without reference to axiological theories but based on them. Attempting to highlight universal and non-core emotions is untenable. There is no finally a given categorical structure of emotions. It changes from one theory to another. Here it is appropriate to recall that the conceptual mechanism of theories is realized thanks to the methods of conceptual transduction. Managing emotions is possible and necessary [8]. Nevertheless, without engaging the potential of conceptual transduction, it is unlikely to succeed. The same applies to measures of emotion. They are necessary to ensure the process of managing emotions. [9] As it turned out, emotions are measurable; they can be controlled by building them into conceptual ranks. That is why emotional representations of theories are possible. So far, unsurpassed masters in this business are the actors of the theater and cinema, representing the fate of their heroes as a multilink relay of emotions. Apparently, scientists will have to learn from the actors the ability to manage emotions.

Emotions are omnipresent. Therefore, it is not surprising that they accompany all social and cultural processes. In recent years, much attention is paid to the epistemic emotions (such as for example, surprise, curiosity, uncertainty). [2; 4;] As Peter Carruthers notes, «[t]here is a perennial temptation to regard epistemic emotions as metacognitive in nature, involving some form of representation of one's own cognitive states. Indeed, such an interpretation is seemingly forced on us by the limitations of common-sense psychology. But in fact, epistemic emotions may be neither implicitly nor explicitly metarepresentational. Moreover, one can only continue to regard them as implicitly metacognitive by defining "metacognition" in such weak terms that we would have to allow that human and animal cognition is almost ubiquitously metacognitive. This drains such a claim of any of the interest that might otherwise attach to it. » [4, 76] However, any metacognitive reasoning is not complete without appropriate emotional accompaniment. Of course, for their understanding, common sense is not enough.

A long-term study of the phenomenon of emotions was accompanied by numerous achievements. From a philosophical point of view, the most important of them is that along with the intellective representation of theories, there is their affective representation. It can and should be considered in the context of conceptual transduction. The use of affective representation of theories by psychologists opens up broad prospects for enriching the understanding of literally everyone, and not just psychological theories. These perspectives could be considered optimistic if the emotion trend in psychology were organically combined with the achievements of the philosophy of science. In my opinion, unfortunately, this combination leaves much to be desired.

References

1. Almada, L.F., Pereira, A. Jr and Carrara-Augustenborg, C. (2013) What affective neuroscience means for science of consciousness. Mens Sana Monogr 11(1), 253-273.
2. Arango-Muñoz, S. (2014) The nature of epistemic feelings. Philosophical Psychology 27(2), 193-211.
3. Berninger, A. (2016) Thinking sadly: In favor of an adverbial theory of emotions. Philosophical Psychology 29(6), 198-217.
4. Carruthers, P. (2017) Are epistemic emotions metacognitive? Philosophical Psychology 30(1-2), 58-78.
5. Carter, J.A., Gordon, E.C. and Palermos, S.O. (2016) Extended emotion. Philosophical Psychology, 29(2), 198-217.

6. Griffiths, P.E. (2013) Current emotion research in philosophy. Emotion Review 5(2), 215-222.
7. Johnson, G. (2020) Theories of Emotion. Internet Encyclopedia of Philosophy. Available at: https://www.iep.utm.edu/emotion/#H5/
8. Koole, S.L. (2009) The psychology of emotion regulation: an integrative review. Cognition and Emotion 23(1), 4-41.
9. Mauss, I.B. and Robinson, M.D. (2009) Measures of emotion: a review. Cognition Emotion 23(2), 209-237.
10. Moors, A. (2014) Flavors of appraisal theories of emotion. Emotion Review 6(4), 303-307.
11. Scarantino, A. and de Sousa, R. (2018) Emotion. The Stanford Encyclopedia of Philosophy. Available at: https://plato.stanford.edu/archives/win2018/entries/emoti on/

15.5. Specificity, irreducibility, and interdependency of psychology

All scientific theories, being participants of interdisciplinary relations, pass a kind of test for their own worth. In this regard, as a rule, the ratio of the chosen science with its closest neighbors is primarily considered. With regard to psychology, they are physics and even more neurobiology. As soon as physics is mentioned when considering interdisciplinary relationships, a formidable shadow of physicalism immediately arises. In all cases where physical theories are in contact with theories, the principles of which differ from their principles, physicalism is untenable. For example, economics with its principle of maximizing profits is not reducible to physics, in which the principle of least action dominates. Accordingly, economic psychology, which is also headed by the principle of profit maximization, cannot be reduced to physics. The same applies to all psychological theories, for their principles cannot be replaced by the principle of least action.

The difference in the principles of theories turns out to be an insurmountable obstacle to reductionism. In my opinion, when considering physical reductionism, in particular, the possibility of reducing psychology to physics, this circumstance should be kept in mind first. Nevertheless, many researchers act in a different way. Frederique Janssen-Lauret proves the failure of physicalism, considering the logical forms of psychology and physics, respectively. The first-personal theoretical statements are relevant to psychology, but not to physics. By virtue of this circumstance, psychology cannot be reduced to physics. [5] In my opinion, the same conclusion follows from consideration of the fundamentally different nature of psychology and physics. Unlike physics, psychology is an axiological, rather than a natural, science. That is why it is guided by the first-personal theoretical statements.

Joungbin Lim proves the failure of physicalism due to the lack of physical solutions to many problems. One of them is as follows: animals, being similar in their physical properties to humans, nevertheless sharply yield to them as thinkers. [6] In my opinion, such an argument has a metaphysical character. In order to clarify its content, one way or another one should refer to the conceptual nature of psychological and physical theories, respectively.

James Tartaglia attempts to rehabilitate physicalism to a certain degree. The question involuntarily arises: Is physicalism substantial really? The argument of Tartaglia is that, in contrast to physics, psychology does not fulfill its ontological obligations, and yet their observance is obligatory. «Theories that combine physicalism with phenomenal concepts abandon the phenomenal irrealism characteristic of 1950s physicalism, thereby leaving physicalists trying to reconcile themselves to concepts appropriate only to dualism. Physicalists should instead abandon phenomenal concepts and try to develop our concepts of conscious states. » [12, 817]

Contrary to the position of Tartaglia, the ontology of psychological theories are built as strictly as the ontology of physical theories. The entities of psychological theories are people, psychological subjects. We know this thanks to psychological, not physical theories.

My conclusion is that any attempt to reduce psychology to physics is untenable to the extent that it ignores the peculiarities of the conceptual nature of psychological theories.

I now turn to the question of the possibility of reducing psychology to neurobiology. As it turns out, researchers are interested not so much in the question of the reduction of psychology to neurobiology, but in the possibility of combining their strengths. Autonomy of psychology is denied, but not it specificity. One of the options for combining offers Gualtiero Piccinini and Carl Craver: «Our argument against the autonomy thesis is *not* an argument for reductionism, either as it has been classically conceived (as the derivation of one theory from another) or as it is now commonly conceived (as the idea that lower-level mechanisms are explanatorily privileged). Instead, our argument leads to a new understanding of how psychology and neuroscience should be integrated – explanatory unification will be achieved through the integration of findings from different areas of neuroscience and psychology into a description of multilevel mechanisms. » [9, 284-285] Eric Hochstein offers his version of the union of two sciences. «[C]ontra the autonomy position, I propose that the theories of psychology and neuroscience are deeply dependent on one another for further refinement and improvement. In this respect, there is an irreconcilable codependence between psychology and neuroscience that is necessary for both domains to improve and progress. » [4, 135] It is not enough to consider psychology only by itself. It is still an organic part of the cognitive science cluster. [1]

Of course, diminishing the specifics of psychology as part of the cognitive sciences is unacceptable. In my opinion, it takes place in the event of a proclamation by Bernard Lonergan the generalized empirical method, which «operates on a combination of both the data of sense and the data of consciousness: it does not treat of objects without taking into account the corresponding subjects; it does not treat of the subject's operations without taking into account the corresponding object.» [7, 141] This method is widely promoted by Robert Henman. [3] Its content, in fact, is, reduced to fixing the correlations between the data of neurobiology and psychology. However, this statement is not enough to give it a loud title 'generalized empirical method'. It should not be forgotten that not only experimental data from psychology and neuroscience correlate in a certain way with each other, but also these theories themselves in all the richness of their dynamics.

Since we are particularly interested in the foundations of psychological theories, it is reasonable to turn to the program of nativism, which, according to Eric Margolis and Stephen Laurence, «is the most promising» [8, 693] Nativists believe that the main factors of cognition are innate. Their main opponents, empiricists, argue that all knowledge is based on experiments. The conception of nativists is often surprising due to the following two circumstances. First, they did not present the mechanism of the origin of the foundations of knowledge. Secondly, by themselves, these foundations are by definition material entities that, seemingly unlike our consciousness, are not responsible for unfolding the learning processes. In recent years, certain hopes of overcoming the paradoxical traits of nativism have been associated with the Bayesian inference as a type of learning mechanism, which allows, through the process of probabilistic modeling, to identify hypotheses that can be considered as the basis of knowledge. Nevertheless, it is not yet clear whether Bayesian inference is a means sufficient for a decisive clarification of the nature of nativism. [2]

In my opinion, the nature of nativism is perfectly explained through the theory of conceptual transduction. As is known, it is implemented as a cyclical process, in which not only experimental data but also principles clearly appear. Natural selection leads to the inheritance by each species of organisms of the ability to realize not all, but only selected types of transduction with their specific principles. They are inherited in object form. However, as it was repeatedly noted earlier, objects, like language and mentality, are a form of representation of the theory. The theory is inherited, along with all its representations. In their present form, nativism and empiricism express the essence of the process of knowledge extremely fragmentary. The basis of the cognitive process is conceptual transduction, represented by mentality, language, behavior, practice, and objects also.

Above, considerable attention was paid to the correlation between neurobiology and psychology. Proceeding from it, it is not difficult to understand the correlation between the brain and the mind. It, in turn, leads to the idea of a modular structure of mind. This structure is questionable. [10] However, it is obvious that to some degree or another, the structures accordingly of brain and mind must be isomorphic to each other. As it turns out, the brain networks have extremely extensive modularity and numerous overlapping functional areas. [11] How exactly this circumstance is expressed in psychology is determined by neurobiologists and psychologists in their joint activities.

References

1. Boone, W. and Piccinini, G. (2016) The cognitive science revolution. Synthese 193(5), 1509-1534.
2. Colombo, M. (2018) Bayesian cognitive science, predictive brains, and the nativism debate. Synthese 195(11), 4817-4838.
3. Henman, R. (2013) Can brain scanning and imaging techniques contribute to a theory of thinking? Dialogues in Philosophy, Mental and Neuro Sciences 6(2), 49-56.
4. Hochstein, E. (2016) Giving up on convergence and autonomy: why the theories of psychology and neuroscience are codependent as well as irreconcilable. Studies in History and Philosophy of Science 56, 135-144.
5. Janssen-Lauret, F. (2018). Logical form, the first person, and naturalism about psychology. The case against physicalist imperialism. In Pinto, M.F., Mäki, U. and Walsh, A. (Eds.). Scientific Imperialism: Exploring the Boundaries of Interdisciplinarity. Abingdon and New York: Routledge, 237-253.
6. Lim, J. (2016). Physicalism and neo-Lockeanism about persons. Philosophical Psychology, 29(8), 1229-1240.
7. Lonergan, B. (1985). Religious Knowledge, a Third Collection. New York: Paulist Press.

8. Margolis, E. and Laurence, S. (2013) In defense of nativism. *Philosophical Studies: An International Journal for Philosophy in the Analytic Tradition* 165(2), 693-718.
9. Piccinini, G. and Craver, C. (2011) Integrating psychology and neuroscience: functional
    analyses as mechanism sketches. Synthese, 183(3), 283-311.
10. Prinz, J.J. (2006) Is the mind really modular? In Stainton. R.J. (Ed.). Contemporary Debates in Cognitive Science. Malden MA: Blackwell, 22-36.
11. Seeley, W.W., Menon, V, Schatzberg. A.F., Keller. J., Glover, G.H., Kenna, H., Reiss, A.L., Greicius, M.D. (2007) Dissociable intrinsic connectivity networks for salience processing and executive control. The Journal of Neuroscience 27(9), 2349-2356.
12. Tartaglia, J. (2013) Conceptualizing physical consciousness. Philosophical Psychology 26(6), 817-838.

15.6. Psychological ethics

Discussion of the problems of the philosophy of psychology led us, as a rule, to the conceptual nature of psychological theories. If axiological theories are presented in the most complete form, then they acquire a distinct ethical status. Only then comes the hour of psychological ethics as such. In my opinion, two principles determine the ethical status of axiological theories, the principle of maximizing the prosperity of all stakeholders and the principle of responsibility. However, they are not enough to ensure the fullest ethical content of axiological theories. It appears only when the group axiological theory is supplemented by individual theories. For example, economic theory is complemented by economic psychology. Prosperity in the composition of economic psychology is determined in accordance with economic principles. Prosperity can be economic, political, technical, pedagogical, etc. It is determined in accordance with the principles of one or another axiological theory.

The expression 'psychological ethics' has an unusual meaning. The interpretation of its content should take into account the rather unusual status of psychology. Consider, for example, three branches of science, namely, medicine, economics, and psychology. Medical and economic ethics do not complement each other. Psychological ethics complement both of them. Medical and economic ethics - group theories. Psychological ethics is a collection of individual theories. This raises a natural question about the support of individual theories of an ethical project, which is usually associated with the ethical principle of maximizing the prosperity of all stakeholders. As it turns out, it is complemented by the principle of maximizing the prosperity of the individual stakeholder. The new principle does not come into conflict with the principle of maximizing the prosperity of all stakeholders, which is related not to the individual, but to the group theory.

I presented psychological ethics in the form in which it emerges from the standpoint of the theory of conceptual transduction. At the same time, I did not have to deviate in the slightest degree from the main path of the development of science. Other authors construct psychological ethics in a different way. In this sense, the article of Richard Walsh is particularly illustrative, in which he summarizes the experience of developing the ethical code of the American Psychological Association (APA) and the Canadian Psychological Association (CPA). [13] It is necessary to pay tribute to a large group of researchers who worked purposefully and with great enthusiasm. In the shortest possible form, their design strategy as an ethical theory of ethical code was as follows.

First, they stated numerous situations that deserve condemnation, for the overcoming of which it was proposed to turn to ethics. Secondly, they chose principles that would serve as the main guidelines for a successful life. Thirdly, they proposed standards of action in situations of a similar type. Fourth, selected conceptual tools were evaluated from the standpoint of such popular ethical directions as, for example, deontology and consequentialism.

The recommendation in the case of life's adversities immediately turn to ethics causes some perplexity. If, for example, not everything were in order in the field of economy, then it would seem expedient to turn not to ethics, but to economic theories and their implementations. In this case, an appeal to ethics looks like some disregard for the possibilities of science.

Principles are designed to give the ethical code a conceptual thoroughness. The APA activists have chosen the following five principles: a) beneficence and nonmaleficence, в) fidelity and responsibility, c) integrity, d) justice, and E) respect for people's rights and dignity. The CPA activists trusted four principles, namely: 1) respect for the dignity of persons and peoples, 2) responsible caring, 3) integrity in relationships, 4) responsibility to society. [3, 4] For completeness, I also note the position of Russian psychologists, who are as well guided by four principles, namely, i) the principle of respect for personal dignity, human rights, and freedoms, ii) the principle of competence, iii) the principle of responsibility, iv) the principle of integrity. [9]

Is it possible to count codes designed according to the considered recipes to be full-fledged scientific theories? Of course not. The fact is that the realization of their potential does not imply a targeted use of scientific methods. As for the concepts used, in particular, the concepts of beneficence, nonmaleficence, fidelity, responsibility, integrity, justice, rights and dignity, they need to be as precise as possible, and this cannot be done far from scientific theories. Considered ethical codes, so popular in not only the United States, Canada, and Russia but also in other countries, are quasi-scientific conceptions.

In my opinion, the authors of the projects of psychological ethics underestimate the need to focus on science. They rather hastily and without distinctly expressed regrets remove in the direction of metaphysics. Owen Flanagan, unlike many other authors, at least mentions 'moral science', but does not make any effort to constitute it. [5] Joshua Knobe believes that moral judgments as autonomous entities impose their stamp on scientific competence; therefore, it is untenable to reduce them to the latter. A person as a scientist and person as a moralist are fundamentally different subjects. It seems we are through and through not scientific but moralizing creatures. [6, 328] Let me use the idea of the superiority of ethics over science; ethics is primary - science is secondary. I believe that the most meaningful ethics must be scientific. To be convinced of this, it is enough to appeal to any moral judgment. It will immediately become clear that its content needs clarification and it cannot take place without science.

Modern ethics are willing to talk about the need for people's responsibility. At first glance, there is no doubt about the viability of responsibility, as well as the fact that it imposes a certain stamp on numerous scientific conclusions. However, it turns out that the phenomenon of responsibility itself needs to be clarified. Scientists that are not satisfied with superficial assertions will certainly plunge into the conceptual and methodological content of science. As a result, the thesis of the superiority of ethics over science is dissolved in this content, which is precisely the best proof of its inconsistency.

It is necessary to pay tribute to Knobe, he tried, although unsuccessfully, to prove the truth of the thesis under consideration. Numerous other authors use this thesis uncritically, in its original intuitive shell. This is the case, for example, when it is groundlessly referred to the authority of ethical directions with their unclear ethical content. In such cases, they are wholly or partially included directly in psychological theories. Frank Richardson is most committed to the ethics of virtues. As a result, he proposes to enrich psychology with it. [8] In my opinion, scientific psychological theories do not need any intervention from ethical directions at all. The study aims to reveal its own content. Richard Walsh argues that «overall, the two salient perspectives in the APA and CPA Codes are consequentialism and deontology.» [13, 73] They did not appear by chance. They were entered into codes from the outside. In addition, the code developers did not take into account that consequentialism and deontology are in many ways contradictory.

As we can see, ethical codes do not express the vitality of genuine scientific psychological theories. They are to a certain extent foreign to them. Nevertheless, it is in them that many authors see the essence of psychological ethics. [2; 8] Henderikus Stam opposes this position: «Originating in ordinary language, psychological terms circulate not merely as science but also as history, making such claims historical artifacts about what kind of beings we are, and most important, what we can portend to be. » [11, 117] In my opinion, the expression "not merely as science but also as history" does not accurately represent the true nature of psychology. Psychology is scientific and as such, it does not need to be supplemented with references to the historicity of human existence. This historicity itself is expressed in the sciences, including psychology.

A number of authors highlight relevant aspects of psychological ethics, considering its place in modern society. [7; 12] Together with economic and political relations, the status of psychology also changes. In a society of economic and political liberalism, psychology also becomes liberal. [12] The so-called positive psychology supports existing social relations, despite their flaws. In this case, psychological ethics is in the shadow. It becomes known when it assumes critical functions relative to existing social relations, i.e. becomes an organic part of critical psychology. [7; 12]

In my opinion, the dynamics described in the previous paragraph, to a certain extent, confirms my views. I mean the following circumstances. First, psychology accompanies every science: economics is accompanied by economic psychology; political science is accompanied by political psychology, and so on. Second, researchers may mistakenly underestimate the ethical potential of psychology; this is the case with positive psychology. Thirdly, the inclusion of the ethical potential of psychology puts it in a critical phase in relation to its fellow travelers, in particular, to economics and political science. Fourth, psychology, in its critical phase, acquires a metascientific character, towering above group theories as awareness and criticism of the shortcomings.

Let me also turn to such a strange formation, which is moral psychology. [4] All science as a whole is an exceptional complex event. In complex ways, psychological ethics is constituted as a collection of individual theories. Highlighting their similarities come to ethics. It is formal in nature. Ethics, in turn, is accompanied by its individual companions, which form the moral psychology. Thus, it turns out that there are no such sciences, which are not accompanied by psychological ethics.

Thus, my main point is that awareness of the status of psychological ethics implies a clear focus on the scientific imperative. This circumstance, as a rule, is not taken into account. In this case, metaphysics comes to the fore, in particular, in the form of the thesis on the supremacy of ethics over science. In its present form, psychological ethics is mostly in the grip of metaphysics. The current challenge is to free her from these clutches.

References

1. American Psychological Association. (2010) Ethics Code. Available at: https://www.apa.org/ethics/code/
2. Allan, A. (2015) Ethics in psychology and law: an international perspective. Ethics and Behavior, 25(6), 443-457.
3. Canadian Psychological Association. (2017) Canadian Code of Ethics for Psychologists. Fourth Edition. Ottawa, Ontario.
4. Doris, J., Stich, S., Phillips, J. and Walmsley, L. (2017) Moral psychology: empirical approaches. The Stanford Encyclopedia of Philosophy. Available at: https://plato.stanford.edu/archives/win2017/entries/moral-psych-emp/
5. Flanagan, O. (2009) Moral science? Still metaphysical after all these years. In Narvaez, D. and Lapsley, D.

(Eds.). Personality, Identity, and Character: Explorations in Moral Psychology. Cambridge: Cambridge University Press, 52-78.

6. Knobe, J. (2010) Person as scientist, person as moralist. Behavioral and Brain Sciences 33(4), 315-329.

7. Prilleltensky, I. and Walsh-Bowers, R. (1993) Psychology and the moral imperative. Journal of Theoretical and Philosophical Psychology, 13(2), 90–102.

8. Richardson, F.C. (2012) On psychology and virtue ethics. Journal of Theoretical and Philosophical Psychology 32(1), 24-34.

9. Russian psychological society. (2012) Eticheskiy kod psikhologa [Ethical code of psychologist]. Available at: http://psyrus.ru/rpo/documentation/ethics.php/ [In Russian].

10. Schwartz-Mette, R.A. and Shen-Miller, D.S. (2018) Ships in the rising sea? Changes over time in psychologists' ethical beliefs and behaviors. Ethics and Behavior 28(3), 176-198.

11. Stam, H. J. (2015) The historical boundedness of psychological knowledge and the ethics of shared understandings. Journal of Theoretical and Philosophical Psychology 35(2), 117–127.

12. Sugarman, J. (2015) Neoliberalism and psychological ethics. Journal of Theoretical and Philosophical Psychology 35(2), 103–116.

13. Walsh, R.T.G. (2015) Introduction to ethics in psychology: historical and philosophical grounding. Journal of Theoretical and Philosophical Psychology 35(2), 69–77.

15.7. Unity of psychology and pluralism of its directions

Many researchers are surprised and even shocked by the diversity of psychological directions. Let us recall in this connection about the associative, structuralist, functional, gestalt, behavioral, activity, cultural-historical, humanistic and cognitive philosophy. The variety of psychological trends is striking, but not their unity. This circumstance, especially against the background of the strife of representatives of various philosophical directions, causes well-founded concern. It is indicative that researchers characterize the problem situation in modern psychology in a wide range of moods.

Adrian Brock believes that psychology has always consisted of fragments, which do not enrich each other and testify against the myth of its transformation into a mature science. [3] Most authors characterize the state of modern psychology with stoic restraint. They describe in detail the history of the growth of pluralism in psychology and approve it, without insisting on any cardinal measures. [7; 10; 15] Suzanne Kirschner believes, «that efforts to devise a unified theory of psychological knowledge are problematic, and that the cultivation of multiple theoretical lenses contributes to more useful and self-aware psychology. » [7, 1] Luis Augusto «in order to fill in the puzzle of a unified mind» notes «[m]oreover, the need to look for transitions, rather than dissociations. » [1, 287].

Frederick Wertz in his search for ways of confronting fragmentation and eclecticism in psychology places his main hopes not on pragmatism, but on Continental philosophy, primarily on phenomenology and hermeneutics. [15] Amedeo Giorgi places his hopes on phenomenology. [5] Stephen Yanchar holds the strongest position. He does not doubt the need for urgent measures to overcome the pernicious fragmentation of psychology. «[U]nity will not be achieved until competing ideas regarding morality, ontology, epistemology, and so forth are critically examined and evaluated. Ideas that pass theoretical muster and that cohere with human moral interests will provide a theoretical starting point for unification efforts. » [16, 150] In strategic terms, an alternative to objectivism and relativism should be the project of evaluation. [8]

Like Stephen Yanchar, I am convinced that pluralism, characteristic of modern psychology, should be the primary concern of researchers, psychologists, and philosophers. Pluralism must be properly understood, which is impossible without theory and relevant ethics. Expressing agreement with the Yanchar project, I, nevertheless, should note that his project is not concrete enough. In my opinion, the theory I developed in the previous sections of this chapter has the potential that it is necessary for a correct understanding of the status of modern psychology with its aspects of unity and diversity. Below I will demonstrate this circumstance.

Thus, I assess the state of modern psychology from the standpoint of the theory of conceptual transduction, including the principle of theoretical representation. First, let me consider which forms of representation are the most popular in psychology.

Table 15.1. Forms of representations of psychological directions

Representation forms of theories	Psychological directions
Mentality	Associative, structuralist, gestalt, humanistic psychology
Practice + mentality	Functional psychology

Body + language	Psychoanalytical psychology
Behavior	Behavior psychology
Collective activity	Activity psychology
Language + thinking	Cultural historical psychology
Thinking + body	Cognitive psychology

As a rule, it is considered that psychological directions are separated from each other. The content of table 15.1 on the contrary, testifies to their unity. The fact is that the forms of representations belong to the same theory, which is precisely psychology. The presence of theories makes the unity of all psychological areas. I will give an illustrative example in this regard.

In physics, a long time talked about quantum-wave dualism. After the creation of quantum mechanics, the idea of the dualism of waves and particles turned out to be superfluous. According to quantum mechanics, there is no dualism. If phenomena are covered by the same theory, then they are characterized by a special type of pluralism. It does not divide the phenomena, but on the contrary, brings them into unity. This rule is relevant not only for physics but also for psychology. Supporters of various psychological directions are irreconcilable towards each other only when they are not guided by the principle of theoretical representation. The unity of psychological trends is outside their field of vision.

Each psychological direction is itself heterogeneous. As a rule, it appears as a certain number of theories related in some respects. Let me demonstrate this fact on the example of mentally oriented psychological directions. The first forms of scientific psychology were associative and structuralist psychology. The concepts of psychology are definitely interconnected with each other. Psychologists understood this relationship as an association, and very simplistic.

«Associationism was a project united by a shared explanandum phenomenon, rather than a theory united by a shared theoretical posit». [4, 31] The founder of structural psychology, E.B. Titchener, did not reject associationism, concentrating on the complexes of associations, i.e. structures. [13, 450] At the same time, he resolutely rejected the acceptability of functional psychology with its emphasis on the connection of the mind with the practical activities of people. In contrast to supporters of functional psychology, Gestalt psychologists remain in the bosom of mentalism, but they reject the principle of association. Entire consciousness is explained through holistic forms, Gestalts. [13, 272] However, it cannot be denied that associative, structuralist and Gestalt psychology form a certain unity. Connections that exist between different psychological directions indicate their unity. Each psychological direction achieves relative success. In this sense, the history of Freudianism is very curious.

The conception of Sigmund Freud as a whole is not considered scientific. [2]. As a rule, his doctrine of the unconscious is denied. This means that the transition language → body failed. Nevertheless, Freud was good as an enthusiast of focused communication with the patient. His language innovations were undoubtedly progressive for the development of psychology.

The fate of behavioral psychology is also indicative. Its supporters believed that they gave the only correct presentation of the content of psychology. In fact, they absolutized one of the representations of psychology, namely, behavioral. It is enough to refer to the article B.F. Skinner, to be convinced of his rather strange argumentation. [11] He examines mental phenomena one by one, giving them the behavioral interpretation. Since such an interpretation is possible, he decides that mental phenomena do not exist.

Nevertheless, he could make a different conclusion, namely that the behavior and mentality of people represent the same content. Not only the content but also the form of its presentation is actual. Therefore, in some cases, it is advisable to use a behavioral view, while in others mental, for example, when thinking is studied.

Activity psychology is focused on collective object-oriented practice. [9] Initially, the practice was understood as abstract labor, the notion of which was developed by K. Marx in his economic doctrine. This interpretation of activity was later set aside. The basic ideas of activity psychology were developed by Lev Vygotsky. Then he moved to a special variant of cognitive psychology, becoming the author of the language turn in psychology. [14]

To date, the most flexible position is demonstrated by supporters of cognitive philosophy. They pay primary attention to the thinking + body presentation of psychology but as a rule, are not limited to it.

Unfortunately, I have to admit that not a single psychological direction uses the whole range of representations of psychological theories. This circumstance leads to a widespread view of the absence of unity in modern psychology. This unity exists, but, unfortunately, it is poorly understood.

After the above, it is obvious that there is a wide network of links between psychological directions. Here, of course, there are leaders and outsiders. For example, mental representation is expressed in cognitive psychology in a brighter form than in humanistic psychology. Assessing the shortcomings and achievements of the philosophical directions, one can construct their interpretative ranks, putting in the first place the most developed ones. [6, 156-157]

Table 15.2. Interpretative series of psychological directions

Forms of representations of psychological theories	Series of psychological directions
Mental	Cognitive → humanistic → Gestalt psychology
Procedural	Behavioral → activity psychology
Language	Cultural historical → humanistic → psychoanalytic psychology

Of course, the reader has the right to disagree with my assessments of the achievements of various philosophical directions. Nevertheless, I hope that he will not deny the existence of a certain subordination between the psychological directions. Moreover, this means that modern psychology possesses unity and at the same time progresses. Thus, in my opinion, the theory of conceptual transduction allows one to assess adequately the unity and diversity of psychological directions, as well as ways of opposing eclecticism in psychology.

References

1. Augusto, L.M. (2018) Transitions versus dissociations: a paradigm shift in unconscious cognition. Axiomathes 28(3), 269-291.

2. Borch-Jacobsen, M. and Shamdasani, S. (2007) Interprefactions: Freud's legendary science. History of the Human Sciences 21(3), 1-25.

3. Brock, A.C. (2011) Psychology's path towards a mature science: an examination of the myths. Journal of Theoretical and Philosophical Psychology 31(4), 250-257.

4. Dacey, M. (2015) Associationism without associative links: Thomas Brown and the associationist project. Studies in History and Philosophy of Science. Part A 54, 31-40.
5. Giorgi, A. (2013) Reflections on the status and direction of psychology: an external historical perspective. Journal of Phenomenological Psychology 44(2), 244-261.
6. Kanke, V.A. (2014) Istoriya, filosofiya i metodologiya pedagogiki i psikhologii [History, Philosophy and Methodology of Pedagogy and Psychology]. Moskva: Yurait. [In Russian].
7. Kirschner, S.R. (2006) Psychology and pluralism: toward the psychological studies. Journal of Theoretical and Philosophical Psychology 26(1-2), 1-17.
8. Kristensen, K.B., Slife, B.D., and Yanchar, S.C. (2000) On what basis are evaluations possible in a fragmented psychology? An alternative to objectivism and relativism. *The Journal of Mind and Behavior 21(3), 273-288.*
9. Leontiev, A. (2009) The Development of Mind. Ohio: Erythros Press and Media.
10. Shaw, R. L. and Frost, N.A. (2015). Pluralism and mixed methods - breaking out of the silo mentality. The Psychologist 28(8):638-641.
11. Skinner, B. F. (1977) Why I am not a cognitive psychologist. Behaviorism 5(2), 1-10.
12. Titchener, E.B. (1898) The postulates of a structural psychology. The Philosophical Review 7 (50), 449-465.
13. Von Ehrenfels, C. (1890) Über «Gestaltqualitäten». [About «Gestaltqualitäten»]. Avenarius, R. (Hrsg.). Vierteljarsschrift für wissenschaftliche Philosophie. Leipzig: Reisland, 249-292.
14. Vygotsky, L.S. (1962) [1934]. Thinking and Speaking. Ed. and transl. by E. Hanfmann, G. Vakar, and N. Minnick. Cambridge, MA: The MIT Press.

15. Wertz, F.J. (1999) Multiple methods in psychology: epistemological grounding and the possibility of unity. Journal of Theoretical and Philosophical Psychology 19(2), 131-166.
16. Yanchar, S.C. (1997) Fragmentation in focus: history, integration, and the project of evaluation. Journal of Theoretical and Philosophical Psychology 17(2), 150-170.

15.8. The relevance of the union of psychology and philosophy of science

I hope that the reader has long been convinced of the need for a philosophy of psychology and, therefore, a union of psychology and philosophy of science. However, in the literature, it is difficult to find a sufficiently clear description of their unity. My position is that psychologists, forced by their own efforts to implement the conceptual and methodological content of their theories, form not the philosophy of psychology, but metapsychology. The latter gives psychology fullness and thoroughness, but only partially because it does not take into account the unity of psychology with other sciences. In order not to remain in the metascientific isolation, psychologists are forced to turn to the philosophy of science. It summarizes the conceptual achievements of all the sciences, often providing nontrivial achievements from other fields to a particular science. Thus, the ascent - psychology → metapsychology → philosophy of psychology - has undoubtedly scientific relevance. Psychology needs a philosophy of psychology insofar as it is an organic part of the modern family of sciences.

The dynamics that I described at first glance can be implemented without any particular difficulty. In fact, the situation is much more problematic. The heights of

787

metapsychology and philosophy of psychology are achieved with great difficulty. Many psychologists confine themselves to the gold standard, i.e. an experiment to find out the causal relationships. They do not reach metapsychology. This is largely due to the difficulties associated with the development of the achievements of the philosophy of science. The philosophy of science is always accompanied by a thick cloud of metaphysics, from which it is difficult to free it. Many psychologists, as well as philosophers, mistakenly take metaphysics for the philosophy of science. In order to give our discussion of the union of psychology and philosophy of science a more specific character, I turn to some of those plots in which attention is drawn precisely to this union.

According to Arthur Staats for a modern disunified science of psychology, a special philosophy should be created that will ensure its Unification. [5] In my opinion, the urgent task is to fully develop the potential of metapsychology and philosophy of psychology so that all relevant problems of modern psychology, and not just the problem of unification, fall into the field of vision of psychologists.

Paul Thagard notes that philosophy occupies a worthy place in the alliance of cognitive sciences. He sees the main mission of philosophy in the fact that it provides aspects of generality and normativity in this alliance. [7] This is obviously true. Of course, it should also be borne in mind that the philosophy of science combines cognitive disciplines with all other sciences. This interaction takes place not only along lines of generality and normativity.

The actual significance of philosophy is invariably remembered when it is regarded as a savior from a crisis in psychology. In this article, not necessary to consider all the vicissitudes of ideas about the crisis of psychology. [6] I will note only three works demonstrative for the issues at hand.

Rudolf Willi proclaimed the crisis in psychology first. [9] He was dissatisfied with the fact that in psychology people lost their proximity to the outside world. He proclaimed his assessment on behalf of the empirio-criticism of Richard Avenarius.

Lev Vygotsky tried to cope with the crisis in psychology, which he saw, above all, in the struggle of various psychological directions, through the methodology of Karl Marx. [8] Despite his undoubted philosophical talent, he did not succeed.

Two modern authors Steve Brown and Paul Steiner once again offer a way to overcome the crisis of psychology. [1] They mostly do it on behalf of post-structuralism, in particular, the philosophy of Michel Foucault and Gilles Deleuze. In my opinion, this attempt is unsuccessful also.

The failures of all authors who outline ways to overcome conceptual and methodological problems relevant to psychology indicate that they do not sufficiently thoroughly understand the content of the philosophy of science. The same is characteristic of those researchers who uncritically attract philosophy for the development of specific forms of psychology, oriented towards particular philosophical directions. In particular, one can point to the phenomenological [2; 3], hermeneutic [4] and poststructuralist [1] psychology. I will take the liberty of asserting that the authors of these works do not clearly separate the philosophy of science from the metaphysically oriented philosophy. Phenomenology, hermeneutics, and poststructuralism in their modern form are largely focused on metaphysics. Therefore, it is not surprising that psychologists very often under the auspices of these philosophical trends fall under the influence of metaphysics. All areas of modern psychology are oriented towards certain philosophical directions, be it Marxism (activity psychology), existentialism (humanistic psychology), analytical philosophy (cognitivism). Everywhere the philosophy of science is under the unrelenting pressure of metaphysics. Psychologists, free yourself from metaphysics! Otherwise, you will not achieve conceptual and methodological success.

Thus, the purposeful strengthening of the union of psychology with the philosophy of science is crucial in the development of psychology. While the state of this union is alarming. Meanwhile, it is obvious that this alliance should be developed and that there are many previously unused reserves in this matter.

References

1. Brown, S.D. and Steiner, P. (2009) Psychology without Foundations: History, Philosophy and Psychosocial Theory. London: Sage Publications.
2. De Jesus, P. (2016) Autopoietic enactivism, phenomenology and the deep continuity between life and mind. Phenomenology and the Cognitive Sciences 15(2), 265–289.
3. Gallagher, S. and Zahavi, D. (2008) The Phenomenological Mind: an Introduction to Philosophy of Mind and Cognitive Science. London: Routledge.
4. Sandage, S.J., Cook, K.V., Hill, P.C., and Strawn, B.D. (2008) Hermeneutics and psychology: a review and dialectical model. Review of General Psychology 12(4), 344-364.

5. Staats, A.W. (1989) Unificationism: philosophy for the modern disunified science of psychology. Philosophical Psychology 2(2), 143-164.

6. Sturm, T. and Mülberger, A. (2012) Crisis discussions in psychology – new historical and philosophical perspectives. Studies in History and Philosophy of Science Part C: Studies in History and Philosophy of Biological and Biomedical Sciences 43 (2), 425-433.

7. Thagard, P. (2009) Why cognitive science needs philosophy and vice versa. Topics in Cognitive Science 1(2), 237-254.

8. Vygotsky, L. S. (1997) [1927] The historical meaning of the crisis in psychology. In Rieber, R.W. and Wollock, J. (Eds.). The collected works of L.S. Vygotsky. Vol. 3. New York, NY: Plenum Press, 233-344.

9. Willy, R. (1899) Die Krisis in der Psychologie. [The Crisis in Psychology.] Leipzig, Germany: Reisland. [In German].

Chapter 16. The nature of sociology

16.1. Sociological theory

Sociology consists of theories. It is obvious that the phenomenon of the theory should cause every researcher, who is trying to understand the original content of sociology, of paramount interest. Gabriel Abend reasonably notes that «'[t]heory' is one of the most important words in the lexicon of contemporary sociology. Yet, their ubiquity notwithstanding, it is quite unclear what sociologists mean by the words 'theory', 'theoretical,' and 'theorize'. I argue that confusions about the meaning of 'theory' have brought about undesirable consequences, including conceptual muddles and even downright miscommunication. » [1, 173]. He himself made a very revealing attempt to find out the true meaning of the term 'sociological theory'.

Abend singled out seven different senses of the word 'theory'. [1, 177-181] They deserve a mention. I present their formulations in the most concise, partly "trimmed" form, solely in order to acquaint the reader with the issues at hand as soon as possible.

Theory$_1$ – the relationship between variables.

Theory$_2$ –an explanation of the particular social phenomenon.

Theory$_3$ – an interpretation of some social phenomena.

Theory$_4$ – the views of eminent authors, presented in their works.

Theory$_5$ – worldview.

Theory$_6$ – the etymology of the term.

Theory$_7$ – opinions of sociologists about various topical problems of sociology.

Abend concluded all seven definitions of the nature of the theory do not have the proper semantic clarity. In this regard, he proposes a therapy for sociology, his own way of overcoming the semantic difficulty in question. It consists in the fact that the definition of the meaning of a sociological theory should be guided, firstly, by the principle of practical reason, secondly, by the principle of ontological and epistemological pluralism.

It is not difficult to see that, ultimately, Abend expressed his obvious pragmatic predilections. Very little is said directly about the sociological theory. The reader remains completely unaware of its conceptual and methodological content.

Christopher Dandeker and John Scott reveal the nature of the sociological theory from a fundamentally different position than Abend. The subject of their interest is the internal structure of the theory. This approach, of course, deserves every support. Without an understanding of the internal structure of the theory, it is hardly possible to give a clear idea of its nature. In their study, Dandeker and Scott proceed from a certain position, which is that the production of sociological knowledge implies definite answers to a number of basic questions. Just these answers reveal the structure of the theory.

The answer to the fundamental question "What?" implies information about objects and their characteristic statics. The question "How?" indicates methods and their inherent dynamics. [3, 305] Four structural units, namely, 1) objects, 2) statics, 3) methods and 4) dynamics, need to be characterized carefully. In this regard, Dandeker and Scott discuss numerous dilemmas, in particular, the confrontation of materialism and idealism, nominalism and realism, conditional and symbolic, surface and generative, and characterize empiricism, subjectivism, objective materialism, and objective idealism. I got the impression that the authors substituted the question of the structure of sociological theory with a discussion of the topical philosophical problems of sociology. The structure of the theory gets its expression only when its parts, their relationship with each other and the mechanisms of realization are indicated.

Unfortunately, sociologists rarely give a detailed description of the theory as a fundamental conception. In this regard, it is reasonable to refer to the conclusions of philosophers who seek to characterize the phenomenon of the theory, regardless of its belonging to a particular science. [6] Strictly speaking, their generalizations relate mainly to physics and mathematics. However, they are also of some interest to sociology.

In the twentieth century, philosophers paid special attention to syntactic, semantic and pragmatics views. Syntactic view: theory is a syntactic logical reconstruction; semantic view: theory is mathematical modeling; pragmatic view: theory is an amorphous entity consisting of sentences, models, standards and practices. [6, sec. 1; 4, 137] It turned out that the most accurate formulation of the theory is achieved only if the achievements of logic and mathematics are used. [5] In all cases, the ways to reconcile the theory with empirical facts were considered without fail however, without much success. At this point, it is fitting to recall the cycle of intratheoretical conceptual transduction. Scientific prediction and planning, actualization, data processing and the revision of the principles of the theory form a coherent whole. I call the indicated whole a theory. In my opinion, there are good reasons for this.

There is no doubt that the prediction and planning of experiments and practical actions is a frankly theoretical action. Nevertheless, is it permissible to say that the sphere of influence of the theory is over? Obviously, this is not the case. The purpose of the conceptual transduction cycle is to refine the theory. This means that the actualization, data processing and improvement of principles are certain phases of the metamorphosis of the original theory. In the language of Hegel, the theory returns to itself, but at a higher phase of its development. Such is the life of a scientific theory of any type, also of sociological conception.

Returning to the discussion of the nature of sociological theory, I note that there is every reason to give it a characteristic based on ideas of intratheoretical conceptual transduction. The subjects of sociological theories are various communities of people. They are guided by principles, and, therefore, also by the laws. There are a prediction and actualization, in particular in the form of practice, and the comprehension of its lessons, and the improvement of the initial principles (of motives of action). In sociology, obviously, it cannot do without deduction, adduction, induction, and abduction, as well as methods of intertheoretical transduction. In the matter of comprehending these actions, it is quite appropriate to take advantage of the achievements of mathematics, as well as many other sciences. As an axiological science, sociology is more organically combined with a pragmatic one than with the previously mentioned syntactic and semantic approaches.

So what is a sociological theory? This is the life of communities of people in its entirety. Of course, the term 'life' has been used in this case exclusively for translating the text into the space of everyday language, perhaps familiar to some readers. As for the scientific interpretation of the concept 'sociological theory', it implies an appeal to the concepts of conceptual transduction. Sociological theory is the management of sociological concepts and the realization of all their functions.

Unfortunately, many researchers underestimate the exceptional relevance of the concept of 'sociological theory'. In this regard, the unusual appeal of Max Besbris and Shamus Khan caught my attention: «Less Theory. More Description. » [2] Sociology - axiological science. All its concepts are not descriptions, but values. Only at first glance can a sentence, for example, the answer to a question with the sociological content of an interviewer, be a description. Nevertheless, with a detailed understanding of the answer, it becomes clear that it deals with value and, therefore, not descriptions, but value judgments. Obviously, Besbris and Khan suggest increasing the share of empiry in scientific research. The fact is that theory and empiry are in agreement with each other. The empiry is part of the theory.

References

1. Abend, G. (2008) The meaning of 'theory'. Sociological Theory 26(2), 173-199.
2. Besbris, M. and Khan, S. (2017) Less Theory. More Description. Sociological Theory 35(2), 147-153.

3. Dandeker, C. and Scott, J. (2007) The structure of sociological theory and knowledge. Journal for the Theory of Social Behavior 9(3), 303-325.
4. Mormann, T. (2007) The structure of scientific theories in logical empiricism. In Richardson, A. and Uebel, T. (Eds.). The Cambridge Companion to Logical Empiricism. Cambridge: Cambridge University Press, 136-162.
5. Suppes, P. (1967) What is a scientific theory? In Morgenbesser, S. (Ed.). Philosophy of Science Today. New York: Basic Books, pp. 55–67.
6. Winther, R.G. (2016) The structure of scientific theories. The Stanford Encyclopedia of Philosophy. Available at: https://plato.stanford.edu/archives/win2016/entries/structure-scientific-theories/

16.2. Sociological groups and individuals

The ontology of any scientific theory is primarily represented by certain entities, objects in the case of natural science, and humans when axiological science. Properties and relationships, in particular, in the form of laws and principles, belong to entities. By virtue of the noted, researchers pay special attention to entities. The humans of sociological theories are social (sociological) groups and individuals as members of these groups. Their nature deserves special consideration.

Strictly speaking, humans are representations of the relevant theories. Wishing to determine their nature, one should turn directly to sociological theories and present the humans in the form in which they appear in these conceptions. Determining the nature of sociological humans bypassing sociological theories is a frank metaphysics, therefore, a departure from the scientific line. Unfortunately, this approach is characteristic of the modern philosophy of sociology. In particular, it is characteristic of compositions [1–12]. At the same time, the ratio of individuals and groups is partly productively considered in these works. It is commendable. Of course, it provided that humans are defined as ontological representations of sociological theories.

Studying the ratio of individuals and groups, some authors consider individuals as the determining factor, while others, on the contrary, give a clear preference to groups. The first position is most strongly advocated by Michael Bratman and Ludwig Kirk. [3; 4; 8; 9] Bratman raises the question of what exactly constructs modest social reality and concludes that it is shared intentions. [3, 149]. Apparently, it is permissible to assume that Bratman outlined the strategic vector – *individuals → social reality*. However, he implemented it with extraordinary caution, limiting himself to the consideration of simple cases.

A fundamentally different approach than Bratman develops Raimo Tuomela. [12]. He distinguishes between we-mode and I-mode attitude. We-mode expresses the thinking and doing of members of social groups. I-mode is the attitude of a private person. We-mode is not to reduce to I-mode. Understanding the we-mode Tuomela shares with the position of Michael Bacharach, who developed the concept of team reasoning from the standpoint of decision theory. [1; 2] He believed that we-thinking is possible only as a transition to the appropriate conceptual frame. It is complemented by the presence of common interests among members of a social group, as well as the desire and need for common success. [2, 121] The desired success is achieved with a certain degree of probability. The higher it is, the more adequate the identification of group members.

In my opinion, the approach of both Bratman and Tuomela has significant drawbacks. First, it should be noted that sociological theories, like all other scientific conceptions, are not reducible to any other knowledge. This means that they have an emergency character. Any attempt to present the emergence of sociological theory in the form of a systematic mechanism represents a relapse of unjustified reductionism. Together with sociological theory, a social group is also born. A social group is a collection of individuals representing the same social theory. They do this with varying degrees of completeness, which, nevertheless, is consistent with the status of members of the groups.

There is no reason to oppose, as Bratman and Tuomela do, individuals to social groups. Bratman postulates the existence of individuals with certain intentions that are not part of the social reality until a certain time. However, what exactly are the intentions? Bratman leaves this question unanswered. However, it is of fundamental importance. The fact is that any attempt to construct a social reality from something in an implicit form revives reductionism. The social erroneously is reduced to the non-social. This error was also not avoided by John Searle, who constructs the social world from intentions and speech acts. [12] Their non-social nature is as mysterious as the status of individuals in the Bratman conception.

Tuomela and Bacharach postulate the existence of I-mode, the members of which, unlike the members of we-mode, only care about themselves. Only altruists are allowed into the social world, but not egoists. In fact, in any social group, there is a wide range of ethical attitudes. Social does not mean ethically monotonous and preferable. Its nature is determined by the principles of the corresponding theory. Members of the football team are guided by the principles of the game of football, and members of nations by the principles of national constitutions. They can do this, arbitrarily approaching those or other ethical poles, for examples such as egotism and altruism.

The lack of reasoning of Bratman and Tuomela is that they do not essentially consider sociological theories. The discussion is translated into an ethical plane. At the same time, ethics is not considered in the context of sociological theories. This approach is, of course, metaphysical. As we have shown, it ultimately boils down to reductionism.

As I have already noted, members of a social group represent one and the same theory. This circumstance gives them identity. This seems to contradict the fact that members of a social group adhere to various theories. The views of the American Democrats and the Republicans differ from each other; however, they are representatives of the same nation. Is such a combination of one and the many, which does not destroy the identity of a social group possible? Yes, it is if the manifold acts as a combination of different interpretations of one and the same. This circumstance is not taken into account in the theories of Bratman, Tuomela, and Bacharach.

Many times bewilderment was expressed about the nature of mentality, language, and activity of a social group. All these forms of representation of the theory are implemented by members of the social group. The bodily nature of people is such that it can be a carrier of the most varied, including social theories.

In conclusion, I shall look at another trend. His supporters seek to argue about the nature of social groups very concretely, bottom-up. This approach can be called empirical. Catherine Ritchie believes that groups are implementations of structures. «Some thing, x, is a member of group G with structure S at time t and world w if, and only if, x occupies a node(s) of S and is functionally related (in the ways required by S) to other occupiers of nodes in S of G. » [10, 270] I would like to know what and how determines the structure of the group. In my opinion, it is often determined by the strategic line of the theory that the group implements.

Brian Epstein, characterizing the nature of social groups, considers their four profiles: 1) construction, 2) extra essentials, 3) anchor, and 4) accident profiles. [6] He believes that realizes a certain metaphysics, according to which the formation of a group, its essentials and accident properties, as well as the facts that, according to the anchor profile, determine the existence of these properties, should be considered. As with any form of metaphysics, the conception of Epstein is formulated by means of terms that are not grounded to scientific, authoritative social, including sociological, theories. The empirical approach suffers from the understatement of the status of theories. I see no other way to overcome it, except as an appeal directly to social theories.

The main point of this section is that a social group is a collection of individuals who, in their reflections, speech acts and actions, represent the same theory, but in different interpretations of it. The nature of social groups is determined by the social theories that they implement. An attempt to characterize the nature of social groups without regard to social theories leads to metaphysics. Upon closer examination, it turns out that all the metaphysical characteristics of the nature of social groups lack conceptual solidity.

References

1. Bacharach, M. (1999) Interactive team reasoning: a contribution to the theory of cooperation. Research in Economics 53(2), 117-47.
2. Bacharach, M. (2006) Beyond Individual Choice. Ed. by N. Gold and R. Sugden. Princeton: Princeton University Press.
3. Bratman, M. (2014) Shared Agency: A Planning Theory of Acting Together. Oxford: Oxford University Press.
4. Bratman, M.E. (2009) Modest sociality and the distinctiveness of intention. Philosophical Studies 144(1), 149-165.
5. Epstein, B. (2015) The Ant Trap: Rebuilding the Foundations of the Social Science. New York: Oxford University Press.
6. Epstein, B. (2017) What are social groups? Their metaphysics and how to classify them. Synthese. Available at: https://doi.org/10.1007/s11229-017-1387-y
7. Epstein, B. (2018) Social ontology. The Stanford Encyclopedia of Philosophy. Available at: https://plato.stanford.edu/archives/sum2018/entries/social-ontology/
8. Kirk, L. (2015) Shared agency in modest sociality. Journal of Social Ontology 1(1): 7–15.
9. Kirk, L. (2017) Methodological individualism, the we-mode, and team reasoning. In Preyer. G. and Peter, G. (Eds.). Social Ontology and Collective Intentionality: Critical Essays on the Philosophy of Raimo Tuomela with His Responses. Cham, Switzerland: Springer, 3-18.
10. Ritchie, K. (2013) What are groups? Philosophical Studies 166(2), 257-272.
11. Searle, J.R. (2010) Making the Social World: The Structure of Human Civilization. Oxford: Oxford University Press.
12. Tuomela, R. (2013) Social Ontology: Collective Intentionality and Group Agents. New York, NY: Oxford University Press.

16.3. Scientific methods of sociology: survival and development

Many philosophers are of the opinion that under the pressure of discoveries of the philosophy of the second half of the 20th century, the concept of the scientific method has lost its scientific legitimacy and has become a myth. [1; 2; 11] This circumstance is especially obvious in the field of not natural, but social sciences. This position is distinguished by its obvious radicalism, which, as a rule, is not supported by scholars and university professors. First, they are not in a hurry to give up science. As applied to sociology, Jonathan Turner put it quite energetically.

If sociological theory is not scientific, then what is it? My answer is that it becomes various mixes of journalism, ideological preaching, critique of perceived wrongs, and vague philosophizing. Such alternatives to the epistemology science do not, I believe, take sociology in a very healthy direction. They assure that we will be a watered-down humanities and that we will be irrelevant to policymakers and even our fellow academics. [12, 3]

Many researchers organically combine the institute of science with the concept of the scientific method, as does, for example, Carlo Cellucci. [5] Of course, not all philosophers deny the institution of science. Many believe that, due to its repeated transformations, it needs new thinking. [4; 8] Before addressing sociology directly, I will note some relevant events that occurred in the history of philosophy and were crucial for understanding the nature of scientific methods. Not always, these events are adequately evaluated in the modern philosophy of the social sciences.

Before Francis Bacon, scientists associated the nature of science mainly with Aristotle's deduction, it was assessed in the context of two-tier transduction, induction ↔ deduction. This type of transduction was successfully mastered in the middle of the 19th century by John Stuart Mill and William Whewell. Mill made an outstanding contribution to the development of the inductive method. Nevertheless, he understood it simplified, not in the context of mathematical statistics, which will be developed in the first quarter of the 20th century. Both Mill and Whewell misunderstood the meaning of actualization and its method of implementation through observation, experimentation, and practical action. That is why they were not able to develop three-tier transduction, which would include, along with induction and deduction the actualization method, adduction.

At the end of the 19th century, Charles Peirce developed the concept of three-tier transduction: *abduction → deduction → induction*. It was a conceptual innovation, worthy of an outstanding philosopher of science. However, unfortunately, in his striving to develop a method of science, Peirce encountered considerable difficulties. He promoted the transition from abduction to other methods but ignored the transition *induction → abduction*. Without it, the nature of abduction could not be determined, which he reduced to an intuitive guess. Regardless of Peirce's work, an absolute majority of scientists and philosophers continued to use the two-tier concept of transduction, while continuing to focus on deduction and induction.

At the end of the 19th century, Karl Pearson devoted considerable attention to the development of the scientific method. He characterized the scientific method in three of its main features: 1) careful classification of facts, 2) discovery of laws through imagination, 3) self-criticism as a criterion of all normally functioning minds. [10, 45] In fact, he remained within the two-tier concept of the scientific method. Thus, ultimately, the philosophy of science of the XIX century did not go beyond the two-tier concept of the scientific method.

What happened in the 20th century? Here one could expect innovative ideas primarily from neo-positivists and critical rationalists. The now widely known deductive-nomological model of scientific explanation of the neopositivist Carl Hempel attracted widespread attention. The emphasis on the deduction, characteristic of it, naturally, did little to update the understanding of the nature of the scientific method. Deduction is known since Aristotle. The emphasis on the deduction is a characteristic sign of critical rationalism with its leader Karl Popper. Hempel expressed the aspirations of critical rationalists also. It is not by chance that the Hempel model is also often called the Popper-Hempel model.

From a neopositivist standpoint, Rudolf Carnap gave priority to the method of induction. He had the opportunity significantly to clarify the content of the method of induction, using the achievements of mathematical statistics. His path was to try to use probabilistic inductive logic to characterize the degree of truth of a theory. In this connection, induction has ceased to be an intratheoretical method. However, even in the understanding of the relationship between theories, neither Carnap nor other neopositivists did not succeed.

As for the critical rationalists, they in the development of intratheoretical methods suffered a clear fiasco. In the context of the universal use of two-link transduction, *deduction* ↔ *induction*, Popper denied induction. Of course, scientists did not follow this advice and did not abandon induction. The genuine innovation of critical rationalists belonged to the field of not intratheoretical, but intertheoretical methods. Popper proclaimed the need to critique of theories, which initiates the replacement of outdated theories with new conceptions. Thus, Popper opened the gate to the field of methods of intertheoretical transduction.

Thus, on the eve of the second half of the 20th century, scientific methods were presented by deduction and induction, as well as criticism of theories. Now was the time for relativists. It is widely believed that Thomas Kuhn and Paul Feyerabend substantially transformed or even destroyed the institute of scientific methods. However, this is just a common opinion.

As for the methods of deduction and induction, Kuhn and Feyerabend did not propose to abandon them or replace them with others. Feyerabend's radical position was as follows: «My intention is not to replace one set of general rules by another such set: my intention is, rather, to convince the reader that all methodologies, even the most obvious ones, have their limits.» [10, 32] It is hardly worth opposing the revealing of the limits of one method or another. As for the intertheoretical transduction, the influence of Kuhn and Feyerabend on its development turned out to be negative. As is well known, they insisted on the incommensurability of theories. In this case, the methods necessary for expressing the relationship of theories are not needed.

To complete the picture of scientific methods, it is also necessary to at least briefly to review the positions of representatives of such authoritative philosophical directions as phenomenology, hermeneutics, and poststructuralism. They did not skimp on criticism of neopositivism, critical rationalism, and analytical philosophy. Scientifically, their criticism has always been superficial. It did not reach the scientific conceptions and methods. Achievements of science, including the methods used in it, remained unshakable.

Thus, my historical excursion shows that the most important achievement of the natural sciences, primarily physics, was the two-tier conceptual transduction: induction ↔ deduction. This achievement was not overturned by representatives of any philosophical direction. Unfortunately, many philosophers have misunderstood the relevance of methods and their necessity. Why are they needed? Because without them, the nature of a scientific theory, its dynamics, and mode of functioning cannot be revealed. Rejection of scientific methods closes access to the nature of scientific theory.

The phenomenon of conceptual transduction was realized in the middle of the XIX century, in particular, Mill and Whewell. In this historical period, all social sciences with the exception of the economics were in their infancy. Under these conditions, many argued about the difference between social theories from physics. Much has been clarified on this point only by now.

In all modern social sciences methods of deduction and induction, as well as adduction as the method of actualization, is fruitfully used. Without them, it is impossible to understand the structure of not only physics but also sociology. [3]

Variables and other concepts of the social sciences are values. Scientists constantly overestimate the degree of their relevance. Because of this, all concepts of the theory have a pronounced changeable, not universal character.

All social sciences deal with quantitative relationships between variables. This means that the concept of the law is no strange to these sciences. The idea of universal law essentially not used. The difficulties of adequately representing the variability of the laws of the social sciences stimulate partial or complete abstraction from them. In the first case, is realized a mixed, and in the second - a qualitative study.

The value character of all concepts of social theories means that they are subject to a constant process of optimization.

In the past decade, the theory of the causal mechanisms has attracted widespread attention. [7] Many authors believe that causal mechanisms express the main methodological content of social theories. Daniel Little, sticking to this position, does not even mention the methods of intratheoretical transduction. [9] In my opinion, this position misses the most important of the methodological forms. It is not the case that by all possible means, researchers are trying to identify the causal mechanisms, which mark the pinnacle of the social sciences. These mechanisms appear in a distinct form only when the consequences of people's actions are considered. Nevertheless, the meaning of these actions is determined by the value aspirations of people, which ultimately boil down to their principles. To understand their meaning, as well as cause and effect, one has to go through all the stages of conceptual transduction. The methods of conceptual transduction are of paramount methodological importance.

The meaning of the above is that the debate around the status of social, including sociological theories, accompanied by numerous radical statements, did not disprove the importance of scientific methods. On the other hand, one can only regret that many philosophers, zealous in their metaphysical radicalism, did not contribute to the development of scientific methods. In modern sociology, I do not see any alternative to methods of intratheoretical, as well as of intertheoretical, transduction. Unfortunately, their meaning is often misunderstood.

References

1. Andersen, H. and Hepburn, B. (2016) Scientific method. The Stanford Encyclopedia of Philosophy. Available at: https://plato.stanford.edu/archives/sum2016/entries/scientific-method/
2. Bauer, H.H. (1992) Scientific Literacy and the Myth of the Scientific Method. Urbana: University of Illinois Press.
3. Bryman, A. (2012) Social Research Methods. Fourth Edition. Oxford: Oxford University Press,
4. Bschir, K., Lohse, S., and Chang, H. (2019) Introduction: systematicity, the nature of science? Synthese 196(3), 761-773.
5. Cellucci, C. (2016) Is there a scientific method? The analytic model of science. In: Magnani, L. and Casadio, C. (Eds.). Model-based reasoning in science and technology. Studies in Applied Philosophy, Epistemology and Rational Ethics 25, 489-505.
6. Feyerabend, P.K. (1978) Against Method. London, New York: Verso.
7. Hedström, P. and Ylikoski, P. (2010) Causal mechanisms in the social sciences. Annual Review of Sociology 36(1), 49-67.

8. Hoyningen-Huene, P. (2013) Systematicity: The Nature of Science. Oxford: Oxford University Press.
9. Little, D. (2015) Mechanisms and method. Philosophy of the Social Sciences 45(4-5). 462-480.
10. Pearson, K. (1892) The Grammar of Science. London: Walter Scott.
11. Rowbottom, D.P. and Aiston, S.J. (2006) The myth of 'scientific method' in contemporary educational research. Journal of Philosophy of Education 40(2), 137-156.
12. Turner, J. H. (2002) Sociological theory today. In Turner, J.H. (Ed.). Handbook of Sociological Theory. New York: Kluwer Academic / Plenum Publishers, 1-17.

16.4. The way out of the dualism of individualism and holism

As I see it, the content of the previous sections of the chapter allows for a certain review of the ratio of individualism and methodological holism. [5, 10] The doctrine of methodological individualism was developed by Max Weber due to difficulties encountered in understanding the status of social collectivities, which are any social groups of people. He decided that these collectivities should be understood solely as the result of the particular acts of individual persons. [9, 13] In contrast to Weber, Emile Durkheim believed that sociology deals with social facts, to which he attributed values, cultural norms and social structures. Social facts, above all a social whole, exist independently of the consciousness and actions of individuals. [2, 110] This is the doctrine of methodological holism.

Conceptions of both methodological individualism and methodological holism are intended to clarify the issue of the status of sociological theories. It should be noted that they are represented on behalf of individuals and social structures. The existence of theories is assumed, but they are not presented in a clear form. It cannot be ruled out that otherwise, the question of the status of individualism and holism would have received a more distinct expression.

The first, rather obvious fact is that in the process of cognition, structures are encountered at every step. Why are they omnipresent? Apparently, in part, due to the omnipresence of the language. [3] However, it should be noted that the structures of the language studied by linguistics are not within the competence of the social sciences. Structures are relationships. [1, 6] They are ineradicable from all regions of human life. Structures are not only in the world of Robinson. Since people do not live separately from each other, but together, the structures invariably accompany them. The type of structure is determined by the relevant theories. Sociological structures are presentations of sociological theories. Their atoms are individuals considered in the context of these structures. It is obvious that individuals and structures have always existed in unity. That is why there is no separate theory of individuals and the theory of structures. Once having arisen, social theory supplies both individuals and structures in unity.

The second, also obvious fact is that individuals and structures influence each other. Following Giddens, William Sewell argues in this connection about the duality of structures. «Structures shape people's practices, but it is also people's practices that constitute (and reproduce) structures. In this view of things, human agency and structure, far from being opposed, in fact presuppose each other. » [8, 4] In my opinion, it is hardly legitimate to introduce an idea of the duality of structures, as well as of individuals. Perhaps we should talk about something else, about the fact that in the process of unfolding the potential of sociological theory, one has to switch from an atomic approach to a structural-functional one. Two approaches follow each other. From the standpoint of an atomic approach, structures are embodiments of the general features of individual actions, mental and speech acts of humans. From the standpoint of the structural approach, each individual embodies a certain structure node, performing certain functions. [1] Atomic and structural-functional approaches complement each other. The absolutizing of any of them is untenable. Classical structuralism (Lévi-Strauss, Lacan) absolutized the structural-functional approach, losing individuals out of sight. Post-structuralists (Derrida, Lyotard), proceeding from the atomic approach, declared war on the structures. However, it was not possible to get rid of them. In the absolute majority of poststructuralist theories, structures are present as rules for language games.

From the recognition of the mutual influence of individuals and structures does not follow the conclusion about their causal dependence. Individuals do not give rise to structures, and structures do not give birth to individuals. They change each other, but do not create. Changes in individuals and structures can be traced in any sociological theory. Only in the transition to a new sociological theory arise, as their object representation, individuals and structures of a fundamentally new nature.

It has been repeatedly stressed that, unlike individuals, structures do not have a body and mind. This circumstance, of course, has to be taken into account when determining the nature of the structures. The unusual plasticity of the brain is well known. The brain of the same person is the material carrier of diverse theories, in particular, physical, biological, psychological and economic. It is not surprising that he is also able to represent the reality of social structures. The brain of people is their carrier, both as social individuals and social structures. In either case, the brain acts as a carrier of social concepts, not being one of them. The type of reality that is characteristic of social subjects implies the existence of the human brain. At the same time, it, to be related to physiological phenomena, is not a direct characteristic of either social structures or individuals. This circumstance, as a rule, is not taken into account by supporters of methodological individualism, who believe that the brain itself is a social quality. Having rejected their notion it is not difficult to understand that, as a reality, social structures are no less fundamental than social individuals are.

Due to the presence of social structures, appropriate ones are possible, structural explanations. [4; 11] However, they should not be reduced to deductive explanations. The status of both social individuals and structures is revealed only in the process of implementing full-weight conceptual transduction. It can be carried out for the sake of improvement including social structures, for example, organizations and institutions.

Gustav Ramström compares the ratio of individuals - social structures with the ratio of micro-macro outside the social sciences. Behind the specified limits of the macro-phenomena supervenes on micro-phenomena. «Social macro phenomena are micro-based macro phenomena rather than macro-manifest macro phenomena. The relationship between micro and macro in social science is thus analytical; that is, the social macro level merely consists of concepts and statistics, which summarize and describe the empirical micro level. The argument for macro causation borrowed from philosophy of mind, which builds on the presence of an empirical micro–

macro relationship, thus cannot be applied to social science. »
[7, 496]

In my opinion, Ramström does not use a criterion that would allow us clearly to judge in which cases there is supervenience or something else. Such a criterion is the content of the relevant scientific theory. Supervenience takes place only if there is a connection between the phenomena explained, but they themselves form part of various theories. If phenomena are represented by the same theory, then they are not characterized by superventive connection. It is not necessarily analytical. This is exactly the case that is characteristic of the ratio of individuals and social structures. Coexisting, they are not derivable from each other. Their attitude is neither analytic nor superventive. As for causal mechanisms, they are equally characteristic of both individuals and structures.

The recognition of the complementarity of individuals and structures is not a relapse of dualism. Dualism takes place when phenomena are unjustifiably opposed to each other and, therefore, their unity is not expressed. The juxtaposition of methodological individualism and methodological holism is an example of dualism. Svetlana Kirdina suggests finding a way to synthesize them. Not finding it, she suggests considering two principles to be complementary. [6] I see another way out of a difficult situation.

I believe that representatives of the social sciences, in dealing with their subjects and getting lost, came up with the dualism of individuals and social structures. In reality, the subjects of social theories are bilateral. There are no individuals and social structures separately. Genuine subjects of social theories are bilateral. Before their researchers, they appear in two ways. In this regard, they are in one case mistaken for individuals, in the other - for structures. The dualism of individuals and structures is continued in the dualism of the two methodologies, individualism and holism. Thus, a single entity was torn apart, which were mistakenly opposed to each other. If we proceed from the existence of bilateral subjects, then there is no need for methodological individualism and methodological holism.

One should not think that bilateral entities are characteristic exclusively for the social sciences and, therefore, recognition of their reality is exotic, and it is possible, unscientific. Indicative of the situation in physics, namely, in the subject of her pride, i.e. in quantum field theory. Here the ratio of particles and fields is constantly discussed. Often, fields are considered a collection of particles, and particles as field excitations. Nevertheless, both of these positions are criticized. Physicists 'suffer' with an understanding of the correlation of particles and fields, and representatives of the social sciences with an understanding of the relationship between individuals and structures. In both cases, researchers are not in a hurry to recognize the reality of bilateral entities.

References

1. Burns, T. R. (2006) The sociology of complex systems: an overview of actor-system-dynamics theory. World Futures, 62(6), 411-440.
2. Durkheim, E. 1938 [1895] The Rules of Sociological Method. New York: The Free Press.
3. Giddens, A. (1987) Structuralism, post-structuralism and the production of culture. In Giddens, A. and Turner, J.H.

(Eds.). Social Theory Today. Stanford, CA: Stanford University Press, 195-223.
4. Haslanger, S. (2016) What is a (social) structural explanation? Philosophical Studies 173(1), 113-130.
5. Heath, J. (2015. Methodological individualism. The Stanford Encyclopedia of Philosophy. Available at: https://plato.stanford.edu/archives/spr2015/entries/methodological-individualism/
6. Kirdina, S. (2015) Methodological individualism and methodological institutionalism for interdisciplinary research. Montenegrin Journal of Economics 11(1), 53-67.
7. Ramström, G. (2018) The analytical micro–macro relationship in social science and its implications for the individualism-holism debate. Philosophy of the Social Sciences, 48(5), 474–500.
8. Sewell, W.H. Jr. (1992) A theory of structure: duality, agency, and transformation. American Journal of Sociology 98(1), 1-29.
9. Weber, M. (1922) Economy and Society. Ed. by G. Roth and C. Wittich, Berkeley: University of California Press, 1968.
10. Zahle, J. (2016) Methodological holism in the social sciences. The Stanford Encyclopedia of Philosophy. Available at: https://plato.stanford.edu/archives/sum2016/entries/holism-social/
11. Zahle, J. and Kincaid, H. (2019) Why be a methodological individualist? Synthese 196(2), 655-675.

16.5. Bounded rationality and the scientific method

The concept of 'social sciences', one of which is sociology, is consistent only if all of these sciences are characterized by certain invariants. In this regard, the principle of utility maximization and the theory of rational choice attracts particular attention. Hartmut Kliemt believes that the origins of the theory of rational choice are contained in the works of Thomas Hobbes and his follower Benedict Spinoza. [9, 135-136] Hobbes believed that, firstly, social theories should be derived from the fundamental (a priori) principles, secondly, acting, people pursue their own goals; thirdly, each action should be explained in according to its place in the causal relationship caused by it. [7, chap. 4, 10] Spinoza found «universal law of human nature» in that «everyone will, of two goods, choose that which he thinks the greatest; and of two evils, that which he thinks the least.» [17, 203]   In the 19th century, utilitarians Jeremy Bentham and John Stuart Mill developed the concept of utility. As a result, they came to the principle of utility maximization.

As for the concept of 'maximization', it was largely inspired by the ideas of mathematicians (A. Cournot) and economists with a good mathematical background (W. Jevons, L. Walras). Using the apparatus of differential and integral calculus for describing economic processes, researchers linked the definiteness of them with finding the maxima and minima of functions. In this regard, the concept of utility maximization seemed quite natural. In this place, I must certainly make one actual clarification. The maximization of utility in economics is not a certain function, but an extreme principle from which economic laws are derived. Extreme principles are characteristic of physics. Often their presence is considered evidence of the scientific character of a theory. In his Nobel lecture, Paul Samuelson repeatedly stressed that the principles of maximization are relevant to many sciences, including the economy. [13] He meant that they give scientific theories a high degree of thoroughness.

It should be noted that mathematicians quite often introduce unexpected innovations into the social sciences. When it turned out that, economists should operate on the concept of not utility, but subjectively expected utility, beneficial ideas were found on this subject in the works of Blaise Pascal and Thomas Bayes. [8, 415] In 1654, Pascal showed that states of uncertainty could be quantified using probabilities and expectations. In 1763, Bayes used the probability calculus theorem he proved to describe the learning process. Of course, the ideas of mathematicians must be taken critically.

Thus, the search for invariants of social sciences led to the principle of maximizing (subjectively expected) utility. As for the concept of utility, it was associated with all concepts of the individual social sciences. The utility is the same as what is value. All concepts of the social sciences are values as well as norms if they are approved by some authority. Values are preferences designed to ensure the steady progress of individuals and social groups. [11, 38] It is reasonable to assume that people strive for progress, not regression. In this case, you cannot do without the maximization of values. This, in turn, implies a distinct (rational) way of choosing development paths, i.e. rational choice theory. What is a rational choice and why is it possible? According to Ruth Chang, it is possible due to the comparability of social facts. [1] If it were not possible to compare the facts, then a rational choice would be impossible.

Now, I go to the revolution in the field of the philosophy of social sciences, which was initiated by the psychologist Herbert Simon with his conception of bounded rationality. A special piquancy of the situation under consideration is attached to the strife that has arisen between representatives of two sciences, economics and psychology. Typically, representatives of various sciences have no complaints to each other. Everyone does his own job, without worrying about the representatives of other sciences. In this case, despite the division of scientific labor that exists between economists and psychologists, they began to make claims to each other. Why?

Bounded rationality is simply the idea that the choices people make are determined not only by some consistent overall goal and the properties of the external world, but also by the knowledge that decision makers do and don't have of the world, their ability or inability to evoke that knowledge when it is relevant, to work out the consequences of their actions, to conjure up possible courses of action, to cope with uncertainty (including uncertainty deriving from the possible responses of other actors), and to adjudicate among their many competing wants. Rationality is bounded because these abilities are severely limited. Consequently, rational behavior in the real world is as much determined by the "inner environment" of people's minds, both their memory contents and their processes, as by the "outer environment" of the world on which they act, and which acts on them. [16, 25]

This definition of Simon is beyond doubt. However, one should pay attention to the fact that he opposes bounded rationality to perfect rationality [16, 26] It would be quite consistent to call it imperfect rationality. The development of knowledge leads to the fact that the degree of perfection of rationality grows. However, this idea seems to be Simon banal. It does not allow any claims to be made to economists who are guided by the principle of utility maximization.

The main idea of Simon is that the bounded rationality is compatible not with the principle of maximization or optimization, but with the principle of satisfaction. Therefore, the inevitable necessity is «involving satisficing instead of optimizing criteria». [16, 33]

> *Problem solving by recognition, by heuristic search, and by pattern recognition and extrapolation are examples of rational adaptation to complex task environments that take appropriate account of computational limitations - of bounded rationality. They are not optimizing techniques, but methods for arriving at satisfactory solutions with modest amounts of computation. They do not exhaust, but they typify, what we have been learning about human cognition, and they go a long way toward explaining how an organism with rather modest computational capabilities can adapt to a world that is very complex indeed.* [14, 11, Italic of Simon]

Simon was in many ways an exceptionally versatile explorer. He showed the greatest interest not to any single factor, including even bounded rationality, but to the scientific method of all cognitive and social sciences. He sought to present it in the most distinct form, avoiding «fuzzy labels like 'intuition' and 'creativity'» [15, 471] Simon, commendably, did not allow any form of irrationalism. In what form did Simon imagine the scientific method? To this question, perhaps, the best answer is his article on invariants of human behavior. [14] In this connection, I have to point out that, unfortunately, the integral scientific method as a sequence of methods of deduction, adduction, induction, and abduction, as well as methods of intertheoretical transduction, he did not present in a distinct form, the same applies to methods mathematical modeling. This circumstance, in my opinion, allows explaining some of the costs of its methodological positions.

Repeatedly noting that economists as adherents of mathematical modeling do not carry out empirical research in due amount and do not take into account the relevance of the results obtained by psychologists, Simon was right. Nevertheless, accusing all economists of the false substitution of the principle of satisfaction with the principles of maximization and optimization, in my opinion, he himself made a grave mistake. The meaning of mathematical modeling is not to solve all disputable situations in an exhaustive way. By definition, there is no limit to improving the methods of mathematical modeling. This just means that new knowledge is achieved in portions. Simon's principle of satisfaction does not conflict with the principles of maximization and optimization. In fact, he calls as satisfaction not full, but partial optimization. In any case, optimization takes place. People are creatures that optimize. Of course, in this skill, they are significantly different from each other. Many, including scientists, do not manage to avoid the fate of unsuccessful optimizers.

The main invariant of all social sciences is not the principle of satisfaction, but the principle of maximizing and optimizing the values that are part of the individual sciences. There is no universal utility, but there are values, respectively, of sociological, economic, political, legal and historical theories. These values are constantly being improved and complemented by new ones. That is why it is so difficult to take into account their nature through computer and mathematical modeling.

Let me return to the question of the relationship between psychology and economics, bearing in mind, above all, the influence of the concept of bounded rationality on the transformation of the scientific method of the social sciences. This ratio has no clear content. According to Stefano Fiori, «BR has been incorporated into different theories (characterized by distinctive methods and aims), and assumes distinctive meanings in each of them. For this reason, we may assume that there is an implicit challenge in redefining what constitutes BR, given the different applications of this notion» [4, 609]

Enrico Petracca believes that the thread associating bounded rationality with the economy is partly lost due to the development of situated, distributed, and embodied cognition. [10, 34] Don Ross believes that

> no general model of bounded rationality should ever be expected to feature in the economist's toolkit, regardless of the extent to which psychologists successfully identify specific human cognitive limitations. Use of moderate rational expectations assumptions should be understood in this light. Such assumptions are readily relaxed in specific applications, and in ways customized to modeling circumstances, that modelers, experimentalists, and econometricians are making steadily more sophisticated. [12, 411]

In my opinion, the strategic idea of Simon to revise the content of the scientific method of the social sciences in connection with bounded rationality did not lead to the expected success. The framework of the scientific method remains the same. Realizing the methods of conceptual transduction, people, of course, are limited in their abilities. But no matter how modest they are, only the implementation of conceptual transduction methods gives theories a scientific status. The rational choice theory remains in force. With regard to heuristic methods, they are only relevant to the extent that they contribute to the implementation of scientific methods.

The above history of the invariants of the social sciences, of course, is also directly related to sociology. Here, the rational choice theory was met with some caution. The fact is that usually, this theory considers the actions of individuals. [5] In sociology, attention to social institutions predominates. James Coleman overcomes this difficulty more successfully than others have in a book with the remarkable title «Foundations of Social Theory». [2] Rational choice theory he considered the basis of both sociology and all other social sciences. [3, 119] This common opinion is questioned by Peter Hedström and Petri Ylikoski, speaking on behalf of analytical sociology. [6] They believe that rational choice theory uses a flexible vocabulary, which does not express the characteristics of analytical sociology, which is founded on a mechanism-based theory. It is obvious that a similar remark can be made on behalf of other varieties of sociology. The foundations of social knowledge have value along with the methods of the corresponding social theories.

References

1. Chang, R. (2016) Comparativism: the grounds of rational choice. In Maguire, B. and Lord, E. (Eds.). Weighing Reasons. Oxford: Oxford University Press, 213-240.
2. Coleman, J. S. (1990) Foundations of Social Theory. Cambridge, MA: Belknap Press of Harvard University Press.
3. Coleman, J. S. (1992) The vision of foundations of social theory. Analyse and Kritik 14(2), 117-128.
4. Fiori, S. (2011) Forms of bounded rationality: the reception and redefinition of Herbert A. Simon's perspective. Review of Political Economy 23(4), 587-612.

5. Hedström, P. and Stern, C. (2008) Rational choice and sociology. The new Palgrave Dictionary of Economics. Vol. 2. London, UK: Palgrave Macmillan, 1-8.

6. Hedström, P. and Ylikoski, P. (2014) Analytical sociology and rational choice theory. In: Manzo, G. (Ed.). Analytical Sociology. Hoboken; John Wiley & Sons Ltd., 57-70.

7. Hobbes, T. (1968) [1651]). Leviathan. Harmondsworth: Penguin Books.

8. Joyce, J. M. (2011) The development of subjective bayesianism. In Gabbay, D.M., John Woods, J. and Kanamori, A. (Eds.). Handbook of the History of Logic. Volume 10: Inductive Logic. Oxford: North Holland, 415-475.

9. Kliemt, H. (2018) On the nature and significance of (ideal) rational choice theory. Analyse and Kritik 40(1), 131-159.

10. Petracca, E. (2017) A cognition paradigm clash: Simon, situated cognition and the interpretation of bounded rationality. Journal of Economic Methodology, 24(1), 20-40.

11. Portales L. (2019) Generation of values by social innovations. In: Social Innovation and Social Entrepreneurship. Cham: Palgrave Macmillan, 33-40.

12. Ross, D. (2014) Psychological versus economic models of bounded rationality. Journal of Economic Methodology 21(4), 411-427.

13. Samuelson, P. A. (1972) Maximum principle in analytical economics. The American Economic Review 62(3), 249-262.

14. Simon, A. (1990) Invariants of human behavior. Annual Reviews of Psychology 41(1), 1-19.

15. Simon, H.A. (1973) Does scientific discovery have a logic? Philosophy of Science 40 (4), 471-480.

16. Simon, H.A. (2000) Bounded rationality in social science: today and tomorrow. Mind and Society 1(1), 25-39.

17. Spinoza, B. de (1951) [1670] A Theologico-Political Treatise. New York: Dover.

16.6. Pluralism of sociological directions. What would it mean?

Sociology differs from other social sciences in particular diversity of its directions. Among them are positivist (Comte, Durkheim), neopositivist (Neurath), critical rationalistic (Popper, Albert), analytical (Hedström, Bearman), phenomenological (Schütz, Berger, Luckmann), hermeneutical (from Weber to Habermas), structuralist (Durkheim; Mauss, Lévi-Strauss), structural-functional, or systemic (Parsons, Luhmann), poststructuralist (Foucault; Bourdieu), Marxist (Marx), critical (Horkheimer, Adorno, Benjamin, Marcuse), rational choice (Coleman, Esser), symbolically interactive (Mead, Blumer) sociology. This diversity of sociological trends causes a mixed feeling of amazement and bewilderment. In this connection, the German authors question whether it is a question of the need for many directions, or whether they signify some transitional norms to unified sociology. [2] Is it possible to combine various sociological directions into a single scientific picture and should we try to do this? Burrell Gibson and Garreth Morgan did not find an answer to this question. [4] They concluded that sociological trends should be assessed within the framework of four paradigms (metatheoretical positions), functionalist, interpretive, radical humanist and radical structuralist. Show unity of paradigms they failed. Gibson and Morgan themselves favored the functionalist approach.

The question of the diversity of sociological theories was prominent in the work of the Austrian sociologist Andreas

Balog. His findings were mostly negative. [1, 180] As he believed, it is wrong to assume that the existence of different approaches certainly deserves a positive assessment because they complement each other. In the case of sociological theories, this is not the case. These theories are so significantly different from each other, that all together they do not give a holistic result. They are controversial, for, highlighting individual issues, narrow the explanatory possibilities of sociology as a whole. Only its individual aspects are considered. Supporters of different theories are mainly interested in defending their own positions. The point of view of opponents is not taken into account. The subject area of sociology is lost from view. All this does not promote but destroys productive intellectual disputes. Balog, assessing negatively the atmosphere in which the diversity of sociological conceptions resides, did not outline the way to improve it.

Many authors sought to evaluate not so much the negative as the positive content of the pluralism of directions and, as often expressed, paradigms. According to Stephan Kornmesser und Gerhard Schurz, when assessing the state of any science, one should avoid isolating paradigms from each other, attempts at their eclectic combination or their differentiation, based on ideological premises. In this case, the way is open to the constructive rivalry of paradigms. [6, 35] The normal stage of science is characterized by one paradigm. The paradigm competing with it helps to clarify its weak points. The second situation is that there is no dominant paradigm. In this case, the rivalry of paradigms contributes to the formation of new science. This is just a hypothesis that, in relation to sociology, needs proof.

The efforts of Gabriel et al aimed at clarifying the paradigm structure of sociology. They conclude that it contains three levels. [5, 29] The first level is formed by two rival superparadigms, actor-centered and system-theoretical. They consist of higher order paradigms, which in the case of actor-centered superparadigms consist of families of paradigms. The position in question is that the paradigmatic structure of sociology should be taken for granted, for it is precisely it that expresses the uniqueness of sociology.

Of undoubted interest is the article by Joachim Fischer, in which he summarizes the experience of understanding sociological pluralism gained in German sociology. [4] First, attempts are being made to explain the very existence of the pluralism of theories. Its origins are seen in the complexities of the process of establishing sociology as a full-fledged science, in the features of the cognitive process oriented towards conceptual competition, and in the complexity of social processes, especially at the present stage of their development. [4, 350-353] Secondly, moving to the meta-theoretical level, theories are distinguished by a number of criteria. In this regard, there are theories of the social and society, actions and structures related to the micro and macro levels, focusing on quantitative and qualitative research, with critical or descriptive potential. [4, 343-347] Third, the comparison criteria themselves are evaluated. This is done in three ways, eliminatory, hermeneutic and integrative. [3, 356] In the first method, a comparison is made on behalf of elected theories. The second method is an attempt to establish a dialogue of theories. The third method is to try to integrate theories. Fourth, and most importantly, it is proposed to compare theories as applied to specific cases. Here, when speculations are inappropriate, the strengths and weaknesses of sociological theories are identified in the most effective way. [4, 357-365] The analysis stages reviewed by Fischer are certainly of interest.

However, questions remain about the true meaning of sociological pluralism. Does it destroy or build up sociology as a holistic science?

In my opinion, the ways of understanding the pluralism of sociological directions discussed above are unsuccessful. They are helpless in ascertaining the unity of various directions. The variety of directions is not accompanied by their unity. This means that the disunity of directions is not overcome. I believe that when assessing the degree of relevance of various sociological directions, one should proceed from their conceptual and methodological unity. In my opinion, it is represented by the theory of conceptual transduction, in particular, by its eight main methods. This or that conception is evaluated in terms of conceptual transduction. A direction is welcomed only if it is compatible with the theory of conceptual transduction and contributes to its development. Otherwise, it is subject to criticism. In this regard, let me turn to the phenomenological, hermeneutic and poststructuralist sociology.

In my opinion, the main advantage of phenomenological sociology is the emphasis on the sphere of mentality. This means that the mental representation of sociological theories is in her field of vision. In this capacity, it occupies a very worthy place in sociology. Unfortunately, in phenomenological sociology, the methods of conceptual transduction have not received a distinct expression. In this context, it is scientifically unsatisfactory. Hermeneutic and poststructuralist sociology has its strengths. Both focus on the language representation of sociological theories. At the same time, hermeneutists consider the processes of finding agreement between members of social groups, but poststructuralists emphasize that human freedom should not be suppressed by social groups. Both hermeneutists and poststructuralists actualize issues that in no way go beyond sociology in the unity of all its parts. Nevertheless, there are also legitimate claims against them about their ignoring the methods of scientific sociology. In part of them in which they are consistent, phenomenological, hermeneutic, and poststructuralist sociology does not fall out of scientific sociology. As already noted, they have shortcomings that can be overcome only through scientific criticism.

Balog believed that representatives of separate conceptions narrow the field of sociology. However, this, strictly speaking, is not in their power. In my opinion, his mistake was that he did not consider separate theories in the context of sociology, its conceptual and methodological content as a whole. He considered the separate conceptions in their own frame of reference, which is wrong.

German sociologists, fascinated by the selection of rival paradigms, also make a fundamental mistake. In fact, they oppose each other parts of a single whole, for example, individuals and social groups as systems. Within the framework of a consistent sociological theory, individuals and social groups do not oppose each other. If, however, they are extracted from a theoretical whole, then immediately the thought of their opposition is born. These are all the costs of an inconsistent understanding of the conceptual and methodological content of sociology as a combination of scientific theories.

All sociological directions are the result of a metascientific and philosophical-scientific analysis of the content of sociological theories carried out with greater or less thoroughness. Unfortunately, while many philosophers are guided not by the philosophy of science, but by the philosophy with its reverence for metaphysics. Partly for this reason, In sociological directions, there are many scientifically untenable metaphysics. Fortunately, the stream of achievements of the philosophy of science does not stop. It is thanks to them that sociology is an organic part of science as a whole.

Until now, I have considered the correlation between sociological directions. However, the theme of pluralism is directly related to what is taking place within each direction. Consider for definiteness hermeneutic sociology. In the course of its development, it was fueled by the ideas of Weber, Mead, Schütz, Garfinkel, and Habermas. Paying tribute to each of them it is reasonable to build a hermeneutic league-theory beginning with the name Habermas. I mean that of these five authors, he is the creator of the most developed socio-hermeneutic conception. Finally, I note that, depending on the specific situation, various sociological directions may come to the fore.

Sociology is similar to a starfish, the disc of which is its conceptual and methodological structure, and the rays are represented by sociological directions. Like other branches of science, it is so multifaceted that it cannot be represented by just one direction. Pluralism of sociological directions is a manifestation of the diversity of sociology.

References

1. Balog, A. (2003) Theorienvielfalt in der Soziologie. [Theories diversity in sociology.] SWS-Rundschau 43(2), 167–181. [In German].

2. Balog, A., Schülein, J.A. (Hrsg.) (2008) Soziologie, eine multiparadigmatische Wissenschaft. Erkenntnisnotwendigkeit oder Übergangsstadium? [Sociology, a Multi-paradigmatic Science. Knowledge Need

or Transitional Stage?] Wiesbaden: VS Verlag für Sozialwissenschaften. [In German].

3. Burrell, G. and Morgan, G. (1979) Sociological Paradigms and Organizational Analysis. London: Routledge.

4. Fischer, J. (2014) Multiparadigmatizität der Soziologie. Übersichten, Unterscheidungen, Ursachen und Umgangsformen. [Multiparadigmaticity of sociology. Overviews, distinctions, causes and manners.] In Kornmesser. S., Schurz, G. (Hrsg.). Die multiparadigmatische Struktur der Wissenschaften. Wiesbaden: Springer, 305-335. [In German].

5. Gabriel, M., Gratzl, N., Gruber, D. (2014) Zwischen akteurszentrierter und systemtheoretischer Soziologie. Eine Klassifikation der soziologischen Paradigmenstruktur. [Between actor-centered and system-theoretical sociology. A classification of the sociological paradigms structure.] In Kornmesser. S., Schurz, G. (Hrsg.). Die multiparadigmatische Struktur der Wissenschaften. Wiesbaden: Springer, 337-370. [In German].

6. Kornmesser, S., Schurz, G. (2014) Die multiparadigmatische Struktur der Wissenschaften: Einleitung und Übersicht. [The multiparadigmatic structure of the sciences: introduction and overview.] In Kornmesser. S., Schurz, G. (Hrsg.). Die multiparadigmatische Struktur der Wissenschaften. Wiesbaden: Springer, 11-46. [In German].

16.7. Sociological ethics

As I noted earlier, the ethical factor must dominate in any axiological theory. Unfortunately, this circumstance, as a rule, is not realized. Not by chance, it is usually not discussed in a systematic manner. In sociology, there is such a situation. The prevailing trend here is that the relevance of the union of

831

sociology and ethics is generally recognized. Nevertheless, the conceptual content of this union leaves much to be desired. Often do not distinguish between social and sociological ethics. Sociological ethics is exclusively sociology. Social ethics express the unity of the ethical factors of all social sciences, i.e. sociology, economics, political science, law, and history.

Special attention should be paid to those researchers who express a point of view that the majority do not share. In this case, I mean the position of the outstanding German sociologist Niklas Luhmann. The first representatives of scientific sociology hailed ethics. [5; 8]. Especially popular was the position of the founder of the positivist sociology Émile Durkheim. In the division of labor, he saw the possibility of rallying people, an antidote to the growth of the autonomy of their individual moral consciousness. Individuals are forced to complement each other. The division of labor and similar factors contributing to the growth of people's solidarity, they have moral content. Sociology is not intended to update morality, but to create it on scientific grounds. [5, 406]

Luhmann notes that more than a century after Durkheim, it is time to reconsider the relationship between sociology and morality, based on a new level of theoretical analysis. He gives the following arguments. [9, 28-31] First, the one who studies moral phenomena should not bring in them anything personal, but in this case, the communication, which is a condition of morality, is broken. Secondly, people as moral beings are guided by the good/bad binary code. It is not proved but taken for granted. This is contrary to the status of science. Thus, the sociology of morality will never acquire the status of an ethical scientific theory. «Sociology is not ethics and ethics is not sociology». [9, 32]

The argument of Luhmann, of course, does not hold water. The researcher, studying morality or something else is not able to turn off his larger or smaller interest in the subject of the research. In practice, this means that he is initially guided by some theory, which he then refines. Luhmann proceeded from the ideal of objective knowledge, which is incompatible with the achievements of the modern philosophy of science.

The argument regarding the binary code of ethics is also untenable. Ethicists, like scientists, can evaluate values in relative terms, one is better than the other is. It is not necessary to associate the nature of ethics exclusively with binary evaluation.

In connection with the discussion of creativity of Durkheim, I will also note the position of Gerard Dalcourt. Like Durkheim, he believes that sociology complements ethics, but emphasizes that it differs from ethics in its status. Sociology deals, in contrast to ethics, not with what should be, but with what is. [3, 320] This remark is also untenable. Sociology, like ethics, consider not only the existing but also various stages of improvement of axiological phenomena. In this regard, it is proposed to follow the paths of social progress. Scientists do not impose absolute guidelines on actors, but offer estimates of various alternatives. Actors are free to dispose of them, being aware of the undesirable consequences of ignoring scientific recommendations.

Along with Luhmann, the contenders for the honorary title of the main troublemakers in the field of sociological ethics are authors adhering to the line of philosophical poststructuralism. These authors, as a rule, oppose ethical fundamentalism, do not recognize traditional values, question the principle of responsibility, see the game of diversity and uncertainty everywhere, gravitate more towards aesthetics than towards ethics. In some cases, their efforts are welcomed [1], in others, they are criticized. [10] There is a stubborn search for authentic sociological ethics; the achievements of essentially all philosophical trends are attracted. [11] But what exactly ethics represents is still a big mystery. A bold attempt to solve it was undertaken by Yesim Isil Ulman.

Her attempt to define the principles of social, including and above all, sociological ethics deserves approval. She made her choice in favor of the principles of justice and public health. [12] Obviously, she showed her passion for medical ethics, which uses both of these principles. However, in my opinion, the principle of justice should be left to political scientists.

A thorough conversation about scientific theories always begins with principles. This rule is relevant in the case of sociological ethics. So, what are the principles of sociological ethics? In my opinion, this question was given a noteworthy answer by members of the American Sociological Association. They developed a code of ethics for themselves. However, it is reasonable to assume that they consider the principles outlined by them as relevant not only for themselves but also for all who deal with sociology. The following six principles are involved: A) Professional Competence. B) Integrity, C) Professional and Scientific Responsibility, D) Respect for People's Rights, Dignity, Diversity, E) Social Responsibility, F) Human Rights. [2, 4-6] If we keep in mind the current practice of compiling ethical codes, the choice of ASA members deserves approval. The trouble, however, is that the principles mentioned above do little to clarify the content of sociological ethics. Similar principles appear in the ethical code of other associations. They are borrowed from metaphysical ethics that do not take into account the content of scientific theories. Exit from the embarrassing situation under discussion is the same as in the case of psychological and pedagogical ethics. Principles of ethics should not be sought outside scientific theories, but in their composition.

There is no sociological ethics along with sociology. There is sociology enriched by two ethical principles, namely, the principles of maximizing the prosperity of all stakeholders and the principle of responsibility. In this case, prosperity is based on the principles of sociological, and not medical, political or any other non-sociological theories. Members of social groups often seek to develop their unity. In this case, the specificity of the principles of maximizing prosperity and responsibility is determined by the principle of developing the unity of the relevant social group of people. Thus, sociology culminates in sociological ethics. It is untenable to oppose each other sociology and ethics. This circumstance did not come into the view of Luhmann.

The conjugation of two ethical principles with other principles of sociological theories immediately reveals the most pressing questions of ethics. This is primarily the understanding of social groups as stakeholders. It is in this context that so much attention is paid to corporate social responsibility and collective thinking. [4; 6; 7] Thanks to sociology, it became clear that the subjects of ethical creativity are not only individuals but also social groups of people.

References

1. Ajana, B. (2008) In defense of post-structural ethics in sociological praxis: Derrida, Lévinas and Nancy. Enquire 1(1), 23-31.

2. American Sociological Association. (2018) Code of Ethics. Available at: https://www.asanet.org/sites/default/files/asa_code_of_et hics-june2018.pdf/

3. Dalcourt, G.J. (1973) The sociological approach to ethics. Metaphilosophy 4(4), 298-320.

4. Dietz, A. (2016) What we together ought to do. Ethics 126(4), 955-982.

5. Durkheim, E. (1893) De la division du travail sociale. [From the division of social labor.] Paris: Félix Alcan. [In French].

6. Frynas, J.G. and Yamahaki, C. (2016) Corporate social responsibility: review and roadmap of theoretical perspectives. Business Ethics: A European Review 25(3), 258-285.

7. Garriga, E. and Melé, D. (2004) Corporate social responsibility theories: mapping the territory. Journal of Business Ethics 53(1-2), 51–71.

8. Hoffding, H. (1905) On the relation between sociology and ethics. American Journal of Sociology, 10(5), 672-685.

9. Luhmann, N. (1996) The sociology of the moral and ethics. International Sociology 11(1), 27–36.

10. Morgan, M. (2014) The poverty of (moral) philosophy: towards an empirical and pragmatic ethics. European Journal of Social Theory 17(2), 129-146.

11. Reed, I. (2008) Justifying sociological knowledge: from realism to interpretation. Sociological Theory 26(2), 101-129.

12. Ulman, Y. I. (2015) Social ethics. In: ten Have, H. (Ed.). Encyclopedia of Global Bioethics. Cham: Springer, 2632-2641.

Chapter 17. The nature of economics

17.1. On the definition of economics

The economy is a collection of exclusively economic theories. It is legitimate to recognize them as a science because the potential of any theory is revealed through the methods of conceptual transduction. The same is true of any scientific theories, in particular, physical and medical conceptions. Economics meets the criteria of science. Of course, it has a certain specificity. Its nature should obviously be clarified at the very beginning of the chapter. In this regard, it seems to me that the generalization that Michael Bleaney and Ian Stewart developed is very relevant.

What is it, then, that unifies economics? This is a difficult question to answer, but the key must surely lie in the existence of certain axioms that are implicitly accepted by all economists. These axioms can be summarized in the maxim that people and institutions are in rational pursuit of goals that are defined by a set of preferences that can be taken as stable. [...] The rational pursuit of goals is usually taken to mean the maximization of some objective functions, although it does not necessarily exclude other formulations, such as 'satisfying' behavior, provided that they can be justified as a rational response to uncertainly and lack of information. [...] Human behavioral as viewed by economics, is essentially a question of choice under constraints; indeed, some writers would regard economic theory as a general theory of choice. [2, 730]

Obviously, we are talking about the fact that people, guided by their preferences, set goals that they are trying to achieve under the auspices of the principle of utility maximization. Similar content was expressed by Lionel Robbins, defining economics as «the science which studies human behavior as a relationship between ends and scarce means which have alternative uses. » [7, 15] Its wording does not contain a reference to the maximization principle. Meanwhile, it is known that the definitions of sciences should include a reference to principles. In my opinion, some comments on the definitions of Robbins are quite appropriate.

Frank Knight considered it not wide enough, instrumental, and not taking into account the importance of social communities and ethics. [5] Unfortunately, he himself did not bring his comment to the proper determination of the nature of economics. John Hart, a follower of the position of Knight, was also unable to do this. [4] Roger Backhouse and Medema Steven correctly note that the definition of Robbins helped consolidate the efforts of economists. [1, 231] At the same time, they believe that «lack of agreement on a definition does not necessarily pose a problem for the subject. Economists are generally guided by pragmatic considerations of what works or by methodological views emanating from various sources, not by formal definitions [...]. ». [1, 231] With this remark, it is difficult to agree. The so-called pragmatic considerations are not an alternative to a decent understanding of the content of economics. Its absence always leads to scientific confusion.

Mehrdad Vahabi correctly notes that Léon Walras was one of the first to express important features of economics. [8] «Pure economics is, in essence, the theory of the determination of prices under a hypothetical régime of perfectly free competition. The sum total of all things, material or immaterial, on which a price can be set because they are scarce (i.e. both useful and limited in quantity), constitutes social wealth. Hence, pure economics is also the theory of social wealth. » [9, 40] In my opinion, the definition of Walras leads to an actual conclusion: economic science always considers the totality of prices as an organic whole, which is expressed through the concepts of either economic equilibrium or disequilibrium. If social wealth did not possess internal unity, then the concepts of equilibrium and disequilibrium would lose all meaning.

Of even more fundamental importance are the comments addressed to the definition of Robins, who, on behalf of the representatives of the Austrian school in economics, makes Carmelo Ferlito. He concluded that economics is a science of subjective meaning. [3] Mises explains that «[h]uman action is purposeful behavior. Or we may say: Action is will put into operation and transformed into an agency, is aiming at ends and goals, is the ego's meaningful response to stimuli and to the conditions of its environment, is a person's conscious adjustment to the state of the universe that determines his life». [6, 11] The main meaning of the position of the representatives of the Austrian school is that prices of goods and services are generated by people due to their consciousness and actions. Prices are not real characteristics of goods and services, but only interpretations. As for goods and services, they do not exist, for they are unreal. In this position, it is difficult to detect weak spots, but they exist.

First, I note that economic phenomena are the result of supervening; they cannot be reduced to processes of non-economic, for example, physiological, content. Secondly, once having arisen, the economic world began to be vigorously improved by people. Thirdly, since time immemorial, the economic world has acted in various forms of representation of economic theories, including mental, linguistic and objective. The mistake of the adherents of the Austrian school in economics is that they notice only two presentation of economic theories. They reveal economic consciousness and economic activity, but not economic entities, i.e. *homo economicus* and goods and services. They would not exist if they did not have the appropriate material correlates, namely, people, things and processes

Thus, the economic world is people in their economic quality, goods, and services (a collection of prices). The world of prices has an internal unity, which is expressed through, for example, the concepts of equilibrium and disequilibrium. The economic world is a representation of economic theories. They are improved through conceptual transduction techniques. People have the ability to compare prices, economic utility in, as a rule, monetary units. The most important economic principles are the maximization of profit entrepreneurs and of wages of employees. Everything that happens in economics has a certain justification and, therefore, is rational. The economic opportunities of people are not limitless; they are limited by their own abilities, as well as natural and social phenomena. Economics is a set of economic theories that are improved through their forms of representations and conceptual transduction methods and. Its specifics are most fully expressed by the principles of maximizing profits and wages.

References

1. Backhouse, R.E. and Medema, S.G. (2009) On the definition of economics. Journal of Economic Perspectives 23(1), 221-233.
2. Bleaney, M. and Stewart, I. (1991) Economics and related disciplines. In Bleaney, M., Greenaway, D., and Stewart. I. (Eds.). Companion to Contemporary Economic Thought. London and New York: Routledge, 729-741.
3. Ferlito, C. (2018) Economics: a science of meaning. ZBW – Leibniz Information Centre for Economics. Kiel, Hamburg.
4. Hart, J. (2014) Frank Knight's 'categories' and the definition of economics. Journal of Economic Methodology 21(3), 290-307.
5. Knight, F. H. (1934) Review of Robbins (1932). International Journal of Ethics 44(3), 358–361.
6. Mises, L. (1998) [1949] Human Action. A Treatise on Economics. Auburn, AL: Ludwig von Mises Institute.
7. Robbins, L.C. (1932) An Essay on the Nature and Significance of Economic Science. London: Macmillan.
8. Vahabi, M. (2012) A Note on Backhouse and Medema: on Walras' Contribution to the definition of economics. MPRA Paper 42673, University Library of Munich, Germany.
9. Walras, L. (2003) [1826] Elements of Pure Economics. London, Routledge.

17.2. Search for methodological foundations of economics

The question of the methodological foundations of economics remains unanswered. It seems that everyone knows what the methods of economics are, but they have difficulty in defining them. In this regard, I will consider some trends that seem to be relevant in terms of clarifying the methodological foundations of economics.

Thinking about the nature of economics, many researchers consider, first, the relationship between theory and experiment. The theory is understood in this case as the connection of concepts that allow predicting the course of economic processes. The experiment is an interference with the economic processes themselves, without which it is impossible to obtain information about them. In my opinion, Vernon Smith expresses interesting thoughts on the relationship between theory and experiment. Theories motivate specific design experimental tests. Their actual implementation most often leads to a mismatch of observations with predictions. In this case, theories are modified in such a way that the harmony between predictions and observations is restored.

As experimentalists we have come to the realization that people's decisions, consistent with their cultural experience, are often as sensitive to the specific context as to variation in the structure of the game. That is how brains work. An understandable fault we share is the error of thinking too much like economists and game theorists when interpreting the decision choices of our subjects. The standard game-theoretic assumptions are an important generator of precise theorems, but this desirable property should never be confused with the *precision of the tests the theorems motivate*. Modeling skill is essential when constructing abstract first-cut representations of socioeconomic systems and their underlying function. Moreover, these representations are often accurate predictors of the outcomes we observe – as in markets, various auction institutions and in two-person games under private information – but those skills fail to enable us to see how and why people who do not have our professional expertise, can or cannot reach our predicted outcomes across the spectrum of games we study. [8, 13]

In essence, the main idea of Smith is that economics is realized through multiplying cycles of mutual correlations between theories and experiments. Moreover, he notes that the state of affairs in economics resembles the situation in physics at the beginning of the 20th century. Smith clearly advocates the position of economic naturalism. Daniel Hausman thinks that «[...] social scientific naturalism, like social scientific anti-naturalism, is not a clear position [...]». [2, 306] To me, the position of Vernon Smith seems to be as accurate as possible. I do not see any need to doubt the relevance of economic naturalism. Pursuing a harmony of predictions and experimental results, there is no need to go beyond the limits of scientific methodology.

Robert Sugden considers two research programs in which experiments act as either tests or exhibits. In the first case, as a rule, it turns out that already existing theories are insufficient for the explanation. They do not need cancellation; they only need to be corrected. «What do deviation theories have in common? Each of them is constructed by making a relatively small number of revisions to a received theory, usually encompassing the received theory as a limiting case. Generalise expected utility theory, prospect theory, rank-dependent theory and regret theory involve different revisions of expected utility theory.» [9, 295] In the case of experiments as exhibits, it is not enough just to correct already existing theories; we have to invent a fundamentally new conception. «The function of the exhibit is not so much to falsify the received theory as to provide positive evidence of a particular regularity. [...]An exhibit, properly understood, is an experimental design that reliably induces a surprising regularity.» [9, 299-300] Sugden seeks to describe in the most detailed way the origin of the idea of the experiment as exhibits and, equally important, its design. It turns out that there is no shortage of applicants for the invention of new theory; they usually include the creators of exhibits. In essence, Sugden sets forth the beginnings of the concept of intertheoretical transduction, explaining the emergence of new theories. Not all economists are able to assess the relevance of experiments. As a result, they adhere to the theory-centrism position. [1, 83] Smith and Sugden safely avoid both theory-centrism and experiment-centrism. The foundations of economics they see in economic theories and experiments. Both of them do not get tired of noting the possibility of coming from theory to experiment, and from experiment to theory.

When moving from theory to experiment, thought experiments are relevant. They are not real experiments, for they are not interference in the course of economic processes. They are not reducible to formal models. [10] In my opinion, their purpose is to prepare the design of real experiments. Actual experiments themselves allow us to estimate the range of applicability, reliability, and predictive ability of a theory, to present economic phenomena in the most distinct form, and to play the role of material models. [7]

Thus, I considered the first way to determine the foundations of economics, which was to clarify the relationship between theory and experiment. The second way of analysis is to consider either abduction as such [3; 4; 11], or the unity that it makes up with deduction and induction. [5; 6; 12] Why exactly abduction is given paramount attention? Because people, constantly improving their economic theories, meet with significant difficulties in understanding the mechanism of this creative process. At the initiative of Charles Peirce, abduction is called in the philosophy of science to explain this mechanism. Abduction is understood as a transition from facts to their explanatory hypothesis.

Ramzi Mabsout considers three positions about the interpretation of the process of inventing a new theory. Carl Popper believed that there was no logical way from facts to theory. Herbert Simon, on the contrary, believed that there was such a path. The correct position is to recognize abduction as a weak form of logical inference. With regard to the situation under consideration, it is not the logical definiteness of abduction that is decisive, but the recognition of its significance in understanding scientific discoveries. [3, 22]

Fernando Tohmé and Ricardo Crespo, representing the potential of abduction, brings it closer to inference to the best explanation. [11, 4219] In my opinion, this approach can be misleading. Being realized, abduction leads, at least initially, to one hypothesis. It can be recognized as the best only if it is compared with an already existing conception, the one that initiated the cognitive cycle, which led to the need for an abduction operation. Consequently, abduction provides the generation of such a new theory, which is better than its predecessor in relation to the studied phenomena is. But perhaps there is another, really the best theory. This conclusion does not contradict what James J. Heckman and Burton Singer. They define abduction as « [...] a strategy for growing knowledge and not for pretending to have it. » [3, 301]

Let me now turn to authors who in one way or another view deduction, induction and abduction together. Adrian Moroşan assesses deduction, induction, and abduction as logical methods that are in perfect harmony with the nature of the economics. [5, 94] Each of these methods should be used where it is particularly effective.

Dumitry Zait defines the stages of the study, starting with the identification of the problem and the definition of the research objective, and ending with the consistent use of abduction, induction, and deduction. These three categories of the methodological association are neither the only possible nor strictly defined. The researcher is free in his choice, but he must comply with certain methodological conditions of compatibility, otherwise, his research may lead to incorrect results. [12, 67]

Richard Ormerod seeks to determine the content and specifics of rational inference. In this regard, he pays tribute to deduction and also to induction, among the varieties of which abduction is credited, but gives priority to the probabilistic orientation and Bayesian approach. [6] This means that the value of deduction and induction should be determined from the standpoint of the Bayesian approach. His interest is focused not on the sequence of research stages, but on their common nature.

It is time to take stock of my brief excursion into the search for methodological foundations of economics. Anyway, his various options are grouped around intratheoretical and intertheoretical transduction with its methods. Sugden and Smith consider the process of generating new theories and their relationships with their predecessors much better than Popper did. Nevertheless, It does not come to distinguish the sequence of methods for problematization, discovery, interpretation, and ordering. It is not noticed that the comparison of theory and experiment is not quite correct. The experiment must be related not to theory, but to prediction. It is the prediction that precedes the experiment.

The situation with understanding the nature of abduction is somewhat disappointing. Peirce understood it as a stage in the generation of a new theory, which we cannot reduce to either deduction or induction, apparently, also to the Bayesian approach. [3, 300] He was an outstanding logician. Nevertheless, he did not understand deduction, induction, and abduction solely as logical operations. With regard to economics, they, being its methodological foundations, possess exclusively economic specificity. Logical methods are not the basis of economics. In my opinion, the observed increase in researchers' attention to abduction should lead, ultimately, to the recognition of intratheoretical transduction cycles, including the successful transition - abduction - deduction - adduction - induction. It is possible that in the near future, researchers will pay due attention to the adduction. It is customary to speak of an experimental method. However, the experiment is not a method, but a stage of intratheoretical transduction. Another thing is that he himself has a certain methodological content, which is precisely the adduction.

Thus, in my opinion, the search for the methodological foundations of economics should lead to methods of intratheoretical and intertheoretical transduction.

References

1. Guala, F. (2011) Theory-centrism in experimental economics. Journal of Economic Methodology 18(1), 83-86.
2. Hausman, D.M. (2012) Social scientific naturalism and experimentation in economics. Handbook of the Philosophy of Science. Volume 13: Philosophy of Economics. Ed. by M. Uskali. North Holland: Elsevier, 287-307.
3. Heckman, J.J. and Singer, B. (2017) Abducting economics. American Economic Review: Papers & Proceedings 107(5), 298-302.
4. Mabsout, R. (2015) Abduction and economics: the contributions of Charles Peirce and Herbert Simon. Journal of Economic Methodology 22(4), 491-516.
5. Moroşan, A. (2014) The use of inductive, deductive or abductive rezoning in economics. Revista Economică 66(3), 89-96.
6. Ormerod, R.J. (2010) Rational inference: deductive, inductive and probabilistic thinking. Journal of the Operational Research Society 61(8), 1207-1223.
7. Schmidt, K.M. (2009) The role of experiments for the development of economic theories. Perspektiven der Wirtschaftspolitik 10(Issue Supplement), 14–30.
8. Smith, V.L. (2009) Theory and experiment: what are the questions? Journal of Economic Behavior and Organization 73(1), 3-15.
9. Sugden, R. (2005) Experiments as exhibits and experiments as tests, Journal of Economic Methodology 12(2), 291-302.
10. Thoma, J. (2016) On the hidden thought experiments of economic theory. Philosophy of the Social Sciences, 46(2), 129-146.
11. Tohmé, F. and Crespo, R. (2013) Abduction in economics: a conceptual framework and its model. Synthese 190(18), 4215-4237.

12. Zait, D. (2015) Methodological options in economic and management research. Cross-Cultural Management Journal 17(1), 59-67.

17.3. Models

David Hausman is inclined to emphasize that philosophers and economists evaluate scientific knowledge differently. «Most philosophers have argued that science proceeds by the discovery of theories and of laws, but economists are more comfortable talking about *models* than about laws and theories. » [4, 9]. Some philosophers later began to also consider the problems of models, but this, it is said, is not fully characteristic of them. Economists concentrated their attention on models. Daniel Klein and Pedro Romero devoted a special article to the correlation between economic theories and models. Their conclusion was surprising in many ways. In a special journal devoted to economic theories, only 12 percent of the articles were devoted to theories. In all other articles, models were considered [5]. These authors even suggested renaming the «Journal of Economic Theory» into the «Journal of Economic Models».

«The really pressing philosophical task for those interested in economics is to come up with an understanding of scientific *models*, because economic theorizing relies mainly on models. Models in the sciences, unlike theories, may be material (like the scale models of airplanes tested in wind tunnels) as well as linguistic; however, like laws and theories, they are representational. Unlike laws and some theories, models are manipulated, explored, and modified. Although it is sometimes appropriate to ask whether parts of models are true or false, economists more often assess models in terms of their fruitfulness or usefulness. » [4, 11]. Interestingly, in this passage D. Hausman, arguing about the representativeness of the models, in fact, uses the correspondence conception of truth. Then, emphasizing its usefulness appeals to the pragmatic (instrumentalist) conception of truth.

What is a model? Uskali Mäki believes that the model must necessarily have a resemblance to what it models. «Models conceived as representations can be considered four placed: Model M is an entity used by agent A to represent target system S for purpose P. The inclusion of purpose or function suggests pragmatic constraints on the required respects and degrees of resemblance. The desired sort of resemblance is a function of the uses to which models are put, the purpose they are supposed to serve. » [6, 305]. Ideally, the model should have a complete similarity with the object. Nevertheless, to achieve a certain goal, it suffices to restrict ourselves to partial similarity. [7]

Another expert on economic models is Mary Morgan. She specifically emphasizes that representations become models only if they have the resources to manipulate them. [8, 27] I explain her thoughts as follows. The elephant figurine is not a model of a real elephant, for by manipulating with it, it is impossible to get relevant answers regarding the nature of the animal. Morgan believes that the mainline of the reasoning of economists is systematic. [8, 217–225] The first step is that a model is formed in accordance with some interest; the second step is asking about the world or model; the third step - using the resources of the model, looking for the answer to the question posed; the fourth step is a narrative, i.e. a narrative that combines a question with the resolution found. Both Mäki and Morgan believe that working with models is a kind of experiment. [6, 81-89; 8, 31]

Thus, the economic model, as a rule, is interpreted as a representation, the starting point of which is real economic phenomena. Many economists discuss the realism of both theories and models. Theories and models are considered representations of the real world, but at the same time, models are closest to it. According to the principle of theoretical representation, such a representation is false. In accordance with this principle, not theories are representations of the real world, but he himself acts as their representation. Similar can be said about the models. Not models are representations of economic phenomena, but, on the contrary, these phenomena represent models. They cannot be understood without theories, including models.

Models in economics are donor conceptions for economic theories. In this connection, formal theories from the arsenal of linguistics, logic, mathematics, and computer programming fall primarily into the field of economists. In this case, the main attention is drawn to mathematical models, which, as a rule, are accompanied by computer calculations. In economic modeling, in the chain 'economic theory - a mathematical model - a computer model' prevails economic theory. Of course, logical models of economic phenomena can also be used. Therefore, for the reproduction of processes saturated with probabilities and uncertainties, it may be advisable to use multi-valued logic. Its use, in fact, is possible only in connection with the construction of a logical model. Linguistic models can also be used. If the content of the same economic theory is presented sequentially in English, Russian and Chinese, then there are three linguistic models of economic theory.

When economists turn to donor theories, they do it not to saturate the economy with an alien content. It is important for them to express the full potential of economic theory as much as possible. In this regard, everything foreign to economics should be avoided. This goal is achieved as follows: all concepts of the mathematical theory are considered symbols of economic theory. When a mathematical model expresses the specifics of economic theory, it is not independent of it. Eaten candy is not a candy, because it has become a substance of the body. The meaning of economic and mathematical modeling is not that the researcher moves away from economic theory into the realm of models. He presents an economic theory in a more developed form than before.

Why is an economist interested in mathematical theories? Due to the division of labor among scientists of various specialties. Mathematics expresses some similar features of various theories. The mathematicians themselves describe the similar as morphisms (isomorphism, homeomorphism, etc.). This similarity is first extracted from non-mathematical theories, then improved in mathematics, and then returned to its native sources.

Scientists of various specialties are often perplexed about the relevance of mathematical knowledge. The famous physicist Eugene Wigner not without perplexity stated the inconceivable effectiveness of mathematics [9]. The sources of its effectiveness are hidden in the non-mathematical sciences themselves, for mathematics develops in a certain sense theirs own content. Moreover, mathematicians do this in a highly non-trivial way, offering scientists some quantitative calculus.

Without mathematics, economics would not be able to present its content in the most complete form possible.

Is it permissible to assume that mathematical modeling is an experiment? In our opinion, is unacceptable. The fact is that an experiment involves some interference in the course of events [3]. In the case of observations, this intervention is minimal; however, it cannot do without it. So-called mental, mathematical, and computational experiments are not genuine experiments. They do not allow you to check deductive predictions. It is widely believed that deduction takes place in a unique, unambiguous way. Mathematical modeling allows you to vary the deduction in accordance with the selected scenarios. The potential of mathematical modeling can be used beyond the limits of deduction, in particular, at the stage of the experiment, data processing and updating of deductive principles. The specificity of all stages of the study is determined by the economic (acceptor) theory, and not by mathematical models.

In 1953, Milton Friedman proclaimed the thesis of descriptively false assumptions. «To be important, therefore, a hypothesis must be descriptively false in its assumptions; it takes account of, and accounts for, none of the many other attendant circumstances, since its very success shows them to be irrelevant for the phenomena to be explained. » [2, 153]. It is not quite clear why, using the model with its abstractions (some phenomena are not taken into account) and idealizations (the phenomena are partially embellished), one should depart from reality, in fact, apparently, never going back to it completely. The overwhelming majority of authors who argue about these amazing moves of knowledge, as a rule, are guided by the corresondence conception of truth, sometimes supplemented by its pragmatic (instrumental) rival. Our position, however, is that we should be guided by the metascience-oriented concept of truth. In this case, the relevance of the appeal to the models is as follows.

Already at the stage of prediction by means of exclusively economic theory, reality acts as its representation. If the potential of a mathematical model is connected to economic theory, then reality appears in a new form, more developed. Thus, the essence of the matter is not that, with models, the reality is torn into pieces that cannot be glued together, but in the development of the image of reality. The use of mathematical models allows enriching the theory; as a result, reality looks different from before. In this regard, it is obvious that the model does not lead away from reality in any way. It is wrong to talk about theories and models, starting from reality. The correct way is that reality is viewed as a representation of economic theory, first in its form, when the potential of mathematical models is not used, and then in a form enriched with this potential. The expressions 'descriptively false premises' and 'unrealistic models' are essentially meaningless. If the model is economically relevant, then it can be neither unrealistic nor false.

The use of mathematical models made it possible to evaluate the status of economic theory in a new way. It seems that the theory should unfold like some kind of linear deductive structure. However, the same economic theory can use the potential of many mathematical models [1]. The essence of the process under consideration is that economic theory has many possibilities for its development. Mathematical modeling allows you to implement them. Of course, while economists make full use of their creative abilities.

Above, relevance for the economics of mathematics, which grows from depths of economics, and then returned to it in an updated form, was explained. Similarly, we can explain the relevance of models from the field of any other formal branch of science, in particular, for example, logic and programming. How to explain the relevance of not only formal but also, for example, physical models? In our opinion, economists are forced to take into account the physical environment of economic processes. Physical concepts are considered as symbols of economic processes. They are forced to 'tune in' to each other. Because of this, they become somewhat similar to each other.

In interpreting the relationship of economic theories, models, and experiments, researchers face certain difficulties. In this regard, models are often wrongfully contrasted with theories. In the interpretation of the nature of mathematical models, as a rule, two concepts of truth are used, the correspondent and the pragmatic (instrumental). In the first case, the idea is that the mathematical model due to abstractions first leads away from reality, and then allows you to get closer to it. In the second case, the problems of economic truth go into the shadows. The model is considered a means to achieve the goals.

I propose, in interpreting the nature of formal models, to be guided by the metascience-oriented concept of truth. In this case, for example, the mathematical model does not oppose economic theory but contributes to its development. Accordingly, the changing image of economic reality. Every economically relevant mathematical model is true initially. The model does not depart from reality in any way.

References

1. Aydinonat, N.E. (2018) The diversity of models as a means to better explanations in economics. Journal of Economic Methodology 25(3), 237-251.
2. Friedman, M. (2008) [1953] The methodology of positive economics. In Hausman (Ed). Philosophy of Economics. An Anthology. Cambridge: Cambridge University Press, 145-178.
3. Hacking, I. (1983) Representing and Intervening: Introductory Topics in the Philosophy of Natural Science. Cambridge, UK: Cambridge University Press.
4. Hausman, D. (2008) Introduction. In Hausman, D. (Ed). Philosophy of Economics. An Anthology. Cambridge: Cambridge University Press, 1-38.
5. Klein, D.B. and Romero, P.P. (2007) Model building versus theorizing: the paucity of theory in the journal of economic theory. Econ Journal Watch 4(2), 241-247.
6. Mäki, U. (2005) Models are experiments, experiments are models. Journal of Economic Methodology 12(2), 303-315.
7. Mäki, U. (2011) Models and the locus of their truth. Synthese 180(1), 47-63.
8. Morgan, M.S. (2012) The World in the Model: How Economists Work and Think. New York: Cambridge University Press.
9. Wigner, E. (1960) The unreasonable effectiveness of mathematics in the natural sciences. Communications on Pure and Applied Mathematics 13(1), 1-14.

17.4. Misunderstanding of the status of theories

In the previous section, the place of models in theories was considered. This question occupies a significant place in the modern philosophy of economics. I decided to supplement what was said earlier about theories and models. The above-mentioned article by Daniel Klein and Pedro Romero has a strange name, which is about the «paucity of theory». [3] The authors of 66 articles were asked three test questions: 1) Did you create a theory of what? 2) Why was your theory/model created? 3) What are the achievements of your theory/model? Successfully answer these three questions could only authors of eight articles. It was concluded that the authors of 58 articles, in fact, are engaged not in theorizing, but in modeling. The pathos of the critical article by Klein and Romero was that they defended theorizing. Without vigilant care about the relevance, importance, and usefulness of theories, the model building can turn into a genre of creative writing (literature). Modeling, which has lost contact with reality, with unclear positive goals and achievements, largely, is scientifically untenable.

The article by Klein and Romero attracted the attention of many researchers; it was reviewed critically by Robert Goldfarb and Jon Ratner [2]. They believe that the concepts of theory and model should be clarified. Klein and Romero have three requirements for mathematical models. First, they must describe the conditions and mechanisms leading to some real phenomena. Secondly, the model is necessary for a better explanation of real phenomena. Thirdly, as an explanation, the model deserves recognition as some achievement. According to Goldfarb and Ratner, eminent economists understand the ratio of theories and models differently. In this regard, some examples are given. Their conclusion is:

> A widespread use of "theory and "model" is that "theory" is a broad conceptual approach— as in "price theory" — while "models," typically in mathematical (including graphical) form, are

applications of a theory to particular settings and/or represent explorations of different sets of assumptions conditionally allowable by the theory approach. [2, 97]

Models do not necessarily reach real phenomena they may be abstract. However, they can also describe real phenomena. Unlike their opponents, Goldfarb and Ratner believe that they do not prescribe some mandatory features to models, but only describe the work methods of prominent economists, in particular, Robert Solow. In my opinion, such an argument leads away from the substance of the matter, which in this case consists of presenting in a clear form that part of economic theory where interdisciplinary relations are considered. Indeed, the dispute is about correlation, on the one hand, economic, and on the other hand, mathematical theory. Naturally, the question arises about its correct interpretation.

In my opinion, Goldfarb and Ratner are on the wrong path. The essence of their approach is that economic theory finds its continuation in mathematical theory. Two different types of theories line up. Mathematics is more relevant than economics and closer to data. The transition to data is accomplished through mathematics. My position is fundamentally different.

Mathematics does not continue economic theory but goes on parallel to it at all its four stages, predictions, experiment, data processing, and updating of deductive principles. Economics is clearly more specific then mathematics. Mathematics is not something applied to economics. To reach the stage of experiment and data, the economy does not need intermediaries, because it is originally related to them. Economic data are representations of economic theory. Mathematics is necessary for the economy not for accessing data, but for presenting the management of concepts in a more verified form. With the help of mathematics, economics realizes its own potential.

In determining the status of mathematical models, many economists somehow very unambiguously characterize the ratio of two different branches of science. Genuine interdisciplinary relationships are not expressed. One way or another, the acceptor role of economics is belittled, and this is fundamentally wrong.

Continuing to clarify the relationship between theories and models, I will consider another pair of duelists. John Kay seeks to show the fallacy of many of the ideas of the most zealous proponents of using mathematical models. His opponent, Michael Woodford, believes that all the critical remarks of Kay can be disproved by the most justified handling of models. I give below the main arguments of Kay.

- Proponents of models lose contact with reality so much that they refuse to give realistic predictions. [2, 4]
- They use models for some problems even if in reality it is impossible. [2, 6]
- Proponents of models do not stop using obviously false premises (for example the so-called Ricardian equivalence, according to which some premises of the theories evoke response actions, leveling their meaning). [2, 6]
- They use universally applicable ideas in which all the basic links are predetermined. [2, 7]
- They blindly follow the rule of ensuring absolute rigor and consistency. [2, 7]

- They, in an effort to justify the relevance of comprehensive mathematical models, introduce an idea of rational expectations, always performed according to the same rules. [2, 10]
- They do not take into account that the world of the economy depends much more than the physical world on our ideas. [2. 12]

Kay's crucial arguments against proponents of the models are as follows:

- Economic behavior is influenced by technologies and cultural forms that are not developed randomly, but one that cannot be completely described using variables and equations familiar to economists; [2, 7]
- Economic theory is not a task search technique, but a set of tasks that must be solved. These tasks are heterogeneous, their solutions will inevitably be eclectic; [2, 11].
- One should adhere to pragmatic thinking, thanks to which one can use various tools for solving short-term tasks. [2, 12]

Woodford is ready to take into account the arguments of Kay, but he believes that they in no way disprove the relevance of formal models. Woodford gives a brief but very impressive description of the merits of the models.

Models allow the internal consistency of a proposed argument to be checked with greater precision; they allow more finely-grained differentiation among alternative hypotheses, and they allow longer and more subtle chains of reasoning to be deployed without both author and reader becoming hopelessly tangled in them. Nor do I believe it is true that economists who are more given to the use of formal mathematical analysis are generally more dogmatic in their conclusions than those who customarily rely upon more informal styles of argument. Often, reasoning from formal models makes it easier to see how strong are the assumptions required for an argument to be valid, and how different one's conclusions may be depending on modest changes in specific assumptions. And whether or not any given practitioner of economic modeling is inclined to honestly assess the fragility of his conclusions, the use of a model to justify those conclusions makes it easy for others to see what assumptions have been relied upon, and hence to challenge them. As a result, the resort to argumentation based on models facilitates the general project of critical inquiry that represents, in my view, our best hope for some eventual approach toward truth. [4, 14]

In this passage, in my opinion, everything is correct, except for the thesis of approaching the truth. Economic truth does not loom somewhere ahead of theory but is a concept, according to which they get rid of false knowledge. According to Woodford, if necessary, formal models take into account the real state of affairs, either directly or in a more subtle way. He agrees with Kay regarding the inconsistency in the interpretation of rational expectations, which are always carried out according to the same rules and therefore forever true. Many models can be considered approximately true at the present moment, not necessarily believing that they will remain true forever. [4, 16]. This statement seems to me to be correct if we understand 'the present moment' as a certain period. I will add on my own that any theory enriched with a model will certainly correspond to some of the time horizons. Models designed for eternal times are untenable.

Woodford somehow uncertainly refutes Kay's statement about the need to take into account the variability of people's ideas about the economy. In economics, representations are a more significant factor than in physics. This circumstance, according to Kay, limits the possibility of using universal models in economics as boldly as in physics. He is right in many ways. For physics, as a rule, first-order predicate logic is sufficient. It is enough to consider the features of physical objects, the nature of which does not depend on people's assessments. A fundamentally different state of affairs is characteristic of economics. Here all features are constantly evaluated by people whose priorities continually change. In economics, the first-order predicate logic is sometimes not enough. In this regard, it is necessary to use the logic of predicates of the second and higher orders.

Arguing with Kay, Woodford had to decide on the contexts of economics, political, social, and psychological and others. He comes to the strange conclusion that it follows from the rational expectations postulate that these contextual factors are insignificant. [4, 17] In fact, he did not consider them at all. Kay's thesis was that mathematics was powerless to take into account the features of various phenomena. He did not take into account that in any branch of science mathematical models are used. In this regard, it is untenable to assert the impotence of mathematics.

The peculiarity of Woodford's article is that he concentrates entirely on models, and does not even recall theories. In this regard, it is necessary to recall that, strictly speaking, economists operate with theories, and not with models. The opposite statement inevitably leads to the absolutizing of the formal sciences and replacement of the economics by them.

One group of methodologists considers formal models to be a direct continuation of economics, not a donor conception accompanying it. These economists exaggeratedly exalt the virtues of mathematical models. Another group of methodologists does not consider formal models as a continuation of economic theory. In this regard, they are right. They are met with another difficulty, namely, they do not know how to attach formal models to economic theories. As a result, they often refuse to recognize the relevance of formal models at all.

References

1. Goldfarb, R.S. and Ratner J. (2008) 'Theory' and 'models': through the looking glass. Econ Journal Watch 5(1), 91-100.
2. Kay, J. (2012). The map is not the territory: models, scientists, and the state of modern macroeconomics. Critical Review: A Journal of Politics and Society 24(1), 87-99.
3. Klein, D.B. and Romero, P.P. (2007) Model building versus theorizing: the paucity of theory in the journal of economic theory. Econ Journal Watch 4(2), 241-247.
4. Woodford, M. (2012) Chto ne tak s ekonomicheskimi modelyami? (Otvet Dzhonu Keyu) [What is wrong with economic models? A response to John Kay]. Voprosy ekonomiki 5, 14-21. [In Russian].

17.5. Three types of economic pluralism

As a branch of science, economics consists of many economic schools. This alone is enough to understand the relevance of the theme of pluralism for the economy. Perhaps, there is no other branch of science, in which this topic would be discussed as contradictory as in economics. The works, specified in the reference, testify to this inconsistency. They discuss the relationship between pluralism and monism, as well as, and most often, the orthodox and heterodox approaches. As a rule, all these four positions are considered without their direct correlation with the variety of schools that is characteristic of economics. In this connection, I considered that it is necessary, first, to consider, at least in a brief form, those schools that are interpreted through the concepts of pluralism and monism, orthodoxy and heterodoxy.

Perhaps, in economics, there is no brighter opposition than the ratio of microeconomics and macroeconomics. The reduction of macroeconomics to microeconomics is impossible in principle. [8] Of course, they are in some way related to each other, while maintaining relative independence. This is precisely what means the case of pluralism. As for econometrics, as a theory of economic measurements, it accompanies both microeconomics and macroeconomics. It is not the third link in the union of microeconomics and macroeconomics.

Turning to economics again, we meet with classical, historicist-institutionalist, neoclassical, Keynesian, monetarist, Austrian schools. The allotment of schools itself indicates their originality, the impossibility of reducing one school to another. Another circumstance also attracts attention: each school is unique and consists of theories of individual authors. Thus, the classical school includes the theories of Smith, Ricardo and J.S. Mill. The neoclassical school combines the conceptions of Jevons, Menger, Walras, and Marshall. Theories that form schools are combined according to some criteria of the greater or lesser degree of relevance, for example, of cost-of-produvtion theory of value (for classical school) or marginal theory (for neoclassical school). Thus, a well-known pluralism is characteristic of every economic school. It should be expected that another type of pluralism is characteristic of the ratio of individual economic schools.

Of particular note is the continuity of some schools. Keynesian economics includes Neo-Keynesian, New Keynesian, and Post-Keynesian economics. Post-Keynesian economics is most closely associated with the original views of the Keynes itself. In Neo-Keynesian economics and New Keynesian economics, there is some departure from the original ideas of Keynes. Both of these schools developed under the strong influence of the attitudes of not only Keynes but also of the neoclassical school. The fate of the latter has so far been the most successful. Its starting point was the marginalist revolution. Later, its conceptual content found an organic continuation in the theory of Marshall, in the neoclassical synthesis of Hicks and Samuelson, in the theory of rational expectations of Muth, Lucas, as well as in the theory of rational choice of Buchanan, Arrow. The successful fate of the neoclassical school allows us to consider it the dominant economic school today. Together with the Keynesian approach, it forms the modern mainstream.

Continuing the inventory of economic schools, let us pay attention to the conceptual distance between them, it may be larger and smaller. This distance is determined by the degree of similarity and differences in the principles of economic schools.

If the indicated difference is maximal, then among the supporters of theories there is often a persistent opposition. In this regard, introduces the idea of the orthodox (mainstream) and heterodox economics. Heterodox economics opposes to the mainstream. [9, 484] Tony Lawson believes that heterodox economics include «post-Keynesianism, (old) institutionalism, feminist, social, Marxian, Austrian and social economics, among others.» [9, 484] How exactly heterodox economics relates to orthodox economics is a matter for further discussion. In the meantime, I note that the abundance of economic schools is very acute in raising the question of the need to develop a concept of economic interschool relations.

Judging by the available literature, not monistic, but the pluralistic approach enjoys universal sympathy. [3; 4] The proponents of the orthodox and heterodox economics declare themselves, as a rule, as supporters of a pluralistic approach. However, what is pluralism? Randall Holcombe believes that «[Pluralism] is the concept that there is no single methodology that is always the correct one for discovering scientific truths, so multiple approaches and methodologies are required for a complete scientific understanding of a subject.» [7, 51] Bruce Caldwell compared the standards of monism and pluralism and concluded that the standards of pluralism provide a comprehensive understanding of the strengths and weaknesses of the studied programs. [2, 238-240] Holcombe claims that heterodox economists speak on behalf of pluralism only when they criticize mainstream. In the case of the characteristics of the schools to which they themselves belong, these schools are considered in isolation from each other. [7] As a result, the pluralism program is not implemented by heterodox economists. [1]

What is the situation with orthodox economists' pluralism? Heterodox economists blame them for grossly rejecting pluralism. [5; 6; 9; 10;] Other economists hold a more moderate position. Holcombe believes that supporters of the orthodox economics adhere to three competitive methodologies, a positive (according to Friedman), general equilibrium and a strictly empirical. Therefore, orthodox economics is pluralistic. [7, 57] Apparently, one can agree with this conclusion. However, it should be borne in mind that critics of orthodox economics blame it for the absence of not intraschool, but interschool pluralism. Intraschool pluralism is implemented under the auspices of general principles. For example, supporters of all theories included in the neoclassical school are distinguished by their commitment to mathematical modeling. Intraschool pluralism consists in the fact that the principles common to all theories of a given school are implemented in various ways.

The mechanism for implementing intraschool pluralism is mostly clear. Much more complicated is the situation with interschool pluralism. The difference between economic schools is striking. But what is their unity? Pluralism implies unity. Otherwise, it cannot be implemented. In my opinion, the trouble of heterodox economists is that they, justifiably insisting on the need for the interschool pluralism, do not name the integral principle that gives it unity and scientific validity. This principle is a set of scientific methods relevant to economic theories. These methods are the result of the hard research work of economists. In my opinion, we should talk about the methods of conceptual transduction. Thus, scientific pluralism does not consist of combining the methods of different schools in one way or another. All of them are critically evaluated from the standpoint of the integral principle. And then it immediately turns out that all economic schools are on an equal footing in the system of scientific pluralism. The advantages and disadvantages of the neoclassical school and all other schools are evaluated equally demanding. In this regard, the confrontation of the orthodox and heterodox schools in a scientific sense is out of business. Its meaning turns out to be purely ideological.

Interschool pluralism is that a round of all economic schools is performed, the result of which is the selection of their achievements and shortcomings. Consider in this connection, for example, the concept of equilibrium. It was very productively used in the neoclassical school, where, in particular, they distinguished the Stackelberg equilibrium from the Nash equilibrium. On the other hand, representatives of the Austrian school, noting that the methodology of equilibrium does not take into account the active nature of entrepreneurs, contributed to the growth of attention to the concept of imbalance. We are talking about two different positions, which - and this is especially true - do not contradict, but complement each other. Pluralism is realized as a system of not contradictory, but additional provisions. Pluralism is criticism. Nevertheless, this is not a criticism from the standpoint of individual schools. The conceptual framework of criticism is not these positions, but the integral scientific method developed in metaeconomics. In the absence of a metascientific work, scientific pluralism is impossible; it inevitably degenerates into eclecticism. Thus, interschool pluralism is possible and necessary.

Continuing the analysis of economic pluralism, I refer to the concept of neoclassical synthesis, which seems to be evidence of the merger of two different schools, neoclassical and Keynesian. There was a lot of talk about this merger, but in fact, it was not there. [11] For the merger, the synthesis of microeconomics and macroeconomics, the similarity of their scientific methods were adopted, first of all, the methodology of equilibrium. In fact, macroeconomics is not reducible to microeconomics. «Reductionism in macroeconomics, the program of the microfoundations of macroeconomics, faces as twofold challenge. First, the agent-by-agent analysis that is its natural end state, at the least, cannot be practically implemented. Second, even if it could, it would fail to provide the right conceptual resources for the problems that motivate macroeconomics in the first place. Macroeconomics requires different conceptual resources because the interactions of individuals generate stable relationships that are not simply the sum of individual behaviors regarded atomistically, and these relationships in aggregate are frequently independent of the details of the individual behavior. » [8, 708] Macroeconomics supervenes on microeconomics. They are united by the phenomenon of supervenience.

So, at least three types of pluralism, intraschool, interschool and micro-macro are realized in economics. As for the dominance of the neoclassical school in modern economics, it is determined solely by the productive use of scientific methods by its supporters.

References

1. Bouwel, J. van. (2004) Explanatory pluralism in economics: against the mainstream? Philosophical Explorations: An International Journal for the Philosophy of Mind and Action 7(3), 299-315.

2. Caldwell, B.J. (1988) 'The case for pluralism'. In Marchi, N. de. (Ed.). The Popperian Legacy in Economics. Cambridge: Cambridge University Press, 231-244.

3. Callahan, G. (2008) Economics and its modes. Collingwood and British Idealism Studies 14(2), 128-157.

4. Courvisanos, J., Doughney, J. and Millmow, A. (Eds.) (2016) Reclaiming Pluralism in Economics. Abingdon: Routledge.

5. Fullbrook, E. (2014) 'New paradigm economics versus old paradigm economics; interview with Edward Fullbrook, conducted by Paul Rosenberg'. Real-World Economics Review 66, 131-143.

6. Heise, A. (2016) 'Why has economics turned out this way?' A socio-economic note on the explanation of monism in economics. The Journal of Philosophical Economics: Reflections on Economic and Social Issues 10(1), 81-101.

7. Holcombe, R.G. (2008) 'Pluralism versus heterodoxy in economics and the social sciences'. Journal of Philosophical Economics, 1(2), 51-72.

8. Hoover, K.D. (2015) Reductionism in economics: intentionality and eschatological justification in the micro foundations of macroeconomics. Philosophy of Science 82(4), 689-711.

9. Lawson, T. (2006) The nature of heterodox economics. Cambridge Journal of Economics 30(4), 483-505.

10. Lee, F.S. (2011) The pluralism debate in heterodox economics. Review of Radical Political Economics 20(10), 1-12.

11. Vroey, M. de and Duarte, P.G. (2013) In search of lost time: the neoclassical synthesis. The B.E. Journal of Macroeconomics 13(1), 965-995.

17.6. Philosophical-economic pluralism

In the previous section, I reviewed economic pluralism, which is the result of a metascientific analysis of economic theories. Along with it, there is also another type of economic pluralism, which is ensured by the philosophy of science or, in its absence, by traditional philosophy. Philosophers offer their services to economists, believing, for the most part, arrogantly that they were able to generalize the achievements of all the sciences. Economists, to a greater or lesser extent, use the workings of philosophers. This allows them to integrate economics into science as a whole. As for the achievements of philosophy, they usually act as some directions, for example, such authoritative ones as positivism, neopositivism, critical realism, analytical philosophy, phenomenology, hermeneutics, and poststructuralism. Unfortunately, each of these areas, as a rule, is not presented in a carefully detailed form. This circumstance makes it extremely difficult to use philosophical ideas in economics. Nevertheless, the union of economics and philosophy is realized, in connection with which philosophical and economic pluralism is constituted. That it is the subject of further discussion. I will turn first to the fate of positivism in the economy. The scientific authority of positivism is extremely high; from it the philosophical status of any science, in particular, economics, begins.

As soon as it comes to economic positivism, the image of John Stuart Mill immediately pops up. Along with Auguste Comte, he was the founder of philosophical positivism. At the same time, Mill was a prominent representative of the classical school in economics. Because of his brilliant philosophical and economic education, one should have expected that he should have become the founder of economic positivism. Nevertheless, this did not happen. He concluded that the method of political economy is deduction. [17] As a positivist, he had to declare primacy not of deduction, but induction. Mill did not take this step insofar as in the political economy it is extremely difficult to conduct experiments.

Mill's case shows that in the middle of the XIX century, economics was not ready to assimilate positivistic ideas. The same applies to the end of the century. This circumstance was clearly demonstrated by the famous Methodenstreit of German and Austrian economists. [2] The German Gustav von Schmoller defended the ideals of an ethically and historically oriented economy that does not need mathematical analysis. Austrian Carl Menger insisted on the need to discover economic laws and emphasized the significance of subjective factors. Both positions were very far from positivism. Their historical perspective turned out to be connected not with positivism, but with hermeneutics.

As for the English authors, at the end of the XIX century, they also remained in certain methodological confusion. Their positions tried to consolidate John Neville Keynes. He concluded, «[A]ccordingly to the special department or aspect of the science under investigation, the appropriate method may be either abstract or realistic, deductive or inductive, mathematical or statistical, hypothetical of historical». [9, 20] This position is not sufficiently defined; in particular, it does not allow isolating the special role of positivism. However, it was not without its influence. Keynes adopted the position that positive and normative economics should be distinguished. All value issues relate to the normative economy. Positive economics acts as a science refined from values. There is no doubt that the definition of positive economics correlates with the attitudes of positivism, and not of any other philosophical direction. Nevertheless, it should be borne in mind that the nature of positive economics must not be considered without fail in accordance with positivism.

A valuable testimony to the state of economic methodology in the first half of the twentieth century is the article by Terence Hutchison. [8] During the period under review, there was no distinct economic logical positivism, economic critical rationalism, or economic hermeneutics.

The famous article Milton Friedman contributed significantly to the consolidation of the philosophical position of English economists. [7] In its basic content, it should be attributed to critical rationalism. It argues that the facts cannot prove the truth of the theory, but only to refute it; the facts themselves cannot be understood without theory; it is necessary to ensure continuous progress of theories; the invention of new theories is an intuitive act. [7, 9, 34, 42, 43] All these four provisions are typical of critical rationalism. Friedman's article also contains neopositivist propositions, in particular, the postulation of the relevance of positive economics and the interpretation of logical and mathematical propositions as tautologies. [7, 3, 8].

Thanks to Friedman, economic critical rationalism took place. This fact deserves special mention. The enrichment of theories with philosophical content is always difficult and ambiguous. The fact is that extremely rarely philosophical concepts are presented in a detailed form. This circumstance makes it difficult to use them. In the case of critical rationalism, a unique situation has developed. Economists had a book by Carl Popper, in which the main provisions of critical rationalism were presented in a systematic way. [18] This circumstance contributed to the success of Friedman. A similar favorable situation did not happen in cases with positivism and logical positivism. The same applies to hermeneutics and phenomenology. However, it was not without the union of economics and philosophy in these cases. Let me turn to various options for this union.

Economic positivism

Lawrence Boland gave a very balanced assessment of economic positivism. [5] He called the main supporters of economic positivism V. Smith, P. Samuelson, J. Stigler, G. Becker, and R. Lipsey. Positivist puts experiment and data processing first. As a rule, he dislikes the concept of 'theory'. Many authors hide their lack of experimental and inductive training behind the rhetoric that positivism is outdated in all respects.

Economic logical positivism

This direction differs from economic positivism by the active use of mathematical, logical and computer models. Absolutizing of these models leads to the oblivion of the experiment and, consequently, to the rejection of positivism in general. Such a refusal is usually carried out in favor of critical rationalism. Supporters of logical positivism must be sought among active adherents of mathematical, logical and computer modeling. In my opinion, Terence Hutchison was close to the attitudes of economic logical positivism; however, he did not make a clear distinction between it and critical rationalism.

Economic critical rationalism

Along with Friedman, the most prominent representatives of economic critical rationalism were Mark Blaug and Hans Albrecht. [4; 1] Blaug adhered to the concept of rigorous falsifications: all parts of the theory should be subject to a refutation procedure. Unfortunately, it should be noted that supporters of economic critical rationalism do not properly develop the most valuable content of Popper's theory, namely, his theory of intertheoretical relations. The main mistake of the supporters of the teaching in question is the unjustified denial of the inductive method.

Economic hermeneutics

The most prominent representatives of economic hermeneutics are representatives of the Austrian school Don Lavoie and Ludwig Lachmann. [10-12] For the Don Lavoie conception, the following two quotes are especially indicative.

We only understand our world because we understand one another. We only understand each other, in turn, because we all spent some substantial part of our lives being enculturated into the life-world, a specific domain we have in common. [12, 111].

The problem of theory choice can be "solved" not algorithmically but intersubjectively; not logically within one mind but dialogically among several. Adherents of alternative interpretive frameworks must endeavor to make their statements more intelligible to one another, to interpret one another's meaning, to pose one another's problems, to persuade one another. Through a spontaneous interplay of mutual criticism, a kind of tug of war of rivalrous interpretations, the evolution of knowledge can continue to be progressive, so long as enough of its participant minds remain genuinely committed to discovering the truth. [12, 124]

The common position of all representatives of economic hermeneutics is that supporters of a positive economy in their quest for objective knowledge emasculate the world, they lose its original features, subjectivity, and intersubjectivity. Because of this, 'objectivists' are not able to ensure the true progress of mankind, as evidenced, in particular, by economic crises.

The critics of the hermeneutists blame them for the inability to present in a detailed, truly effective way the rules of economic understanding.

Economic phenomenology

Most impressively, economic phenomenology is represented by a monograph of Till Düppe. [6] He comes from the ideas of Edmund Husserl, who argued in the 1930s that all science, replacing the human sensual world with abstractions, idealizations, and formalisms, is in crisis. Düppe, considering the history of economics, concludes that economics is in a deep crisis. To save it as a science is impossible. Consequently, it must be abandoned, leaving room for those who perceive the economy with a genuine vital interest. It is not science that should be revived, but the vital world of man. Unlike Husserl, Düppe does not offer specific methods of phenomenological research. In my opinion, this is precisely the main weakness of his project. He failed to imagine the potential of Husserl's philosophy in economic form. This potential is particularly relevant for understanding the mentality of economists.

Economic rhetoric

This is a concept developed by D. McCloskey. [15; 16] She managed not only to develop an interesting philosophical project but also to present it in economic form. Rhetoric is directed against the well-established standards of modern economic methodology that limit creativity in the economy. The rhetoric of economics is of literary matter. Economics is heavily metaphorical. Metaphors in economics are used to convey novel thoughts. Rhetoric is bricolage, that is, the implementation of its own project through metaphors. It constitutes a poetics of economics.

How to evaluate the project? Is it a skeptical, nihilist, or relativistic program, does it significantly expand the economy? On this account, there is no consensus. Economic rhetoric, not have disproved the traditional methodology of economics, forces economists to be more attentive to their conclusions, without imposing any restrictions on economic creativity. According to its philosophical orientation, economic rhetoric belongs to the field of philosophical poststructuralism. [3] Attempts have been made repeatedly to use in the interests of the economics the conceptions of such outstanding poststructuralists as Michel Foucault and Jacques Derrida. Nevertheless, so far the best project of economic poststructuralism is McCloskey's rhetoric.

Conclusion

I considered the most well established philosophical-economic directions. Of course, many other projects claim the status of a philosophical-economic direction. Many of them in one way or another are guided by the naturalism of W. Quine or the paradigmatic pragmatism of Thomas Kuhn. I did not consider them. In my opinion, the enormous potential of analytical philosophy has not yet been realized economically. It is not clearly visible either in the critical realism of Tony Lawson or in the realism of Uskali Mäki. [13; 14].

The presence of various philosophical-economic directions naturally raises the question of the possibility of their combining. I concluded that the pluralism of philosophical-economic trends is implemented in the same key as the pluralism of economic schools. By all means, there should be a round of all philosophical-economic directions. Their strengths and weaknesses are evaluated from the standpoint of the integral scientific method. It should be a generalization of the methodological achievements of all the sciences, including economics. Ignoring the status of the integral scientific method necessarily leads to the degeneration of scientific pluralism into eclecticism.

References

1. Albert, H. (1985) Treatise on Critical Reason. Princeton University Press, Princeton.
2. Backhaus, J. und Hansen, R. (2000) Methodenstreit in der Nationalökonomie. [Method dispute in the national economy.] Journal for General Philosophy of Science 31(2), 307–336. [In German].
3. Balak, B. (2006) McCloskey's Rhetoric: Discourse Ethics in Economics. New York: Routledge.
4. Blaug, M. (1980) The Methodology of Economics, or, How Economists Explain. Cambridge, England; New York: Cambridge University Press.
5. Boland, L.A. (1991) Current views on economic positivism. In Bleaney, M., Greenaway, D., and Stewart, I. (Eds.). Companion to Contemporary Economic Thought. London and New York: Routledge, 86-104.

6. Düppe, T. (2011) How economic methodology became a separate science. Journal of Economic Methodology, 18(2), 163–176.

7. Friedman, M. (1966) [1953] The methodology of positive economics. In Essays In Positive Economics. Chicago, University of Chicago Press, 3-16, 30-43.

8. Hutchison, T.W. (2009) A formative decade: methodological controversy in the1930s. Journal of Economic Methodology 16(3), 297-314.

9. Keynes, J.N. (1999) The Scope and Method of Political Economy. Kitchener: Batoche Books.

10. Lachmann, L.M. (1991) Austrian economics: a hermeneutic approach. In Lavoie, D. (Ed.). Economics and Hermeneutics. New York: Routledge, 132-143.

11. Lavoie, D. (1990) Understanding differently: hermeneutics and the spontaneous order of communicative processes. History of Political Economy 22(annual supplement), 359-377.

12. Lavoie, D. (2011) The interpretive dimension of economics: science, hermeneutics, and praxeology. The Review of Austrian Economics 24(2), 91-128.

13. Lawson, T. (1997) Economics and Reality. London: Routledge.

14. Mäki, U. (2011) Scientific realism as a challenge to economics (and vice versa). Journal of Economic Methodology 18(1), 1-12.

15. McCloskey, D. (1983) The rhetoric of economics. Journal of Economic Literature 21(2), 481-517.

16. McCloskey, D. (1985) The Rhetoric of Economics. Madison: University of Wisconsin Press.

17. Mill, J. S. (1967) [1844] On the definition of political economy; and on the method of investigation proper to it.

In Robson, J.M. (Ed.). Collected Works of John Stuart Mill.
Vol. IV. Toronto: Toronto University Press, 309-339.
18. Popper, C. (1935) Logik der Forschung. [Logic of Scientific
Discovery]. Vien: Springer. [In German].

17.7. Economic ethics in a vice of dichotomies

In economics, ethics is on the rights of Cinderella. It seems
that she should be here, but not be visible. This state of affairs
is far from accidental. It is a consequence of the ideas about the
nature of the economics of some highly respected
methodologists. In this regard, Milton Friedman was extremely
expressive.

Positive economics is in principle independent
of any particular ethical position or normative
judgments. As Keynes says, it deals with "what is,"
not with "what ought to be." Its task is to provide a
system of generalizations that can be used to make
correct predictions about the consequences of any
change in circumstances. Its performance is to be
judged by the precision, scope, and conformity
with experience of the predictions it yields. In
short, positive economics is, or can be, an
"objective" science, in precisely the same sense as
any of the physical sciences. [2, 4]

Economics is understood as a positive science, which is
accompanied by normative economics. The latter is not
scientific, but an applied discipline, a field of manifestation of
the achievements of scientific economics. Scientific economics
is the science of what is, about facts; applied economics is the
theory of what ought to be, about values. Like normative

economics, ethics is also a theory of what ought to be and is guided by value judgments. According to its status, ethics is close not to scientific, but to applied economics. The achievements of positive economics make it possible to explain a lot about the content of not only applied normative economics, but also ethics. [4; 5] It is recognized that some conceptual confusion is characteristic of the relationship between economics and ethics. Nevertheless, this confusion is considered insurmountable. [7]

My position is that this confusion, firstly, is completely avoidable, and secondly, there is a way for giving the scientific economy the ethical aggravation so lacking for it to date. In this regard, it is necessary to abandon the three dichotomies: positive economics / normative economics, facts/values, the theory of what is / the theory of what should be.

The failure of the positive/normative dichotomy

The realization of the potential of theories always occurs in specific situations. In order to correctly judge the nature of theories, all their content should be considered, not depleting it. Scientists often identify common features of situational (special) theories. This approach is formal insofar as the researchers abstract away from certain aspects of phenomena. General theories after their improvement are used in specific situations. Special theories are conceptually richer than general theories; therefore, it is by their content that the nature of some science should be judged. The above fully applies to the economy. Positive microeconomics is a formal general theory that does not represent all the specific features of economic micro-phenomena. Its content does not provide an adequate understanding of microeconomics. The mistake of all supporters of contrasting positive and normative economics consists of absolutizing the status of general microeconomics.

It should resolutely abandon the identification of microeconomics with positive microeconomics. That is what Tony Lawson and Daniel Hausman offered. [8; 3, 95] Both believes that positive economics is economically poor. David Colander and Huei-Chun Su, objecting to Hilary Putnam and John Davis, point out that economists' use of the positive-normative distinction was developed not in the logical positivist, but the pragmatic tradition of Mill-Keynes. «[T]he best way forward is not to eliminate it, but to reposition it within the Mill–Keynes tradition from which it initially developed.» [1, 157]

In my opinion, Colander and Su complicates the situation. The positive-normative distinction does not have a favorable future. It should be clearly stated that the classification of economic theory does not imply its division into positive and normative economics. I also see no need for an addition to economics the art of economics, as Su suggests. [10, 388] The true economic theory is one; it does not need appendages to it.

The failure of the facts/values dichotomy

The facts/values dichotomy was proposed by logical positivists. Facts are fixed in experiments by means of sentences-descriptions, they are objective and do not depend on theories, the bases of which they are. Scientific theories are based on facts. Values are expressed through sentences-prescriptions. From them proceeding, it is possible to construct theories, but they are unscientific, for they are guided not by objective, but by subjective principles and laws. Physical theories and other natural sciences, for example, chemistry, are scientific. All theories about humans with their preferences are unscientific. Such are economics and ethics. Criticism of logical positivism revealed the dependence of facts on theories. This led to the discrediting of the facts/values dichotomy. In this regard, Hilary Putnam behaved especially vigorously. [12] «All statements of fact presuppose one kind of conceptual and theoretical scheme about the world rather than another, and the facts can never fully determine which scheme to choose.» [9, 199-200] «But if the whole idea that there is a *clear* notion of fact collapsed with the hopelessly restrictive empiricist picture that gave rise to it, *what happens to the fact/value dichotomy*?» [9, 30]. It collapses also. It turns out that logical positivists have mistakenly written economics and ethics into the field of unscientific theories.

The reader should keep in mind that in the modern philosophy of science the terms 'fact' and 'value' are used in a different sense than in the framework of fact/value dichotomy. Facts are understood as experimental data, and values are all concepts exclusively of the sciences of man and society, including their inherent facts. From this point of view, economists, and ethicists, but not for example physicists, operate with values.

The failure of the is/ought dichotomy

Hume's problem or Hume's guillotine is the ability to output ought-sentences from is-sentences. [6, 335] Hume believed that only is-sentences are scientific. If the ought-sentences characteristic of ethics is not deducible from is-sentences, then ethics is unscientific. The failure of the fact/value dichotomy evidence the failure of the is/ought dichotomy. [11] This means that the question of the scientific nature of ethics goes beyond the competence of the natural sciences. The same applies to economics. Economists, proving the scientific nature of economics likened it to physics. It turns out that we should take a closer look at the economics itself. The failure of the three considered dichotomies leads precisely to this conclusion.

Economics is scientific because it is guided by the methods of conceptual transduction. Does this conclusion relate to ethics? Should economists perceive ethics as a kind of axiological science, like, for example, medicine and sociology, or its status is some other? In the first case, it would be sufficient to consider the interdisciplinary relations of economics and ethics. Exactly this does the absolute majority of economists. Ethics is relevant along with other axiological sciences, and therefore economists should take into account its findings. Nevertheless, it turns out that they are wrong.

When analyzing various ethical situations, it always turns out that they all have meaning only in the context of a certain theory. This meaning is, for example, economic (while reducing wages of workers), medical (with poor medical care), and pedagogical (abusing students). Ethics is somehow present in the theories themselves. Therefore, it is necessary to establish its actual status. The appeal of economists to ethics is not just a voluntary gesture of educated people who want to expand their area of expertise. It is directly related to the scientific status of economics itself. Since economic ethics is in the economy itself, it is impossible to establish the scientific status of the economy without assigning it to ethics.

The described problem situation is resolved if two ethical principles, namely, the principle of maximizing the prosperity of all stakeholders and the principle of responsibility, are introduced directly into economic theories. I have pointed out the relevance of these principles previously, repeatedly, in particular, when considering technical, agrarian, medical, pedagogical, psychological, and sociological ethics. At this point, I can confine short explanations. The principle of maximizing prosperity is necessary for the implementation of an ethical project as such; it expresses the main content of the ethical project. The principle of responsibility ensures the highest possible level of development of ethical ideas and decisions made.

The introduction directly into the structure of economic theories of ethical principles raises concerns that they violate the consistency of economic principles. However, there is no reason for concern. Having entered into the composition of economic theories, ethical principles appear exclusively in the economic shell. There is not a grain of something uneconomic in them. They lead to a certain subordination of economic principles, leading their pyramid. The subordination of economic principles is not given finally. People change it in accordance with the goals that they seek to achieve. For example, the principle of maximizing sales can dominate the principle of maximizing the profits of entrepreneurs. However, more often, as you know, it is precisely the principle of profit maximization that dominates over other economic principles. In accordance with the ethical orientation of economic theories, it has to give primacy to the principles of maximizing the prosperity of all stakeholders and the principle of responsibility.

My main conclusion is that the essence of ethics lies in every economic theory, and not only, for example, in the theories of welfare and in the moral codes of economic communities. Contrary to Friedman, scientific economic theories are not only not devoid of ethical content, but literally saturated with them. We can only guess at the exceptionally rich content of economic ethics. The disadvantages of economic methodology has led to the neglect of ethics. It is time to extract economic ethics from the methodological dungeon. Its future is entirely determined by an understanding of the nature of scientific economic theories.

References

1. Colander, D. and Su. H.-c. (2015) Making sense of economists' positive-normative distinction. Journal of Economic Methodology 22(2), 157-170.
2. Friedman, M. (1966) [1953] The methodology of positive economics. In Essays in Positive Economics. Chicago, University of Chicago Press, 3-16, 30-43.
3. Hausman, D. (1992) The Inexact and Separate Science of Economics. Cambridge: Cambridge University Press.
4. Hausman, D., and McPherson, M. (1993) Taking ethics seriously: economics and contemporary moral philosophy. Journal of Economic Literature 31(2), 671-731.
5. Hausman, D.M. (2018) The bond between positive and normative economics. Revue d'économie politique 128(2), 191-208.
6. Hume, D. (1738) A Treatise of Human Nature. London: John Noon.
7. Kliemt, H. (2009) Conceptual confusions, ethics and economics. In Brennan, G. and Eusepi, G. (Eds.). The Economics of Ethics and the Ethics of Economics: Values, Markets and the State. Cheltenham: Edward Elgar Pub., 51-72.
8. Lawson, T. (2009) The current economic crisis: its nature and the course of academic economics. Cambridge Journal of Economics, 33(4), 759-777.

9. Putnam, H. (2002) The Collapse of the Fact/Value Dichotomy. Cambridge, MA: Harvard University Press.
10. Su, H.-c. (2012) Beyond the positive-normative dichotomy: some remarks on colander's lost art of economics. Journal of Economic Methodology, 19(4), 375-390.
11. Wolf, A. (2015) Giving up Hume's guillotine. Australasian Journal of Philosophy 93(1), 109-125.
12. Zammito, J.H. (2012) The "last dogma" of positivism: historicist naturalism and the fact/value dichotomy. Journal of the Philosophy of History 6(3), 305-338.

Chapter 18. The nature of political science

18.1. Political science status

The policy is usually understood as activities involved in running a governmental entity or state. In order to judge policy meaningfully, it is necessary to know the relevant theories. In this connection, researchers who turn to political knowledge encounter surprises whose analogs can hardly be found in sociology or economics. At first glance, the state of affairs in the political field might resemble a situation with economic phenomena. Economists consider economics as the scientific theory of the economy. The controversy surrounding economics, its positive and normative aspects, does not question its central position in economic knowledge. In the field of political phenomena, it would seem possible to consider politics as the scientific theory of policy. The researchers chose a different path; they called the scientific theory of politics (policy) political science. Occasionally it is also called politology. However, English-speaking authors, as a rule, consider politology as the whole area of political knowledge. It is the same thing as political theory. We have political philosophy instead of political science. Philosophy equals theory. It is not divorced from politology, being with it in a syncretic unity. Political philosophy is contrasted with political science. [2; 4; 7; 9] As noted by Dennis Chong and James Druckman, the framing of theory can be very strange. [5] In this respect, politics provides, perhaps, one of the most prominent examples: politology = political science vs political philosophy. Nevertheless, despite this oddity, the sources of which will be clarified below, the formation and development of political science was as natural as the corresponding processes in the case of sociology and economics.

Gabriel Almond, considering the development of political science, highlights its three successive stages, namely, the Chicago school, the behavioral approach and the use of logical-mathematical models. [1] The first two stages organically express a positivistic understanding of science, which then passes mainly onto the rails of analytical philosophy, which absorbed the fruitful impulses of logical positivism and critical rationalism. All three social sciences, sociology, economics, and political science pass along the same mainstream: positivism → logical positivism → critical rationalism → analytical philosophy. He is accompanied by contributions from less scientifically oriented philosophies. With regard to political science, they are particularly vividly represented by the works of Hannah Arendt (existentialism), Jürgen Habermas (hermeneutics) and Michel Foucault (poststructuralism).

Almond believes that the process of the development of political science is progressive-eclectic. [1, 51] In my opinion, eclecticism is overcome by a comprehensive review of this process. Another conceptual move by Almond is that he considers a long series of authors, including, in particular, Plato, Aristotle, Machiavelli, Hobbes, Locke, Rousseau, Kant, Hegel and Marx as precursors of political science. I personally, this proposal seems to be quite relevant. Nevertheless, the following circumstance should be considered. Any science can be viewed in two ways with the selection of a decisive event in its history, or without it. In the first case, scientific physics begins with Newton, scientific biology - with Darwin, and scientific economics - with Smith. Galileo, Linnaeus, and Petty are among the forerunners of genuine science. In the second case, they do without highlighting decisive events. Now, for example, not only Galileo, but also Aristotle and Archimedes are recognized not as predecessors of scientific physics, but as full-fledged creators of it. Both points of view are legitimate, but the second is more democratic. According to it, for example, Plato and Aristotle are not predecessors, but representatives of political science. I will immediately consider the question of the legality of enrolling them in the number of representatives not only of philosophy and political science but also of political philosophy.

Plato and Aristotle, as well as, for example, Hobbes and Rousseau, were philosophers and political scientists. They clearly used the philosophical systems created by them for the development of political science. In modern terms, they implemented an interdisciplinary attitude – *philosophy ↔ political science*. At the same time, philosophy, on the one hand, and political science, on the other hand, remained relatively independent branches of science. This means that there is no reason to introduce the idea of philosophical political science or political philosophy as independent theoretical entities. A centaur-shaped term 'political philosophy' in an extremely unfortunate form expresses the presence of interdisciplinary connections between philosophy and political theories. Of course, there are no grounds for identifying 'political philosophy' with 'political theory'. In this context, both of these terms, unlike the term 'political science', are unsuccessful. Therefore, there is no reason to oppose political philosophy to political science. However, there is every reason to welcome in every way the interdisciplinary connections of philosophy and political science. It should be recognized that in this respect a whole galaxy of philosophers, starting with Plato, looks particularly impressive.

The main reason for the popularity of political philosophy is that its representatives successfully implement interdisciplinary connections of philosophy and political science. In this regard, they probably have no equal. Vittorio Bufacchi, fascinated by the book of Brian Barry on Social Justice, concludes that political philosophy matter. [4] His compliment was not sent to the correct address. The fact is that the term 'political philosophy' has no clear meaning. Barry's book demonstrates the success of philosophically oriented political science, not a political philosophy.

It is considered that, in contrast to representatives of political science, representatives of political philosophy do not use the scientific method insofar as they do not conduct experiments. This argument does not hit the point. Representatives of political philosophy themselves really, as a rule, do not conduct experiments. Nevertheless, they are guided by numerous facts known to them from documentary sources. This is enough to reason scientifically, i.e. in accordance with the canons of scientific methods. Thus, in my opinion, opposition to political science and political philosophy is the result not of scientific analysis, but of rhetoric. Ian Shapiro, noting that representatives of political science do not take into account the theoretical loading of observations, draws from this a conclusion in favor of the political theory. [9, 616] Strictly speaking, his argument makes sense only within the framework of political science, so it testifies political science, not its opponents, in particular, political theory.

It is time to turn to the main features of political science. It is usually seen in the phenomenon of power. [6, 7.] «The power of a person or group, in the most general sense, is their ability, as given by particular means in a particular context, to bring about, if desired, future states of the world. » [8, 711] Political science is not meant just to record the phenomenon of power; it must ensure the improvement of its efficiency. In this regard, it is obvious that we are talking about a principle, namely, the principle of improving the efficiency of power. The power principle in the field of social phenomena is omnipresent. This circumstance is rarely paid attention to. Meanwhile, it is of paramount importance for characterizing the nature of political science.

Let me compare the economic principle of profit maximization with the political principle of improving the efficiency of power. The first principle is relevant exclusively in the field of economics. Outside of economics, it is not. The principle of improving the efficiency of power is characteristic of any type of social phenomena, including economic processes. We, of course, usually speak of economic and political processes as if they are independent of each other. Nevertheless, we have no opportunity to distinguish, on the one hand, economic phenomena, and, on the other hand, political phenomena. This means that, unlike the sociology and economics previously discussed, political science is not a basic branch of science, but a superstructure one. It deals with some general and therefore formal features. Within economics, there is no political principle of power, but there is a principle of economic power. Accordingly, in sociology everywhere there is a principle of social, not political power. An extremely common mistake is that political science is taken as a basic branch of science instead of a superstructure.

If political science were a basic branch of science, then its intrinsic internal dynamics would be realized under the auspices of the principle of improving power by the methods of conceptual transduction. This principle is not independent, it is therefore not given to him to form his own separate family of concepts. It is designed to accompany the main principle of the basic branch of science, in particular, economics. In economics, it accompanies, for example, the principle of profit maximization. It is this principle, and not the principle of improving power, that primarily determines the dynamics of economic concepts. Karl Marx, who asserted the primacy of economics over politics, could justify his position by referring to the superstructure nature of political science.

In 1962, Isaiah Berlin asked 'Does the Political Theory Still Exist?' [3] This was not about any, but about scientific political theory. He took it for granted the need to develop precisely political science. In my opinion, his appeal remains valid. Political science took place, but its understanding leaves much to be desired. We need not only a consistent political science, but also a philosophy of political science

References

1. Almond, G.A. (1998) Political science: the history of the discipline. In Goodin, R.E. and Klingemann, H.-D. (Eds.). A New Handbook of Political Science. Oxford: Oxford University Press, 50-96.
2. Ball, T. (2007) Political theory and political science. Can this marriage be saved? *Theoria: a Journal of Social and Political Theory* 54(113), 1-22.
3. Berlin, I. (1962) 'Does political theory still exist?' In Laslett, P. and Runciman, W.G. (Eds.). Philosophy, Politics and Society, second series. Oxford: Blackwell, 1-33.
4. Bufacchi, V. (2008) Why political philosophy matter. European Journal of Political Theory 7 (2), 255-264.
5. Chong, D. and Druckman, J.N. (2007) Framing theory. Annual Review of Political Science 10, 103-126.
6. Goodin, R.E. and Klingemann, H.-D. (1998) Political science: the discipline. In Goodin, R.E. and Klingemann, H.-D. (Eds.).

A New Handbook of Political Science. Oxford: Oxford University Press, 3-49.
7. Grant, R.W. (2002) Political theory, political science, and politics. Political Theory 30(4), 577-595.
8. Lovett, F. (2012) Power. In   Goodin, R.E., Pettit, P. and Pogge, T. (Eds.). A Companion to Contemporary Political Philosophy. Second ed. Vol. I.   Malden, MA; Oxford: Blackwell, 709-718.
9. Shapiro, I. (2002) Problems, methods, and theories in the study of politics, or what's wrong with political science and what to do about it. Political Theory 30(4), 596-619.

18.2. Methodology of political science

Over the past three decades, the methodology of political science has significantly strengthened its position. In order to verify this, it is enough to refer to the popular manuals. [4; 5; 7; 9; 14] Modern political scientists carry out laboratory, field, and natural experiments, implement quantitative, qualitative and mixed research, use mathematical and computer models. All this is done in the context of certain philosophical trends. Political scientists to a significant extent adopted the methodological experience of economists and psychologists. Nevertheless, in spite of all this, they have trouble understanding their own methodological experience. In the most visible way, they are manifested in the popular conception of methodological pluralism. In the past ten years, it has become the hallmark of the methodology of political science. That it is the subject of further discussion.

Donatella delta Porta and Michael Keating distinguish four approaches in the methodology of the social sciences, namely, positivist, post positivist, interpretive and humanistic. Each of them is characterized by a special type of ontology and epistemology [13, 23] and, obviously, methodology. «We believe that social science knowledge is a collective enterprise, built using various techniques, methodologies, and methods. » [12, 316]. Michael Coppedge and David Kuehn distinguish «four methodological 'disruptions' over the past 60 years: the behavioral revolution of statistical methodology; the introduction of formal theory; the sophistication of qualitative, set-theoretic and multi-method research; and the increasing use of experimental methods. » [6, 1] They note that in recent years quantitative and multi-method research has been developing at a particularly fast pace. [6, 1] Amel Ahmed believes that multi-method research brings into dialogue different research traditions. [1].

Multi-method research has been developed in many books. [3; 8; 11; 15] Not always, its content is presented in a distinct form. A pleasant exception to this is the review article of Derek Beach. [2] The arguments presented there deserve special consideration. Beach considers two approaches, a variance-based 'top-down' and a bottom-up, case-based approach. The first approach expresses the mean causal effect, the second - the individual cases. Each approach leaves its opponent in the shadow. There is no way to combine them with each other. Therefore, we should talk about two different methods. This is the main rationale for the relevance and inevitability of multi-method research.

After reading the article by Beach, I was surprised to find the striking similarity of its argumentation to the meaning of intratheoretical transduction. It includes both 'top-down' (deduction) and 'bottom-up' (induction). At the deduction stage, new phenomena (cases) are judged based on a theory that operates with averaged data. Information about cases is predicted, but in the experiment, they are always to some extent not confirmed. Therefore, the prediction does not reach the actual characteristics. Adduction provides information on specific phenomena, but not on those averaged effects, which are indicated by deduction. It seems that after Beach, I must proclaim the triumph of multi-method research, expressing the incommensurability of prediction with its deductive method and data processing carried out by means of an inductive method. What keeps me from this step is the presence, along with deduction and induction of adduction and abduction. Adduction connects deduction with induction; abduction is a transition from induction to deduction. It turns out that 'top-down' and 'bottom-up' are commensurate with each other insofar as they are links in the conceptual transduction cycle. Pluralism of methods really exists, but it is accompanied by their unity. The pluralism of methods without their unity dangerously draws closer to eclecticism. In my opinion, supporters of multi-method research implement intratheoretical transduction, but in a reduced form, ignoring, in fact, abduction. They represent transduction exclusively in the form of reasoning about causal mechanisms. This leads to an underestimation of the relevance of laws and principles, as well as the theoretical position as a whole. As for the inter-theoretical transduction, unfortunately, it is not discussed.

Of particular note is the connection of the methodology of political science with the philosophical directions and philosophy of science. Its comprehension leaves much to be desired. With this circumstance, I associate the desire for analytic eclecticism and, as a result, for theories of the average level. From tradition-bound scholarship, analytic eclecticism differs in its three features. « The first is a broadly pragmatist ethos, whether implied or proclaimed; the second is an effort to formulate problems in a manner that seeks to trace rather than reduce complexity; and the third is the construction of causal stories focused on the complex processes through which different types of mechanisms interact. » [16, 416] As a follower of analytic eclecticism, David Lake states that the Great Debates that took place in international relations did not yield any significant results. In this regard, he proposes steadily to focus on analytic eclecticism. [10] Let me remind readers that the debate took place between idealists and realists, traditionalists and behaviorists, supporters of liberalism and realism, rationalists and reflectivists.

Nowadays, most often talk about the opposition of positivists, post-positivists, critical realists, interpretivists, and constructivists. All of them form a wide range of ideas that are far from useless, but, on the contrary, highly relevant. For their understanding, the program of analytic eclecticism is clearly insufficient. It did not express the following relevant rule for scientific research: when studying a problematic issue, no matter how difficult it was, it should be considered in the context, of firstly, the science to which it relates, secondly, its interdisciplinary connections with other sciences, including philosophy. The methodology of political science does not need eclecticism, in whatever form it is proposed. Its demand for interdisciplinary connections with the philosophy of science is highly relevant. I see nothing wrong with proposing the issue of pluralism and unity of methods of political science as the subject of the next Great Debates. Pluralism without unity is untenable. The methodological unity is provided by the corresponding theory, which unites at first glance disparate formations.

References

1. Ahmed, A. (2019) Multi-methodology research and democratization studies: intellectual bridges among islands of specialization. Democratization 26(1), 97-139.
2. Beach, D. (2018) Multi-method research in the social sciences: a review of recent frameworks and a way forward. Government and Opposition. doi:10.1017/gov.2018.53.
3. Beach, D. and Pedersen, R.B. (2016) Causal Case Studies: Foundations and Guidelines for Comparing, Matching, and Tracing. Ann Arbor: University of Michigan Press.
4. Brady, H.E. and Collier, D. (Eds.). (2010) Rethinking Social Inquiry: Diverse Tools, Shared Standards. Second ed. New York et al.: Rowman and Littlefield.
5. Cappelen, H., Gendler, T.S. and Hawthorne, J. (Eds.) (2016) The Oxford Handbook of Philosophical Methodology. Oxford: Oxford University Press.
6. Coppedge, M., and Kuehn, D. (2019) Introduction: absorbing the four methodological disruptions in democratization research? Democratization 26(1), 1-20,
7. Druckman, J.N., Green, D.R., Kuklinski, J.H., and Lupia, A. (Eds.). (2011) Cambridge Handbook of Experimental Political Science. Cambridge: Cambridge University Press.
8. Goertz, G. (2017) Multimethod Research, Causal Mechanisms, and Case Studies: An Integrated Approach. Princeton: Princeton University Press.
9. Goodin, R.E. and Klingemann. H.-D. (Eds.) (2008) A New Handbook of Political Science. Oxford: Oxford University Press.
10. Lake, D.A. (2013) Theory is dead, long live theory: the end of the great debates and the rise of eclecticism in international relations. European Journal of International Relations 19(3), 567-587.

11. Lieberman, E. S. (2005) Nested Analysis as a Mixed-Method Strategy for Comparative Research. American Political Science Review 99 (3), 435-451.

12. Porta, D. della, and Keating, M (2008) Comparing approaches, methodologies and methods. Some concluding remarks. In Porta, D. della and Keating, M. (Eds.). (2008). Approaches and Methodologies in the Social Sciences: A Pluralist Perspective. Cambridge, New York: Cambridge University Press, 316-322.

13. Porta, D. della, and Keating, M. (2008)   How many approaches in the social sciences? An epistemological introduction. In Porta, D. della and Keating, M. (Eds.). Approaches and Methodologies in the Social Sciences: A Pluralist Perspective. Cambridge, New York: Cambridge University Press, 19-39.

14. Porta, D. della, and Keating, M. (Eds.). (2008) Approaches and Methodologies in the Social Sciences: A Pluralist Perspective. Cambridge, New York: Cambridge University Press.

15. Seawright, J. (2016) Multi-Method Social Science. Cambridge: Cambridge University Press.

16. Sil, R. and Katzenstein, P. J. (2010) Analytic eclecticism in the study of world politics: reconfiguring problems and mechanisms across research traditions. Perspectives on Politics 8(2), 411-431.

18.3. The principle of power

The specificity of political science is determined by the concept of power. Theories, of course, are headed not by separate concepts, but by principles. In this case, we should be talking, in fact, about the principle of power. Due to its relevance, it should obviously be given priority attention. The perennial debates about the nature of the concept of power indicate that it is difficult properly to assess the nature of the principle of power. In my opinion, the right way of understanding the principle of power was described by Leslie Lipson.

> Without power, no government can perform its functions. All political systems, therefore, involve the acquisition and exercise of power. [...]We entrust our government with the power to serve us, while we reserve enough power to impose a limit. This ambivalent relationship which results from creating a power over which we retain control involves a deeper implication. What we are doing in a democracy is to take this phenomenon of raw power - of naked power, if you will - and clothe it in ethical garments. [...] Such is our basic theory. Such are our underlying principles. [10, 1]

It is great that Lipson talks about principles. He considers, in fact, two principles, the principle of power and the principle of democracy. In my opinion, this logic deserves attention. The same applies to his conviction that the principle of power must be under ethical control. More controversial is his idea that the two principles of political science are different in nature. Perhaps it would be more correct to say that both of them are either related or not related to ethics.

In recent years, when considering the nature of power, the concepts of *power over* and *power to* are often addressed. [8; 9; 11; 12] The content of *power over* is closely linked usually to the understanding of power as domination, which is criticized. The true nature of power is related to *power to*, but its content remains a hotly debatable issue. In my opinion, it is closely correlated with the understanding of the principle of power as of the principle of effective management of some social whole. People cannot leave its future to the mercy of fate, so they are forced to rule it. This obligation is relevant; nevertheless, it still leaves in the shadow of an extremely important feature of the power principle, namely, its personified character. Subjects of management are appointed some individuals and social groups of people. In this regard, Mark Haugaard quite legitimately connects the concept of power with the concept of not only democracy but also authority. [5] The one who controls is the subject of power. The origin of power was one of the first to realize Mary Follet: «Group organization is to be the new method in politics, the basis of our future industrial system, the foundation of international order. Group organization will create the new world we are now blindly feeling after, for creative force comes from the group, creative power is evolved through the activity of the group life.» [2] She also noted, «[w]e can confer authority; but power or capacity, no man can give or take». [4, 115] Authentic authority accompanies genuine power, not preceded by it.

The most difficult thing is understanding the principle of power, to determine its place in the composition of the relevant scientific theories. The prevailing view is that it is the principle of power that leads to the conceptual structure of political science. I agree with this position. Nevertheless, it means little if one does not take into account the formal and superstructure nature of political science. Given this circumstance, the principle of power loses its preeminent position. I will demonstrate this circumstance with the example of an interdisciplinary connection between political science and economics. At the same time, it is also necessary to take into account the connection of economics with ethics, which was considered in section 16.7. It explained that a consistent consideration of the ethical factor is carried out by introducing directly into the structure of economic theories of two ethical principles, the principles of maximizing the prosperity of all stakeholders and responsibility.

Directly the specificity of economic theories is expressed most often by the principles of maximizing the profits of entrepreneurs and wages of workers. These two types of maximization are impossible without proper management of economic processes. It is in the connection that the hour of the principle of power comes and behind it of the principle of democracy. I have presented a certain hierarchy of ethical, economic, and political science principles. It is essential that the principles under consideration should follow each other in a certain order. Ethical principles should lead the hierarchy in question; otherwise, there are those costs that are determined by the uncontrolled expansion of the principles of profit growth and the principle of power. Economic principles cannot be lowered below the place that I have defined for them in the hierarchy of principles. Otherwise, the entire analysis will be scholastic. It is only in the light of these principles that the relevance of the appeal to the principle of power becomes clear. In this case, it largely determines the ways of implementing the content of the principles that precede it in the structure of principles. Its content is not autonomous from these principles. If a political scientist does not know the content of ethical and economic principles, then he will not succeed in implementing the principle of power. I demonstrated the content of the principle of power by the example of the relationship of political science with economic theories. Similarly, is the situation at any other interdisciplinary connections of political science. The attempt to get rid of them gives political science a purely speculative character. As a result, the path to understanding the true content of the principle of power is closed.

Above, considering the position of Leslie Lipson, I noted that the content of the principles of power and democracy should be uniform. He attributed democracy to ethics. In fact, it, as well as the principle of power, has no ethical, but political nature. The ethical control of the principle of power ensures the principle of responsibility, according to which every person vested with political rights should be guided in his actions by the most developed theories. This requirement applies among other things to democracy. *Power to* is when a specific social whole is flourishing. It is not enough to say that *power to* is a family resemblance' concept. [8] In this family resemblance, a central content is determined by the place of the principle of power in the structure of the theories to which it belongs.

Among the many projects to rethink the content of the phenomenon of power, special attention was attracted by the ideas of Michael Foucault. Like no other, he expresses the omnipresence of power, in politics, it is not isolated from the world, and it is everywhere. Power imposes its power on organizations and individuals, enforces discipline and order, forms the subjectivity of people. Power as the dominance of some people over others causes a strong protest of Foucault. His analytic of power is directed primarily against the repressive function of power. How to resist her? By the development of freedom of discourses, their release from numerous prohibitions. Criticism of discourses, consideration of their genealogy and problematization is the key to the release of society from violence. Further study needs not only the nature of power in general but also the techniques and tactics of its domination. [3, 102]

The main opponent of Foucault is Jürgen Habermas. [1] He believes that power is «the formation of a *common* will in communication directed toward reaching an agreement» [5, 4] The nature of power is communicative. Power may have a repressive function. However, it does not exist if the discourse is built according to the rules of logic, rhetoric, and dialectics, which constitutes discursive ethics of responsibility. Habermas clearly believes that he, unlike Foucault, had developed a positive program for the development of political science.

In my opinion, the projects of Foucault and Habermas have considerable potential, especially in terms of confronting the uncritical perception of existing political relations. Unfortunately, they have general weakness. Foucault and Habermas speaking on behalf of philosophy, in fact, do not show a special interest in the nature of political science. Its specificity is not taken into account. On the other hand, thanks to them, it became clear that researchers should take into account the interdisciplinary connections of political science with philosophy. Of course, the interdisciplinary connections of political science with all axiological sciences should be equally rigorously studied. This idea is close to the installations of Foucault, who found traces of the concept of power in all areas of human activity.

References

1. Allen, A. (2009) Discourse, power, and subjectivation: the Foucault/Habermas debate reconsidered. Philosophical Forum 40 (1), 1–28.
2. Follet, M.P. (1918) The New State: Group Organization the Solution of Popular Government. London: Longmans, Green.

3. Foucault, M. (1980) Power/Knowledge. Brighton, UK: Harvester.
4. Graham, P. (Eds.). (2003) Mary Parker Follett. Prophet of Management. Washington: Beard Books.
5. Habermas, J. (1977) Hannah Arendt's Communications Concept of Power. Social Research 44(1), 3–24.
6. Haugaard, M. (2010) Democracy, political power, and authority. Social research 77(4), 1049-1074.
7. Haugaard, M. (2010) Power: a 'family resemblance' concept. European Journal of Cultural Studies 13(4), 419-438.
8. Hearn, J. (2014) On the social evolution of power to/over. Journal of Political Power 7(2), 175-191.
9. Karlberg, M. (2005) The power of discourse and the discourse of power: pursuing peace through discourse intervention. International Journal of Peace Studies 10(1), 1-23.
10. Lipson, L. (1989) Power, principles and democracy. Political science 41(2), 1-17.
11. Pansardi, P. (2012) Power to and power over: two distinct concepts of power? Journal of Political Power 5(1), 73-89
12. Shokri, M. (2017). What is political power? (Theory of political consciousness and integrated concept of power). Arts and Social Sciences Journal 8(3), 269.

18.4. The principle of justice

Considering the foundations of political science, of course, due attention should be paid to the principle of justice, especially in connection with the relevance of the theory of justice of John Rawls. [5] As you know, he managed to draw everyone's attention to the concept of justice. On the very first page of the main text of his book, he states « [j]ustice is the first virtue of social institutions, as truth is of systems of thought. »

[5, 3] «The only thing that permits us to acquiesce in an erroneous theory is the lack of a better one; analogously, an injustice is tolerable only when it is necessary to avoid an even greater injustice. Being first virtues of human activities, truth and justice are uncompromising. » [5. 4] According to the explanations of Rawls, the subject of his book is political philosophy. [6, 223]. In this regard, it is reasonable to assume that he, in fact, adheres to the conviction that the first principle of political philosophy is the principle of justice. However, Rawls talks about the theory of justice, and not about political philosophy as a theory. I see in his position a certain inconsistency.

It should be noted that Rawls, in response to the criticism of its many opponents, had repeatedly to clarify the content of his theory. His main clarification was that «the public conception of justice is to be political, not metaphysical» [6, 223]. «It should also be stressed that justice as fairness is not intended as the application of general moral conception to the basic structure of society, as if this structure were simply another case to which that general moral conception is applied». [6, 225] Rawls is tolerant of the content of philosophical and ethical conceptions but emphasizes that it is not crucial for forming a political theory. So, how does the theory of justice come about?

The construction of the theory begins with the intuitive idea of "cooperation between free and equal persons". [6, 231] As rational beings, they realize the ability to form a sense of justice. In this regard, they must make decisions that would not be distorted by unimportant circumstances. «The principles of justice are chosen behind a veil of ignorance. This ensures that no one is advantaged or disadvantaged in the choice of principles by the outcome of natural chance or the contingency of social circumstances. Since all are similarly situated and no one is able to design principles to favor his particular condition, the principles of justice are the result of a fair agreement or bargain. » [5, 11]. The development of a collective decision involves the consent of the negotiators. This consent Rawls calls reflective equilibrium. [5, 18] The outcome of the negotiations are two principles of justice.

«First: each person is to have an equal right to the most extensive scheme of equal basic liberties compatible with a similar scheme of liberties for others.

Second: social and economic inequalities are to be arranged so that they are both (a) reasonably expected to be to everyone's advantage, and (b) attached to positions and offices open to all. » [5, 53]

Such is the theory of Rawls in its most concise form. In my opinion, its main advantage consists in a rather distinct presentation of one of the principles of political science, namely, the principle of justice. Starting from Plato, hundreds of authors, philosophers, and political scientists argued about this principle, but not as convincingly as Rawls did.

What is convincing? The attribution of the principle of justice to the foundations of political science. Whenever the foundations of theory become known, the understanding of the content of the theory gaining clarity. Rawls excelled in understanding the foundations of political science. I give him credit, primarily, to this circumstance. Of course, the Rawls theory is not devoid of numerous weaknesses. One of them, rarely seen, is the attempt to present step by step the process of the emergence of a theory.

Realizing the cycles of conceptual transduction it is possible to show how the theories are improved. Nevertheless, it is impossible to imagine the birth of the first theory in the same systematic mode. Why? Because it is an act of emergence. Rawls tried to express the design of political theory gradually. Because of this striving, he makes a mistake. His 'free and equal persons', being pregnant with the idea of good, in essence, are original products of the principle of justice. They are equal because they are originally representations of the principle of justice. Rawls struggled to avoid metaphysics. Nevertheless, his reasoning about how free and equal persons supposedly, by virtue of these qualities, give rise to the principle of justice, is a vivid example of unrestrained metaphysics.

In characterizing Rawls's theory, his controversy with Jürgen Habermas is often remembered. [3; 7] The dispute between two prominent humanitarians promised a lot, but these hopes were not fully realized. Habermas believed that Rawls shun philosophy; he «hopes to develop political philosophy into a sharply focused discipline and thereby to avoid most of the controversial questions of a more general nature. » [3, 131] These controversial questions were, above all, the design of the original position, the fact of pluralism and the idea of an overlapping consensus. Rawls was not at all ashamed of his philosophical modesty. He, contrary to Habermas, believed that he rightly focused his efforts precisely on political theory. [7, 132] The conversation of the philosopher Habermas and the political scientist Rawls did not clarify decisively the foundations of political science.

Critics of Rawls's theory found many weaknesses in it. In this regard, Richard Arneson reasonably notes that « [f]rom its first elaboration, Rawls's theory of justice has been scrutinized by an

909

enormous amount of criticism. In my view, Rawls's theory has been broken on the rack of this critique. But the upshot is not a defeat for the theory of justice. New suggestions, not yet fully elaborated for the most part, point in a variety of promising, albeit opposed, directions. » [1, 50] As a rule, ways were suggested to improve the principle of justice, and not to abandon it. Indicative in this respect is the criticism of Amartya Sen and John Harsanyi. [4; 8]. They both came from the social choice theory. With all the merits of this theory, it does not properly express the foundations of political theory. [2, 20] It is worth thinking about them, and then the grandeur of the Rawls' project immediately comes to light.

References

1. Arneson, R.J. (2008) Justice after Rawls. In Dryzek, J.S., Honig, B. and Phillips, A. (Eds.). The Oxford Handbook of Political Theory. Oxford: Oxford University Press, 45-64.
2. Boot, M. (2012) The aim of a theory of justice. Ethical Theory and Moral Practice 15(1), 7-21.
3. Habermas, J. (1995) Reconciliation through the public use of reason: remarks on John Rawls's political liberalism. Journal of Philosophy 92(3), 109-131.
4. Harsanyi, J.C. (1975) Can the maximin principle serve as a basis for morality? A critique of John Rawls's theory. The American Political Science Review 69(2), 594-606.
5. Rawls, J. (1999) [1971] A Theory of Justice. Revised Edition. Cambridge, MA: Harvard University Press.
6. Rawls, J. (1985) Justice as fairness: political not metaphysical. Philosophy and Public Affairs 14(3), 223-251.
7. Rawls, J. (1995) Political liberalism: reply to Habermas. The Journal of Philosophy 92(3), 132-180.

8. Sen, A. (2006) What do we want from a theory of justice? Journal of Philosophy 103(5), 215-238

18.5. Why freedom is not a principle

Robert Nozick and Friedrich Hayek subjected Rawls' theory of justice to particularly sharp criticism. In one form or another, they opposed liberty to justice. «Believing with Tocqueville that it is only by being free that people will come to develop and exercise the virtues, capacities, responsibilities, and judgments appropriate to free men, that being free encourages such development, and that current people are not close to being so sunken in corruption as possibly to constitute an extreme exception to this, the voluntary framework is the appropriate one to settle upon. » [9, 328] (Hereinafter I use the terms 'freedom' and 'liberty' as synonyms - V.K.). Nozick did not get tired to speak for liberty and against force. He even regretted that Rawls did not put the principle of natural liberty ahead of the principles of justice. [9, 204] However, Nozick does not make an attempt to present the principle of liberty in a distinct form.

In many respects, the fundamentally different is the position of Hayek, who, according to his opinion, clearly thought out the foundations of political science. Hayek came to a very indicative conclusion.

Liberty not only is a system under which all government action is guided by principles, but it is also not likely to last if this ideal is not itself accepted as the most general principle to be observed in all the particular acts of legislation. Where no such fundamental rule is stubbornly upheld as an ultimate political ideal about which there must be no bartering for material advantages – as an ideal which, even though it may have to be temporarily infringed during a passing emergency, must form the basis of all permanent arrangements – freedom is almost certain to be destroyed by piecemeal encroachments. [3, 240]

At the same place, that is, in the foundations of political science, where Hayek saw the principle of liberty, Rawls approved the principles of justice. There is a clear confrontation between the two conceptual positions. According to Hayek political science starts from the principle of freedom and according to Rawls from the principle of justice. Not surprisingly, Hayek called the idea of social justice a "mirage." [4]. Ultimately, Hayek largely reconciled with Rawls, seeing in him a supporter of liberalism. [7] However, this reconciliation never referred to the legality of replacing the general principle of freedom by the general principle of justice.

The comparison of the positions of Rawls, Hayek, and Nozick clearly indicates a problematic situation. Rawls is guided by the principle of justice. In his theory, there is no principle of freedom. His recognition of people as being free in their decisions cannot be considered a recognition of the relevance of the principle of freedom. Hayek is guided by the principle of freedom, dispensing with the principle of justice. Nozick, unlike Rawls and Hayek, avoids serious discussion about the foundations of political science. The considered problem situation is that there is no answer to the following questions. Are both principles, of justice and freedom relevant, and only one of them? If they are both relevant, what is the relation between them? Before giving a definite answer to this question, I will take a little excursion into the history of the question of the meaning of the concept of freedom.

The founders of liberalism, in particular, Hobbes and Locke, as a rule, did not consider freedom as a principle. An exception to this rule is John Stuart Mill, who in his "On freedom" used the concepts of 'the principle of liberty', 'the principle of individual liberty', and 'the general principle of liberty'. [8, 174, 180, 198] He clearly sought to give the concept of freedom the status of a principle of political theory. This project was not implemented. Mill was not able to explain that not only individuals but also governments should be guided by the principle of freedom. This meant that the concept of freedom in his interpretation did not have the universal character that is inherent in the principles.

An important milestone in understanding the content of the concept of freedom was the article of Isaiah Berlin «Two concepts of liberty». The question is whether individuals are masters of their political life. If they are, then there is a negative concept of freedom. If not, then it is a positive concept of freedom. [1] This conception is most often used in the fight against liberals. As a rule, they themselves adhere to the negative concept of freedom. The liberal concept of freedom of Berlin denies any interference in the behavior of individuals by political institutions. This circumstance attracted the attention of supporters of another understanding of freedom, namely republican. They draw attention to the role of social institutions. These institutions should not dominate, but along with it, they are relevant for strengthening the position of supporters of the concept of freedom. [10; 11] Many researchers believe that the differences between supporters of liberal and republican conceptions of freedom indicate the difficulties of developing the concept of freedom and the need for its further development. [5; 6]

The distinction of negative freedom and positive freedom is not sufficient to resolve the issue of the status of freedom as a principle. Meanwhile, due to its staging, there is a paradox. It consists in the fact that we, on the one hand, value the concept of freedom, on the other hand, it is often violated; however, we do not know how to consistently explain this situation. Alan Carter believes that he resolved this paradox in relation to morality. [2] Help came from the very concept of freedom. Individuals who are guided by the value of freedom must take into account each other's position. In this case, they voluntarily agree with such values that limit individual freedoms. Then they claim not individual freedom, but freedom in general. In my opinion, the paradox under consideration did not receive its permission insofar as the contradiction between the concepts of individual and general freedom remained.

After all this, it is time to present my version of the status of the concept of freedom. It consists in the fact that when discussing the status of the concept of freedom, one should proceed not from metaphysical premises, but achievements of the philosophy of science. The essence of the matter is as follows. In all scientific theories, there are principles whose potential is revealed through intratheoretical transduction. Principles, for example, the principle of least action in physics or the principle of profit maximization in economics, are always represented by concepts that express the specifics of a theory. In the case of the concept of freedom, this requirement is not fulfilled. Therefore, it should be recognized that the concept of freedom is not a principle. However, it also has some status. What is it like? To answer this question, one should find the place of the concept of freedom in intratheoretical transduction. The suggested answer is that the concept of freedom expresses the individual's desire to carry out independently and creatively intratheoretical transduction cycles in the form in which they are characteristic of political science. There is room for creativity here, but, of course, to the extent, that is determined by the state of political science. The demand in the name of political science to be free of it must be attributed to unrestrained metaphysical fantasy.

Now we understand the mistake of Berlin and all those numerous researchers who implemented the program of distinguishing or even identifying the concepts of negative and positive freedom. They, in fact, did not take into account the nature of political theory. The concept of freedom seemed obvious to them in many aspects. However, it was a superficial impression. Otherwise, it was necessary to trace its dynamics in the cycles of conceptual transduction.

Thus, the Rawls vs Hayek dispute is resolved in favor of Rawls. It is legitimate to introduce the principle of justice, but not the principle of freedom. There is no coordination between them since the concept of freedom is not a principle. Both of these circumstances did not attract the attention of Nozick. In the theory of justice of Rawls, there are no principles of freedom and equality. In my opinion, the refusal of Rawls from the principles of freedom and equality is quite legitimate. Their numerous formulations, as a rule, do not properly take into account the specific characteristics of political phenomena. Therefore, they are not genuine scientific principles. In my opinion, the most important mistake of Rawls was to ignore the principle of power. In his absence, it is impossible to single out the specifics of political science. In this case, it is considered something of applied ethics. At the level of principles, the specificity of political science is represented by the subordination - the principle of power → the principle of justice. Of course, it is also necessary not to forget that political science does not exist by itself, but is woven into the content of all axiological sciences.

References

1. Berlin, I. (1958) Two concepts of liberty. In Four Essays on Liberty. Oxford: Oxford University Press, 1979, 118-172.
2. Carter, A. (2003) Morality and freedom. *The Philosophical Quarterly 53(211), 161-180.*
3. Hayek, F.A. (1958) Freedom, reason, and tradition. Ethics 68(4), 229-245.
4. Hayek, F.A. (1976) Law, Legislation and Liberty. Vol. 2. The Mirage of Social Justice. Chicago: University of Chicago Press.
5. Kukathas, C. (2012) Liberty. In Goodin, R.E., Pettit, P. and Pogge, T. (Eds.). A Companion to Contemporary Political Philosophy. Second ed. Vol. I.   Malden, MA; Oxford: Blackwell, 685-698.
6. Larmore, C. (2003) Liberal and republican conceptions of freedom. Critical Review of International Social and Political Philosophy, 6(1), 96-119.
7. Lister, A. (2013) The «Mirage» of Social Justice: Hayek against (and for) Rawls. A Journal of Politics and Society 25(3-4), 409-444,
8. Mill, J.S. (2011) On Liberty London: Walter Scott Publishing Co.
9. Nozick, R. (1974) Anarchy, State, and Utopia. New York: Basic Books.

10. Pettit, P. (1999) A Theory of Freedom and Government. Second Ed. Cambridge: Cambridge University Press.
11. Skinner, O. (1998) Liberty before Liberalism. Cambridge: Cambridge University Press.

18.6. Lessons from critical theory

The concept of the theory, of course, is of paramount importance for political science. In this regard, the concept of critical theory deserves attention, the non-trivial content of which makes it possible to clarify the status of political theory. Max Horkheimer contrasted the concepts of traditional and critical theory with an extensive article. [10] In the "Postscript" to it, he noted

> I pointed out two ways of knowing: one is based on the *Discourse on Method*, the other on Marx's critique of political economy. Theory in the traditional sense established by Descartes and everywhere practiced in the pursuit of the specialized sciences organizes experience in the light of questions, which arise out of life in present-day society. [...] The critical theory of society, on the other hand, has for its object men as producers of their own historical way of life in its totality. The real situations which are the starting-point of science are not regarded simply as data to be verified and to be predicted according to the laws of probability. Every datum depends not on nature alone but also on the power man has over it. Objects, the kind of perception, the questions asked, and the meaning of the answers

all bear witness to human activity and the degree of man's power. [9, 244]

The purpose of the critical theory is not the accumulation of knowledge, not a display of reality as it is. «Its goal is man's emancipation from slavery.» [9, 246] Horkheimer noted that the idea of critical theory is in agreement with the German idealism of Kant and Fichte, i.e. is its natural continuation, which has received not only dialectical but also materialistic expression in the works of Marx.

According to the findings of Fabian Freyenhagen, the program to deploy a critical theory is associated with the fulfillment of the following obligations. [4, 466-476] First, it must be a critical analysis of real social processes with an indispensable focus on the distress of people. Secondly, it is necessary to identify how much it is determined by the existing social structures. Thirdly, conceptual monism should be avoided, because not all social phenomena are described in a uniform way. Fourth, the requirement of pluralism is relevant to the conceptual representation of social pathologies. Fifth, ethical judgments should not be avoided. Who implemented the program for the development of critical theory and how?

Karl Marx, apparently, was the first to introduce a critical theory, namely, through his famous work 'Capital'. He believed that the fundamental substance, abstract labor determines the uniformity of the entire capitalist society. Such an approach is clearly insufficient to represent the entire spectrum of diverse processes of capitalist society. [11]

The joint book of Horkheimer and Adorno "Dialectic of Enlightenment" (1947) is hardly permissible to be considered a full-fledged version of the critical theory. [2] The book is a propedeutic to it. The main idea of the book is that the enlightenment ideal of rationality not only does not close the path to the monstrosities of the 20th century, in particular, National Socialism and World War II, but also, on the contrary, brings them to life.

The book of Theodor Adorno "Negative Dialectics" (1966) is his main philosophical work. [1] Negative dialectics, unlike Hegel's dialectic, negates the synthesis of opposites, which leads to the synthesis of identities. There is a somewhat curious situation. Based largely on Hegel's dialectic, Horkheimer, working closely with Adorno, formulated a program of critical theory. Then, Adorno, proceeding from this program, transformed the dialectic. All these events took place exclusively in the field of metaphysics. Neither Horkheimer nor Adorno managed to create a variant of critical social theory. In this respect, more than others succeeded Jürgen Habermas and Axel Honneth. Their work is especially significant for the fate of social critical theory.

Habermas presented his critical theory project in the two-volume edition «The Theory of Communicative Action». [5] The decisive course of his thought was that avoiding the detrimental effects of the traditional mind, one should form rationality in a mature discourse. It promotes both individualization and solidarity. «From this point of view, characteristical social pathologies may be explained as disruptions of a communicatively mediated social integration. Since the issue, then, is the analysis of patterns of systematically distorted communication, philosophy can no longer solve the problem on its own. » [6, 441] In this regard, the social sciences are connected to philosophy. However, this is done somehow timidly. Habermas constantly balances on the border of philosophy and social sciences. In this case, guidelines come from philosophy.

Axel Honneth along with Habermas made a particularly great contribution to the development of the concept of critical theory. He presents her main question in a very distinct form.

> The idea that human beings have a deep-seated interest in overcoming dependencies and heteronomy has always been a hallmark of the tradition of critical social theory deriving from Marx. Some of the Left Hegelians already held that in the absence of such an emancipatory interest on the part of the entire species, the demand for social progress would remain a merely moral "ought," lacking any support in historical reality. [7, 908]

The main merit of Honneth is the development of the theory of recognition. [8] Unlike Habermas, he is primarily interested in the fate of individuals fighting for their recognition. They are the starting point of everything else, including rationality and language. Based on this link, Honneth explains the phenomena of practice, knowledge, rationality, justice, and morality. All of them turn out to be as contradictory as the subjects, which fight for their recognition. Marco Angella has shown well how Honneth has been developing the theory of recognition for a dozen years, expanding the scope of its applicability. [3] Honneth does not doubt the need for critical theory to the extent that, as in society today, as before, critical theory expresses emancipatory interest. [7] Of course, there is no lack of criticism of the theory of Honneth. In this place, I am interested not so much in criticism of individual variants of the critical theory, as in the consistency of this theory as a whole.

In my opinion, the main misfortune of the representatives of the critical theory is that they oppose their normative guidelines with a non-scientific, traditional theory. They are not fully aware of the fundamental difference between a truly scientific theory and the image of a scientific theory, which they are guided. In order to have an adequate understanding of social scientific theory, it is necessary to carry out significant work on the understanding of these, including political theories. This is a metascientific assessment of the status of social theories. As far as I know, the supporters of the critical theory project did not develop such an assessment. As a result, they cannot get out of the snares of metaphysics, which prescribes its canons to the special social sciences, without properly taking into account their content. In this regard, you can point to the scandalous history of Hegel's dialectical method. All prominent representatives of the critical theory, including Marx, Habermas, and Honneth, are guided by him, but none of them gave any detailed scientific assessment of his viability, and it should be negative. In my opinion, the main lesson in the development of a critical theory project is the conclusion that insensitivity to the philosophy of social sciences, including political science, isolates researchers from science. It has a detrimental effect even on prominent thinkers, which, no doubt, are Habermas and Honneth. Each of them united the ideas of hundreds of researchers, which allowed them in many ways, even contrary to the project of critical theory, to join political science.

References

1. Adorno, T.W. (1990) [1966] Negative Dialectics. London: Routledge.

2. Adorno, T.W. and Horkheimer, M. (2002) [1947] Dialectic of Enlightenment. Trans. by E. Jephcott. Stanford: Stanford University Press.

3. Angella, M. (2018) On the consistency of Axel Honneth's critical theory: methodology, critique, and current struggles for recognition. Philosophical Forum 49 (4), 483-509.

4. Freyenhagen, F. (2017) Was ist kritische Theorie? [What is orthodox critical theory?] Deutsche Zeitschrift für Philosophie 65(3), 456-469. [In German].

5. Habermas, J. (1981, 1984) The Theory of Communicative Action, vols. 1 and 2. Boston: Beacon Press.

6. Habermas, J. (1999) Hermeneutic and analytic philosophy. Two complementary versions of the linguistic turn? Royal Institute of Philosophy Supplement 44, 413-441.

7. Honneth, A. (2017) Is there an emancipatory interest? An attempt to answer critical theory's most fundamental question. European Journal of Philosophy 25(4), 908-920.

8. Honneth, A. (1995) [1992]) The Struggle for Recognition: The Moral Grammar of Social Conflicts. Cambridge, Massachusetts: The MIT Press.

9. Horkheimer, M. (2002) [1937]. Postscript. In Horkheimer, M. Critical Theory. Selected Essays. New York: Continuum, 244-252.

10. Horkheimer, M. (2002) [1937]. Traditional and critical theory. In Horkheimer, M. Critical Theory. Selected Essays. New York: Continuum, 188-243.

11. Postone, M. (1993) Time, Labor, and Social Domination: A reinterpretation of Marx's critical theory. Cambridge: Cambridge University Press.

18.7. Political science and ethics

In all axiological theories, the same situation is observed; researchers in determining their status encounter considerable difficulties in establishing the relationship of these theories with ethics. It seems that ethics is needed to give theories proper moral weight, usually highly valued in society. On the other hand, it seems you can do without ethics. The first impression is that the relationship between axiological theory and ethics is marked by the unbiased ambivalence print. This circumstance with reference to political philosophy has alarmed Bernard Williams.

Given his qualifications, from him should have been expected propaganda of the relevance of ethics for the political philosophy. Contrary to expectations, he focused on the possibilities and relevance of political realism as opposed to political moralism as teaching that exaggerates the importance of ethics for political philosophy. His main argument was that the legitimation of the problematic issues of political philosophy in relation to specific situations is achieved through the age-old political concepts, such as, for example, power. [6, 4-6] It is interesting that Williams chose Rawls as the main representative of political moralism. [6, 1] There were certain grounds for this choice. However, Rawls's commitment to political moralism is ambiguous. I will cite two quotes that unequivocally indicate this ambiguity.

While a political conception of justice is, of course, a moral conception, it is a moral conception worked out for a specific kind of subject, nimby, for political, social, and economic constitutions. [3, 224]

It should also be stressed that justice as fairness is not intended as the application of general moral conception to the basic structure of society, as if this structure were simply another case to which that general moral conception is applied. In this respect justice as farness differs from traditional moral doctrines, for these are widely regarded as such general conceptions. Utilitarianism is a familiar example [...] The essential point is this: as a practical political matter no general moral conception can provide a publicly recognized bases for a conception of justice in a modern democratic states. [3, 225]

A supporter of political realism, or, as I would say political ethical minimalism, may well agree with the second, but not with the first quote. It is not clear why the «conception of justice is, of course, a moral conception», and why it applies not only to political but also to social and economic constitutions. A supporter of political realism, obviously, considers it a purely political, and not some other, conception.

Williams compares its position also with the theory of Habermas. He approves of his attempts to legitimize political philosophy through discursive technique, but not about his rapprochement with Kant's ethics. [6, 9-10]

At this point, I refrain from a detailed description of the positions of Rawls and Habermas, which, in my opinion, did not present the correlation of political science and ethics in a sufficiently distinct form. This circumstance is another evidence in favor of Williams' distinction between political moralism and political realism. His comprehension opens the way to understanding the positions of individual authors, including Rawls and Habermas.

Let me state my position about the relationship between political science and ethics. First, I note that one should clearly distinguish between metaphysical and scientific ethics, as well as political science and political philosophy. Williams, judging by the terminology he used, considered the relationship between metaphysical ethics and political philosophy. Both of these disciplines are so loaded with metaphysical and, therefore, arbitrary components, that it is hardly possible to express their correlation in a clear way. Such an opportunity opens up only if they are transferred to scientific rails. In this case, of course, I will not do this. Thus, my attention is drawn to scientific ethics and political science.

The next actual situation is that, along with political, economic, medical, psychological, there are no special ethical phenomena. If they were, then ethics would be as independent as, for example, economics and political science. As a result, the relationship between political science and ethics would have to be considered as a special type of interdisciplinary relationship. However, as it turned out, this is not necessary.

Not being a separate science, existing in the same status as, for example, economics and political science, ethics, nevertheless, in a sense, is also a relatively independent entity. It cannot have another status as being a generalization of certain features of the axiological sciences, including political science. Which ones? Two principles that give axiological sciences ethical specificity. I have repeatedly called these principles. It is about the principles of maximizing the prosperity of all stakeholders and the principle of responsibility. Thus, scientific ethics is an expression of the general ethical features of the axiological sciences. In this capacity, it is a formal discipline.

Having determined the status of ethics as a formal discipline, I can pose two important questions. The first question is can ethics bring political science to life? The second question: does the ethically oriented component of political science contradict purely political content of this theory?

Obviously, the first question has a negative answer. As a formal discipline, ethics does not express the specifics of any axiological science, including political science. The formal does not give rise to the specific; the specific is not applied to the formal. Just as physics is not applied mathematics, political science is not applied ethics.

The second question is directly related to the distinction between political moralism and realism. Why did ethical-oriented principles appear in political science? Do they not contradict other political principles? They did not appear by chance, but by virtue of the development of political science itself. In the absence of these principles, political science leads to numerous atrocities so characteristic, for example, of dictatorial and authoritarian regimes. Thus, political science without ethically oriented scientific principles is untenable.

Does political science need ethics? Yes, need, because political science presents the achievements of all axiological sciences. If political scientists were not interested in these achievements, they would largely lose contact with other axiological sciences. The development of knowledge includes constant transitions from the specific to the formal and vice versa, from the formal to the specific. Such transitions take place in the case of a relationship between political science and ethics. Thus, political science should contain ethically oriented principles; there is nothing in it that is non-political in nature.

What does the Williams distinction of political moralism / political realism look like in the light of the above? Political realism rightly raises the question of the purity of political science, the absence of non-political components in it.

Nevertheless, at the same time, its ethically oriented principles and the connection of political science with ethics are forgotten. In political moralism, in the name of the metaphysical systems alien content is imposed on political science. In my opinion, this circumstance was of decisive importance in defending by Williams of political realism. The weakest point in his conception is his uncritical perception of metaphysical ethics and political philosophy.

Scientific ethics are also not mentioned in the works of Rawls and Habermas. In my opinion, it is hardly legitimate to accuse Rawls of dragging into political science an ethical content alien to it. In his theory of justice, he was guided not by the ethics of duty or utilitarianism, but by the idea he developed about the initial state, the participants of which own the techniques of analytical analysis.

Habermas, in fact, does without traditional ethical systems. He believes that in an ideal discourse an ethic of responsibility is developed. The trouble is that it is weakly consistent with scientific canons. I am inclined to believe that Williams, Rawls, and Habermas basically do without the philosophy of political science. As a result, the relationship of political science with ethics does not receive a clear expression.

Thus, I presented my concept of assessing the strengths and weaknesses of political moralism and political realism. It is reasonable to compare it with other concepts of a similar focus.

Matt Sleat claims that Williams was unable to implement his program in such a way as to present in a new realistic form the content of liberalism. [4] I agree with this position. In contrast to Sleat, I see Williams failing in the absence of a thorough metascientific analysis of the content of liberal theories. I also agree with Cristina Voinea, who notes that in his program of developing political realism, Williams made no concessions to political moralism. [5]

David Estlund, dissatisfied with the position of supporters of political realism, comes to the defense of methodological moralism. He examines the fundamental principles of political realism and argues that they all «even if they were correct, would raise any difficulty for the thesis that political arrangements are subject to moral standards of what is right or just». [1, 365] The basis of this position is the fact that no one is able to give a clear definition of the content of morality and political philosophy. As a result, various kinds of doubts are legitimate regarding the correlation between morality and political philosophy. But it is unlawful to deny «the whole moralized framework of social justice and injustice, as many authors do [...] ». [1, 376] Estlund's conclusions are irrefutable if speaking from positions of metaphysical ethics and political philosophy. If we move to the positions of scientific ethics and political science, then the arguments about their correlation acquire quite a clear meaning. Then it turns out that there is no need for methodological moralism.

Sebastian Nye believes that supporters of political realism and moralism should be guided by metaethical arguments. For supporters of political realism, it is advisable to deny the reliability of the fact/value dichotomy and the possibility of a priori justification of political values and principles. The position of supporters of political moralism should be the exact opposite. [2, 99] In my opinion, these recommendations are unsuccessful. The fact is that meta-ethics in its modern form is a theory of metaphysical ethics, not scientific. In the context of the embryonic state of scientific ethics, the conclusions of metaethics are not commendable. It is also necessary to take into account that the entire project of distinction of political moralism and political realism was started to clarify the nature of political science, and not ethics. In this connection, meta-political science is of primary interest. The appeal to her highlights the content of all major controversial issues concerning the relationship between political science and ethics.

The controversy of supporters of political moralism and realism once again convinces us that the task of developing a coherent philosophy of political science is urgent. This conclusion applies to the chapter as a whole.

References

1. Estlund, D. (2017) Methodological moralism in political philosophy. Critical Review of International Social and Political Philosophy 20(3), 365-379.
2. Nye, S. (2015) Real politics and metaethical baggage. Ethical Theory and Moral Practice 18(5), 1083-1100.
3. Rawls, J. (1985) Justice as fairness: political not metaphysical. Philosophy and Public Affairs 14(3), 223-251.
4. Sleat, M. (2010) Bernard Williams and the possibility of a realist political theory. European Journal of Political Theory 9(4), 485-503.
5. Voinea, C. (2016) A realist critique of moralism in politics. The autonomy of Bernard Williams's basic legitimation demand. Public Reason 7(1-2), 81-92.
6. Williams, B. (2005) In the Beginning Was the Deed: Realism and Moralism in Political Argument. Ed. by Hawthorn, G. Princeton: Princeton University Press.

Chapter 19. The nature of law

19.1. Foundations of legal theory

It is time to turn to the foundations of law as a branch of science. As it turns out below, there is reason to believe that law in its content is closest to political science. In this regard, it is reasonable to consider law right after political science. Any branch of science consists of related theories. The same is true for law. It follows that a clarification of the nature of law presupposes, first, a definition of the nature of legal theory. There are so many concepts about this theory. Everyone who addresses them directly runs the risk of getting lost in their wilds. Avoiding this fate, I will present the structure of the principles of axiological social substantive theories, i.e. theories whose concepts are values or norms (if values are approved by some authority).

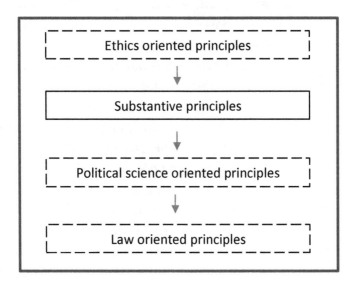

I believe it will be not difficult for the reader to understand the meaning of Figure 19.1. Earlier, I repeatedly explained that there are no ethical and political phenomena as such. Ethical and political theories are justified only insofar as researchers mentally isolate from the field of some substantive theories, for example, economic and social conceptions, their similarities. Thanks to their isolation, it seems that the ethical and political phenomena represented by the relevant theories exist independently. However, this view is erroneous. As for legal phenomena, they, like ethical and political phenomena, also do not exist on their own. This means that the principles of legal theories should be sought as part of substantive theories. Let me explain this fact by the example of economic theories. In the composition of theories, principles are especially significant concepts; therefore, I characterize theories by principles.

The specificity of economic theories is most often expressed by the principles of profit and wage growth. As previously explained, ethics is represented by the principles of prosperity growth of all stakeholders and political science by the principles of power and justice. In accordance with my research, the basic principle of law is the principle of growth of the permissible. The narrowing of the permitted area usually leads to an increase in repressive factors, which causes quite reasonable criticism. Of course, the permissible cannot be arbitrary. This is clear insofar as any law-oriented principle is under the auspices of substantive principles. The economist approves the law to ensure the implementation of effective substantive principles. Any other variant of the law is considered defective. Thus, the law is a set of theories, the general feature of which is the principle of growth of the permissible. The permissible cannot be arbitrarily determined; for its constitution, a scientific theory is needed.

Any axiological scientific theory operates with the concepts of humans, principles, laws, and variables. These concepts are also inherent in legal theories. The humans of legal theories are individuals and organizations. The description of these theories uses specific terminology regarding the designation of laws and variables. Laws are called rules (and often norms), and variables are called rights (including liberties). Thus, the law is a set of theories representing the dynamics of the principle of growth of the permissible, rules and rights of humans.

When discussing the nature of law, they usually pay particular attention to the origin of it and its relationship with morality. [6] There is no doubt that throughout the history of humankind, the law has been changed by people. Therefore, it is constructed in a certain way. In asserting this, it should be borne in mind that scientists represent a mechanism for changing the law, but not its initial occurrence. It is reasonable to consider that this occurrence was a spontaneous emergent act. As regards the issue of the relationship between law and morality, it is considered particularly relevant. About it, a sharp controversy erupted between two prominent jurists Herbert Hart and Ronald Dworkin.

Hart argued that, contrary to Dworkin, legal theory is «both descriptive and general» and not «in part evaluative and justificatory». [5, 240] He admitted the legitimacy of interpreting the law as normative, interpretive or evaluative theory, believing, however, that in this case the canons of the scientific impartial approach are violated. Disagreeing with this approach, Dworkin noted that Hart fixes only the «abstract part of legal argument». [2, 2098] In my opinion, both were largely right. Therefore, each of them had reason to persist in their position. Let me comment on the positions of Hart and Dworkin.

based on the understanding of the structure of the axiological social theory.

Hart, in fact, focuses on that part of the axiological social theory, which has a legal orientation. If a researcher characterizes exclusively law, then this is correct. However, there are two weaknesses in his position. First, he clearly distances himself from axiological theories as such. Secondly, he is at odds with the principles of law. This is clearly an erroneous position. Dworkin, reproaching Hart that he is limited to considering the abstract part of the law. Hart really uses only part of the theory, but not of law, of substantive conception. Hart, refusing to include morality in law, is right. [4] However, he clearly underestimated the relevance of ethics. Dworkin takes into account the completeness and integrity of axiological social theories. It is right. Unfortunately, he absolutizes law, in essence, identifying it with a whole set of theories, including political science and ethics. Dworkin includes ethics in law, and yet there is no place for it. He pays great attention to principles. This circumstance distinguishes him from Hart. The trouble is that he does not mention the basic principle of law, the principle of growth of the permissible. Dworkin often mistakenly equates the principles of law with the principles of political science, primarily with the principle of justice.

A comparison of the positions of Hart and Dworkin shows that law is an axiological science, as the principle of growth of what is permissible is a value. There is no reason to consider this principle as a descriptive concept. It represents the fullness of the legal activities of people. I examined the nature of law from the perspective of the theory of conceptual transduction. Of course, it is also advisable to consider other approaches to characterizing the nature of law.

John Finnis, characterizing law and the philosophy of law, speaks on behalf of natural law theory. «Since "natural law," in the present context, has the same reference as "the normative principles and standards of ethics and politics" (or "normative political philosophy"), everything said so far in this article is a piece of natural law theory. » [3, 137-138] «The philosophy of law is not separate from ethics and political philosophy, but dependent upon them. » [3, 133] As you can see, Finnis incorporates the philosophy of law into the unity that political science and ethics form. In reality, the philosophy of law, and therefore the law, is separated from political science and ethics. Three entities, ethics, political science, and law have different contents. In order to find out the type of dependence of law, political science and ethics from each other, one should carefully study those conceptual transitions that take place inside axiological theories. Of course, law depends on ethics and political science, but above all, on substantive axiological science. Finnis, in fact, seeks to consider a whole, whose parts are ethics, political science and law. This whole is supposedly a natural law theory. I believe that in this context, natural law theory is a metaphysical attempt to express the content of the philosophy of substantive social sciences.

Quite informative about the nature of law argued Robert Alexy.

The arguments addressed to the question of the nature of law revolve around three problems. The first problem addresses the question: In what kinds of entities does the law cosmists, and how are these entities connected such that they form the overarching entity we call «law»? The answer is that law consists of norms as meaning contents, which form a normative system. The second problem addresses the question of how norms as meaning contents are connected with real world. This connection can be grasped be means of the concepts of authoritative issuance and social efficacy. The latter includes the concept of coercion of force. The third problem addresses the correctness of legitimacy of law, and, by this the relationship between law and morality. To ask about the nature of law is to ask about necessary relations between the concepts of normative meaning, authoritative issuance as well as social efficacy, and correctness of content. [1, 156]

I completely agree with this position, but with one significant addition. The answers to the question «What is the nature of law? » which are developed in the field of legal philosophy are the result of a thorough analysis of the content of substantive social sciences. Of decisive importance is precisely the nature of these sciences and not the connection of law with political science and ethics. Law in itself is not a substantive axiological, but a formal and superstructure science.

References

1. Alexy, R. (2004) The nature of legal philosophy. Ratio Juris 17(2), 156-167.
2. Dworkin, R. (2017) Hart's posthumous reply. Harvard Law Review 130(8), 2096-2130.
3. Finnis, J. (2014) What is the philosophy of law? The American Journal of Jurisprudence 59(2), 133–142.
4. Hart, H.L.A. (1958) Positivism and the separation of law and morals. Harvard Law Review 71(4), 593–629.

5. Hart, H.L.A. (1994) The Concept of Law. Second ed. Ed. by P. Bulloch and J. Raz. Oxford: Oxford University Press.
6. Marmor, A. (2012) The nature of law: An introduction. In Marmor, A. (Ed.). The Routledge Companion to Philosophy of Law. New York and London: Routledge, 3-15.

19.2. The methodology of law does matter

The previous section examined the nature of legal theory. Some of its aspects were left without due attention. I mean, first, the dynamics of the concepts of the theory. These dynamics are clarified in the methodology, so it is time to turn to it directly. I have done something like that many times throughout this book. As applied to all sciences, it turned out that the dynamics of concepts act as intratheoretical conceptual transduction. In this regard, it is reasonable to assume that the methodological content of the law is similar, in particular, to the similar content of political science expressed in conceptual transduction. I remind the reader that the four methods of intratheoretical transduction are deduction, adduction, induction, and abduction. There is every reason to believe that all these methods are characteristic of law.

Like the state of affairs in economics, sociology and political science, in the law observations are carried out, and various experiments, in particular, laboratory and field ones, as well as quantitative, qualitative and mixed. [1; 6] There is no doubt that the mechanism of intratheoretical transduction is implemented together with experiments. However, intratheoretical transduction methods, as a rule, are not called. Usually, as Denis Galligan does, an empirical method of investigation is mentioned. «The method of empirical research is: to pose questions about an aspect of law; to gather evidence; to interpret the evidence; and then draw conclusions. » [4, 980] It is not difficult for a reader who is familiar with the conception of intratheoretical transduction to find that the cited text organically corresponds to the content of this transduction. Let me state that the scientific methodology of law has taken place. Unfortunately, I must immediately note that awareness of this circumstance is carried out with great difficulty. In this sense, the following statement by Galligan is very characteristic.

> There are two main ways legal theory could be relevant to empirical research: one would be the use of empirical research to test the factual basis on which theories are based, the other to rely on the ideas and concepts of legal theory in framing questions for empirical research. Empirical research has not embraced legal theory in either way. Researchers have not seen legal theory as a source of research questions and it is hard to find examples of its tenets being directly examined empirically. [4, 982]

Denis Galligan is an exceptionally thoughtful author. However, he makes a strange statement that «[e]mpirical research has not embraced legal theory in either way.» What theory did he mean? From the context of his article, it is clear that he was referring to the famous Hart theory set forth in his book, The Concept of Law. [5] Researchers, not being soulless automata, were of course guided by some theory. Designing an experiment, its implementation, processing the results of observations and experiments, drawing conclusions is nothing more than a legal theory in action. Researchers were guided by their theories, but not Hart's theory. Obviously, this state of affairs is not accidental. Hart's theory seemed to them divorced from life. This circumstance indicates some fundamental difficulty that remains to be clarified.

Many authoritative authors, determining the nature of the legal methodology, invariably turn, first, to Hart's theory. Obviously, they proceed from the correct assumption about the necessity of correlation of methodology and theory. Of course, it requires proper reflection. Many authors believe that since Hart's theory, performed by its founder, had no empirical justification, the proposed scientific standard is not valid. This position is vigorously advocated by Brian Leiter. [8, 183-199; 7, 679] He even believes, what is in my opinion very risky, that we are talking about the concept of "which is the methodology of almost all legal philosophy these days". [7, 679] The conception of Leiter is most often criticized by those authors who, in their work, continue the Hart tradition, in particular, Julie Dickson. [2; 3]

> My own view of jurisprudence is more informed by the thought that there may be many different types of inquiry which can yield knowledge of different aspects of the multifaceted phenomenon that is law, and that it is likely that there are several different routes, and combinations of routes, to such knowledge. For example, in some recent work, I have suggested that jurisprudential inquiry must investigate both issues concerning the social reality or 'social fact-ness' of law, and issues concerning the ideals to which law aspires, and any overall moral purpose it may have in virtue of its nature, and that focussing on only one of these lines of inquiry at the expense of the other is a weakness and not a strength of certain theories of

law. [...] I am also open to the idea of empirical inquiries of various kinds being potentially able to assist with jurisprudential inquiry, and would also support the view that valuable jurisprudential work remains to be done as regards law's contingent properties as well as any essential properties it has. [3, 496-497]

I also mention the position of Aaron Rappaport. He identified four methods, namely, intuitive, empirical, categorical, and contingent analysis, and concluded that each of them cannot be considered the main method of the law. Not the search for the main method should be put at the center of the methodological work but the resolution of topical regulatory issues through the rational reconstruction of all methods.

Rational reconstruction offers a plausible method for doing legal theory, but it may not be the only candidate worthy of consideration. The point here is not to demonstrate that one methodology is the correct one. Rather, it is to challenge legal theorists to rethink their traditional commitment to conceptual analysis and to encourage further debate on the proper methodology of jurisprudence. [9, 106]

From the standpoint of the theory of conceptual transduction, three authors Leiter, Dickson, and Rappaport do not take into account the most important circumstance, namely, the methodological achievements already achieved in modern science. I mean, first, cycles of conceptual transduction. Leiter offers a program of naturalizing of jurisprudence. This appeal is certainly relevant to all friends of science. Nevertheless, in itself, without the methods of conceptual transduction, it is insufficient. Since the time of Charles Sanders Peirce, methods of deduction, induction, and abduction have been known. No one has proven their fallacy. Why not to consider them as methods of legal research?

Julie Dickson has proclaimed many different types of inquiry. This sounds in tune with our age of pluralism, which does not tolerate prohibitions and restrictions. There are many methods. However, the fact is that they are interconnected with each other, not in an arbitrary way. By cycles of conceptual transduction, we present the dynamics of theories. Refusing the methods of conceptual transduction, we lose these dynamics from view.

Aaron Rappaport, like Leiter and Dickson, searches for relevant scientific methods without taking into account the centuries-old tradition of Aristotle-Bacon-Mill-Peirce. He believes that the diversity of regulatory issues specific to law forces to implement some version of the reconstruction of known methods for their resolution. Rappaport is unable to characterize these options in detail. In fact, any of the most complex issues are resolved in a very definite way. It is embedded in cycles of conceptual transduction. This is not difficult to comprehend. There is no other way to understand a certain issue than its inclusion in theory, for without theory there is no understanding. If this is done, then this issue itself begins to bear the imprint of all stages of conceptual transduction. The more stages of conceptual transduction it goes through, the more thoroughly its understanding.

Unfortunately, modern legal methodology clearly does not pay enough attention to the principle of theoretical representation. Every now and then, arguments about legal practice are presented as if one could judge It without regard to theory. Researchers who give due weight to theories run the risk of being called an armchair philosopher far from legal practice. This is a clearly outdated understanding of the nature of legal theory. The modern legal methodology is in urgent need of not only naturalizing but also theorizing. As a scientific phenomenon, it has largely taken place. This circumstance is hardly recognized because the organic unity of legal theories with experiment-oriented research is artificially torn. The banal statement is that the law differs from other branches of science, in particular, sociology and economics, and, therefore, this difference should be taken into account in legal methodology. It, of course, is. However, there are also significant similarities between law, economics, sociology and political science. In my opinion, this circumstance allows lawyers to take advantage of the development of the legal methodology into account of the achievements of other social sciences.

References

1. Cane, P. and Kritzer, H.M. (Eds.). (2010) The Oxford Handbook of Empirical Legal Research. Oxford and New York: Oxford University Press.
2. Dickson, J. (2004) Methodology in jurisprudence: a critical survey. Legal Theory 10(3), 117–156.
3. Dickson, J. (2011) On naturalizing jurisprudence: some comments on Brian Leiter's view of what jurisprudence should become. Law and Philosophy 30(4), 477-497.
4. Galligan, D.J. (2010). Legal theory and empirical research. In Cane, P. and Kritzer, H.M. (Eds.). The Oxford Handbook of Empirical Legal Research. Oxford and New York: Oxford University Press, 976-1001.

5. Hart, H.L.A. (1994) The Concept of Law. Second ed. Ed. by J. Raz and P. Bullock. Oxford: Clarendon Press.
6. Hoecke, M. van. (2011) (Ed.). Methodologies of Legal Research. Oxford and Portland, Oregon: Hart Publication.
7. Langlinais, A. and Leiter, B. (2016) The methodology of legal philosophy. In Cappelen, H., Gendler, T.S. and Hawthorne, J. (Eds.). The Oxford Handbook of Philosophical Methodology. Oxford: Oxford University Press, 671-689.
8. Leiter, B. (2007) Naturalizing Jurisprudence. Oxford: Oxford University Press.
9. Rappaport, A.J. (2014) On the conceptual confusions of jurisprudence. Washington University Jurisprudence Review 7(1), 77-106.

19.3. Evidence

The problem of evidence has gained particular importance in law. Every day the fate of thousands of people depends on court decisions, the quality of which is determined primarily by the content of the evidence. Of course, they are associated with many problems, some of which will be considered in the future. Modern law is mainly focused on the achievements of science. Therefore, jurists strive to conduct evidence operations at the proper scientific level. However, this is extremely difficult to do, primarily because of the superficial acquaintance of many researchers with the theory of conceptual transduction. Its content is crucial in understanding the essence of evidence. Scientific evidence is implemented by cycles of conceptual transduction. Something is proved if it is embedded in scientifically sound cycles of conceptual transduction. This crucial circumstance is usually underestimated. It is significant that the evidence includes all stages of conceptual transduction, in particular, experiment. The evidence is not reduced, for example, to the deduction. I recall in this connection that the intratheoretical transduction is not limited to its deductive stage.

The most common mistake is completely to ignore the superstructural nature of law. This means that legal evidence is not completely autonomous it is involved in the cycles of conceptual transduction of substantive sciences. As applied, for example, to economics, this means that its legal aspects are realized in cycles of economic conceptual transduction. It is in them that it becomes clear what is permitted in the economy and to what extent, whether, for example, the resale of goods is a crime.

How to distinguish and understand the legal part of the cycles of conceptual transduction? Obviously, this can be done solely through the operation of abstraction. Lawyers do not realize it, because they, as a rule, implement evidence bypassing the theory of conceptual transduction. As a result, some common notion of legal theory is applied to practical situations. Theory acts as some kind of procedural specific history, in which a combination of facts and rules is realized. An exemplary legal theory, approved by a certain authority, first of all, by the state, abstracts from procedural histories. It determines their invariant part in the form of the need to evaluate facts through rules. Deviation from these rules is crucial in determining what is permitted and not permitted. In accordance with rules, legal decisions are made. As a result, a conflict is generated between the two theories, exemplary (institutional) and situational.

In the issue, the impression is recognized that legal theory is only a correlation of facts and rules. The facts are explained by the rules. The anomalies that arise are explained by the deviation of situational theories from exemplary concepts. Any need to consider the stages of conceptual transduction seems to disappear. However, we must remember that facts-rules orientated theory is an extremely simplified image of conceptual transduction. Moreover, usually, a focus on facts is clearly superior to a focus on rules. Therefore, fact-oriented theory prevails. The antinomian tradition of Jeremy Bentham, which rejects the dictates of fact, does not have widespread support. [4]

The phenomenon of evidence, it is usually associated with the concepts of justice and truth. Deviation from the truth is not allowed. «However, the search for truth is not the highest level, or overarching, aim of adjudication. The overarching aim is securing substantively just treatment of individuals. » [2, 164] In my opinion, the concept of harmony of evidence and justice, which is very popular, is doubtful. The fact is that justice is a principle not of law, but of political science. The first principle of law is the principle of growth of the permissible. A close examination always reveals that relevant evidence implements this principle. In everyday language, the term 'justice' is not assigned either to political science or to law. Unfortunately, the uncritical use of the term 'justice' is widespread in law. This is a direct result of insufficient attention to the principle of growth of the permissible.

Of course, the criterion of true knowledge also deserves special attention. As explained in section 1.11, true is knowledge represented by the most advanced scientific theories. The use of scientific methods leads to the elimination of false knowledge. It is not so that, pursuing true knowledge, researchers come to scientific methods. Any phenomena are specific, we must have adequate information about them. The use of scientific methods provides the separation of the true, i.e. scientifically adequate knowledge from false knowledge. This fact is misunderstood in the widespread traditional correspondent, coherent and pragmatic conceptions of truth. In all three conceptions of truth, due attention is not paid to the methods of attaining true knowledge. Because of this, their content is doubtful. Despite this circumstance, most jurists adhere to the corresondence conception of truth. However, the number of adherents of the coherent conception of truth is also multiplying. [1]

Thus, my point of view is that the content of evidence is determined primarily by the consistent use of scientific methods in accordance with the principle of growth of the permissible. However, as already noted, in the modern theory of evidence another conception dominates, namely, fact-oriented. In accordance with it, paramount attention is paid to the formation of a corpus of facts, their legal admissibility, and relevance. [3] The vast majority of items of Federal Rules of Evidence (US) relate to establishing the admissibility and legal relevance of facts. Moreover, a fact is understood to mean any action or state of things that is supposed (at the moment) as occurring or existing. Facts are elements of rules. Of course, attention to the status of facts is justified. One has only to regret that not so much attention is paid to the status of rules, principles and scientific methods.

Actual importance is also given to the objectivity of facts. [7; 11; 10] Lidia Rodak concluded that "[t]he necessity for interpretation and its application make the dream of objectivity unreal." [7, 142] She came to this conclusion considering the semantic level, that is, correlation of language and facts, and focusing on the research of Wittgenstein and Kripke. Of course, I understand the greatness of these philosophical authorities.

However, I will partially disagree with them. Determining the possible objectivity of facts, they did not take into account the nature of substantive theories, including legal concepts. The semantic point of view is not primary; it must itself be interpreted. Only after this can we begin to interpret the nature of the facts. A more economical way of research is that legal facts are recognized by the concepts of legal theories that are implemented by people. From this point of view, facts, of course, cannot be objective, i.e. independent of people. However, they are not arbitrary. It should be borne in mind that the status of facts varies from one stage of the theory to another. At the induction stage, a transition is made from facts to laws. In the deductive case, the situation changes, the rules determine the nature of the facts.

The next relevant aspect of legal evidence concerns the issue of the need to consider conflicting theories, including the adversarial court. In my opinion, this is a very fruitful position. Earlier, in relation to various sciences, I have repeatedly noted that intertheoretical transduction is used much less effective in them than intratheoretical transduction and as a rule, due attention is not paid to the concept of 'theory'. In my opinion, considering conflicting theories is a step towards intertheoretical transduction. It is relevant that theories appear not in the form of lifeless narratives, but as representatives for the most pressing interests of the plaintiff and defendant. Another thing that often raises complaints about their construction. In this regard, it is clear that it is advisable for the conflicting parties to trust their interests to lawyers. Unfortunately, they far from always skillfully present legal theories. This is a consequence of adherence to the fact-oriented theory. Of course, consideration of conflicting theories requires the ability correctly to correlate their relative conceptual power.

Let me note with satisfaction that in the last two decades, in the law the intertheoretical approach was strengthened due to the use by jurists the inference to the best explanation. [1; 5; 6] The core of this approach is the belief that only the most developed theories provide the most scientifically appropriate explanation. Contending parties generate theories. The side that invents the most effective theory wins. Such theory is best determined based on certain criteria, among which the simplicity of the theory, its credibility, and the explanation of a greater number of facts and so on are most often called. Paul Thagard devoted a special article to the theory of selection criteria. [9] Like the vast majority of other authors, he believed that if there are several theories, you could always find criteria for their comparison and decide which theory is better. I doubt the correctness of this position.

The fact is that inference to the best explanation is the heir to the concept of abduction. If the content of abduction is misunderstood, then inference to the best explanation is also misunderstood. Thagard believed that inference to the best explanation "has many advantages over the hypothetic-deductive model of theory confirmation." [9, 76] It is indicative that he contrasts inference to the best explanation and the deductive method. Meanwhile, the tradition from Charles Peirce consists in considering abduction in unity with deduction and induction. Thagard ignores this connection. The approach implemented in this regard is that, on the one hand, legal theory is considered, and, on the other hand, inference to the best explanation as a way of the choice of the best theory. The same approach is applied to legal evidence. [1; 5; 6]

In my opinion, the correct approach is that abduction is considered as a stage of intratheoretical transduction; and inference to the best explanation appears in the composition of intertheoretical transduction. In this case, a comparison of theories appears as an operation of interpreting a less developed theory (T1) from the standpoint of a more developed theory (T2). Symbolically, this operation can be written as follows: $T_2 \rightarrow T_1 \{T_2\}$. The two theories come together through an interpretation operation. In the approach I criticize, theories are compared according to criteria taken from nowhere. Only at first glance do they seem obvious. A closer look always reveals their problematic, unclear nature. In this case, a comparison of theories ignores their inner nature, which contains abduction along with deduction, adduction, and induction.

My criticisms do not mean denying the need to use inference to the best explanation in legal evidence. In this regard, the efforts of Ronald Allen and Michael Pardo, who insist on the need for «shifting from probabilism to explanationism», seem to be very productive. [6, 1] I mean that Bayesian probabilism, widely used in legal evidence, is relevant only if it takes into account the nature of legal theories and their relative strength. An emphasis on the concept of inference to the best explanation puts on the agenda the consideration of the relative strength of legal theories. This is a step in the right direction, namely, towards the conception of conceptual transduction.

Thus, in my opinion, the main problematic aspects of legal evidence are the result of the superficial understanding of the nature of legal theories. Most often, it manifests itself in ignoring their connection with substantive theories and in adherence to fact-oriented conceptions.

References

1. Amaya, A. (2013) Coherence, evidence, and legal proof. Legal Theory 19(1), 1-43.
2. Goldman, A. (2005) Legal evidence. In Goldring, M. and Edmundson, W. (Eds.). The Blackwell Guide to the Philosophy of Law and Legal Theory. Malden, MA: Blackwell, 163-175.
3. Ho, H.L. (2015) The legal concept of evidence. The Stanford Encyclopedia of Philosophy. Available at: https://plato.stanford.edu/archives/win2015/entries/evidence-legal/
4. Jackson, J. and Doran, S. (2010) Evidence. In Patterson, D. (Ed.). A Companion to Philosophy of Law and Legal Theory. Second edition. Malden, MA: Wiley-Blackwell, 177-187.
5. Pardo, M.S. and Allen. R.J. (2008). Juridical proof and the best explanation. Law and Philosophy 27(3), 223-268.
6. Pardo, M.S. and Allen, R.J. (2019) Relative plausibility and its critics. The International Journal of Evidence and Proof 20(10), 1-55.
7. Rodak, L. (2012) Objectivity of legal facts from semantic point of view. Studies in Logic, Grammar and Rhetoric 28(41), 123-143.
8. Rodriguez-Blanco, V. (2010) Objectivity in law philosophy. Compass 5(3), 240-249.
9. Thagard, P.R. (1978) The Best explanation: criteria for theory choice. Journal of Philosophy 75(2), 76-92.

10. Wright, R.G. (2017) Objective and subjective tests in the law. The University of New Hampshire Law Review 16(1), article 5.

19.4. Legal responsibility

The vast majority of authors believe that along with moral responsibility there is also a legal responsibility. [1-9] Unfortunately, the nature of these two forms of responsibility remains largely unclear. This circumstance negatively affects the understanding of the nature of law. My immediate task is to consider the relationship between moral and legal responsibility.

Earlier, I repeatedly turned to the ethical principle of responsibility, understood as an obligation to be guided by the most developed theories. [6.9, 10.10] Since law, like ethics, is rooted in all substantive axiological theories, and these theories are led by ethical principles, it is reasonable to assume that the principle of legal responsibility following the principle of ethical responsibility consists of the obligation to be guided in all cases related to law by the most developed theories. In this regard, it is reasonable to compare my understanding of legal liability with other interpretations of its content.

Defending the concept of responsibility is associated with many difficulties. This circumstance was talentedly presented by Peter Strawson in the article "Freedom and Resentment". [9] He drew attention to the correlation of the concept of responsibility with an understanding of free will and determinism. In the absence of a sufficiently clear understanding of the nature of both free will and determinism, judgments of responsibility become invalid and, therefore, they should be treated critically. The only thing you can be sure of is in interpersonal relationships in which people express their diverse emotions of approval and condemnation of other people's actions. Strawson saw the foundations of responsibility in the psychological practice of people. Moreover, he was clearly at a loss to present the theory of responsibility in its possible conceptual coordinates.

Galen Strawson also notes the correlation between responsibility and determinism. He, unlike Peter Strawson, was completely disappointed in the concept of determinism. Galen Strawson concludes that moral responsibility is not possible at all.

> (1) Nothing can be *causa sui* - nothing can be the cause of itself. (2) In order to be truly morally responsible for one's actions one would have to be *causa sui*, at least in certain crucial mental respects. (3) Therefore nothing can be truly morally responsible. [8, 5]

After the noted difficulties in understanding responsibility, the works of Herbert Hart look especially significant. [4, 5] In an effort to determine the nature of legal responsibility, he examines its typical kinds. Hart does this, which is extremely important, from the standpoint of already known legal theories. Apparently, fearing metaphysical traps, he does not step aside from the law. In the legal theories he knows, the primary focus is on causal mechanisms. Consequently, the concept of responsibility should be defined precisely in their context. [5; 6] Hart constantly takes into account that the purpose of the legislation is to approve such legal norms of behavior that are consistent with the value of individual freedom. [4, 8, 200-201] A lawyer who repeatedly emphasized that legal theory dispenses with principles, considering the concept of responsibility, in fact, was guided by the principle of individual freedom. The mechanism for the implementation of responsibility is causal, and its main semantic horizon is determined not by the desire to punish misconduct, but by ensuring the triumph of legal affairs, people's freedom.

Hart's approach explains the fallacy of the reasoning of both Strawson's. They confine themselves to metaphysical discourse on determinism avoiding a thorough analysis of the nature of legal theories. Hart considers legal determinism as he sees it in law.

In an effort to be extremely specific, Hart identifies four varieties of responsibility: (1) causal responsibility from the point of view of a dynamic source; (2) role-responsibility in connection with the task; (3) capacity-responsibility in terms of a person's ability to fulfill the necessary; (4) liability-responsibility directly related to the assessment of the act. [4, 221-230] The interpretation of the content of liability-responsibility caused Hart the greatest difficulties. [1, 39]

> We may therefore summarize this long discussion of legal liability-responsibility by saying that though, in certain general contexts, legal responsible and legal liability have the same meaning, to say that a man is legally responsible for some act or harm is to state that his connexion with the act or harm is sufficient for liability. [4, 222]

Liability-responsibility is, in fact, the most specific representation of legal responsibility. In my opinion, Hart's analysis is marked by the seal of duality. On the one hand, he seeks to take into account the nature of legal theory. On the other hand, Hart wants to deduce its main points, based on some facts. In addition, he constantly refers to the fruitfulness of common sense, not taking into account its difference from the scientific position. Another extremely significant fact is that Hart ultimately relates responsibility only to misconduct. This means that responsibility is firmly tied to the concepts of guilt and crime. In my opinion, a more solid position is that responsibility is considered primarily in the horizons of the principles of the theory.

In my opinion, Hart's work is indicative especially in the context of the method he uses. His ideas about the nature of legal theory were quite preliminary. Nevertheless, he consistently sought to realize her potential. There is hardly any other author who would be as consistent as he in his desire to take into account when interpreting the content of the concept of responsibility its methodological foundations.

After Hart, it was natural to expect a methodological sequence from modern authors. Unfortunately, many of them, not paying due attention to the methodology, prefer their endless interview with the facts. This remark does not apply to Nils Jansen. It seems to me that his position is also very revealing. He believes that «the idea of civil equality and the principle against unjustified enrichment require citizens to assume responsibility not only for the consequences of their misbehavior, but also for the consequences of lawful actions that non-reciprocally endanger the rights of others. » [7, 221] In my opinion, he is consistent in at least two respects. Firstly, correlating responsibility with 'lawful actions'. Secondly, trying to consider the phenomenon of responsibility in the context of certain principles, primarily of civil equality.

My disagreement with Nils Jansen concerns the issue of methodological substantiation of the concept of responsibility based on the principles of legal theory. In my opinion, in these theories, there is neither the principle of civil equality nor the principle against unjustified enrichment. The principle of civil equality relates to political science, and not to law. However, even there it is inappropriate, for it does not agree with the principle of justice. As for unjustified enrichment, this requirement is hardly a principle, because this provision is a consequence of the basic principles of economics. The true principle of legal theories is the principle of growth of the permissible. Excess of the permissible is punishable. This position can be considered a direct consequence of the principle of growth of the permissible. Having fixed this fact, I am still far from the concept of responsibility. It suggests that the individual is able to evaluate his actions. Otherwise, it is useless to demand responsibility from him. The subject becomes responsible only when he mastered the corresponding, i.e. most developed theory.

I returned to where I started this section. Legal responsibility is a principle according to which an individual should be guided by the theory of such a level of development that allows him to justify his actions. Legal responsibility is a principle, not a rule. If it were a rule, it would be deduced from the principle of growth of the permissible. However, legal responsibility is not deductible. It, therefore, must be recognized as the second principle of any legal theory. Legal responsibility is not a rule, not one of the rights of citizens, not an abstract idea, but the principle of legal theories. Of course, in the absence of moral responsibility there would be no legal liability.

References

1. Boxer, K. (2014) Hart's senses of 'responsibility'. In Pulman, C. (Ed.). Hart on Responsibility. London, UK: The Palgrave Macmillan, 30-46.
2. Fletcher, G.P. (2010) Punishment and responsibility. In Patterson, D. (Ed.). A Companion to Philosophy of Law and Legal Theory. Second ed. Malden, MA and Oxford: Willey and Blackwell, 504-512.
3. Golding, M.P. (2005) Responsibility. In Golding, M. and Edmundson, W. (Eds.). The Blackwell Guide to Philosophy of Law and Legal Theory. Malden, MA and Oxford: Blackwell, 221-235.
4. Hart, H.L.A. (1968) Punishment and Responsibility. Essays in the Philosophy of Law. Oxford: Oxford University Press,
5. Hart, H.L.A., and Honoré, T. (1985) Causation in the Law. Second ed. Oxford: Clarendon Press.
6. Honoré, A. and Gardner, J. (2010) Causation in the law. The Stanford Encyclopedia of Philosophy. Available at: https://plato.stanford.edu/archives/win2010/entries/causation-law/
7. Jansen, N. (2013) The idea of legal responsibility. Oxford Journal of Legal Studies 34(2), 221-252.
8. Strawson, G. (1994) The impossibility of moral responsibility. Philosophical Studies 75(1-2), 5-24.
9. Strawson, P. F. (1962) Freedom and resentment. Proceedings of the British Academy 48, 1-25.

19.5. Punishment as principle

Legal punishment is the application of measures to individuals or organizations by the authority, which sanctioned a certain right that applies to these individuals and organizations, but is violated by them. Simon Blackburn believes punishment is « [t]he deliberate infliction of harm upon somebody, or the withdrawal of some good from them, by an authority, in response to their being supposed to have committed some offence». [2, 375] This definition is inconsistent because the authority that executes the punishment does not at all consider that it inflictions «of harm upon somebody». Nevertheless, many authors adhere to the opposite position. For them, the issue of the moral admissibility of any, including the legal punishment, is extremely relevant. [8] They insist on the acquittal of punishment. If it is impossible, then the institution of punishment should be recognized as unlawful.

Punishment often qualifies as retribution, reparation, reformation, and deterrence. [2, 236; 3, 629]. The content of these characteristics is interpreted, as a rule, in accordance with two approaches, cconsequentialist (or utilitarians) and retributivist (or deontological). [1: 4; 9; 11] Consequentialists attach paramount importance to deterrence, retributivists to retribution. Both sides believe that the framework for legal punishment is applied philosophy. Such a choice seems extremely strange. It must be assumed legal punishment should be judged properly, first, based on legal theories. Unfortunately, this approach is implemented with great difficulty. In this regard, let me turn to the work of Herbert Hart. This choice, of course, is not accidental. We are talking about the author, who, unlike many of his opponents, always sought to clarify the nature and content of legal theories when clarifying urgent legal problems.

At the very beginning of his founding report, Hart states that his task is to show that the morally tolerable report of criminal punishment is «a compromise between distinct and partly conflicting principles.» [8, 1] We are talking about the principles of utilitarianism and retributivism. Hart does not show much respect for these principles he clarifies them. It is significant that we are talking about the principles of ethical theories, and not about the principles of legal theory. Hart further states that he, comparing legal punishment with property, discuss issues of definition, general justifying aim, and distribution. [8, 2] These are undoubtedly urgent issues, but their formulation looks like just an a priori act. Indeed, it is not explained why exactly these issues should be discussed. Hart, from a scientific point of view, was supposed to attempt to show the place of the concept of legal punishment as part of a legal theory in which legal principles and rules play a key role. Nevertheless, that Hart did not. Douglas Husak, commenting on the work in question, concludes that Hart's analysis was unsuccessful because he did not find out the reason for the introduction of criminal punishment. [10, 107] I agree with the first part of this statement. Husak and I explain the reasons for the failure of Hart in different ways. He is interested in the cause of legal punishment; I strive to determine its place in the composition of legal theory.

In the search for methodological grounds for the characterization of criminal punishment, a well-known article by John Rawls 'Two Concepts of Rules' deserves attention. [12] In concluding the article, he expressed satisfaction that he was able to reconcile the retributive and utilitarian justification of punishment. [12, I] Rawls, as well as Hart, did not enter the concept of legal punishment directly into the context of legal theory. Most modern authors avoid this inclusion. In my opinion, this means that the required legal analysis is replaced by ethical research, and far from scientific standards. I have no choice but to offer my own version of understanding the concept of legal punishment.

The legal theory is headed by two principles, namely, the principles of growth of the permissible and the principle of responsibility. Guided by these principles, people control various kinds of axiological systems, in particular, economic, social, pedagogical, psychological, and technical. Any type of management, including legal, is not without errors. Their correction is necessary for any, including the legal system. These corrections are not considered crimes until the case reaches the excess of the permissible established by the relevant legal acts. Punishment is prescribed only for those acts that exceed the permissible limits. They are a prerequisite for the successful functioning of the axiological system.

Obviously, the management of the system involves the mandatory elimination of errors. This condition is hardly reasonable to question. It may be called into question whether such levels of the permissible are established that be worthy of punishment. The indicated expediency is a conclusion that is established in the process of conducting multiple cycles of conceptual transduction, which, as you know, contain their practical stages. This conclusion refers exclusively to the already completed cycles of knowledge, and not to eternity. The very existence of law indicates that punishments are necessary at this stage in the development of humankind. Of course, the punishment in its meaning is closely related to the principles of growth of the permissible and responsibility. However, the concept of punishment cannot be deduced from these two principles. It is added to these two principles. This means that the concept of punishment is not a separate value, not a rule, but a principle. Separate value is part of principles or rules. Rules are derived from principles. Punishment is not inferred from principles and is not part of principles.

Thus, the legal theory is headed by three principles, the principles of the permissible, responsibility and punishment. I determined the place of punishment as part of legal theory. After that, it is not difficult to give answers to those questions that Hart considered defining, namely, questions of definition, general justifying aim, and distribution. The correct definition of punishment says that it is the principle of legal theory, which, together with the principles of the permissible and responsibility, determines the meaning of the rules and individual values. In the light of this definition, the definition of legal punishment as «deliberate infliction of harm upon somebody, or the withdrawal of some good from them» is deeply mistaken. Punishment is a concept of legal rather than ethical theory. For this reason, it is impermissible to correlate it directly with harm or good.

If you want to determine the connection of punishment with ethical concepts, the nature of axiological theories should be taken into account, the hierarchy of principles of which is headed by the principle of multiplying the prosperity of all stakeholders. Suppose that, in view of this provision, we decided to define of harm and good. In this case, good is that all stakeholders are subject to punishment because otherwise, it is impossible to ensure the successful functioning of the axiological system. Harm is that someone is freed from being subject to punishment. As you can see, scientific analysis has led to conclusions that are directly opposed to common-sense attitudes, to which, in my opinion, Hart has overly trusted. In the light of the clarifications made, it is not difficult to characterize the expediency of characterizing the punishment from the point of utilitarianism and retributivism.

Utilitarianism, including consequentialism as its developed version, does not in itself have any a priori power that would allow characterizing legal punishment. He himself acquires a distinct meaning only as a generalization of the achievements of axiological sciences in the form of the statement that it is necessary to maximize the utility function. If desired, this requirement can be quite successfully fulfilled on behalf of legal theory. The trouble with utilitarianism is that emphasizing the result, it does not take into account the nature of the internal dynamics of axiological theories. In this regard, it immediately becomes clear that on its behalf the legal punishment can be characterized only extremely unilaterally.

Retributivism, with its emphasis on the concept of retribution in itself, regardless of the axiological sciences, is a purely a priori construction. There is no reason to follow its instructions. Its conceptual apparatus does not allow characterizing what exactly is a legal punishment. In this case, the concept of punishment turns out to be devoid of a specific address. Retributivism acquires a distinct meaning only if it is understood as a well-known generalization of the achievements of legal theories. In this case, it turns out that retributivism states the need for punishment of legal crimes.

Retributivism does not add anything substantial to what is known of legal punishment. Its supporters are forced to invoke people's intuition as the evidence base of their theory. In my opinion, Nathan Hanna convincingly showed that people at the level of their intuition, i.e. statements that are accepted without justification do not have common views which retributivists insist on. [7] Common sense with its addiction to intuition is not something obvious and therefore acceptable. It himself needs to be interpreted through scientific theories. The failure of retributivism is clarified if it is considered from the standpoint of scientific legal theories. It turns out that the actual potential of these theories is not available to it.

In my opinion, the conviction of most researchers that some form of moralism is the basis of legal punishment is deeply erroneous. [4; 9] Instead of interpreting legal punishment from a scientific point of view, i.e. in accordance with the nature of legal theories, it is considered from the standpoint of superficially based ethical conceptions. The connection of law with ethics should certainly be taken into account, but not through moral fundamentalism. It is not a worthy alternative to the scientific analysis of the concept of punishment.

As for the concepts of retribution, reparation, reformation, and deterrence, their rational meaning is also clarified through a scientific analysis of scientific legal theories. Contrary to the widespread methodological position, they are not the key to understanding the nature of legal punishment. The opposite position leads directly to metaphysics far from science. It should be especially noted that legal punishment is often carried out in an unacceptable form, for example, those, which are justifiably criticized by Michael Foucault. [6] This criticism in no way cancels the relevance of legal punishment as a principle of scientific legal theories.

References

1. Bedau, H.A. and Kelly, E. (2017) Punishment. The Stanford Encyclopedia of Philosophy. Available at: https://plato.stanford.edu/archives/win2017/entries/punishment/

2. Blackburn, S. (2005) Oxford Dictionary of Philosophy. Oxford: Oxford University Press.
3. Brooks, T. (2016) In defense of punishment and the unified theory of punishment: a reply. Criminal law and philosophy 10(3), 629-638.
4. Duff, A. and Hoskins, Z. (2018) Legal punishment. The Stanford Encyclopedia of Philosophy Available at: https://plato.stanford.edu/archives/fall2018/entries/legal-punishment/
5. Duff, R.A. (2014) Towards a modest legal moralism. Criminal law and Philosophy 8 (1),217-235.
6. Foucault, M. (1977) Discipline and Punish: The Birth of the Prison. New York: Pantheon.
7. Hanna, N. (2019) Hitting retributivism where it hurts. Criminal law and Philosophy 13(1), 109-127.
8. Hart, H.L.A. (1968) Prolegomenon to the principles of punishment. In Punishment and Responsibility: Essays in the Philosophy of Law. New York: Oxford University Press, 1-27.
9. Hoskins, Z. (2020) The moral permissibility of punishment. Internet Encyclopedia of Philosophy. Available at: https://www.iep.utm.edu/m-p-puni/
10. Husak, D. (1994) A framework for punishment: what is the insight of Hart's 'Prolegomenon'? In Pulman, C. (Ed.). Hart on Responsibility. London, UK: The Palgrave Macmillan, 91-108.
11. Murtagh, K. (2020) Punishment. Internet Encyclopedia of Philosophy. Available at: https://www.iep.utm.edu/punishme/
12. Rawls, J. (1955) Two concepts of rules. The Philosophical Review 64(1), 3-32.

19.6. Law in interdisciplinary relations

Each science is in an interdisciplinary relationship with all other sciences. In all such respects, its specificity leaves an essential stamp on these relations. With regard to the law, this circumstance is manifested in a very specific way, in particular, in the relationship of law with economics, political science, and ethics.

Law and economics

The most striking thing in the relationship between law and economics is that economic research methods were transferred to the field of law with their emphasis on the concept of efficiency. [2; 8; 9; 12] Opponents of such a transfer put forward various arguments against it, in particular, indicating that it did not take into account the normative nature of law and the freedom of judges in their decision-making. Refuting these arguments, Richard Posner replied, « [j]udges can hardly avoid using some criterion of social welfare in fashioning rules of decision, and efficiency is a more libertarian criterion than any other I know. » [9, 777] His arguments regarding the need for a positive approach and following the rules of utilitarianism in the name of the triumph of freedom and justice are much more controversial than the thesis about the relevance of the efficiency approach. Successful use of this approach in the analysis of torts, property, and procedure led to the spread of the opinion that economic research methods are used in law. This opinion is erroneous due to at least a few circumstances.

Research methods must not be considered in isolation from their conceptual content. Because of this, economic methods are not identical to legal methods. They have different contents. An economist increases the financial well-being of people, and a lawyer expands the field of possibilities that are acceptable to them. Despite their different content, economic and legal methods have some similarities insofar as they focus on the criterion of efficacy. The lawyer, impressed by the successes of the economics, abstracts from their economic content. He transfers this bare abstract image into the sphere of law and loads it with legal content. Thus, two metamorphoses take place. At first, the economically concrete turns into the abstract, and then this abstract into the legal concrete. Further, as a rule, the quantitative characteristics of legal concepts are compared to the prices of goods and services. In this regard, the temptation again arises to believe that there is a reduction of the legal to the economic. In reality, there is modeling, namely, prices act as symbols of the quantitative characteristics of legal phenomena. Modeling never identifies heterogeneous entities. In the case under consideration, there is also no identification of the quantitative characteristics of legal phenomena with prices. Thus, the successful use in the economics of research methods that use the efficiency criterion has served as an impressive example for lawyers. They did not transfer them to the field of law but developed their legal counterparts. They transformed economic methods, giving them, ultimately, and legal specificity.

Robert Cooter and Thomas Ulen posed two interesting questions: Why should lawyers study economics? Why should economists study law? They themselves, in particular, believe that

> [f]rom economists, lawyers can learn quantitative reasoning for making theories and doing empirical research. From lawyers, economists can learn to persuade ordinary people – an art that lawyers continually practice and refine. Lawyers can

describe facts and give them names with moral resonance, whereas economists are obtuse to language too often. If economists will listen to what the law has to teach them, they will find their models being drawn closer to what people really care about. [2, 9-10]

Let me give you an answer to the questions of Cooter and Ulen. When considering the relationship between law and economics, researchers usually do not take into account that these two sciences are not disconnected from each other. In their original meanings, legal provisions are directly part of the economy. Economists should study law primarily for a better understanding of the economics itself. The position of jurists is fundamentally different from the situation with economists. Economics is not part of the law. Therefore, legal scholars should study economics not because it is part of the law, but due to another circumstance. The fact is that law is "extracted" from the substantive sciences, that is, it is contextual in its origin. If this circumstance is not taken into account, then the nature of law is misunderstood. Economics is an authoritative representative of the substantive sciences. Lawyers must study economics to understand the contextual significance of the law. Without this, they misunderstand the content of the law.

Law and political science

According to widespread belief, political science and law are particularly closely related to each other. Much more often than the economics, each of them is not considered as an independent conceptual entity. To my surprise, the opinion that law and political science are inseparable is extremely widespread. In this regard, a sharp objection was raised to the statement of Duncan Kennedy that the reduction of law to politics is impossible. [7, 72] Objecting to him, John Schlegel claims, « [l]aw participates in the unmeetable ethical demand for rationality in the world as much as does politics, and economics in some hands seem only to dispute the "unmeetable" part of this objective.» [11, 28] He emphasizes that for him are equally apparent «Law is politics» and «Politics is the law.» [11, 35] Julen Etxabe considers law as politics. [4] Miro Cerar believes that «politics can define certain predominantly legal values or institutions as its goal.» [1, 1] It is not clear why legal values do not refer to the law, but to politics. Obviously, Cerar does not clearly distinguish between law and political science. Meanwhile, such a division seems to be extremely relevant.

The researchers mentioned in the previous paragraph do not consider conceptual, epistemological and methodological subtleties. Nevertheless, without them, determining the status of law, as well as political science, is in principle impossible. By the way, in order to avoid misunderstandings, I must certainly note that they are not talking about political science, but about politics. Nevertheless, we are still talking about the ratio of two scientific units, i.e. law and political science. Should they be distinguished? In my opinion, it follows, and that is why. The history of the development of social sciences has led to the formation of two heterogeneous units, political science, and law with fundamentally different principles. Political science implements the development of the principle of power, law – the principle of permissible. Theories with different principles cannot be identical; they cannot be reduced to each other. In this regard, both the proposals «Law is political science» and «Political science is law» are unacceptable.

Despite their fundamental difference, law and political science are, in a certain respect, really close to each other. This proximity is indicated by the following circumstance. As superstructure sciences, their genealogy begins with substantive theories. In this capacity, they certainly accompany each other as parts of any substantive axiological theory. Perhaps it is precise because of their similar fate that law and political science often are being identified with each other.

Being abstracted from the substantive sciences, law and political science lose touch with each other. In this position between them, there is no interdisciplinary relationship. Their need makes itself felt in connection with the realization of the potential of law and political science as parts of substantive theories, for example, economic and sociological. Without this realization, law and political science remain lifeless abstractions. The status of substantive theories is such that it requires the unity of law and political science. Within these theories, political scientists are forced to take an interest in the admissible factor, and legal scholars as a factor in power. It is in this connection that law and political science meet each other. In my opinion, this is precisely the nature of the interdisciplinary connection between law and political science.

Law and Ethics

An analysis of legal literature shows that the relationship of law with ethics is discussed much more often than its relationship with economics and political science. This indicates that the connection of law with ethics is of especially exceptional importance for understanding its nature. Unfortunately, the vast majority of authors prefer to talk not so much about the relationship of law with ethics, but with morality or morals. This conceptual move seems erroneous to me since talking about morality, regardless of ethics, acquires a distinctly quasi-scientific character.

Outstanding philosophers of law Hart, Dworkin, Rawls, and Habermas have devoted many pages to the correlation of law and ethics.

Herbert Hart has established himself as the main representative of the exemption of law from ethics. [6] With this approach, the question of the relationship between law and ethics is squeezed out of science and, therefore, it if not completely, then largely loses its relevance.

Ronald Dworkin resolutely returns ethics to the scene of law, calling it as the main guideline of integrity. [3] The trouble is that he does not represent integrity ethics in any coherent form, which would be consistent at least to the same extent as the traditional expositions of utilitarianism and deontological ethics.

Hart and Dworkin introduced ethics as adherents of law. In contrast, John Rawls considered ethics in the context of political science, and Jürgen Habermas from the standpoint of social theory. The law did not fall out of their field of vision. Rawls and Habermas, having carefully examined utilitarianism and deontological ethics, considered them insufficient for the development of law and political science. This meant that ethics, in its main traditional meanings, was recognized as largely incapable. Both refused to justify law and political science based on traditional ethics because it itself needs justification. They presented two drafts of the new ethics. A reasonable question arises: in what form did the updated ethics appear? What are the principles of truly relevant ethics?

It can hardly be considered that Rawls gave clear answers to these questions. His main work carefully examines the principle of justice. [10] This is the principle of political science, not ethics. I am far from the idea of asserting that there is no ethics in Rawls's works. It appears in the desire of the drafters of the constitution to ensure the possibility of successful coexistence of all citizens.

The main idea of Habermas is that in its modern form, "the moral point of view" culminates in the form of "procedural theory of justice", three models of which were presented by J. Rawls, L. Kohlberg and he together with K.-O. Apel. [5, 242-243] If justice is considered the principle of political science, which, in my opinion, is quite reasonable, then ethics equates to the moral point of view.

What lessons should be learned from the studies of Hart, Dworkin, Rawls, and Habermas? A radical rethinking of the status of ethics has taken place. Traditional ethical systems, in particular, utilitarianism and deontological ethics were previously perceived as separate conceptual entities so independent that they could be opposed to the law. Now, ethics is a component of substantive theories. Interdisciplinary relations of law and ethics are implemented in the context of these theories, and not outside of them. In my opinion, this lesson is completely insufficiently taken into account by many researchers who continue to compare ethics and law outside the context of substantive theories. In addition, they usually consider traditional economic theories instead of modern ethical conceptions.

References

1. Cerar, Dr. Miro. (2009) The relationship between law and politics. Annual Survey of International and Comparative Law: 15(1), Article 3.

2. Cooter, R. and Ulen, T. (2016) An introduction to law and economics. In Cooter, R. and Ulen, T. (Eds.). Law and Economics. Sixth Ed. Boston: Addison-Wesley.
3. Dworkin, R. (1986) Law's Empire. Cambridge, Massachusetts: Harvard University Press.
4. Etxabe, J. (2016) Law as politics: four relations. Law, culture and the humanities, 1-18.
5. Habermas, J. (1986) Law and morality. The Tanner Lectures on Human Values. Harvard University, 219-279.
6. Hart, H.L.A. (1958) Positivism and the separation of law and morals. Harvard Law Review 71(4), 593–629.
7. Kennedy, D. (2006) Three globalizations of law and legal thought: 1850–2000. In Trubek, D. and Santos, A. (Eds). The New Law and Economic Development: A Critical Appraisal. Cambridge: Cambridge University Press, 19-73.
8. Kornhauser, L. (2017) The economic analysis of law. The Stanford Encyclopedia of Philosophy. Available at: : https://plato.stanford.edu/archives/fall2017/entries/legal-econanalysis/
9. Posner, R. (1975) The economic approach to law. Texas Law Review 53(4), 757-782.
10. Rawls, J. (1971) Theory of Justice. Cambridge, Massachusetts: Harvard University Press.
11. Schlegel, J. H. (2015) Three globalizations: An essay in inquiry. Law and Contemporary Problems 78(1 -2), 20-35.
12. Winter, H. (Ed.). (2017) Issues in Law and Economics, University Press, Chicago, IL: Chicago University Press.

19.7. The main legal schools

Each science is realized through a cluster of its directions or schools. Its very existence explains a lot about the nature of the corresponding science, in particular, law. I will consider the following schools of law: 1) natural law conception, 2) legal positivism, 3) legal realism, 4) interpretivism (Dworkin's version), 5) legal hermeneutics, 6) legal deconstruction. I confine myself to considering only the main foundations of these schools. It is important for me to show their originality, coherence, and unity.

1. Natural law conception

This is the earliest legal philosophical conception, dating back to the names of Plato, Aristotle, and Thomas Aquinas. The foundation of law is universal ethics, a practical form of philosophy. Proper legal action implements universal virtues. Law follows ethics. [3; 7]

Comment

In the vast majority of legal schools, the uniqueness of law is strongly emphasized. Only against this background is the question of the relationship between law and ethics. In my opinion, supporters of the natural law conception interpret the correlation between ethics and law in a straightforward manner. Law is applied ethics. As a result, the specifics of the law are decisively underestimated. The second weakness of the natural law conception is the postulation of the existence of some universal ethics with universal virtues. This is an exaggeration. Within the framework of the school in question, ethics is present in its metaphysical shell, which is not consistent with the scientific nature of law.

2. Legal positivism

Its founders were John Austin and Jeremy Bentham. In its modern understanding, the status of legal positivism is mainly associated with the conception of H.L.A. Hart.

Hart's version of what we earlier called substantive positivism can be summed up in two claims: (1) that the validity of legal rules is strictly a function of their recognition by law-applying institutions according to criteria established by the system's rule of recognition; and (2) that the rule of recognition exists, and has its status as a rule, strictly by virtue of the fact that it is practiced by law-applying officials. Law so identified leaves entirely open the question of what moral respect, if any, it is due. [12, 46]

According to the authoritative opinion of Julie Dickson, «law's existence does not determine what ought to be done». [5, 58]

Comment

In all sciences since the days of Auguste Comte, the defining criterion of positivism is relying on facts obtained in experiments and comprehended by the inductive method. Legal positivism does not meet this criterion. The emphasis is on factuality but the process of obtaining facts is not explained. Another criterion of authentic positivism is exception ethics from the theory. Legal positivism strictly meets this criterion. In all social sciences, the same situation is observed. At first, ethics is completely driven out of science, and then at the subsequent stages of research, attempts are being made somehow to resume contact with it. Abstracting from ethics allows isolating the features of social science. Legal positivists have successfully passed this way. Nevertheless, they do not know how to get in touch with ethics. In my opinion, this is largely the result of a misunderstanding of the correlation between law and basic axiological sciences. Legal positivists, in fact, extract the law from the substantive social sciences, but subsequently, do not return it to its original place. Another mistake of legal positivists is that they consider law as general science. In this case, a natural question arises. What theory deals with specific situations? Of course, there are sciences that deal exclusively with the general. They are formal theories to which special theories certainly correspond. Considering the law, we can distinguish in it the general and special law. In my opinion, legal positivists ignore this issue. They clearly absolutize general law.

3. Legal realism

Legal realism is an extremely ramified conception with centuries of history. It is extremely difficult to identify its crucial positions. In my opinion, Brian Leiter made an interesting attempt at this score. He formulated the core claim of legal realism: «in deciding cases, judges respond primarily to the stimulus of the facts of the case, rather than to legal rules and reasons. » [11, 52] Secondly, realists advocated «naturalized jurisprudence, that is, a jurisprudence that eschews armchair conceptual analysis in favor of continuity with a posteriori inquiry in the empirical sciences. » [11, 56] In this regard, they met with significant difficulties. In practical situations, judges had to use the canons of interpretation contained in legal texts, but they turned out to be contradictory.

Comment

The program of legal realism is, in fact, a program very consonant with positivism and its emphasis on empirical knowledge and exclusion ethics from the sciences. The trouble is that the realists cannot create a consistent theory, which, as I have repeatedly emphasized earlier, should be based on the methodology of conceptual transduction. In this case, it turns out that the opposition of reliability of facts and indeterminacy of rules, often carried out by legal realists, is untenable. Conceptual transduction captures the transition from facts to rules and from rules to facts. Of course, the desire of legal realists to transfer the law to scientific footing and resolve real, rather than far-fetched legal issues in the interests of citizens deserves high praise.

4. Legal interpretivism (Dworkin variant)

I decided to pay special attention to the Dworkin variant of legal interpretivism, which is most often considered in conjunction with the previously discussed schools. Together, they most fully express the analytical tradition in jurisprudence. Dworkin's concept found its fullest expression in his main book 'Law's Empire'. I give its main points on the epilogue of this book «What is law?».

> «We should accept integrity as a virtue of ordinary politics because we should try to conceive our political community as an association of principle [...] ». [6, 411] Integrity stands beside and sometimes conflicts «with the more familiar virtues of justice and fairness ». [6, 411] Law is «integrity, which units jurisprudence and adjudication » [6, 410]. «Law is an interpretive concept. Judges should decide what the law is by interpreting the

practice of other judges deciding what the law is»
[6, 410]

Comment

Dworkin's attention to principles is commendable. There are no more information-rich concepts in theories than principles. Therefore, their oblivion is a gross methodological error. Dworkin avoids it. However, the choice of principles that he makes, in my opinion, is unsuccessful. First, he mistakenly identifies legal principles with ethical principles. The first ones are absent at all. Secondly, he chooses the principles of metaphysical ethics, namely, integrity, justice, and fairness. This means that he does not distinguish between the principles of scientific theories and the principles of metaphysical conceptions. In my opinion, he should have given to the principles of ethics a scientific interpretation, but he did not. As for the subordination of the principles of justice and honesty to the principle of integrity, this move is purely arbitrary. An attempt to identify the correlation between law and ethics is also commendable. However, Dworkin does not distinguish ethics from the law, and this again is a mistake. It is no coincidence that he characterizes law as an interpretive conception. He needs to be given an idea of the mechanism for developing legal knowledge. Simple forms of thinking do not suit him. It is necessary to find such a sublime form of the thought process that will ensure the achievement of integrity. Dworkin calls this form of thinking interpretation. It has little to do with the hermeneutic category verstehen (understanding). Verstehen puts in the first place the mutual understanding of people, and not the ideals of moral progress, achievable, according to Dworkin, only to intellectual Hercules. According to Dworkin, the interpretation is realized by analyzing the precedents that have taken place and finding the best solution by the judges or by those who make legal decisions. In this regard, it would be reasonable to consider abduction as a method of inventing new principles. Nevertheless, it is not considered by him. It is difficult to find anything reminiscent of cycles of conceptual transduction in his works. In my opinion, Dworkin does not give a clear definition of the scientific method. The program of naturalizing of law is clearly alien to him.

5. Legal hermeneutics

Legal hermeneutics is mainly based on the ideas of the German philosophers Rudolf Schleiermacher, Wilhelm Dilthey, Hans-Georg Gadamer, and Jürgen Habermas. All of them, dissatisfied with the positivist methodology, offer some ways of interpreting texts and various forms of human activity. Lawyers use these interpretations in the interests of jurisprudence. Carl von Savigny was guided by the ideas of Schleiermacher, Emilio Betty - by the hermeneutics of Dilthey, Arthur Kaufman - by the hermeneutics of Gadamer, Robert Alexy - by the hermeneutics of Habermas.

The canons of interpretation proposed by von Savigny and Betty turned out to be very significant for the fate of hermeneutics. Von Savigny examined the grammatical, logical, historical, and systematic elements of interpretation. [13] Betty suggested: 1) The canon of hermeneutical autonomy of the text: 2) The canon of totality and coherence (of all parts of the text); 3) Canon of the actuality of understanding (which is determined by the subject); 4) The canon of the hermeneutic correspondence and consonance (congeniality of the interpreter and author of the work). [2] According to Gadamer, interpretation involves the inclusion of an interpreter in the history of a certain tradition, the dialectics of questions and answers, the practical use of each new portion of knowledge, and the triumph of a common cause. [8] Habermas proposes to be guided by the rules of logic (avoiding contradictions), dialectics (to be sincere), rhetoric (give everyone a word) and take into account the peculiarities of the situations. [10]

Comment

The main problem of hermeneutists is that they are always at odds with scientific methods. Ultimately, it turns out that they are unsuccessfully trying to surpass them. Hermeneutists reveal new interesting problems, for example, about the need for mutual understanding between people. It is one thing to identify problems, another to solve them successfully. It invariably turns out that scientific methods are needed to solve problems.

6. Legal deconstructivism

Any of the directions of post-structuralism, whether it be the archeology of Michel Foucault, the deconstructivism of Jacques Derrida or the differentism of Juan-François Lyotard opens up new possibilities for a corresponding reorientation of law. I will present the possibilities of poststructuralism on the example of Derrida's deconstructivism. Deconstruction consists in the fact that a chosen phenomenon is considered in tandem with its opposition. Together they make up the aporia, which then, due to its previously unaccounted features, is brought into an endless movement, aporetic transgression. Techniques for introducing new features of the aporia vary from one work of Derrida to another. Jack Balkin concluded that after many years of trying to use deconstruction in law, his future is «remain – as a deconstructionist might say – indeterminate». [1, 367]

To the delight of his supporters, Derrida himself demonstrated how the deconstruction technique in law could be used. [4] Simon Glendinning presented the argumentation of the article as follows.

First, that there is a history of laws. Second, that the history of laws relates a history of power. Third, that might is not right. Additionally, though these additions are unlikely to be immediately affirmed by its signatories, we might say, fourth, that law is constructed and can therefore be deconstructed. Fifth, that justice is undeconstructible. And, finally, sixth, that this work of deconstruction belongs to a movement of progress in the history of law. [9, 188]

Derrida, unexpectedly for the vast majority of jurists, called justice to be deconstruction. It never remains in a steady-state and is in touch with the mystery.

Comment

Derrida's proposed model for the implementation of deconstruction in law seems not only strange but also uncomplicated. It cannot be properly substantiated or verified. Justice is the principle of political theory. In my opinion, Derrida's proposal to consider the correlation of law and justice an aporia is an arbitrary metaphysical act. Derrida's desire to show the variability of law and justice is laudable. However, his chosen way of showing this variability is doubtful.

Conclusion

After considering six influential legal schools, I offer the reader the following conclusions. Each direction actualizes a certain aspect of law. A critical assessment of the content of legal schools requires some theory. In this connection, I used the theory of conceptual transduction. All the legal schools examined have difficulties in understanding the nature of scientific methods. Attempts to replace them with metaphysical constructs are unsuccessful. Law does not boil down to the position of just one law school. Its nature includes the unity and diversity of all legal schools. The development of law schools is marked by both successes and failures.

References

1. Balkin, J.M. (2010) Deconstruction. In Patterson, D. (Ed.). A Companion to Philosophy of Law and Legal Theory. Second ed. Malden, MA and Oxford: Willey and Blackwell, 361-367.
2. Betti, E. (1990) Teoria generale dell'interpretazione. [General theory of interpretation.]Vol. 1. Milano: Giuffrè. [In Italian].
3. Bix, B. (2010) Natural law theory. In Patterson, D. (Ed.). A Companion to Philosophy of Law and Legal Theory. Second ed. Malden, MA and Oxford: Wiley and Blackwell, 211-227.
4. Derrida, J. (1990) Force of law: the 'mystical foundations of authority'. Cardoso Law Review 11(5-6), 919-1045.
5. Dickson, J. (2012) Legal positivism: contemporary debates. In Marmor, A. (Ed.). The Routledge Companion to Philosophy of Law. New York and London: Routledge, 48-63.
6. Dworkin, R. (1986) Law's Empire. Cambridge, MA: Harvard University Press.
7. Finnis, J. (2012) Natural law theory. Its past and its present. In Marmor, A. (Ed.). The Routledge Companion to Philosophy of Law. New York and London: Routledge, 16-30.
8. Gadamer, H-G. (1975) Truth and Method. London: Sheed and Ward.
9. Glendinning, S. (2016) Derrida and the philosophy of law and justice. Law and Critique 27 (2), 187-203.
10. Habermas, J. (1990) Moral Consciousness and Communicative Action. Trans. by C. Lenhardt and S.W. Nicholsen. Cambridhe, MA: MIT Press.

11. Leiter, B. (2005) American legal realism. In Golding, M. and Edmundson, W. (Eds.). The Blackwell Guide to Philosophy of Law and Legal Theory. Malden, MA and Oxford: Blackwell, 50-66.

12. Postema, G.J. (2012) Legal positivism: early foundations. In Marmor, A. (Ed.). The Routledge Companion to Philosophy of Law. New York and London: Routledge, 31-47.

13. Savigny, F.C. von. (1840). System des heutigen Römischen Rechts. [System of today's Roman law.] Erster Band. Berlin: Veit. [In German].

Chapter 20. The nature of historiology

20.1. The nature of historiological theory

It is time to turn to the basics of what scholars call history, historiography, or historiology. History is usually understood as historical phenomena, as such. Historiography is a description of the history, known facts. This time, the language comes to the fore and with it the concept of theory. Historiography involves the use of certain theoretical concepts. This circumstance does not give grounds to consider it as a pronounced theory. The latter is not limited to a description of the facts. Initially, it is obvious that there is a need for terminology, denotes a scientific historical theory. For this purpose, the term 'historiology' is well suited. Historians rarely use this term, however, there is no alternative to it as a designation of a set of scientific historical theories. As the reader knows, I am guided by the principle of theoretical representation. According to its content, history and historiography are two different forms of representation of historiology.

As applied to historiology, it is appropriate to distinguish between metahistoriology and the philosophy of historiology. Metahistoriology is the comprehension of the conceptual and methodological structure of historiology as such. Metahistoriology is the destiny of historians. The philosophy of historiology presupposes currents of knowledge emanating from all sciences, previously generalized within the framework of the philosophy of science. It involves the collaboration of historians with philosophers. In the existing literature, the philosophy of historiology is called, as a rule, the philosophy of history. The popular 'Stanford Encyclopedia of Philosophe' and the 'Internet Encyclopedia of Philosophy' have articles

'Philosophy of History'. [1; 3] It is easy to verify that in the content they coincide with the philosophy of historiology. What is the nature of historiology? A typical answer to this question is given by Daniel Little.

> In short, historians conceptualize, describe, contextualize, explain, and interpret events and circumstances of the past. They sketch out ways of representing the complex activities and events of the past; they explain and interpret significant outcomes; and they base their findings on evidence in the present that bears upon facts about the past. ... Ultimately, the historian's task is to shed light on the what, why, and how of the past, based on inferences from the evidence of the present. [3, sec. 1]

Anthony Jensen begins his article with the sentence «History is the study of the past in all its forms. » [1] I agree with the authors who believe that historiology studies the past. Nevertheless, I believe that it is unlikely that the study of the past should be considered the main feature of historiology. Let us compare history with four other social branches of science, namely, with sociology, economics, political science, and law. All these branches of science deal with one type of phenomenon. For example, economics studies exclusively economic phenomena. The situation with historiology is fundamentally different. Historiology does not deal with historical phenomena that are as independent as, for example, economic or political phenomena. It deals with sociological, economic, political and legal phenomena in a complex, in unity with each other. This circumstance distinguishes historiology from other social sciences in the first place. Each of them also studies the past. Only historiology studies with respect to the past the unity of all social sciences. Strictly speaking, historiology deals not only with the social but also with all other sciences, in particular, pedagogy, psychology, medicine, and technology. For the sake of brevity, I limit my analysis to the consideration of historiology as a social science.

Earlier, characterizing the nature of the social sciences, every time I primarily singled out their principles. It is reasonable to go this way and in the characterization of historiology. Of course, historians do not cancel the principles of other social sciences. It is not true that they do not do anything with them at all. Combining various social sciences with each other, historians are forced to streamline principles of them. The subordination of the principles of the social sciences depends on specific situations, countries, peoples, historical periods; it is not installed finally. The historiography of respectively a totalitarian and democratic society is significantly different from each other. With that said, I conclude that the subordination of the principles of social sciences that are part of the conceptual complex that historiology deals with is its first principle. The indicated principle of subordination is not singled out even by those authors who pay especially close attention to the conceptual nature of historiology, for example, Reinhart Koselleck. [2] In my opinion, this is the result of insufficient attention to the complex nature of historiology, and of an attempt to liken it to other social sciences.

After streamlining the principles, therefore, in general, the entire set of concepts of those social theories that historiology combines, they are synchronized with each other. Now comes the turn of the principle of diachrony, according to which all concepts realize some temporality characteristic of them. Koselleck believed that "the diachronic principle constitutes

Begriffsgeschichte as an autonomous domain of research". [2, 83] It really does, but only after the principle of subordination of the principles of those sciences, which historiology unites.

Diachrony embraces the past, present, and future. Historians focus on the past. This means that another principle is being implemented, the principle of actualization of the past. Usually, it catches the eye. Perhaps this is why, when characterizing the specifics of historiology, they indicate, first of all, its orientation toward the past. So, the constitution of the uniqueness of historiology is realized through three principles, the principles of subordination of the unified theories, diachrony, and actualization of the past

On the example of sociology, economics, political science, and law, we have repeatedly made sure that the deviation of theories from an ethical project is fraught with undesirable consequences. Avoiding them, it is advisable to include ethical principles of prosperity and responsibility in any axiological theory. Of course, in this respect, historiology is no exception. Thus, the hierarchy of the principles of historiology is as follows: the principle of prosperity → the principle of responsibility → the principle of subordination of unified theories → the principle of diachrony → the principle of actualization of the past. This hierarchy expresses the specificity of historiology most clearly. A more detailed view suggests a demonstration of the conceptual power of this hierarchy of principles in cycles of conceptual transduction.

References

1. Jensen, A.K. (2020) Philosophy of history. In Internet Encyclopedia of Philosophy. Available at: https://www.iep.utm.edu/history/

2. Koselleck, R. (2004) Futures Past: on the Semantic of Historical Time. *New York:* Columbia University Press.
3. Little, D. (2017) Philosophy of History. In The Stanford Encyclopedia of Philosophy. Available at: https://plato.stanford.edu/archives/sum2017/entries/history/

20.2. Historical time and temporal processes

There are certain difficulties in understanding time as a key concept of historiology. Hardly anyone would object physical time is studied in an impressive way. Thanks to the successes of relativistic and quantum physics, we know that each physical reference system has its own time. Time is not an independent separate substance. Physical time, in fact, is a set of durations of physical processes. The longer the duration of the process, the greater part of its life's journey is passed. Duration is an integral quantitative measure of the process from its inception to the end.

It is reasonable to assume that, in historiology, time, being different from physical one, nevertheless, is also a quantitative characteristic of some processes. A researcher, who is well aware of the successes of physics in studying the nature of physical time, turning to historiography, is faced with an extremely unusual situation. Here, for the most part, time is understood not as one of the characteristics of processes, but as these processes themselves with their three modes, past, present, and future. At the same time, historians do not refuse physical time, used, in particular, in chronology. A dual understanding of time in historiology leads to confusion, which with modern lexical norms is hardly possible to avoid. In the future, I will understand time as the totality of durations as characteristics of processes. These processes are not time. The past, present, and future is not time, but a variety of processes with different temporality. Past processes have ended; present ones are continuing, future ones have not yet begun.

It must be assumed that the peculiarity of historiology should be expressed in the peculiarities of historical time. Nevertheless, it is extremely difficult to give a clear answer to the question: «How is historical time different from physical time?». Physical time depends on physical parameters. It does not respond to the features of social systems. Therefore, it should not be taken as an adequate characterization of historical processes. However, historians use it. Do they make a significant mistake uncritically using a characteristic that is alien to historical processes? They may make a mistake, but it is hardly significant.

The fact is that historians evaluate physical durations in the context of historical events. From this point of view, the same chronological year has different meanings as applied, for example, to the economies of the USA, China, and Russia. The physicist does not consider this circumstance. The historian, unlike the physicists, does not consider physical durations on their own, but their historical relativity.

Is it reasonable to consider that historical time is nothing but a combination of physical durations in their historical relativity? I do not think so. [8] In my opinion, the historical duration is a special characteristic expressing the degree to which processes are removed from their inception. If, for example, a three-year history of the development of some social processes, for example, economic, is considered, then each year can be characterized by a quantitative parameter, which is historical, in this case, economic duration. Historical duration and physical duration in its historical relativity are fundamentally different in nature. In the order of self-criticism, I must admit that my understanding of the nature of historical time and its difference from physical time is hardly realized in historiology. In my opinion, most historians identify historical time with the historical relativity of physical time.

A review of the literature shows that historians are interested not so much in understanding historical time as in the understanding of the nature of multiple times. The history of this issue has been qualified by Helge Jordheim. [7] In my understanding, it is as follows.

In 1799, Johann Gottfried Herder suggested that « [i]n reality every mutable thing has its own inherent standard of time; this exists even if nothing else is there; no two things in the world have the same standard of time. ... In other words, there are (one can say it earnestly and courageously) in the universe at any time innumerable different times. » [6, 360] Jordheim believes Herder defined the paradigmatic formulation of theory of multiple temporalities. [7, 512] From an empirical point of view, this theory seems almost obvious, but the problem is that it is extremely difficult to give it a clear theoretical form. In this sense, the reaction to the book of the sociologist Georges Gurvitch «The Spectrum of Social Time» [4] by the French historian Fernand Braudel is very indicative. Gurvitch examined eight types of social time, including time running slowly, quickly and explosively. Braudel's answer was this: «The world's time, historical time is there, but imprisoned, like Aeolus in his goat's skin. It is not history, which sociologists, fundamentally quite unconsciously, bear a grudge against, but historical time - which is a reality that retains its violence no matter how one tries to bring it to order and to break it down. » [3, 49-50] The meaning of his position is that in historical theory appears one time, and not several types of times. Recall in this connection physics.

Physicists up to the discoveries of Albert Einstein recognized the reality of only one, namely, world time. Only when he directly in theory used the concept of types of time did they agree that there are different types of time. It is not enough to affirm the multiplicity of types of times. It should be theoretically justified. Studying various forms of time, in particular, physical and economic time, I was guided by this very position. [8] I considered various theories and it was in them that I tried to highlight specific times. In a clearly articulated form, I could not find them. Therefore, I had no choice but sincerely to assert that, outside the limits of physics, the vast majority of authors are wrong to reduce specific time to the axiological relativity of physical time.

A significant innovation was the work of Reinhart Koselleck of the late 1970s. [9] He considered the problem of historical time in the context of language. Koselleck continued the traditions of German philosophy, Kantianism and hermeneutics. Nevertheless, his addiction to linguistic discourses coincided with the precepts of authors who were guided by French poststructuralism. From now on, historical theory found itself in the shadow of language discourses. Instead of considering the representations of historical theory, they were simply identified with it. The universal approval of the diversity of discourses was accompanied by the same unanimous approval of the multiplicity of time [2; 5] It is significant that like Koselleck François Hartog and Aleida Assmann did not reveal a cardinal difference between historical time and physical time directly in the structure of the historical theory. Without this, the statement of the multiplicity of historical time remains an arbitrary act.

The thesis of the multiplicity of time was relevant in rethinking the boundaries between the three types of temporal processes, i.e. past, present, and future. These boundaries are being broken up and the relationship between past, present, and future is being redefined. [5; 10] According to François Hartog, the relevance of the present is increasing to the detriment of the past and the future. [5] Aleida Assmann claims that the concept of the future has lost its former luster. [2, 7]. Eelco Runia believes that with a correct understanding of the past, it is understood as the initiator of the present; however, it has to be abandoned. [11] Jonas Ahlskog proposes to interpret the presence of the past in the present, drawing on the ideas of R.G. Collingwood. The past is present in the present as it is being rethought. [1]

My position is that the boundaries between the past, present, and future are set by the duration of the processes. If the process is over, then it belongs to the past. If its duration continues to increase, then it refers to the present. If we are talking about a process that has not begun it refers to the future. The boundaries of temporal processes should be determined, first, taking into account their durations. Contrary to a widespread position, the past cannot in any way move into the present. This fact does not contradict the theoretical creativity of people who are perfecting their theories through intertheoretical transduction. The content of the outdated theory of T_1 is interpreted based on a new, more developed theory of T_2: $T \rightarrow T_1\{T2\}$. Theories like all other entities have durations. T_1, unlike T_2 and $T_1\{T_2\}$, belongs to the past, not the present. As you can see, T_1 is not included in the present. Collingwood believed that rethinking the past means the presence of the past in the present. He did not take into account that the past refers exclusively to T_1.

The present always appears as a continuation and at the same time overcoming the past. If people did not make new cycles of knowledge, then the future could be forgotten. Replacing the present with new processes, they demonstrate their indefatigable desire to overcome the present. In my opinion, it is this desire that forces us to introduce the concept of the future. Contrary to the opinion of Aleida Assmann, I do not believe that the concept of the future is losing its luster. Quite the contrary, the development of modern society leads to an increase in the creative activity of people. It is impossible without actualizing the concept of the future.

In conclusion, I note that authors who consider time in the context of history, as a rule, do not pay any attention to those sciences that are united by historiology. This circumstance can hardly be regarded otherwise than as an unreasonable tribute to metaphysics. Better to do without it.

References

1. Ahlskog, J. (2017) R.G. Collingwood and the presence of the past. Journal of the Philosophy of History 11(3), 289-305.
2. Assmann, A. (2013) Ist die Zeit aus den Fugen? Aufstieg und Fall des Zeitregimes der Moderne. [Is the Time out of Fuges? Rise and Fall of the Time Regime of Modernity.] Munich: Carl Hanser Verlag. [In German].
3. Braudel, F. (1982) On History. Transl. by S. Matthews. Chicago: The University of Chicago Press.

4. Gurvitch, G. (1964) The Spectrum of Social Time. Dordrecht: Reidel.

5. Hartog, F. (2003) Regimes d'historicité: Présentisme et expériences du temps. [Regimes of historicity: Presentism and experiences of time.] Paris: Seuil. [In French].

6. Herder, J.G. (1998) [1799]. Eine Metakritik zur Kritik der reinen Vernunft. [A metakritik for the critique of pure reason.] Werke. Band 8. Schriften zur Literatur und Philosophie 1792–1800. Frankfurt am Main: Deutscher Klassiker Verlag, 303-640. [In German].

7. Jordheim, H. (2014) Introduction: multiple times and the work of synchronization. History and Theory 53(4), 498-518.

8. Kanke, V.A. (2018) [1984] Formy vremeni [Forms of Time]. Third ed. Moskva: Librokom Publ. [In Russian].

9. Koselleck, R. (2004) Futures Past: on the Semantic of Historical Time. New York: Columbia University Press.

10. Lorenz, C. and Bevernage, B. (Eds.). Breaking Up Time: Negotiating the Borders between Present, Past and Future. Göttingen: Vandenhoeck and Ruprecht.

11. Runia, E. (2014) Moved by the Past: Discontinuity and Historical Mutation. New York: Columbia University Press.

20.3. Evidence, causation, counterfactuals, and necessity

If I were asked exactly where the analytical epistemology and methodology of historiology is presented most fully, then I would not hesitate to call Blackwell 'Companion to the Philosophy of History and Historiography' Ed. by Avieser Tucker. [10] The second chapter of Companion addresses the main issues of epistemology and methodology. Most of them are worth mentioning: evidence and confirmation, causation, counterfactuals, necessity and contingency, explanation, understanding, colligation, laws, objectivity, the past, narrative and interpretation, ontology, historicism, and ethics. In my opinion, it is the analytical version of the nature of historiology that is the most developed. Compared with other versions of historiology, in particular, hermeneutic and poststructuralist versions, it has the greatest scientific potential. Nevertheless, evaluating its content from the standpoint of the theory of intratheoretical and intertheoretical transduction, I am inclined to believe that it has certain disadvantages. The content of all the problems listed above is greatly clarified if it is considered from the perspective of conceptual transduction cycles. In this case, all of them, covered by the same conceptual framework, receive a uniform interpretation.

I see historiology as the final link in the bundle of social sciences. It is a certain way to links together the achievements of economics, sociology, political science, and law. It is not surprising that, in epistemological and methodological respect, history largely repeats the conceptual achievements of other social sciences. This circumstance keeps me from intending to set out in detail the content of historiological epistemology and methodology. Otherwise, multiple repetitions could not have been avoided. Given this circumstance, I decided to confine myself to comments, which, incidentally, can be considered to have a generalizing character in relation to a cluster of five social sciences, sociology, economics, political science, law, and historiology.

On evidence

Mark Day and Gregory Radick consider « [t]hose beliefs that provide or fail to provide empirical support to hypotheses – that «confirm» the hypotheses or «disconfirm» them – are the evidence. » [3, 88] According to this logic, there are two sides, a hypothesis, and evidence, while research establishes whether there is a correspondence between them. The decisive ratio is correspondence. Everything else is reduced to it. As the reader knows, the cycle of intratheoretical transduction contains four stages, planning the experiment and predicting its results, experiment, processing the results of experiments, constructing a new theory (hypothesis). This multi-link process does not boil down to one concept, correspondence. If the evidence is understood solely in the context of conformity and non-conformity, then it is as dubious as the concept of conformity. In my opinion, evidence should be understood as conducting cycles of intratheoretical conceptual transduction. Reading the numerous works of analytical authors on evidence, I noticed that they somehow reluctantly talk about the role of experiments. As a result, the proof comes down mostly to logic.

On causation

Avieser Tucker begins his article on causation by stating that «[h]istoriography is made of myriad causal links, connecting descriptions of historical events or processes. Arguably, causal links are one of the "glues" that keep historiographic narratives together.» [9, 98] In fact, causation is considered by analytical authors as the core of historical processes. It is clearly more than just one of the «glues». Causation is the dynamic content of actualization, i.e. experiment, including practice. Unfortunately, the vast majority of authors considering causation does not take into account that it is not an autonomous factor. It is implemented as part of a whole. This whole is reproduced through intratheoretical transduction. If this circumstance is not taken into account, then the causality is given the character of an autonomous factor, which it is not. In this case, the idea of social processes is impoverished, becomes boring, mechanistic. In the social sciences, causation is always the interaction of people, which are guided by certain principles. Causation is always, above all, the implementation of principles.

Anton Froeyman, in an effort to express the uniqueness of historiological causality, attaches great importance to three well-known issues. «Historiography consists of giving answers to three different types of questions: What? How? Why? » [5, 119] Without further explanation, it is obvious that these questions even if you add to them four more Who? Where? When? How Match? by themselves, do not give an adequate idea of any science, including historiology. Nevertheless, Froeyman's aspiration to express the true content of historiology and to correlate with it the specificity of historiological causation commendable. The true content of historiology is expressed in cycles of the conceptual transduction.

The absolutizing of causality is unacceptable, as well as its denial. Mark Hewitson provocatively raises the question of the possibility of rejecting the need to consider causal relationships. [7, 26,36] He himself, while not denying their reality, nevertheless concentrates his attention on narratives of history, in which, in essence, causation is not discussed. In my opinion, Hewitson spent a lot of energy searching for the whole to which the causation belongs, but never found it. I have already stated my position on this score. I believe that causation is an aspect of intratheoretical transduction. In any case, the statement remains valid that causation provide the dynamics of historical processes. It consists in the fact that people strive to realize the principles of historical theories. In these acts, of course, there is nothing mysterious.

On counterfactuals

Elazar Weinryb and Yemima Ben-Menahem presented the highly compelling concept of counterfactuals. [2; 11] According to this concept, counterfactuals not complying with the original theory, however, contribute to a sharper emphasis on its merits. A true theory does not establish itself in an airless space but as an alternative to a possible rival. The true theory is consistent with the facts; the non-genuine with counterfactuals, which should have a certain potential for the approval of a genuine theory.

> Counterfactuals are essentially involved in understanding what it means for an event, an action, or an individual to make a difference. Making a difference, in turn, is shown to be a central category of historical reasoning. Counterfactuals, though sensitive to the description they use, make objective claims that can be confirmed or disconfirmed by evidence. [2, 370]

Consider the problem of counterfactuals from the position of conceptual transduction. In this conception, there is no need to talk about the correspondence of the facts of the theory, because they are its integral part. New facts obtained through observations, experiments, and practical actions are part of the process of developing a new theory. New facts are different from old facts, for they are defined in the context of a new theory. As for counterfactuals, they are not genuine facts, because they stand out in the process of not actualization, but imagination. From this point of view, they are akin to abstractions and idealizations, which are also the result of imagination. Imagination does not produce facts, but thought-forms or just thoughts. Strictly speaking, counterfactuals like abstractions and idealizations are not facts, but thought-forms.

All thoughts are necessary to facilitate the process of conceptual transduction. Counterfactuals are similar in status to idealization. They are used temporarily and are ultimately rejected. Yemima Ben-Menahem believes that the central category of historical reasoning is «[m]aking a difference». I believe that making a difference is nothing more than one of the techniques of conceptual transduction. It is extremely important that making a difference applies not only to facts but also to laws and principles. Imaginary counter-laws and counter-principles are no less important than counterfactuals.

On necessity and contingency

These two concepts are considered extremely relevant for historiology. For a long time, it was not possible to give their consistent interpretation. As a rule, the concepts of necessity and contingency were interpreted based on certain ideas about causal relationships. However, what was known about them was not enough to characterize adequately necessity and contingency. Regarding the content of these two concepts, Yemima Ben-Menahem presented an innovative idea.

> On the received view, necessity is associated with causation, contingency with chance or randomness. By contrast, I want to suggest that contingency and necessity be understood in terms of stability, that is, sensitivity or insensitivity to initial conditions and intervening factors. [1, 121]

Ben-Menahem convincingly showed that his conception compares favorably with the metaphysical notions of determinism and freedom. Developing the theory of Ben-Menahem, Rob Inkpen and Derek Turner complimented it with a notion of historical disturbance and noted «contingency and necessity are subject to scaling effects. » [8].

Based on the theory of conceptual transduction, I propose another interpretation of the concepts of necessity and contingency. I mean, first, that about the long-term necessity and contingency we are able judging exclusively due to the league-theory. Theories complement each other in an ambiguous and non-arbitrary way. This circumstance when referring to the concepts of determinism and freedom is understood simplistically. Determinism implies an unambiguous continuity between theories, but it is never like that. Those who insist on free will believe that people are free in their actions largely than this actually takes place.

Using mathematical and computer models of nonlinear processes sheds additional light on the discussed problems. One example of their use is provided by an article by Roberto Franzosi. [4] The use of mathematical and computer modeling can significantly clarify knowledge of the past. In particular, this concerns the construction of long-term time series in which succeeded C.W.J. Granger. [6] It is the time series that are considered in the context of league-theories give the most accurate idea of the ways in which historical processes unfold.

References

1. Ben-Menahem, Y. (2009) Historical necessity and contingency. In Tucker, A. (Ed.). A Companion to the Philosophy of History and Historiography. Oxford: Wiley-Blackwell, 120-130.
2. Ben-Menahem, Y. (2016) If counterfactuals were excluded from historical reasoning... Journal of the philosophy of history 10(3), 370-381.
3. Day, M. and Radick, G. (2009) Historiographic evidence and confirmation? In Tucker, A. (Ed.), 87-97.

4. Franzosi, R. (2017) A third road to the past? Historical scholarship in the age of big data. Historical Methods: A Journal of Quantitative and Interdisciplinary History 50(4), 227-244.
5. Froeyman, A. (2009) Concepts of causation in historiography. Historical Methods: A Journal of Quantitative and Interdisciplinary History 42(3), 116-128.
6. Granger, C.W.J. (1989) Modeling Economic Series: Readings in Econometric Methodology. Oxford: Oxford University Press.
7. Hewitson, M (2014) History and Causality. Basingstoke: Palgrave Macmillan.
8. Inkpen, R. and Turner, D. (2012) The Topography of historical contingency. Journal of the Philosophy of History 6(1), 1-19.
9. Tucker, A. (2009) Causation in historiography. In Tucker, A. (Ed.), 98-108.
10. Tucker, A. (Ed.). (2009) A Companion to the Philosophy of History and Historiography. Oxford: Wiley-Blackwell.
11. Weinryb, E. (2009). Historiographic counterfactuals. In Tucker, A. (Ed.), 109-111.

20.4. Explanation, understanding and colligation

On explanation

The problem of explanation in historiology attracts the close attention of researchers, especially in connection with the difficulties that arise when trying in explanations to combine causes and laws. David Donaldson presented this fact as follows.

The most primitive explanation of an event gives its cause; more elaborate explanations may tell more of the story, or defend the singular causal claim by producing a relevant law or by giving reasons for believing such exists. But it is an error to think no explanation has been given until a law has been produced. Linked with these errors is the idea that singular causal statements necessarily indicate, by the concepts they employ, the concepts that will occur in the entailed law. [4, 698]

The vast majority of representatives of modern analytical philosophy of historiology, continuing the centuries-old tradition of Aristotle-Mill, prefer causal explanations. They could hardly agree with Donaldson in that part of his statement where he considered it possible to call the causal explanation primitive. They believe that causal explanation expresses the most essential, namely, the origin of historical phenomena and the mechanism of their evolution. This circumstance was obscured by the energetic propaganda of Carl Hempel of covering-law or deductive-nomological model of scientific explanation. [7] The law is some functional relation. The type of explanation proposed by him to historians on behalf of the philosophy of science was functional. The question of its causal content remained open. Causation can explain the occurrence of an effect by a cause. It is impossible to explain scientific laws in the same style, because for the most part, at least in nature, they exist initially. On the other hand, few dare to assert that scientific laws are not needed in the matter of explanation. Recognizing the validity of laws and at the same time the impossibility of explaining them by causes, researchers have to acknowledge the presence of not only causal but also non-causal explanations. The findings reached by Graham and Cynthia Macdonald are indicative in this regard.

We have argued that historiographic explanation comes in many forms. Sometimes general claims form an essential component, whereas at other times only the particular circumstances and psychological states of the agent(s) need to be mentioned. In the former case, the generalizations are likely to be laws only in a loose sense, one allowing for the law to be imprecisely formulated and limited in scope. We have suggested that Hempel's fairly broad characterization of those different types of explanation using generality will cover these cases. We have argued in addition that there is room for what has been called narrative explanation, a form of causal explanation that does not make essential use of laws, even if the causal relation requires there to be a law covering that relation. Singular causal explanation works because there is a cause in play, not because there is a law in the background. [9, 140]

In my opinion, McDonald's, like other authors, failed to show the unity of causal and other types of explanations. I refer below precisely to this unity. If there are many types of explanations, then each of them is not complete. Which conceptual framework provides a complete explanation? In my opinion, this is a theory of conceptual transduction. It operates with the concepts of both cause and law, therefore, causal and law-based explanation are its parts. It is equally obvious that a full scientific explanation should include all stages of the intratheoretical and intertheoretical transduction. Both causal and law-based explanations are clearly insufficient. However, forgetting one or the other is also inappropriate. The explanation of any phenomenon is to highlight its full history in the cycles of conceptual transduction. The greater the number of stages of transduction the researcher considers, the clearer the image of the phenomenon being studied. This is precisely the content of the scientific explanation. In my opinion, Hempel gave an extremely poor view of the content of the scientific explanation. He emphasized laws and deduction, but forgot to pay no less attention to the principles, methods of adduction, induction, and abduction, and much more. In light of conceptual transduction, the content of the causal explanation is also rather poor. My main idea is that all types of explanations as aspects of conceptual transduction constitute a unity. There are no grounds for their opposition to each other or for absolutizing some of them.

In recent years, a tendency has clearly become known in the philosophy of science about scientific explanation, taking into account all the features of scientific theories, in particular, in connection with the use of abstractions and idealizations in them. [1; 11; 12] This is certainly a step in the right direction. The explanation must always take into account the fullness of scientific theories. I note once again that this fullness finds its expression in the cycles of conceptual transduction.

On understanding

The concept of understanding (German 'verstehen') is one of the most problematic in historiology. [3] It goes back to the origins of German idealism. Its founder should rightfully be considered Johann Droysen. He noted «[t]he essence of the historical method is researching to understand». [6, 9] The conception of verstehen was developed following Droysen, by W. Dilthey, M. Weber, and many other German hermeneutists. All of them were convinced that we explain nature, and understand human society and ourselves. This means that the methods of the social sciences are fundamentally different from the methods of the natural sciences. This belief was not shared by the absolute majority of Anglo-Saxon authors, brought up in analytical traditions. They believed that both types of sciences had nothing more important than the experimental method. It is not taken into account by hermeneutists. At the same time, they were somewhat alarmed by the difference between the social and natural sciences due to the normativity of the former. Between, on the one hand, hermeneutists and, on the other hand, analytic philosophers, a clear controversy arose that did not dissipate to the present day. One side extols scientific explanation through causation, the other side insists on understanding through interpretation. To emphasize even more sharply the difference between the two positions, let me reproduce a quote from W. Dray, in which he presents in a generalized form the position of another authority, namely, R.G. Collingwood [2]:

> first, that human action, which is the proper concern of history, cannot be described as action at all, without mentioning the thought which it expresses-it has, in Collingwood 's terms, a "thought-side"; second, that once the thought in question has been grasped by the historian, the action is understood in the sense appropriate to actions, so that it is unnecessary to go on to ask for the cause which produced it, or the law which it instantiates; third, that the understanding of action in terms of thought requires the rethinking of the thought in question by the historian, so that, in essence, all history is "the re-enactment of past thought in the historian's own mind. [5,201]

I ask the reader to note this quote carefully. Two famous authors are mainly concerned about the mental side of historians. They believe that causation and laws are beyond mentality. The mental is opposed to the ontological. They, like many other authors, do not notice that the same theory can be given in various forms, including mental and ontological. Given this circumstance, the opposition of explanation and understanding loses all meaning. Two words are not necessary is enough one. Where representatives of two directions act sequentially, they implement the same strategy through cycles of conceptual transduction. The principles of theories, including natural and social conceptions, are different, but not one side can do without them. From the principles begins the line of intentional determination, the active side of which is expressed by causation. In my opinion, this is the essence of the scientific explanation.

On colligation

The linguistic concept of colligation has attracted the attention of historians. [10] In linguistics, colligation refers to the inclusion of a lexical item in a grammatical category. [8, 3]. In historiology, colligation is the unification of disparate elements of knowledge into some construction, for example, into a narrative. As it turned out in the research process, there is a huge variety of collision opportunities, the assessment of the shortcomings and achievements of which meets with great difficulties. It is impossible to cope with them unless you are guided by a developed conception of historiological explanation. If the historian does not have developed colligational competence, then he sees everywhere scattered islands of knowledge that he is not able to combine into a whole, i.e. into the theory.

A qualified historian owns a network of theories, each of which represents a certain collision construct. There are various connections between theories. Each theory is given in some representation, for example, lingual, mental or practical. If the historian skillfully navigates this network of theories, then when he encounters unusual phenomena, knowingly embeds them in existing structures. If this inclusion cannot be achieved, then in accordance with conceptual transduction, a new theory is formed and its relations with existing concepts are established.

My main thought is that only the historian who perfectly knows the theory of conceptual transduction possesses colligational competence and, from its perspective, evaluates any collegiate possibility no matter how strange at first glance it may be.

Thus, all the difficulties associated with explanation, understanding, and colligation, ultimately get their permission with the targeted use of scientific methods.

References

1. Batterman, R. W. and Rice, C.C. (2014) Minimal model explanations. Philosophy of Science 81(3), 349-376.
2. Collingwood, R. G. (1946) The Idea of History. Oxford: Clarendon Press.
3. D'Oro, G. (2009) Historiographic understanding. In Tucker, A. (Ed.). A Companion to the Philosophy of History and Histrography. Oxford: Wiley-Blackwell, 141-151.
4. Davidson, D. (1963) Actions, reasons and causes. Journal of Philosophy 60(23), 685-700.
5. Dray, W. H. (1957) Historical understanding as re-thinking. University of Toronto Quarterly 27(2), 200-215.
6. Droysen, J.G. (1868) Grundriss der Historik [Foundations of History]. Leipzig: Verlag von Veit und Comp. [In German]

7. Hempel, C. (1942) The function of general laws in history. Journal of Philosophy 39(2), 35-48.

8. Lehecka, T. (2015) Collocation and colligation. In Östman, J.-O. and Verschueren, J. (Eds.). Handbook of Pragmatics. Amsterdam: John Benjamins Publishing Company, 1-23.

9. Macdonald, G. and Macdonald, C. (2009) Explanation in historiography. In Tucker, A. (Ed.). 131-141.

10. Mccullagh, C.B. (2009) Colligation, In Tucker, A. (Ed.), 152-161.

11. Reutlinger, A, and Andersen, H. (2016) Abstract versus causal explanations? International Studies in the Philosophy of Science 30(2), 129-146.

12. Reutlinger, A. (2017) Explanation beyond causation? New directions in the philosophy of scientific explanation. Philosophy Compass 12:e12395.

20.5. Scientific theory and metaphysical pretensions to it

Historiology is a wide network of scientific theories. As repeatedly noted earlier, all controversial issues get their explanation no other than with careful consideration of its nature. Most of these contentious issues arise in the midst of historiology itself. New cycles of cognition make it possible to clarify their content. At the same time, there is a large group of questions, the formulation of which is initiated outside the limits of historiology, in the field of metaphysics. Nevertheless, their clarification is expected from historiology. Science has no obligation to metaphysics. Although it has no reason to avoid metaphysical questions. Science makes it possible to clarify the content of many metaphysical questions. The piquancy of the situation lies in the fact that these issues do not always suit the supporters of metaphysics. In this regard, numerous collisions arise. Some of them are connected with questions about the nature of historiological truth and objectivity. Both of these issues are considered extremely relevant to historiology and, at the same time, mysterious. [1, 258; 3, 172] Knowledge is considered objective if it depends solely on the object of study, but not on those who conduct research. [3, 172] The knowledge of the past is objective if it depends only on the past, and not on historians who study and describe it. According to the most authoritative concept of truth, knowledge is true if it corresponds to the object of research (reality), and only to it. It is easy to see that in this context, the concepts of objectivity and truth of knowledge are correlated with the concept of reality.

Having defined the metaphysical concepts of objective and true knowledge, as well as reality, I turn to historiology. Two series of theories are distinguished here. The first series of theories capture the historical tread of problem conceptions and the second their comparison with each other, which is carried out from the standpoint of the most developed theory. For my purposes, it is enough to consider a series consisting of three theories. The most developed theory is T_3.

(I) *The problem series of theories*: $T_1 \rightarrow T_2 \rightarrow T_3 \rightarrow$.

(II) *Interpretative series of theories*: $...T_3 \rightarrow T_2\{T_3\} \rightarrow T_1\{T_3\}$.

Based on the series (I) and (II), the following conclusions can be made.

1. Any historical knowledge, including about the past, is always given not otherwise than in a theoretical form.

2. As theories develop, knowledge is refined from the standpoint of the most developed theories.

3. Knowledge cannot be final.

4. New knowledge is acquired through the work of historians.

5. New knowledge to assess its quality is available to everyone.

6. Knowledge is to a certain extent justified; therefore, it is not arbitrary.

7. To exist means to be a part of scientific league-theory.

8. All representations of theories, in particular, lingual, mental, object and subjective express its content.

As for the metaphysical provisions on the truth and objectivity of knowledge, they, of course, are elevated to the rank of scientific provisions only if they are consistent with conclusions 1-8. According to the metaphysical concept of truth, it must be impeccable. Once opened, it should not be reviewed. This position is incompatible with the content of series (I) and (II), which are open to meet the future achievements of historiology. In this regard, two possibilities are opening up. Either a metaphysical concept of the truth of knowledge should be resolutely abandoned, or it should be transformed in accordance with the contents of series (I) and (II). Additional analysis shows that it is advisable to affirm in its rights a scientific understanding of the truth. The fact is that in metaphysics and in science, false knowledge is denied as an alternative to the truth. Having abandoned the concept of truth, researchers indirectly assert false knowledge. Such a refusal is incompatible with the content of science. Therefore, we get on the rails of scientifically true knowledge. It is recognized as true if included in the content of series (II).

It should be specially noted that it is extremely important to distinguish clearly and consistently between the metaphysical and scientific conceptions of true knowledge. The metaphysical conception of truth proceeds from the provision on the correspondence of mental and lingual knowledge of reality. The scientific conception of truth comes from the most developed knowledge. The corresondence conception of truth is considered far-fetched. By definition, in the composition of theory, all its parts correspond to each other. It cannot be in any other way. Otherwise, you will have to abandon the concept of theory and there will be no conceptual framework for judging true and false knowledge.

The metaphysical position on the objectivity of reality is also not consistent with the series (I) and (II). The invention of a new theory is always identical to the revision of the status of reality. There is no reason to argue that historical reality is just that and no other. Suppose we are studying the question of the basis of Hitler's decision to attack the Soviet Union in June 1941. What guided him, the desire to seize living space for the German people, hatred of the Communists, or the need to deliver a preventive strike on the Soviet Union? There is hardly any definitive answer to this question. It must be assumed that if there was a corresponding testimony of Hitler himself, and then historians called it into question. The question of historical reality cannot be resolved without reference to historical scientific theories. The concept of scientific reality is different from the concept of metaphysical reality. The scientific reality is given by the most developed theories. Accordingly, the concepts of metaphysical and scientific realism also differ.

The failure of the concept of metaphysical reality indicates the failure of the concept of metaphysical objectivity, which suggests that knowledge is determined exclusively by metaphysical reality. The scientific reality is given by the most developed theories; therefore, scientific objectivity is also given by them. Scientific objectivity is that knowledge develops in accordance with the canons of science.

Thus, one should hardly be in a hurry to abandon the concepts of truth, objectivity, and reality. Nevertheless, it is not permissible to keep them as metaphysical categories. In my opinion, the insufficiently clear distinction between metaphysical and scientific concepts is fertile ground for many years of discussion around the question of the viability of the concept of historical truth. Some researchers uncritically focus on the metaphysical concept of truth. Other researchers hastily abandon the concept of scientific truth. Both sides do not always consistently explain their position. In this regard, the article of C. Behan McCullagh, who, defending the concept of historical truth, seeks to clarify many controversial issues, deserves attention. [2]

In particular, he objects to those authors who question the reliability, firstly, of perceptions of the available evidence, secondly, of historical inferences, and thirdly, of the subjectivity of historical interpretations. Regarding the first argument, McCullagh states, «we normally assume the world is as we perceive it to be, under certain conditions. This assumption is not arbitrary, however, because actions based upon it generally produce predicted changes in what we perceive. The truth of the assumption explains the success of these predictions, over and over again. » [7, 101] This argument seems to me clearly insufficient. We judge the state of the world not only based on perceptions but because of full-fledged cycles of conceptual transduction.

Regarding the reliability of historical inferences, McCullagh notes that historians carefully compare the facts of the present and the past so as not to judge the past hastily, solely on the basis of the present. I want to support this statement. However, in my opinion, it does not provide a sufficiently complete picture of how historians combine information about the past and the present.

Regarding the subjectivity of historical interpretations, McCullagh notes that there are various ways to describe the past, but only a few are recognized as true. [2, 106]. Apparently, he means that the subjectivity of historical interpretations does not limit the truth of knowledge in any way.

McCullough repeats some of his arguments more than once. In this regard, let me proceed to consider directly his conception.

> My theory of truth captures perfectly the conditions for a description of something in the present world being true. If the perceptual experiences it implies are confirmed by observation, and if it best explains those observations, implying that they were caused by something in the world, rather than by a dream or imagination, then the description is true. But descriptions of things in the past cannot be proved by direct observation. So how can their truth be established?

> Although one cannot observe past events, historians can often observe their residue: reports by people who did witness them, photos that were

taken of them, descriptions of them by those who interviewed witnesses. The longer the causal chain, of course, the more room there is for error. [2, 73] But if reports by several different witnesses are available, and they correspond in their descriptions of an event, then the best explanation of that correspondence is that they all witnessed the same event and reported it fairly accurately. [2, 106]

McCullough attaches decisive importance to three factors, perceptual experiences, a causal explanation, which, thirdly, should be the best. It is these three factors, and not, for example, the social consensus of historians or the coherence of historical beliefs with diverse cultural circumstances, that support the need for reliance on the concept of historical truth. In my opinion, McCullagh presented one version of the analytic conception of historical truth. Unfortunately, he, firstly, did not pay due attention to the distinction between the metaphysical and scientific conceptions of historical truth. Secondly, only a little was said about the conceptual metamorphoses of historiologic theories.

In my opinion, the release of historiology from the metaphysical pretensions to it leaves much to be desired.

References

1. Ankersmit, F. (2013) Introduction: history and truth. Journal of the Philosophy of History 7(3), 257-265.
2. McCullagh, C.B. (2015) The truth of basic historical descriptions. Journal of the philosophy of history 9(1), 97-117.

3. Newall, P. (2009) Historiographic objectivity. In Tucker, A. (Ed.). A Companion to the Philosophy of History and Histrography. Oxford: Wiley-Blackwell, 172 -181.

20.6. Historicism and historical method

Each branch of science, by virtue of its originality, makes a special contribution to science, marked by the seal of its features. With respect to historiology, it is reasonable to expect that it will actualize the concept of historicity. Nevertheless, many years of expectations in this regard are largely not met. Henning Trüper notes the flatness of historicity. [9] He explains it by the absence of layers of explanatory and semantic depth that would provide a foundation for the term.

Few people manage to achieve a decisive result in the understanding of historicity, which would be approved by the scientific community. It is not by chance that the term 'historicism', which is derived from the word 'historicity' is generally taken critically. [4, 250-251] As a rule, it is understood that the emphasis on the historicity and variability of being does not make a tangible contribution to the development of social sciences. Nevertheless, attempts to give more weight to historicism do not stop. A significant attempt in this regard was made by Mark Bevir in his book on the logic of the history of ideas. [2]

> In the *Logic* I describe and defend a post-analytic historicism. Historicism refers to the view that human life is inherently historical: ideas, texts, actions, and practices are historical objects, and explanations of them must be historical. The word «historicism» appeared in English at the beginning

of the twentieth century to translate the Italian «storicisimo», as used by Benedetto Croce, and the German «Historismus», as used by Wilhelm Dilthey, Friedrich Meinecke, and Ernst Troeltsch. Croce, Dilthey, Meinecke, and Troeltsch were all involved in the crisis of historicism. This crisis consisted of a sense that historicist philosophy might undercut itself, leading to an untenable relativism. In my view, post-analytic philosophy gives support to historicism and also provides us with suitable resources with which to respond to the issues raised during the crisis of historicism. Post-analytic philosophy refers generally to developments in philosophy since the rejection of the distinction between analytic and synthetic propositions. [3, 111-112]

The decisive argument of Mark Bevir is that «[A] historicist ontology implies that texts have meaning only for specific people, whether these be individual authors, particular readers, or the intersubjective beliefs of social groups. Texts do not have intrinsic meanings in themselves. » [3, 111] Critics of Bevir doubt that he has properly revived historicism.

Jeffrey Green blames Bevir for the fact that instead of synthesizing historical (thought moves from the past to the present) and non-historical (past is explained based on the present) explanations, he acknowledges only the first ones. As a result, Bevir recommendations do not so much facilitate the work of historians as they complicate it. [6]

Over and against the figure of the historian of ideas, who interprets political thought only in the manner of a historian, I defend the ideal of the pupil, who in studying past traditions of political thought also seeks to extend and modify them in light of contemporary problems and concerns. Against Bevir, I argue that the mixture of historical and non-historical modes of learning, in the manner of the pupil, need not do damage to the historian of ideas' commitment to scholarship that is non-anachronistic, objective, and non-indeterminate. [6, 84]

Martyn Thompson also makes some claims to the concept of Bevir. He compares the approaches of Bevir and Michael Oakeshott. Thompson believes Bevir failed to show an effective way of highlighting the logic of ideas. «I would like to see a discussion of the logical status of the "past" that is presupposed in that form of the "historical past" that is constructed by historians of ideas. » [8, 607]

To me, the situation with determining the status of historicity seems extremely confusing. Let me try to defuse it somewhat. Each theory contains a time parameter if it is taken into account. About time and, therefore, historicity is judged based on theory. If researchers have to deal with unfamiliar phenomena, then they are looking for a theory with similar phenomena. If such a theory is found, then the durations of unfamiliar phenomena are judged because of these theories. Otherwise, a new theory will be invented in full accordance with the theory of conceptual transduction. Theory of the present, i.e. unfinished processes is also used to reproduce the temporality of processes of the past. As theories improve, it is advisable to consider time in the context of league-theories, which for the case of three theories has the following form: $T_3 \rightarrow T_2 \{T_3\} \rightarrow T_1 \{T3\}$. As a rule, a more developed theory, in this case, T_3 is invented later than less developed theories (T_2 and T_1). This circumstance indirectly indicates that the development of theories correlates with a change in time. It is impossible to judge the principle of the relevance of mature knowledge without taking into account the time factor and, therefore, the historicity of phenomena.

Historians are not content with what has been achieved; they are guided by a special, temporary representation of the theory. This means that the process acts as a certain sequence of its stages. Why do historians use the temporal representation of theories? The fact is that each subsequent stage is closely related to the previous one. By virtue of this, judgments about phenomena that have not yet arrived are made easier when the stages preceding it are known. It is in this connection that historians tirelessly construct time series. Since these series belong to various phenomena, in particular, of an economic, political, sociological nature, they consider combinations of time series, all those conflicts that are associated with the lack of their synchronous development.

In fact, I described nothing more than the historical method that allows us to intensify the process of scientific knowledge. Its main features: a) the use of the temporal representation of league-theories, c) the construction of time series, c) the integration of time series, accompanied by their synchronization. Thanks to this method, researchers express far from the ordinary nature of historicity. Given this circumstance, it is hardly appropriate to insist on 'flatness of historicity'. Equally unfounded is a critical attitude towards all types of historicism. Historians are actively developing the historical method. This is directly indicated by the content of their studies, in which, as a rule, it cannot do without constructing a time series of events. Unfortunately, historians are far from always presenting in due form the foundations of the historical method and, accordingly, the nature of historicity. The main mistake of many researchers is the desire to judge historicity and historical time, regardless of the cycles of conceptual transduction.

I recall once again the conception of Bevir. [1-3] He focused on the logic of the history of ideas. Presumably, he was interested in the foundations of the history of ideas. They are the basic principles of conceptual transduction, which are certainly brought to the historical method. This fact remained out of sight of Bevir. Of course, his desire to realize post-analytical historicism is commendable.

The link to logic when considering the history of ideas deserves special comment. Logicians, like representatives of all other sciences, actively use the historical method in various versions of temporal logic. It is advisable to take into account their achievements. Nevertheless, the identification of the foundations of the historical method with logic is wrong. It is obviously a tradition going back to Georg Hegel, who, calling the dialectic of categories logic, identified the philosophy of variability of Heraclitus with the Absolute Idea. [7, 279] Continuing this line of reasoning, Frederick Engels argued

> The logical method of approach [...] is indeed nothing but the historical method, only stripped of the historical form and diverting chance occurrences. The point where this history begins must also be the starting point of the train of thought, and its further progress will be simply the reflection, in abstract and theoretically consistent form, of the historical course. Though the reflection is corrected, it is corrected in accordance with laws provided by the actual historical course, since each factor can be examined at the stage of

development where it reaches its full maturity, its classical form. [5, 225]

If desired, of course, you can compare the historical method with the methods of logic. In this case, it will be necessary to determine to what extent the methods of conceptual transduction are manifested in logic as a formal science. The results of such a comparison will not lead to the naive conclusion that the logical method is a historical method devoid of its specific features.

The nature of the historical method is determined solely by the content of historiology, not philosophy. In my opinion, this circumstance was misunderstood by Michael Oakeshott, whom Martyn Thompson hastily sets as an example for Bevir. I will not take the liberty of claiming that one of them has a distinctly scientific position. The same applies to the position of Jeffrey Green, who, recommending combining historical and unhistorical explanations, did not consider both in the context of conceptual transduction.

Thus, historicism, understood as giving conceptual transduction of the historical dimension, is completely consistent. A gross mistake is the opposition of historicism to conceptual transduction, giving it independent meaning. Of particular note is the relevance of the historical method. Such a method does exist. His oblivion significantly reduces the potential of modern science.

References

1. Bevir, M. (1999) The Logic of the History of Ideas. Cambridge: Cambridge University Press.

2. Bevir, M. (2000) The logic of the history of ideas. Rethinking History 4(3), 295-300.
3. Bevir, M. (2012) In defense of historicism. Journal of the Philosophy of History 6(1), 111–114.
4. D'Amico, R. (2009) Historicism. In Tucker, A. (Ed.). A Companion to the Philosophy of History and Histrography. Oxford: Wiley-Blackwell, 243-252.
5. Engels, F. (1989) Karl Marx, 'A Contribution to the Critique of Political Economy'. Part One, Berlin: Franz Duncker, 1859, [Review]. In Marx, K. A Contribution to the Critique of Political Economy. New York: International Publishers.
6. Green, J.E. (2012) On the difference between a pupil and a historian of ideas. Journal of the Philosophy of History 6(1), 84-110.
7. Hegel, G.W.F. (1995) Lectures on the History of Philosophy. Vol. 1: Greek Philosophy to Plato. Transl. by E.S. Haldane and F.H. Simson. Lincoln: University of Nebraska Press.
8. Thompson, M.P. (2012) The logic of the history of ideas: Mark Bevir and Michael Oakeshott. Journal of the History of Ideas 73(4), 593-607.
9. Trüper, H. (2019) The flatness of historicity. History and Theory 58(1), 23-49.

20.7. The sluggish ethical turn

In all axiological sciences, the same picture is observed, at the positivist stage of science, ethics are abandoned, and later returned to it, but very uncertainly. In all cases, the fate of ethics is contradictory. This is especially characteristic of historiology. As repeatedly noted earlier, historiology is complex. Historians do not always consider this. In this regard, the development of scientifically oriented historiology, in particular, experimental methods, occurs with great difficulty.

[8] Historians' attempts to translate ethical issues of interest to them on a scientific footing look even foggier. The subject of my interest is precisely the scientifically oriented historical ethics and not metaphysical variations. Modern historiology consists of many schools. Among them, the leading positions are occupied by analytical, hermeneutic, and poststructuralist historiology. The scientific orientation of historiology is approved in its analytical version much more definitely than in the hermeneutic and poststructuralist versions. Thus, I am primarily interested in analytical historical ethics. Is there a need for such ethics? If so, what is it?

At first glance, it is not difficult to give comprehensive answers to the questions posed. I mean the statements about the need for an ethical turn, which, according to many historians, has even taken place. [2; 3; 10] Its origins are usually associated with Hayden White, who noted the sense of the "repressed moral dimension of historical inquiry." [12, 5] The judgment of the ethical turn does not enjoy universal support. Many authors prefer to talk about the practice turn. [4; 7] They usually don't remember ethics at all. So, what does ethics look like in the views of historians?

Michael Dintenfass argues that the Holocaust forces historians, after many years of dominance of the linguistic turn, to refer directly to ethics.

> Taking purposefully the ethical turn that the opponents of postmodernist historiography have unwittingly effected would open up the life-affirming possibilities of a post-linguistic-turn approach to historical inquiry. By directing historical narration to the representation of the good as well as the true, the historian's moral

imagination would be empowered to speak in its own voice and not just through epistemological surrogates that blunt its authority. [3, 20]

Dintenfass proposes to add ethics to epistemology as an external dominant force that affirms the value of the good. It is about intentions, but it is not clear exactly how this should be done. The question of the relationship between epistemology and ethics remains open.

Jonathan Gorman expresses concern that historians are not prepared consider consistently moral issues in their historiographical works. «They would need to have in advance some idea of what it was they were writing about. They would need some way of organizing the complexity of moral material. » [5, 253] He himself does not make any significant recommendations in this regard. A more specific position is taken by Richard Vann. He is also concerned about the poor ethical training of historians. In this regard, he expresses the following argument. «If historians inevitably make moral evaluations, they should examine what philosophical ethicists – virtue ethicists, deontologists, and consequentialists – have said about how to make them; and even if they find no satisfactory grounding for their own moral attitudes, it is a brute fact that they have them. » [11, 3]

Considering the ethical aspects of the most diverse axiological sciences, I have everywhere come across a strongly expressed recommendation to use the achievements of ethics in the form in which it is presented in the works of philosophers. To my great surprise in historiology, this recommendation, by the way, not without its strengths and weaknesses, is rarely expressed. Here, as a rule, they are limited to the statement that in morality it is necessary, to be honest, and sincere. In itself, this statement is, of course, not enough. It is not clear what it means to be honest and sincere.

Kate Jenkins came to a negative conclusion regarding the responsibility of the historian.

> I [...] consider whether historians *qua* historians have some kind of ethical responsibility - to somebody or to something – over and above that of the intellectual *qua* intellectual; I reply negatively. And this negative reply has implications for historians. For *if* historians are to be intellectuals of the type I outline here, then they must end their present practices insofar as they do not fulfill the criteria for the type of ethical responsibility I have argued for. [6, 43]

It is not the conclusion that surprises me, but the way it is received based on the views of Badiou, Lyotard, Said, Derrida, and Rorty, i.e. authors, who are very far from analytical historiology. Their ideas do not form a single whole. Despite this circumstance, Keith Jenkins offers her conclusion on behalf of the whole philosophy and judges all historians, regardless of their belonging to a particular historiological school. The content of her article indicates that a number of authors close to poststructuralism deny the ethical responsibility of historians. Moreover, they do not understand this responsibility as well as hermeneutists and analytical philosophers.

There is no need to continue the presentation of the positions of individual authors. In preparation for writing this section, I reviewed the works of at least two dozen authors, known as active supporters of the ethical turn. None of them considers historical ethics in a systematic way. Many appeals -

little system analysis. It can be stated that the current state of historical ethics is unsatisfactory. This circumstance is especially painfully experienced by history teachers. [3] Students constantly ask them questions that teachers who do not have the proper ethical training are unable to answer.

According to Alan Tapper «[h]istorians seem caught between old-fashioned anti-intellectual empiricism and a new-fashioned kaleidoscopic relativism, which has its own brand of antiintellectualism. It may be that philosophy, even moral philosophy, has something helpful to contribute to this unhappy situation. However, I say that speculatively rather than confidently. » [9, 18] Over the past decade, the situation has not changed much for the better. Ethical turn really takes place, but it is implemented in a sluggishly current form. The main reason for this state of affairs is the lack of understanding by many researchers of the nature of ethics.

Earlier, in explaining the status of sociological and economic ethics, I noted that the ethical content of these theories as substantive concepts lies in the principles of increase of prosperity of all stockholders and responsibility. Superstructure theories will inherit ethical content from substantive theories. Based on the foregoing, the content of sociological, economic, political and legal ethics was determined. History as a complex science combines all these varieties of ethics and, of course, gives them a historical form. Historians do not need to invent a particular kind of ethics. Their task is to ensure the optimal combination of different types of ethics. Jurists are required to condemn the Holocaust from the standpoint of legal ethics. Historians must condemn the Holocaust from the standpoint of the unity of all varieties of social ethics. This is precisely the peculiarity of their positions.

There is no tension between epistemology, methodology, and ethics in historical theories. Ethics contributes to the success of both epistemology and methodology. In the absence of these successes, it becomes weak and lifeless. In this respect, analytic historical ethics clearly outperforms its opponents, the hermeneutic and poststructuralist historical ethics. Of course, this does not mean that hermeneutic and poststructuralist historical ethics have only weaknesses. Just as historiology is called upon to realize the potential of all its schools, historical ethics is called upon to unite the strengths of all versions of historiological ethics.

Should the historian be guided by the principle of responsibility? Unlike Keith Jenkins, I give a positive answer to this question. The fact is that as an intellectual, he must realize the potential of historical theories, and they cannot do without the principle of responsibility. If the historian dispenses with the principle of responsibility, then it is unacceptable to consider him a genuine intellectual. Let me remind the reader that responsibility consists of the obligation to be guided by the most developed theories.

Thus, the chapter has come to an end, crowning the consideration of social theories. Historiology has great potential, but its development leaves much to be desired. In my opinion, the foundations of historiology are less well understood than the beginnings of other social sciences.

References

1. Cole, E.A. and Barsalou, J. (2006) Unite or Divide? The Challenges of Teaching History in Societies Emerging from

Violent Conflict. Washington: United States Institute of Peace Press.

2. De Mello, M.R. and de Araujo, V.L. (2015) Introduction - theory and history of historiography: from the linguistic turn to the ethical-political turn. História da Historiografia: International Journal of Theory and History of Historiography 8(17), 318-332.

3. Dintenfass, M. (2000) Truth's other: ethics, the history of the holocaust, and historiographical theory after the linguistic turn. History and Theory 39(1), 1-20.

4. Epple, A. (2018) Calling for a practice turn in global history: practices as drivers of globalization/s. History and Theory 57(3), 390-407.

5. Gorman, J. (2009) Ethics and the writing of historiography. In Tucker, A. (Ed.). A Companion to the Philosophy of History and Historiography. Oxford: Wiley-Blackwell, 253-261

6. Jenkins, K. (2004) Ethical responsibility and the historian: on the possible end of a history of «a certain kind». History and Theory 43(4), 43-60.

7. Kellner, H. (2016) The practical turn. Journal of the philosophy of history 11(2), 1-8.

8. Roth, P. (2016) Analytic philosophy of history: origins, eclipse, and revival. Graduate Faculty Philosophy Journal 37(2), 1-24.

9. Tapper, A. (2009) Is there an ethics for historians? Studies in Western Australian History (26), 16-36.

10. Thomas, C. (2005) History as moral commentary: ideology and the ethical responsibilities of remembrance. Nebula 1(3), 179-196.

11. Vann, R.T. (2004) Historians and moral evaluations. History and Theory 43(4), 3-30.

12. White, H. (1973) Metahistory: The Historical Imagination in Nineteenth-Century Europe. Baltimore: Johns Hopkins University Press.

Chapter 21. The nature of sciences of arts

21.1. Foundations of art and aesthetics

The art, with its many disciplines, in particular literature, dance, theater, music, is invariably included in the nomenclature of the branches of science. However, they are often not recognized as genuine sciences. This situation is abnormal. Why is art ultimately not allowed into the number of sciences? The situation under consideration is largely the result of introducing the idea of aesthetics. The term 'aesthetics' (from ancient Greek αἴσθησις – perception) to designate a separate discipline was first used in 1750 by Alexandre Baumgarten [1]. He did not consider perception merely a prelude to thinking. Perceptions have an independent meaning and are not subordinate to concepts but in an additional relation to them. Baumgarten introduced the idea of a broad and narrow understanding of aesthetics. In the first case, it is considered a philosophical doctrine of perception. In the second - the theory of liberal arts. The theory itself acted as a doctrine of the beautiful.

Baumgarten sought to put aesthetics on a scientific basis but did not succeed in this matter. At the end of the XVIII, Immanuel Kant's position prevailed, who emphatically denied the scientific nature of aesthetics. I will discuss his argument below. At the time of Kant, the philosophy of individual sciences was not considered. This tradition was established only in the XX century. When it touched on art, it became clear that the philosophy of certain varieties of art, in particular, the philosophy of theater, music, and literature, could not be avoided. Aesthetics was not ready for philosophical pluralism. As a result, a certain tension arose between aesthetics and the philosophy of art. Should art really be seen in the context of both the philosophy (as aesthetics) and philosophy of science? If so, why is not something similar observed with respect to such authoritative branches of science as, for example, physics and economics? In my opinion, the problematic situation under consideration was to some extent discharged by Noël Carroll.

In the broad theoretical sense, briefly mentioned earlier, there need be no difference between the philosophy of art and aesthetics; they might be taken as interchangeable labels for the division of philosophy that investigates art. But in the narrow theoretical sense, the two terms, at least in principle, signal a different primary focus: the philosophy of art is object-oriented; aesthetics is reception-oriented. [3, 158-159]

I agree with the first part of Carrol's statement, but not the second. The separation of the two meanings of aesthetics is relevant in the context of the statements of Baumgarten and Kant. It is not necessary, because within the framework of a correctly understood philosophy of art various other conceptual accents are possible. In my opinion, the philosophy of art and aesthetics are the same thing. The preservation of both terms is explained not by their different content, but solely by questions of lexical convenience.

I believe that art theory if properly developed, has a scientific character. A theory is scientific if all methods of conceptual transduction are implemented during its development. Art theories correspond to this criterion so they are scientific. Illustrating this circumstance, on the example of the implementation of the methods of intratheoretical transduction, for a start I will consider the art deduction.

A deduction is that the meaning of each step of construction, often referred to as composition in art history, determines the initial, most capacious concept, the status of which is often, but not always, indicated by the name 'the artwork'. It is about the idea of the plot, about what determines the meaning of the artwork. This kind of principle is found in every work of art. Here are some examples.

In 'The Tragedy of Hamlet, Prince of Denmark', as the name of the work of W. Shakespeare suggests, it is about the tragedy of the hero, the tragedy of revenge. What is its meaning? Why is Hamlet's fate causing such significant interest both in the audience of the play and in critics? What is the decisive peculiarity of Hamlet? In doubt and indecision? Of course not. In my opinion, we are talking about something else, namely, the responsibility of man in the conditions of tragedy, universal decay. It is not enough to commit a harsh act that will testify not so much of a man's nobility as of his fall. Maximization of the responsibility of a person is perhaps the main principle of Hamlet, its leitmotif, which is emphasized by the behavior of other characters in the play, in particular, Laertes, Ophelia, and Claudius.

Not a single artist can do without principles (intentions). Let us recall in this connection the generalizing principles of the Great Russian writers: a true person in Christ (F.M. Dostoevsky), no resistance to evil by violence (L.N. Tolstoy), traditionalism (M.V. Sholokhov), the enlightened Slavophilism (A.I. Solzhenitsyn). Of course, any type of art, in particular, music, is not without principles. In the fourth symphony, P.I. Tchaikovsky's plan is determined by the movement: rock - the impotence of the individual - going to the people. The famous seventh symphony of D.D. Shostakovich embodies the dynamics of the victory of culture over civilization, wich just imitating culture. It is imperative to understand that a principle is always an expression of not aimless, but a directed movement. Positive values are maximized, and their antipodes, on the contrary, are minimized.

The principle-design in itself, if there is no development of it, is lifeless. Aesthetic events must be connected in a certain way into a single whole. Moreover, this is not possible if certain relationships are not established between them (read laws). The composition is realized as a deduction. However, very peculiar, it does not appear in the form of axiomatic, so familiar to formal sciences.

Naturally, art theory does not end with a stage of deduction. It continues by the experiment. The artist prepares his work for the audience. It is especially significant that the work passes through multiple trials. Each stage of the theory has many faces. Hamlet performed by L. Olivier, V.I. Kachalov, I.K. Smoktunovsky, and V.S. Vysotsky every time is different, but this is the same conception, which, in essence, excludes an unambiguous interpretation. Largely, this is revealed in an art experiment, which method is adduction.

Understanding the experiment is induction, i.e. another way to manage concepts. Numerous not predicted, but occurring, connections of concepts are revealed, which, before the work was realized, were not viewed clearly enough. Together with the identification of what satisfies the authors, directors, and performers, unacceptable moments, circumstances, and causes are found for them. They are not taken for granted; ways to overcome them are outlined. Having fixed this moment, we hit the ground of art abduction.

The transition from induction to abduction especially vividly marks, for example, a series of failures and successes of theatrical works. You can recall in this regard, for example, the failure of the premiere of 'The Seagull' A.P. Chekhov at the Alexandria Theater in St. Petersburg in 1896 and, conversely, a tremendous success two years later in Moscow with the production of the same theatrical performance at the Moscow Art Theater. It is indicative, however, that this success did not open the era of the victorious procession of 'The Seagull'. Both failures and successes continued to happen.

Critics, as a rule, explain artistic failures by the inadequate reading of the author's intention. Naturally, this happens, but another important circumstance should be taken into account. One single adequate reading, understanding of the work, in principle, does not exist. That is why the next stage of realization of the work is a phase of abduction, ending with new assumptions, hypotheses.

Thus, art theory includes the stages of deduction, adduction, induction, and abduction. It can also be convincingly shown that, with the development of art theories, methods of intertheoretical transduction are implemented. That is why the art theories should be included in the family of scientific conceptions. Pushing them beyond science limits the understanding of the conceptual content of art.

It is time to turn to Kant's refutation of the scientific status of art theory. He determined its structure through conceptions of taste, beauty, pleasure, and aesthetic judgment. Taste is the subjective principle of the power of judgment as to such. Aesthetics is judgment of taste. Aesthetic judgment is a free play between imagination and understanding. The object of aesthetic judgment is beautiful. Pleasure is a harmony of imagination and understanding.

> A critique that precedes a science is divided into elementology and methodology. But this division is not applicable to a critique of taste, since there neither is, nor can be, a science of the beautiful, and a judgment of taste cannot be determined by means of principles. [4, 230]

Kant avoided the encounter between aesthetics and science, primarily by two very strong idealizations. First, he has emasculated the content of taste as a principle of theory. Secondly, Kant approved a completely free play of imagination and understanding. Under such conditions, no scientific determination is possible. The refutation of Kant's argumentations is that the principles of aesthetic theories stand out. It turns out that they, as I showed above in the example of the works of outstanding writers, are far from empty.

As for the possibilities of the free play of imagination, they are far from unlimited. Of course, a work of art is always excogitation, but not any. Imagination must certainly keep in touch with reality; otherwise, it will not receive approval. Art science is always the offset of traditional sciences, a kind of counterweight that directs these sciences to further innovations. In my opinion, it is precisely the offset nature of art sciences, which does not so much separate these sciences from other sciences but unites them with them.

Thus, there is not a single argument that would prove the unscientific nature of art theories. The statement that these theories deal with emotions, not thoughts, is not such an argument. Thoughts and emotions are two different forms of expressing the mentality of people. Their content is not arbitrary. Both of these forms are representations of theories. Not a single science can do without an emotional representation of theories, including, for example, physics and economics.

It should be noted that many authors condemn the juxtaposition of science and art, and, as a result, outline the ways of their cooperation. [2; 5; 6] Nevertheless, even they do not dare to call art a branch of science. I explain this state of affairs by insufficient attention to the achievements of the modern philosophy of science. Unfortunately, often the status of art is judged regardless of the achievements of the philosophy of science. In my opinion, this, in particular, occurs when art is considered either representation or mimesis, or expression of emotional content. The disadvantage of such definitions is that they ignore the conceptual dynamics of art as the offset branch of science. It is it that together with other sciences, expresses in the most distinct form the creative aspirations of humankind.

References

1. Baumgarten, A.G. (2014) [1750]. Aesthetica scriptsit Alexander Gottlieb Baumgarten. Delhi: Gyan Books.
2. Bullot, N.J., William P., Seeley, W.P., and Davies, S. (2017) Art and science: a philosophical sketch of their historical complexity and codependence. The Journal of Aesthetics and Art Criticism 75(4), 453-463.
3. Carroll, N. (1999) Philosophy of Art: a Contemporary Introduction. London and New York: Routledge.

4. Kant, I. (1987) [1790]. Critique of Judgment. Transl. by W.S. Pluhar. Indianapolis and Cambridge: Hackett Publishing Company.
5. Radman, Z. (2004) Towards aesthetics of science. JTLA: Journal of the Faculty of Letters, the University of Tokyo. Aesthetics 29(30), 1-15.
6. Richmond, S. (1984) The interaction of art and science. Leonardo 17(2), 81-86.

21.2. Critique of the metaphysical foundations of art and aesthetics

The concepts of taste and beauty are considered central in modern aesthetics. However, their interpretation is very difficult. Michael Spicher notes in his review

> Theories of taste reached their peak in the 18th century. They diminished and then changed in the 19th century. They were left without much significance in the 20th century. Now, in the 21st century, few people really speak about a *theory* of taste. Are these theories merely relics of the past that we should find interesting only as historical artifacts? How can we account for the fact that people speak commonly and meaningfully about aesthetic taste while it seems to have diminished in academic discourse? It is not obvious how we should answer such questions. [6, sec. 5]

The anxiety that he expresses is indeed quite legitimate. It seems that the debate over the concepts of taste, beauty and aesthetic experience has clearly dragged on. [1-5; 7; 9] In my opinion, there is an acute need for fundamentally new ideas that can give additional impetus to the development of aesthetics. Spicher's article leads to this conclusion, but he avoids it by making a reservation «However [...] there have been some notable contributions in the contemporary world». Richard Shusterman took an equally modest position at the end of his article, arguing that «[p]erhaps aesthetic experience, and not just the philosophical value of its concept, has almost reached its end», he hoped that the «aesthetic experience will be strengthened and preserved the more it is experienced [...].» [4, 39] In my opinion, criticism of traditional forms of aesthetics should end with conclusions that are more cardinal.

In my opinion, the concepts of taste and beauty in the form in which they were inherited by modern aesthetics from Immanuel Kant and David Hume, even after repeatedly clarifying their content, remain in the field of metaphysics. There is a need for aesthetics to take a decisive step beyond metaphysics. It consists of the fact that art, like any other branch of science, is understood as a set of related theories, the conceptual and methodological content of which is revealed in the philosophy of art, i.e. in aesthetics. When the metaphysical approach, aesthetics are primordial; it does not have an evidence base. When the metascientific approach, the basis of aesthetics is numerous art theories. With a metaphysical approach, the theory appears as a series of intuitive guesses. Nothing is proved. With a metascientific approach, the content of theories is interpreted from the standpoint of the theory of conceptual transduction. There is an opportunity to use the numerous achievements of the philosophy of science.

As for metaphysical issues, in particular, the nature of taste, beauty and aesthetic experience, their positive content is established from the standpoint of the philosophy of art. As a result, numerous puzzles of metaphysically understood aesthetics overcome. In this connection, I turn to the concepts of taste, the judgment of beauty and aesthetic experience.

In Kant's metaphysic of art, the taste is the first concept with which he begins a deductive presentation of the content of aesthetics. In a certain approximation, it can be said that taste plays the role of principle. This means that the scientific analogs of taste are the principles of people as subjects of art theories. The concept of taste involves some sophistication of people. This means that they are guided by developed theories and not their surrogates. Thus, in the transition from metaphysical aesthetics to its scientific version, the concept of principle developed in art theories appears in place of the metaphysical concept of taste.

I turn now to the concept of aesthetic judgment. It is easy to establish that its analog is the explanation, which, as has been repeatedly noted above, is consistently realized through the stages of intratheoretical and intertheoretical transduction. When considering aesthetic judgment, Sarah Worth and Nick Zangwill focus mainly on its problematic aspects; they do not explain what exactly constitutes an aesthetic judgment. [8; 10]

According to Kant, beauty is the subject of aesthetic judgment. Turning to scientific soil it is reasonable to assume that the principles of theories to varying degrees express the content of the subject of art theories. In this regard, it is reasonable to use value estimates, including such as 'beautiful' and 'ugly'. There are beautiful and ugly entities, but there is no beauty and ugliness as such.

Needs to rethink also the concept of aesthetic experience. In scientific terms, it is the obtaining of facts in the process of observation, experimentation and practical action. It seems that the content of aesthetic empirical experience is fundamentally different from the empirical experience in generally recognized sciences, for example, in physics and economics. It is supposedly more subjective, and so much that it is difficult to consider it a reliable basis for scientific conclusions. This impression is misleading. The experimental experience of people in natural, axiological and offset sciences is not the same. However, in all cases, it is sufficient as a way of obtaining facts. Often art is equated with social sciences. They do not take into account that art is an offset science. Its certainty is set by the aesthetic experience of people.

As for the concept of truth, it appears in art on the same grounds as in other sciences: true knowledge is the most developed theories.

Based on the understanding of art as a set of offset theories, it is not difficult to determine the ratio of ethics and aesthetics. Two ethical principles, the principles of growth of prosperity and responsibility, can be introduced directly into art theory. In this case, it gains ethical weight. It is different from the real sciences, for it refers to offset theory. If there are no ethical principles in art theory, then it remains ethically undefined. Next, you need to discuss the relationship between real and offset ethics. This is an interdisciplinary attitude. It can be realized in the interests of both art and real science, for example, technology and economics. In the first case, art critics consider real ethics as a symbol of offset ethics. In this regard, real ethical conflicts often provide food for art stories. In the second case, offset ethics is considered as a symbol of real ethics. Some of its values can be directly introduced into real theories. There is hardly a country without so-called patriotic literature. Its characters become models of behavior for readers of this literature. Offset ethics is partially or fully converted to real ethics. Of course, this circumstance should not be overestimated. The main ethical teacher is real axiological theories. In relation to them, offset ethics is nothing more than auxiliary material.

In light of my analysis, the frequent exaltation of the unity of truth, goodness, and beauty are rather empty. This trinity is extracted from the depths of not science, but metaphysics. In the framework of metaphysics, its unity is in no way justified. It cannot be explained on behalf of science either. In science, truth is the most developed knowledge. Beauty comes down to signs of entities of art theories. Goodness is reduced to the signs of entities of axiological theories. It is understood that people do not equally express the ethical content of theories. Of course, we should welcome those people who, guided by the most developed theories, are kind and beautiful. At the same time, one should not forget that in the context under consideration, truth, goodness, and beauty do not express the fullness of the sciences, but only some of its aspects. There is no reason to isolate them from science and to extol in every possible way. Science as a whole not its individual aspects deserves the highest praise.

Thus, the translation of art and the philosophy of art (aesthetics) on a scientific footing has matured. In this case, all the controversial aspects of art gain a new understanding. In unity with other sciences, the art looks much more thoroughly than in isolation from them. Unfortunately, I have to admit that in their modern form, art, and after it the philosophy of art, i.e. aesthetics are in a metaphysical shell. The translation of art on a scientific track is the main task of the philosophy of art (aesthetics).

References

1. Ferrari, F. (2016) Disagreement about taste and alethic subrogation. Philosophical Quarterly 66 (264), 516-535.
2. Kneer, M., Vicente, A. and Zeman, D. (2017) Relativism about predicates of personal taste and perspectival plurality. Linguistics and Philosophy 40(1), 37-60.
3. Riggle, N. (2016) On the interest in beauty and disinterest. Philosophers' Imprint 16(9), 1-14.
4. Shusterman, R. (1997) The end of aesthetic experience. The Journal of Aesthetics and Art Criticism 55(1), 29-41.
5. Spicher, M.R. (2013) Distinct basic good of aesthetic experience and its political import. American catholic philosophical quarterly 87(4), 711–729.
6. Spicher, M.R. (2020) Aesthetic taste. Internet Encyclopedia of Philosophy. Available at: https://www.iep.utm.edu/a-taste/
7. Sundell, T. (2011) Disagreements about taste. Philosophical Studies 55 (2), 267-288.
8. Worth, S.E. (2020) Art and epistemology. Internet Encyclopedia of Philosophy. Available at: https://www.iep.utm.edu/art-ep/
9. Wyatt, J. (2018) Absolutely tasty: an examination of predicates of personal taste and faultless disagreement. Inquiry 61(3), 252-280.
10. Zangwill, N. (2019) Aesthetic judgment. The Stanford Encyclopedia of Philosophy. *Available* at: https://plato.stanford.edu/archives/spr2019/entries/aesthetic-judgment/

21.3. Foundations of musicology

Music, by virtue of its universal distribution, attracts the close attention of aestheticists. [1; 4] Related issues are considered in the philosophy of music. Researchers who focus on science in their works believe that music should be discussed only in the context of science, i.e. musicology. For them, the philosophy of musicology has scientific meaning, not the philosophy of music. Directly, music is usually understood a) as a system of sounds that has features characteristic of instrumental music, in particular, the pitch of sounds, tonality and harmony, c) the expression in the music of aesthetic emotions of a person [2, sec. 2]. It is difficult to give such a definition of music that would include not only necessary but also sufficient features of a musical work. Especially if you correlate it with instrumental music that is not accompanied by any verbal libretto. In this regard, Matteo Ravasio rightly notes, «most of the puzzles in the philosophy of music arise with particular strength in the case of pure music. » [4, Introduction] What is music? My answer to this question follows from the theory of conceptual transduction.

According to this theory, there is nothing that would not be a representation of the theory. Consequently, music is also a representation of certain theories. Musical accompaniment of numerous artworks, in particular, operas, films, and ballets, substantively strengthens this idea. There is hardly any doubt that these works are representations of certain theories. It is equally true that these same theories represent the musical accompaniment of the works. Music is a form of representation of art theories. Because of its originality, there is no alternative to it. There is no such form of representation of theories, that would characterize the pitch of sounds, tonality, and harmony as music does. The meaning of a musical work is determined by the theory that it embodied. It is significant that I do not explain the nature of music through its reduction to something that is not music. Music presents the theory, not something different from it. Music is a theory, its peculiar sound form.

When studying the phenomenon of music, researchers encounter significant difficulties, largely because they cannot determine the initial principle, which, like the way it is in traditional sciences, would determine the content of the entire musical work. When analyzing a musical composition, researchers decompose it organized into components. The question of the hierarchy of parts of the organization remains largely open. Nevertheless, the presence of a certain organization in a musical work is its significant characteristic. This circumstance is quite rightly emphasized by Roger Scruton.

> Sounds become music as a result of organization, and this organization is something that we perceive and whose absence we immediately notice, regardless of whether we take pleasure in the result. This organization is not just an aesthetic matter – it is not simply a *style*. It is more like a grammar, in being the precondition of our response to the result *as music*. We must therefore acknowledge that music (or at any rate, tonal music of the kind familiar to the Western listener) has something like a syntax – a rule-guided process linking each episode to its neighbors, which we grasp in the act of hearing, and the absence of which leads to a sense of discomfort or incongruity. [7, 233]

Unlike many other authors, Scruton seeks to liken music to well-studied sciences, primarily linguistics and mathematics. In my opinion, this research path promises the greatest success. Alternative research methods disregard the internal structure and dynamics of a piece of music. The second feature of the Scruton approach is that it is guided by the notion of the famous trinity of syntax/semiotics/ pragmatics. That is why he raises the question of the syntax of a musical work. This approach seems to be doubtful. As far as I know, not a single author, including R. Scruton, has shown that a musical work is a transition from syntax to semantics and from it to pragmatics.

In my opinion, the transition: prediction (deduction) - actualization (adduction) - data processing (induction) - updating of the original foundations (abduction) is crucial in understanding any scientifically sound theory. I assess the status of a piece of music, primarily through the prism of intratheoretical transduction. From this point of view, the innovations of Scruton refer to the stage of prediction, which in this case acts as a preparation for the test of a musical work. It, of course, must certainly come.

The test of a musical work is always contextual: the composer's work is evaluated by the audience. Considering the conditions of a musical work, Aaron Ridley argues, «only some version of contextualism can conceivably be right. » [5, 664]. James O. Young justifies this circumstance as follows: «ontological judgments are apriori and aesthetic judgments are empirical. A priori judgments have no empirical consequences. Neither fundamental ontology of music nor higher-order ontological reflections have any aesthetic consequences. » [8, 1] In my opinion, Ridley and Young do not take into account the stages in the life process of a piece of music. They follow one after another: the creation of a work - its test - the conclusions that follow from the test - a rethinking of the work. This is the same conceptual transduction. It is inappropriate to focus solely on testing.

My central idea is that the status of a piece of music should be judged based on conceptual transduction. Otherwise, the assertion that the researcher proceeds from the ontology of the work or from the idea of its contextuality is proclaimed, but not proved. By turning to the theory of conceptual transduction, one can understand the nature of both musical ontology and musical contextuality.

It is extremely important to determine the status of musicology. Like any aesthetic science, it has an offset character. Nevertheless, as such, it can be of a formal, natural or axiological nature. It is widely believed that all aesthetic sciences have valuable content, i.e. are axiological theories. With regard to musicology, this opinion is incorrect. Like linguistics, musicology is directly related to all sciences. The musical accompaniment of events taking place in the depths of the seas and oceans is as organic as in the case of some social phenomena. Thus, musicology is an offset formal science.

According to Joel Krueger, «from birth, music is directly perceived as an affordance-laden structure. Music, I argue, affords a sonic world, an exploratory space or "nested acoustic environment" that further affords possibilities for, among other things, (1) emotion regulation and (2) social coordination. » [3, 1] It is difficult to disagree with this statement. Nevertheless, it is not enough just to be limited to it. It should be associated with the status of musicology as a science. This circumstance receives a more thorough expression of the analytical philosophy of music than in the continental philosophy of music. Tiger Roholt believes that representatives of the two versions of the philosophy of music misunderstand each other. The main feature of the representatives of the continental philosophy of music is that they oppose the separation of music from its context; representatives of the analytical philosophy of music, as a rule, insist on such a separation. [6, 56] Roholt believes that such a contrasting methodology does not give an advantage to one of the variants of the philosophy of music. Unfortunately, I cannot support the inclination of Roholt to tolerance. I believe that scientific methodology should be put at the forefront. From this point of view, representatives of the analytical philosophy of music have a definite advantage over their opponents. At the same time, I am far from the idea that philosopher-analysts managed to determine the correct way to transfer various theories of music on the scientific footing. In my opinion, they do not pay tribute to the theory of conceptual transduction.

References

1. DeBellis, M. (2001) Music. In Gaut, B. and Lopes, D.M. (Eds.). The Companion to Aesthetics. London: Routledge, 531-544.
2. Kania, A. (2017) The philosophy of music. The Stanford Encyclopedia of Philosophy. Available at: https://plato.stanford.edu/archives/fall2017/entries/music/
3. Krueger, J.W. (2011) Doing things with music. Phenomenology and the Cognitive Sciences 10 (1), 1-22.
4. Ravasio, M. (2020) Analytic perspectives in the philosophy of music. Internet Encyclopedia of Philosophy. Available at: https://www.iep.utm.edu/music-an/
5. Ridley, A. (2012) Musical ontology, musical reasons. The Monist 95(4), 663-683.
6. Roholt, T. (2017) On the divide: analytic and continental philosophy of music. The Journal of Aesthetics and Art Criticism 75(1), 49-58.

7. Scruton, R. (2014) Music and cognitive science. Royal Institute of Philosophy Supplement 74, 231- 247.
8. Young, J.O. (2014) The poverty of musical ontology. Journal of Music and Meaning 13, 1-19

21.4. Foundations of filmology

The extreme popularity of cinema has attracted the attention of philosophers. They began to develop various versions of the philosophy of film. [16] Authors who attach paramount importance to the scientific understanding of the phenomenon of the film prefer to discuss film-philosophy rather than film. At the same time, film science is understood as a science, the subject of which is films. How to justify the scientific nature of film science? In this regard, interesting ideas were put forward by Sergei Eisenstein. He proceeded from the dialectical materialism of Karl Marx with its method of ascension from the abstract to the concrete, from the cell of the system to it in its entirety. Eisenstein believed that only in the era of decline, scientific knowledge does not appear in its original scientific form, but as art and imagery. [8, 126]

> [T]ake such a postulate as the a-priority of the idea, spoken of by Hegel in relation to the creation of the world. At a certain stage, this was the summit of philosophical knowledge. Later, the summit was overthrown. Marx turns this postulate head over heels in the question of the understanding of real actuality. However, if we consider our works of art, we do in fact have a condition that almost looks like- the Hegelian formula, because the idea-satiation of the author,

his subjection to prejudice by the idea, must determine actually the hole course of the art-work, and if every element of the art-work does not represent an embodiment of the initial idea, we shall never have as result an art-work realized to its utmost fullness. It is of course understood that the artist's idea itself is in no way spontaneous or self-engendered, but is a socially reflected mirror-image, a reflection of social reality. But from the moment of formation within him of the viewpoint and idea, that idea appears as determining all the actual and material structure of his creation, the whole "world" of his creation. [8, 127]

Eisenstein was well aware that the scientific method should be presented in detail. His decisive innovation was precisely that.

The shot is by no means an *element* of montage.

The shot is a montage *cell*.

Just as cells in their division form a phenomenon of another order, the organism or embryo, so, on the other side of the dialectical leap from the shot, there is montage.

By what, then, is montage characterized and, consequently, its cell – the shot?

By collision. By the conflict of two pieces in opposition to each other. By conflict. By collision. [8, 37]

Eisenstein should be given credit: his interpretation of the dialectical method as applied to the cinema is extremely original. Unfortunately, this method itself is not valid.

The attention of many researchers was drawn to the book Daniel Frampton 'Filmosophy', in which its author used the concepts of 'filmind' and 'film-thinking'. [10] Most researchers have concluded that Frampton unreasonably uses the anthropomorphic concepts of 'mind' and 'thinking' to characterize the nature of the film. He explained his position as follows.

> The filmind is a philosophical concept; a term to be used when considering the being of film within filmosophy. I would use the term when considering the film-being in philosophical ruminations on the event of film, but when writing about a particular film it is enough to talk about the film giving us things, showing us things (from a non-place of the film itself). Filmosophy simply asks the filmgoer to see the film 'through' the concept of thinking. It is the film that thinks. [11, 366]

In my opinion, the point of view of Frampton is contradictory, but not without meaning. Any film is the embodiment of theory through moving motion pictures. This is a special form of representation of the theory, object-procedural, and not mental. Both forms of presentation of film theory have the same conceptual content. Exactly it is extremely relevant in the interpretation of the nature of the film. In fact, Frampton attracted attention to it. Indeed, traditionally the conceptual content of theories was primarily associated with thinking, and not with feeling. Researchers expected from Frampton scientific discoveries, but they did not happen. His poetic and rhetorically performative language is far from scientific standards.

Of exceptional relevance to the formation of the analytical philosophy of the film were the works of Stanly Cavell. He dispelled the last doubts about the need for purposeful development of the philosophy of the film. Cavell demonstrated that the philosophy of film is not inferior in its potential to other philosophical disciplines. [5] His two main interests are, firstly, things, and secondly, words about them. [7, 194] The first interest unites him with Heidegger and his ontology of things. The second interest relates him to Wittgenstein. Many philosophers argued about the relationship between things and words. The peculiarity of the position of Cavell is that words and things are united by the process of vision. The importance of vision has been recognized throughout the centuries-old history of the development of epistemology. His highest forms are demonstrated by the cinema. This means that the philosophy of the film should be placed at the center of epistemology. It turns out that it gives new impetus to key problems, namely, skepticism a la Descartes and critical philosophy a la Kant.

> The moral I draw is this: the question what becomes of objects when they are filmed and screened—like the question what becomes of particular people, and specific locales, and subjects and motifs when they are filmed by individual makers of film—has only one source of data for its answer, namely the appearance and significance of just those objects and people that are in fact to be found in the succession of films, or passages of films, that matter to us. To express their

appearances, and define those significances, and articulate the nature of this mattering, are acts that help to constitute what we might call film criticism. [6, 256]

Cavell is convinced that «the power of film is to destroy false barriers within audiences, within individual viewers of film.» [6, 175] This power is not accessible to all. To identify it, the philosophy of the film is just what is needed. Thus, it seems that Cavell built a strategy for the development of the philosophy of the film quite strictly. Can it be argued that his philosophy of film satisfies the requirements of the philosophy of filmology? The answer to this question is no. Following Wittgenstein, Cavell believed that philosophy should be limited only to descriptions, avoiding scientific explanations, supposedly not the result of a direct encounter with what we see. [6, 169] This position inevitably left him aside from science alone with ordinary language. A more consistent scientific position, maintaining continuity with analytical philosophy, is based on the theses on objectivity, reproduction, causal relativity, and transparency of knowledge. [14, 268]

The studies of Eisenstein, Frampton, and Cavell demonstrate an extraordinary path to the development of filmology. None of them managed to put it on a scientific track. Given the failures of many other authors as well, I turn to the characterization of perhaps the most fundamental confrontation in the philosophy of film science, namely, two approaches, one of which is related to continental, and the other to analytical philosophy. This confrontation is often characterized as a change of grand-theory by post-theory. Ultimately, it was proposed not to abolish the theory, but substantially to reform it. The key figures in updating the philosophy of the film are Noël Carroll and David Bordwell. [2]

Until the 1980s, the philosophy of the film was represented mainly by the works of representatives of philosophical schools related to European continental traditions, in particular, psychoanalysis, Marxism, existentialism, structuralism, and poststructuralism. [3] Cinema was considered mainly in the broadest possible humanitarian and political context, as a means of both imposing an ideology enslaving large masses of people and possible liberation from it. Issues of the scientific method were not the focus of researchers. Initially, it seemed that they could get consistent development in the semiology of F. de Saussure. These hopes were dispelled because structuralism gave way to poststructuralism. Thus, in the field of film-philosophy, by the early 1980s, the scientific method was clearly in the background. The proposed new theories seemed to have a generalizing character. However, in fact, it was impossible to subject them to scientific examination.

> My reasons go like this. The further up the ladder of abstraction and generality we climb, the less we're inclined to notice quirks, disparities, and exceptions in the things we study. If we pitch our questions at a certain level of generality, we're likely to notice only those general aspects of the film that exemplify what we postulated. [1, 10]

Therefore, David Bordwell proposed developing theories of a level that would be at least portable. We are talking about intermediate theories. What should be the new way of developing theories of cinema? «I've considered the "cognitive" perspective, or the "naturalistic" perspective. [...] I've opted for awkwardness and named this family of theories the *empirical-experiential* one. » [1, 5] Such a choice is perfectly consistent with the basic principles of analytical philosophy. However, ambiguities remain regarding the scientific content of the cognitive perspective. She was chosen as opposed to psychoanalysis. Attention was paid to the psychological characteristics of the audience, however, without any psychoanalytic obligations.

Noël Carroll developed the dialectics of mid-level theories. Consistent scientific criticism was supposed to ensure the truth of theories. Theories whose truth cannot be proved were rejected.

> The dialectical conception of film theory that I am advocating is consistent with trends in the postpositivist philosophy of science. It respects the Kuhnian, antipositivist emphasis on the importance of historical and social contexts for inquiry. It is also not positivist in that it conceives of the process of theoretical argumentation as situated as a debate between existing rivals, rather than as a debate between every conceivable theory, before a court of fully rational participants, endowed with full information. [4, 58-59]

The proposals of Bordwell and Carroll, of course, contributed to the development of the analytical philosophy of the film, but they did not lead to its decisive success. [12; 13] The fact is that they completely ignored the scientific method. In addition, in favor of cognitivism, they did not isolate the filmology as such. After all, it is about it that we should be talking in the first place. Filmology implements a set of interdisciplinary connections with cognitive sciences, but it does not come down to them.

As for my position, I believe that film science really needs to be translated on a scientific footing. To do this, it is enough to be guided by the theory of conceptual transduction. First, it should be taken into account that filmology as an offset science deals with the same sciences with respect to which it implements its offset function. All scientific methods of real sciences are duplicated in relation to filmology. If in the film, political problems are discussed, then their correct interpretation should be carried out with concepts and methods of political science.

Of course, researchers have encountered significant difficulties in interpreting the content of specific films. As a rule, a film is a complex set of various theories that guide its heroes. Each dialogue is an intersection of theories. There can be a lot of them. A variety of plot lines and dialogues complicates the analysis of the film but does not prove its impossibility. To avoid misunderstandings, I note once again that scientific conceptual analysis does not detract in any way from the emotional component of aesthetic experience. Emotions are representations of some theories. We are accustomed to believing that in the mental domain, theories are ideas, but not emotions. This is a clear fallacy, which contributed to a considerable degree to the alienation of art, including filmology from science.

Let me also address the issue of the perspectives of philosophy through film. [9] The philosophy of science is expanding its potential by extending the metascientific achievements of individual sciences to other sciences. The concept of evolution is used in all sciences in many respects thanks to the successes of meta-biology. The concept of time dilation was updated because of the achievements of metascientific studies of relativistic physics. Whenever some metascience develops successfully, it gives rise to the use of its achievements, duly rethought, in other metasciences. There is no reason to deny the corresponding potential of meta-philmology. In my opinion, at the modern stage of its development, this potential is mainly realized in terms of increasing the emotional scientific experience of the audience.

In my opinion, the modern philosophy of film science is in its infancy. There is no other way out of this unpleasant situation than the activation of relevant research.

References

1. Bordwell, D. (2010) A part-time cognitivist: a view from film studies. Projection 4(2), 1-18.
2. Bordwell, D. and Carroll, N. (Eds.). (1996) Post-Theory: Reconstructing Film Studies. Madison: University of Wisconsin Press.
3. Botz-Bornstein, T. (2019) Philosophy of film: continental perspectives. Internet Encyclopedia of Philosophy. Available at: https://www.iep.utm.edu/filmcont/
4. Carroll, N. (1996) Prospects for film theory: a critical assessment. In Bordwell, D. and Carroll, N. (Eds.). Post-Theory: Reconstructing Film Studies. Madison: University of Wisconsin Press, 37-70.
5. Cavell, S. (1971) The World Viewed: Reflections on the Ontology of Film. New York: The Viking Press.
6. Cavell, S. (1978) What becomes of things on film? Philosophy and Literature 2(2), 249-257.
7. Cavell, S. (2005) What Becomes of Thinking on Film?' (Stanley Cavell in conversation with Andrew Klevan). In Read, R. and Goodenough, J. (Eds.) Film as Philosophy: Essays on Cinema after Wittgenstein and Cavell. Houndmills: Palgrave Macmillan, 167-209.
8. Eisenstein, S. (1977) Film form: essays in film theory. Trans. by J. Leyda. New York and London: Harcourt.

9. Falzon, C. (2019) Philosophy through film. Internet Encyclopedia of Philosophy. Available at: https://www.iep.utm.edu/phi-film/

10. Frampton, D. (2006) Filmosophy. London: Wallflower Press.

11. Frampton, D. (2008) Notes on filmosophy: a reply to reviews. New Review of Film and Television Studies 6(3), 365-374.

12. Jarvie, I. (1999) Is analytic philosophy the cure for film theory? Philosophy of the Social Sciences 29(3), 416-440.

13. Lomtadze, A. (2014) From theory to post-theory and beyond: politics and film. Honors Thesis Collection, 170.

14. McGregor, R. (2013) A new/old ontology of film. Film-Philosophy 17(1), 265-280.

15. Sinnerbrink. R. (2016) Cinempathy: phenomenology, cognitivism, and moving images. Contemporary aesthetics 5, e1-e13.

16. Wartenberg, T. (2015) Philosophy of film. The Stanford Encyclopedia of Philosophy. Available at: https://plato.stanford.edu/archives/win2015/entries/film/

21.5. Foundations of theatrology

Getting to the consideration of theatrology, it is natural to compare it with the filmology. The situation with the allocation of grounds of theories in both cases is similar. Considerable attention is paid to the relationship of these art disciplines with philosophy. It is marked by the seal of alertness and anxious hopes. [14] Some researchers have noted the existence of an anti-philosophical trend in theatrology and an anti-theatrical trend in philosophy. [12] Nevertheless, considerable efforts are being made to establish close contacts between the theatrology and philosophy. [2; 5; 6; 8; 12; 14; 16] They are quite rightly expected from this association to clarify the foundations of theatrology. It is well known that the three most important theatrical movements, namely, the realistic theater, the avant-garde theater, and the postmodern theater, were formed and then developed not without the influence of certain philosophical innovations.

For a realistic theater, the concept of mimesis developed by Plato and Aristotle is of paramount importance. Based on the concept of correspondent truth in philosophy, it is hardly possible to avoid the concept of mimesis in the theatrology. According to realism, the stage action should be possible in reality. This requirement is satisfied, for example, by the theory of the psychological realism of Konstantin Stanislavsky.

> We have often been and still are accused of falling into a Naturalistic expression of detail in our pursuit of the Realism of life and truth in our stage actions. Wherever we have done this, we were wrong. ... Realism in art is the method, which helps to select only the typical from life. If at times we are Naturalistic in our stage work, it only shows that we don't yet know enough to be able to penetrate into the historical and social essence of events and characters. We do not know how to separate the main from the secondary, and thus we bury the idea with details of the mode of life. That is my understanding of Naturalism. [13, 333]

Strictly speaking, naturalism supplements the installation of realism with the requirement of its conformity to scientific standards. Criticism of Stanislavsky refers to vulgar naturalism. As for his own theory, it is fully consistent with scientific naturalism. The supertask of all participants in a theatrical performance consists, first, in understanding the main idea of the play and its end-to-end logically substantiated action. In scientific language, this means that you need to know the principle of theory and understand all theatrical actions in its context. Interestingly, Stanislavsky himself avoided characterizing his philosophical preferences. However, the ideological basis of his views clearly goes back to Plato and Aristotle. For him, the theater was a school of moral education of the audience. This is clearly Aristotelian thought.

A significant milestone in the transition from traditional theater to the avant-garde theater was the theory of the epic theater of Bertolt Brecht. The position of theatrical naturalism clearly did not suit him. The purpose of the theater is not to state events, but decisively to transform them. In this regard, his eyes turned to Marxism and its dialectical method.

When I read Marx's Capital I understood my plays...It wasn't of course that I found I had unconsciously written a whole pile of Marxist plays; but this man Marx was the only spectator for my plays... [3, 23, 4n]

[The technique of alienating the familiar] allows the theatre to make use in its representations of the new social scientific method known as dialectical materialism. In order to unearth society's laws of motion this method treats social situations as processes, and traces out all their inconsistencies. It regards nothing as existing except in so far as it changes, in other words is in disharmony with itself. This also goes for those human feelings, opinions and attitudes through which at any time the form of men's life together finds its expression. [3, 193]

Strictly speaking, Brecht used not so much a method of alienation as an appropriation. Alienation is that something is opposed to man as a superior force. Such alienation is a sign of capitalism. The reception of Brecht consists in the denial of alienation, awareness of the previously unconscious. Epic theater pushes everyone the playwright, actors and the audience to an active life position. The transformation is not needed in particular, but in public, primarily political relations. This circumstance enhances the prestige of the theater. It becomes truly epic. B. Brecht's innovation was expressed in many moments, in particular, in the fact that not the mentality of experiences comes to the fore, but the narratives and gestures. The viewer is not included in the play, but is placed in a critical position with respect to it, not empathy is required of him, and the cognitive attitude, argumentation, each part of the production does not go smoothly into another, but acquires an independent meaning (the sequence does not exclude discontinuity).

Perhaps the most piquant in Brecht's theory is his imaginary adherence to the supposedly scientific dialectical method. The dialectical method does not correspond to scientific canons. Nevertheless, Brecht, following Marx, Engels, and Lenin, thought differently. The error of Brecht suggests that understanding of the essence of the scientific method is given to theatrical figures not without difficulty. Sometimes they are simply not well versed in the philosophy of science.

The most revolutionary and radical part of the avant-garde theater was the theater of the absurd of Martina Esslin, Samuel Beckett, and Eugene Ionesco. [9, 7] It is absurd that there is no purpose. [9, 4] Progressive movement is impossible. Every movement invariably returns to its origins. One has to be satisfied with the individual, subjective, imaginary. However, a person's position is not hopeless. He is free to choose from. Responsibility for freedom becomes the main principle of the human being. In the theories of Stanislavsky and Brecht, this principle is not brought to the fore. In a philosophical sense, the theater of the absurd gravitates toward Nietzscheanism and existentialism. Contrary to popular belief, the theater of the absurd is not meaningless. It marks a grandiose attempt to test the viability of a scientific project. As you know, it never succeeds in its full and final form. In this regard, the belief is born that it is in principle impossible and, therefore, there is no need to strive to implement it. All the usual concepts, generalizations, language, communication, morality are put under the fire of theatrical criticism. Myth is opposed to science, philosophy to metaphysics, speech to plastic, concepts to symbols. An alternative to the traditional theater is invented along all its main semantic lines. The onset of the theater of the absurd was most active in the 1960s. Against this background, the postmodern theater with its installations on pluralism and play largely succeeded.

The postmodern theatre is theatre of performance, rather than a theatre of the abstraction of idea, for performance itself is form, essence and idea. [...].

Previous concepts of plot and characterization, no matter whether they are in the Aristotelian or modernist sense, no longer exist in the postmodern theatre. Critical categories of the psychic, dream, distortion and plotlessness in modernist poetics are no longer the defining qualities of the postmodern theatre, which offers a new poetics of collage in playing with discontinuities and inconsistencies always in the making and unmaking. [11, 67]

The postmodern theater is most often interpreted in the context of the poststructuralism of Roland Barth, Gilles Deleuze, and Michel Foucault. The search for unexpected pluralism proposed on his behalf organically coincided with the innovation characteristic of art. Neglect of traditional theoretical forms and the inability to find a poststructural alternative to them would inevitably lead to the actualization of practice. It is in this context that in the 21st century, postmodern theater most vigorously represents performance theater. Performance is the practice of art. Its innovation is largely determined by the fact that the main medium for creating a theatrical action is not the language, but the bodies and energies of the actors. Language is supplanted by corporeality. Together with corporeality, ontology comes to the fore.

The bodily practice of performance is in no way meaningless. In this regard, many researchers considered it necessary to achieve unity of performance with philosophy in the form of performance philosophy. [2; 4-6; 12]

> [T]he study of philosophy has become (appropriately so) the latest breakthrough in theatre studies. What is exciting about this, TO ME, is not that there is an interest in turning to philosophers not in the Continental tradition, but that a whole "new" 2,500-year-old-plus discipline is at our disposal and in our realm of consciousness. That means one thing: "new" ideas (to those of us in the theatre world)! This can only re-invigorate our excitement, our studies, and the possibilities of inquiry! [2, 3]

Michael Bennett is right, there is a difficult search for such a non-standard philosophy that would organically correspond to the specifics of the theater, in particular, of the performance theater. So far, this philosophy has not been found. References to representatives of continental philosophy prevail. At the same time, more and more attempts are being made to take into account the achievements of analytical philosophy. In this sense, the book of Bennett is indicative. In it, with respect to the theater, the relationship between empiricism and rationalism is examined and interpreted in the context of British idealism, phenomenology, analytical philosophy, and pragmatism. [1, 25-26]

In my opinion, the philosophy of the theater is gradually transformed into a philosophy of the theatrology. Any turns, including linguistic, critical, performance, if they are not filled with proper scientific power, come to naught. As for my position, it is known to the reader. I am convinced that conceptual transduction is relevant for theater theories no less than for physical and economic theories. Theatrology does not need non-standard philosophy, but a coherent philosophy of science, which would take into account its specificity as an offset conception.

References

1. Bennett, M.Y. (2012) Words, Space, and the Audience: The Theatrical Tension between Empiricism and Rationalism. New York: Palgrave Macmillan.
2. Bennett, M.Y. (2016) New directions in dramatic and theatrical theory: the emerging discipline of performance

philosophy. The Journal of American Drama and Theatre 28(1), 1-3.

3. Brecht, B. (1992) Brecht on Theatre: The Development of an Aesthetic. Transl. by J. Willett. New York: Hill and Wang.

4. Corby, J. (2019) Failing to think: the promise of performance philosophy. Performance Philosophy 4(2), 576-590.

5. Cull, L. (2018) Notes toward the philosophy of theatre. Anglia 136(1), 11-42.

6. Cull, L. (2018) From the philosophy of theatre to performance philosophy: Laruelle, Badiou and the equality of thought. Labyrinth: An International Journal for Philosophy, Value Theory and Sociocultural Hermeneutics 19(2), 102-120.

7. Daddario, W. and Schmidt, T. (2018) Introduction: crisis and the im/possibility of thought. Performance Philosophy 4(1), 1-8.

8. Dimitrova, Z. (2016) A drama of potentialities – toward an ontology. Journal of Dramatic Theory and Criticism 31(1), 65-85.

9. Esslin, M. (1960) The theatre of the absurd. The Tulane Drama Review 4(4), 3-15.

10. Kornhaber, D. and Middeke, M. (2018) Drama, theatre, and philosophy: an introduction. Anglia 136(1), 1-10.

11. Kwok-Kan, T. (1999) Postmodernist Performance in Contemporary Chinese and Japanese Theatre. In Lie, A.R. (Ed.). Old Worlds, New Worlds. New York: Routledge, 65-74.

12. Puchner, M. (2013) Please mind the gap between theatre and philosophy. Modern Drama 56(4), 540-552.

13. Stanislavski Directs. (1954) Ed. by N.M. Gorchakov. New York: Minerva Press.

14. Stern, T. (2013) Theatre and Philosophy. European Journal of Philosophy 21(1), 158–167.

15. Wilmer, S.E. and Vedel, K. (2019) Theatre and continental philosophy: editorial. Nordic Theatre Studies 31(1), 2-7.
16. Zhu, L. (2012) Aesthetic quality in theatre as a genre of performance. International Journal of English Linguistics 2(5), 55-59.

21.6. Foundations of literature

Literature as creative writing of recognized artistic value is prominent among other art disciplines. It has a pronounced linguistic character. If we keep in mind exclusively this feature of literature, then we should equate it with all the usual scientific texts. In reality, literature differs significantly from them, because it belongs to offset disciplines. This circumstance is crucial in determining its status. In connection with it, many researchers, non-cognitivists do not recognize the scientific status of literature. It, they say, does not develop new knowledge and the concept of truth. Jerome Stolnitz expressed this position clearly.

> Philosophers, critics, and others speak often enough of artistic truth. Considerably less often do they speak of artistic knowledge. How should there be truth without knowledge? We have scientific truth and scientific knowledge, historical truth and historical knowledge. Understandably, for once truth has been established as that and therefore accepted by a judging mind, it is knowledge. Why do we hear so little of artistic knowledge? [9, 192-193]

Stolnitz should be given credit, he is concerned that often relevant artistic knowledge is proclaimed, but in such an indefinite form that even his status is in doubt. In addition, it is desirable to determine its status in relation to the concept of truth, the value of which can hardly be overestimated in determining the nature of certain disciplines. Stolnitz offered to work out a clear, distinct view of artistic knowledge and its relation to truth. The absence of such a representation indicates a lack of understanding by researchers of the true nature of art, including literature. Of course, one cannot put up with this state of affairs.

What needs to be understood first? By definition, each discipline consists of theories. Literature consists of theories that appear, in particular, in the form of novels, stories, tales, and poems. The true nature of literary theories, the mechanism of their functioning, needs understanding. Scientific theories of the real sciences come in the form of conceptual transductions. Is there something similar in literary theories? If not, what exactly is characteristic of them?

The protagonists of not offset theories are people who, guided by motives (principles), do things and adjust their activities in accordance with their results. They do it time after time. This is precisely what cyclic conceptual transduction is all about. The same is true for literary theories. This circumstance is usually not noticed by non-cognitivists. It seems to them that there is no evidence in literary theories. In my opinion, this is a consequence of their lack of competence in the field of philosophy of science. In scientific theories, proof is realized through principles and methods. Clearly, they vary from one theory to another. It is reasonable to expect that something similar takes place in the case of literary theories. This assumption is not empty. I mean the combination of plot and characters of the actors. The plot is the unity of the principles of the theory. It unfolds according to the method of deduction.

Characters mark the methodological originality of the actors, their theories.

> [P]lot is a form of reasonable engagement with the incomprehensible. If narrative denotes our situatedness in the eventfulness of time, plot postulates something to be known as a result of our observing the interconnectedness of events. This is to say, reasons obtain for our countenancing that events are connected. Plot is the locus of that reasoning. The nature of the reasons is correlative with the principle according to which the events narrated seem to cohere and vary according to the specific nature of the mind contemplating those events. To project the coherence of events in the face of difficulty is to admit the necessity of a mind struggling against incoherence. This is true from the seminal moments of literary plotting. [8, 371]

In short, the plotting is the main form of thinking in literature. The plot is a system of interconnected motives in a work that determines the course of all events connected in causal series. The development of the plot cannot be explained otherwise than by references to the motives of the characters. If these motives are highlighted, then there is a literary explanation. The literary explanation is completely in line with those conceptual heights that are characteristic of science. Otherwise, art must be moved beyond science.

Plotting is a form of knowledge. How does it relate to the concept of truth? At first glance, plotting cannot be true, for it refers to the world not of the reality, but of the imaginary. However, this impression is misleading. First, it should be borne in mind that in the context of the theory of conceptual transduction, the most developed theories are recognized as true. Not all theories related to literature are recognized as equally significant, as evidenced by the recognition, for example, of both prominent and ordinary writers. Theories of prominent authors are the first contenders for the honorary title of true theories. Nevertheless, they belong to the imaginary world, where there seems to be no place for true and false. By virtue of this circumstance, the imaginary world is evaluated from the standpoint of real sciences. It is thanks to this that literature is introduced to the concept of true knowledge as part of the sciences of the real world. The literary work that contributes to the development of real sciences should be recognized as true. Thus, a literary work can be true in both the world of the imaginary and the real.

The analysis shows that there is both literary knowledge and literary truth. The arguments put forward by me testify in favor of literary cognitivism. He, as you know, attaches particular importance to the process of thinking. Conceptual transduction does not come down to it. It is realized as not only thinking, but also feeling. The specifics of art, including literature, is usually associated with emotions. At the same time, the significance of literature is underestimated. In fact, thinking and feeling as two forms of mental representation of conceptual transduction accompany each other. There is no reason to attribute thinking to science, and feeling to art.

My version of literary cognitivism follows from the theory of conceptual transduction. Of course, there are other versions. John Gibson believs «that literature's cognitive value resides in its ability not to offer knowledge but rather to act upon the knowledge we already possess» and «that the form of insight we get from this concerns not truth, properly so called, but a certain cognitive orientation toward the "texture" of human experience and circumstance.» [2, 478] In my opinion, there is no reason to deny both literary knowledge and literary truth. Knowledge is the understanding of the manifestation of conceptual transduction. Truth accompanies this knowledge when it is the most advanced. Both are present in the literature. Gibson did not take into account this fact, which is relevant for understanding the nature of literature.

Iris Vidmar, evaluating the status of literary cognitivism, proceeds from the difference between philosophy and literature. It turns out that each of them has a specificity, the relevance of which should not be underestimated.

> If literary cognitivism is not focused on establishing a direct link between literature and truth, but insists instead on embracing a wider account of cognitive gains – deeper understanding, more nuanced appreciation, development of sensibility – there is no reason to exclude literature from cognitively relevant discourses. This is not to diminish literature's artistic value or literary accomplishments of the author; it is simply to acknowledge one aspect of literary experience. With at least some works of literature, we feel cognitively enriched. [10, 384]

This conclusion deserves attention, but its justification is doubtful. Philosophy and literature are fundamentally different sciences. The attributes of deeper understanding, more nuanced appreciation, and the development of sensibility are hardly legitimate to be considered the merits of only literature. Literary cognitivism cannot be distinguished without a thorough analysis of the conceptual content of literature.

Jukka Mikkonen believes, «that the cognitive value of literature is best construed in terms of enhancing the reader's understanding» and «that the place to look for evidence for the cognitive benefits of literature is not the laboratory but the practice of literature.» [4, 273] Both of these statements do not say anything about the mechanisms of literary thinking. The phenomenon of understanding is characteristic of any axiological theory, but in each of them, it takes place in a specific way. Literary cognitivism involves characterizing precisely the type of understanding that is characteristic of literature.

John Harold distinguishes between a strong and a weak version of literary cognitivism. In the first case, we are talking about propositional knowledge, and in the second, of experiential and perspectival. [3] In my opinion, if the cycles of conceptual transduction are considered as the unity of all their stages, then the selection, for example, of experimental knowledge does not make sense. Any literary knowledge is propositional insofar as it testifies to some imaginary world. It is experimental, for it is actualized upon its perception. Thus, highlighting strong and weak literary cognitivism does not seem to be mandatory. The concept of literary cognitivism needs further refinement. Obviously, it should be used in a systematic way. In this regard, I see no alternative to the concept of conceptual transduction.

The concept of literary cognitivism is relevant to determine the nature of literature. It aims to elucidate the internal mechanisms of the functioning of literary theories. In this case, of course, the features of literary schools, in particular, of formalism, Marxism, structuralism, postmodernism, should be taken into account. [7] Each of the literary schools has both strengths and weaknesses. Obviously, weak traits need to be either strengthened or eliminated. As for the strengths, they unequivocally testify to the need to combine different schools. In my opinion, it is not fully understood that a single picture of literary trends can be worked out only by relying on the philosophy of science.

Clarification of the nature of literature, of course, presupposes a correct interpretation of its relations with the philosophy and philosophy of science. There are various positions on this subject, some of which seem rather strange to me. Melvin Chen believes that the ideas about three disciplines are quite appropriate, namely, firstly, about the philosophy of literature, secondly, about philosophy in science and, thirdly, about philosophy and literature. [1] Iris Vidmar believes that there are intersections between philosophy and literature, in particular, they discuss similar topics of philosophical content, but their categorical structure is different; therefore, they should be considered separate disciplines. [11]

Judgments on the relationship between philosophy and literature imply clear ideas about the nature of the natural, axiological, and formal sciences. The content of the natural and axiological sciences is clearly different from each other; their principles, and after them, the laws, are clearly different. Formal sciences, including the philosophy of science, deals with similar content of the natural and axiological sciences. The similarity is not the identity. Within the framework of the philosophy of science, it has been established that the concept of the deductive method is relevant in all sciences. Nevertheless, deduction, for example, in physics and literature is not identical to each other. In this regard, there is no reason to believe that physics and literature intersect with each other. It is correct to state that they have similar methodological content. The concept of similar content refers to the characteristic of the correlation of basic, i.e. natural and axiological sciences. It is not applicable to characterize the ratio of formal and basic sciences. A comparison of basic and formal sciences suggests that they are independent entities in relation to each other. Since this condition is not satisfied due to the superstructural nature of the formal sciences, the comparison operation is also inappropriate.

Thus, the sciences do not have identical content. Iris Vidmar, insisting on the need to distinguish between literature and philosophy, is undoubtedly right. In my opinion, the recognition of this fact is incompatible with the assertion of the existence of «some overlap between the two disciplines». [11, 1] In the context under consideration, 'overlap' implies identity, but, as explained earlier, it does not. It is erroneous, for example, to assert that the same philosophical topics are discussed both in philosophy and in literature. All philosophical topics, by their very definition, are formal. Literary topics are not formal.

When considering the relationship between literature and philosophy, one should bear in mind the difference between philosophy and the philosophy of science. If we keep in mind the scientific context, namely, it is considered in this case, then one science should be recognized, considering it either a philosophy or a philosophy of science. In my opinion, we should focus on the philosophy of science. Only with this choice can one be freed from philosophy as an undesirable metaphysical appendage to scientific philosophy.

Let me now turn to the concept of 'philosophy of literature'. There is nothing formal in literature, which the expression 'philosophy of literature' indicates. Therefore, strictly speaking, there is no philosophy of literature, although much is said about it. In my opinion, if you want to emphasize the methodological and conceptual content of the literature, the term 'meta literature' should be used. Thus, in my opinion, all three concepts discussed by Melvin Chen, namely, 'philosophy of literature', 'philosophy and literature', and 'philosophy in literature' are unsuccessful. In relation to literature, only the concepts 'literature' and 'metaliterature' are relevant.

Finally, the extremely popular notion that literary knowledge is a source of ethical knowledge should be noted. [1; 3; 5; 6; 11] Earlier, when I examined various axiological theories, I repeatedly noted the advisability of including ethical principles in their content. In this regard, the ethical relativity of literary knowledge should be recognized. This knowledge does not have any ethical advantages over other types of axiological knowledge.

References

1. Chen, M. (2017) Philosophy and literature: problems of a philosophical subdiscipline. Philosophy and Literature 41(2), 471-482.
2. Gibson, J. (2009) Literature and knowledge. In Eldridge R. (Ed.). Oxford Handbook of Philosophy and Literature, Oxford, UK: Oxford University Press, 467-485.
3. Harold, J. (2016) Literary cognitivism. In Carroll, N. and Gibson J. (Eds.). The Routledge Companion to Philosophy of Literature. London: Routledge, 382-393.
4. Mikkonen, J. (2015) On studying the cognitive value of literature. The Journal of Aesthetics and Art Criticism 73(3), 273-282.

5. Nussbaum, M. (1990). Love's Knowledge. Second Ed. Oxford, UK: Oxford University Press.

6. Putnam, H. (1976) Literature, science and reflection. New Literary History 7(3), 483-491.

7. Rice, P and Waugh, P. (Eds.). (2001) Modern Literary Theory: A Reader. Fourth Ed. London: Bloomsbury Academic.

8. Singer, A. (2009) Plot. In Eldridge R. (Ed.). Oxford Handbook of Philosophy and Literature, Oxford, UK: Oxford University Press, 369-392.

9. Stolnitz, J. (1992) On the cognitive triviality of art. The British Journal of Aesthetics, 32(3), 191-200.

10. Vidmar, I. (2017) On literary cognitivism from the perspective of difference between literature and philosophy. Synthesis Philosophica 64 (2), 371-386.

11. Vidmar, I. (2015) Literature and philosophy: intersection and boundaries. Arts 4(1), 1-22.

21.7. Foundations of depiction

Considering such basic subdisciplines of the art science as musicology, theatrology, filmology, and literature, it is easy to notice that they all represent some theories through certain intermediaries. These are sounds in musicology, words in literature, words and gestures in theatrology, and motion pictures in filmology. I cited this fact in order to go on to the characterization of another main subdiscipline of art science, namely depiction. Its intermediaries are the traces left by the artist on objects in the form of dots, lines, and spots. It is imperative to understand that any theory can manifest itself through sounds, words, body movements, and expressive means of drawing. In particular, physical and economic theories can be represented in this way. Theories cannot be presented without one or another medium. It should be borne in mind that the same mediums represent both real and offset theories. The depiction is an offset discipline made up of some theories. Its medium is the expressive means of drawing, and the objects themselves are pictures. The humans of depiction are artists and spectators.

Artists and philosophers have repeatedly raised the question of the nature of painting and drawing as parts of depiction. Any discipline consists of theories, depiction too. This conclusion follows from the principle of theoretical representation. A picture is an object of theory. In order to get the most detailed representation of a picture, its history should be considered by the intratheoretical and intertheoretical conceptual transduction. A physicist considers the nature of physical objects, such as electrons, based on physical theories. An economist characterizes the nature of goods based on the content of economic theories. The nature of the pictures should be considered based on depictive theories. This conclusion follows from the theory of conceptual transduction.

Thus, the nature of the pictures lies in the theories that they represent. Turning to these theories, we find a fundamentally different approach. As a rule, it is noted that depiction is an image. [3; 7] In my opinion, the picture is a representation of some depictive theory. How exactly its advantages will be used will depend on numerous situations. It is not necessary that they will be used to depict objects and subjects.

An interesting attempt to develop ideas about depiction was made by Robert Briscoe. According to «the *deep resemblance theory*, pictures work by presenting virtual models of objects and scenes in phenomenally 3D, pictorial space. » [1, 43] Model «is an artifact designed to simulate the outward visual appearance of an actual or possible object or scene – the model's *original*.» [1, 45] In endorsing the theory of Briscoe, let me interpret its content from a position somewhat different from his conception. Briscoe juxtaposes the depictive model and its original. From my point of view, should be compared to depictive and relevant theories. The next step is to implement interdisciplinary connections between theories. Representatives of current theory consider the depictive conception as a donor theory. In this regard, we can assume that they are engaged in depictive modeling. It is possible because there is a resemblance between the two theories. Its origins are obvious.

Creating a depictive theory is hardly possible without relying on actual theory. An artist who is not versed in psychology is unlikely to realize plots dedicated to the effects of rage, humility, and grief. Based on the psychological knowledge known to him, the artist shifts towards the possible imaginary. If an artist avoids obviously impractical leaps into the unknown, then the continuity of the depictive theory created by him with the actual concept is preserved. Later this circumstance can be used by a representative of an actual theory. The two theories under consideration are similar to each other. The deep resemblance of the two theories will be clarified through the comprehensive implementation of their interdisciplinary connections.

Another debatable issue is the realism of depictive theories. The widespread belief is that the purpose of depiction are images. By definition, it is desirable that images are true, i.e. realistic, and not false. The rejection of this false belief leads to a clarification of the question of realism. Realism involves the contact of two theories, imaginary about images and relevant about the originals. It makes no sense to demand identity from them. Of cause in its absence, the image cannot be realistic, true. It turns out that the very concept of an image, due to its loading with metaphysical moments, is not scientific. The portrait does not depict, does not copy the original, but gives it a new interpretation. Noted does not mean that the question of realism is meaningless. It is relevant if depiction reality is considered as irreducible to images.

With regard to current theories, everything that is part of the league-theories developed through conceptual transduction is recognized as existing. The question arises of whether it is permissible to consider the content of offset league-theories as existing. The answer to this question would be simple if the imaginary, included in the content of theories, would not have anything to do with the actual. Meanwhile, as explained earlier, the content of offset theories does not exclude their use in interdisciplinary relations. In my opinion, this means that the imaginary, which is successfully used in interdisciplinary communications, should be recognized as real. Thus, the following two conclusions are relevant in understanding realism as applied to offset theories, including as applied to depiction. Firstly, the concept of a realistic image is untenable. Secondly, it should be recognized that part of the imaginary is translated into the real through the implementation of interdisciplinary relationships between offset theories and relevant actual conceptions.

Back in 1954, Iredell Jenkins noted: "[p]erhaps the greatest obstacle that confronts the philosophy of art is the extreme diversity of the field that it seeks to order." [4, 185]. It is difficult to disagree with this statement even today, including in relation to depiction with its several dozen movements from cubism and fauvism to various variants of postmodernism.

Pluralism is common to all theories, but especially to the artistic conception. Obviously, to some extent, this is due to their imaginary character. In offset theories, the imagination is limited; nevertheless, its boundaries are not identified as strictly as in actual conceptions. This opens up additional room for unexpected assumptions. Of course, the pluralism of depictive theories needs to be explained. In this regard, researchers encounter significant difficulties, in particular, in understanding the role of abstractions. Few people doubt their relevance. Modern artists use abstractions so often and unexpectedly that their status today, like decades ago, still needs additional study. [5, 169]

Trying to comprehend the phenomenon of pluralism in depiction, many researchers paid special attention to the work of Pablo Picasso. This famous artist, willingly continuing the efforts of his predecessors, was distinguished by a pronounced ability to use various styles of painting. «[I]t appears similarly that Picasso's greatness lies not only in his innovations in form and subject but also in his creation of a new model of artistic behavior, that of the versatile conceptual artist who makes frequent and precipitous change in the style and form of his work». [2, 26] It is believed that despite the difference in the styles of painting used by Picasso, his work possessed an internal unity. [9] It is understood that he used the drawing style that was most consistent with the tasks being solved.

Anyone who, avoiding this rule uses one style of drawing, which seems universal to him, commits a methodological error. In the age of pluralism, unity of depiction implies the diversity of depiction schools. This conclusion seems correct to me. Nevertheless, I believe that the unity of depiction should be expressed by the presence of not only various schools, but also transitions between them. The transition to some school is necessary when it provides additional benefits. In the case of cubism, this is shown, for example, in articles by Dan O'Brien and Simon Weir and Jason Anthony Dibbs. [8; 10]

Abstractionism is characterized by an extremely attentive attitude to the expressive means used. Expressionism is good for its attention to the work of the author. Symbolism is appropriate when considering the relationship of depiction with other theories. The concepts of other theories are symbols of depictive concepts. Pop art builds bridges between high and mass painting. Postmodernism has no alternative as the cultivation of pluralism in depiction. My main idea is that the pluralism of theories does not exclude their correlation. It becomes clear if, when comparing theories, their flaws are leveled, and the emphasis is on the synthesis of achievements. Unfortunately, often the pluralism of depictive theories is only proclaimed, but it is not mastered properly conceptually.

Thus, the depiction is art theory with all its attributes, i.e. subjects, themes, relationships of variables, i.e. with the laws. This circumstance is camouflaged by the fact that the picture is a stopped phenomenon. Of course, the artist did not create it overnight. Nevertheless, it seems that the viewer can well perceive it as a finished form, without a systematic detailed understanding. This opinion, of course, is erroneous. Theory always acts as the management of concepts. Painting in this sense is no exception. W. Mitchell notes that «[p]ictures are not just a special kind of signs, they are rather something like an actor at the stage of history, a figure or a character of legendary status in a context that matches and participates in the stories which we tell about the course of our development [...]. [6, 19] He quite rightly emphasizes the procedural nature of the picture as a work of art. The artist does not cancel the time; he encloses it in a spatial and color form.

The development of depiction is an integral part of the achievements of humankind. It has no alternative. As for its foundations, they are far from fully allocated. In my opinion, the main drawback of modern depiction is the lack of attention to the phenomenon of depictive theory.

References

1. Briscoe, R. (2016) Depiction, pictorial experience, and vision science. Philosophical Topics 44(2), 43-81.
2. Galenson, D.W. (2007) And now for something completely different; the versatility of conceptual innovators. Historical Methods: A Journal of Quantitative and Interdisciplinary History 40(1), 17-27.
3. Hyman, J. and Bantinaki, K. (2017) Depiction. The Stanford Encyclopedia of Philosophy. Available at: https://plato.stanford.edu/archives/sum2017/entries/depiction/
4. Jenkins, I. (1954) The unity and the varieties of art. The Journal of Aesthetics and Art Criticism 13(2), 185-202.
5. Lavin, I. (1961) Abstraction in modern painting. A comparison. Metropolitan Museum Bulletin 19 (6), 166-171.
6. Mitchell, W.J.T. (2008) Bildtheorie. [Picture theory]. Frankfurt am Main: Suhrkamp. [In German].
7. Newall, M. (2014) Painting and philosophy. Philosophy Compass 9(4), 225-237.
8. O'Brien, D. (2018) Cubism: art and philosophy. ESPES 7(1), 30-37.
9. Schapiro, M. (2000) The unity of Picasso's art. New York: Braziller.

10. Weir, S. and Dibbs, J. A. (2019) The ontographic turn: from cubism to the surrealist object. Open Philosophy 2(1), 384-398.

Chapter 22. The nature of ethics

22.1. What kind of science is ethics?

I confess to the reader that, starting to write the book, I considered ethics as one of the parts of philosophy. As the book was written, the conviction was ripe that ethics should be recognized to be a full-fledged axiological branch of science along with, in particular, political science and law. Due to the division of labor in the philosophy of science, certain aspects of the basic axiological sciences, namely, the phenomena of power, permissible and prosperity are purposefully studied in special formal sciences. Political science is devoted to the phenomenon of power, the phenomenon of the permissible is expressed in law and, finally, prosperity is studied in ethics. Given this circumstance, ethics should be recognized as a formal axiological science. In full accordance with the developed argumentation, the principle of maximizing the prosperity of all stakeholders should be recognized as the main principle of ethics. This requirement may seem excessive. It can be assumed that under the pressure of unethical factors, the principle of maximizing prosperity will not be feasible. However, the basis of an ethical project is the belief in its feasibility. It is based on a simple assumption. People are able to multiply the total value of income. It is further assumed that this value is sufficient to satisfy the needs of all interested parties.

In the philosophical literature, considerable attention is paid to the problem of substantiating morality. [6] Proponents of this approach believe that it is possible to prove the feasibility of well-defined requirements, for example, those that are discussed as part of the deontological ethics of I. Kant or the utilitarian ethics of Bentham-Mill. In order to avoid misunderstandings, I immediately note that initially, it is necessary to determine the name of the conceptual system that is being discussed. In the case of calling it either ethics or morality, a certain confusion is introduced into the discussion. In accordance with the tradition that formed in Antiquity, I prefer the term 'ethics'. Authors who avoid scientific connotations, as a rule, use the term 'morality'. Justification of ethics is always made from the standpoint of a certain philosophical trend. Illustrative in this regard, for example, the views of the outstanding ethicists of David Hume, Immanuel Kant, John Stuart Mill, Alfred Ayer, John Dewey, Jürgen Habermas, and John Rawls. Their discussions of the nature of ethics are based on empiricism (Hume), early critical rationalism (Kant), logical positivism (Ayer), pragmatism (Dewey), critical hermeneutics (Habermas), and analytical philosophy (Rawls). Each of these authors, being unable to escape the snares of philosophical isolationism, nevertheless speaks on behalf of the supposedly only true universal worldview. This circumstance, considering the nature of ethics, of course, should be borne in mind.

Another feature of the entire body of literature on ethics is that, as a rule, the achievements of the philosophy of science are used extremely inconsistently. Because of this, metaphysics is often recognized to be the key to ethics. All modern ethics are colored with colors of metaphysics. Supporters of metaphysics keep ethics at a very respectful distance from science and the philosophy of science. I believe that in modern ethics the anti-scientific syndrome dominates. This circumstance, especially against the backdrop of the successes of the philosophy of science, is regrettable.

As for me, I consider the status of ethics from the positions of the theory of conceptual transduction, bearing in mind that it combines the achievements of the whole philosophy of science. This means that all metaphysical attempts to determine the status of ethics receive critical coverage. Philosophy is intended to express the conceptual structure of the sciences. This task is beyond the purview of ethics. This circumstance clearly indicates that ethics is not an integral part of philosophy. Ethics is a formal axiological science, guided by the principle of maximizing the prosperity of all stakeholders.

The need for ethics is far from accidental. The fact is that all axiological theories are not immune to some significant flaws. For example, the maximization of the rate of profit in the economy is often accompanied by a sharp and unjustified stratification of citizens into rich and poor. The purpose of ethics is to eliminate all possible undesirable phenomena for people. Under the auspices of ethics, it is advisable to adjust the content of all axiological sciences. It is ethics that gives them completeness and finality favorable to people.

Emphasizing the uniqueness of the conceptual-transduction concept of ethics, let me turn to some popular approaches to substantiating ethics.

David Hume believed that moral distinctions are not determined by reason or facts, but solely by sentiment. As a result « [...] morality consists not in any relations that are the objects of science [...]». [4, III, p. 468] The second line of his argumentation, which is gaining immense popularity, concerns the interconnections of *is*- and *ought*-sentences.

> I cannot forbear adding to these reasoning an observation, which may, perhaps, be found of some importance. In every system of morality which I have hitherto met with, I have always remarked, that the author proceeds for some time in the ordinary way of reasoning, and establishes the being of a God, or makes observations concerning human affairs; when of a sudden I am surprised to find, that instead of the usual

copulations of propositions, *is*, and *is not* , I meet with no proposition that is not connected with an *ought* , or an *ought not* . This change is imperceptible; but is, however, of the last consequence. For as this *ought* , or *ought not* , expresses some new relation or affirmation, it is necessary that it should be observed and explained; and at the same time that a reason should be given, for what seems altogether inconceivable, how this new relation can be a deduction from others, which are entirely different from it. [4, III, p. 469]

As an empiricist, Hume begins with sensory data (feelings). He believes that they determine the content of ethical judgments. Hume does not consider ethical theory as some organized integrality. He does not take into account that feelings operate as part of cycles of conceptual transduction. They represent the theory in its sensual form. The theory can be presented by thoughts, what Hume relates to reason. Between the various representations of the theory, there is certainly coordination. Otherwise, the personality would lose its identity, integrity. Hume also did not take into account that all ethical assessments relate to events, the meaning of which is given by some theory. In particular, ethical assessments of economic and political events should be distinguished.

Hume's reasoning about the difference of *is-* and *ought-*sentences can confuse only a researcher who does not clearly understand the originality of axiological and natural sciences. Of course, it is impossible to derive axiological theories with their ought-sentences from the natural sciences with their is-sentences. Those researchers who are trying to carry out such a derivation quite rightly surprise Hume. However, he himself does not state that the indicated withdrawal, in fact, is not required. The impossibility of deriving axiological theories from natural ones is not a paradox, but a real relationship. Ethics is constituted outside the natural sciences, and not in metaphysics, but in the field of axiological theories.

In my opinion, attempts to deny the scientific nature of ethics from the standpoint of the logical atomism of Ludwig Wittgenstein, the logical positivism of Alfred Ayer and Charles Stevenson, as well as the analytical ethics of John Moore, should be called a scandal. Many supporters of logical atomism and logical positivism implement an extremely straightforward strategy. They reduce the basis of all sciences to the facts of the natural sciences and corresondence conception of truth. Both the first and second are not found in ethics. Then follows the conclusion that ethics is impossible as a theory with clear content (Wittgenstein) or has purely emotive content (Ayer and Stevenson). [8, 88; 1, 102-113; 7] In reality, of course, ethics is intimately connected both with facts and with the concept of truth. Facts are definitions of variables that are implemented in the process of interfering with the course of phenomena, which occurs during observations and experiments or practical actions. So-understood facts are inherent in any axiological theory. For example, the price at which a certain product is sold is an economic fact. In accordance with the theory of conceptual transduction, which, in my opinion, has no worthy alternative, the content of all the most developed theories is recognized as true. Moreover, ethics is present in the most developed axiological theories. The above, in my opinion, is enough to emphasize the complete failure of emotivism.

John Moore, as the founder of metaethics, concluded that good as an elementary concept is indefinable. [5, § 10] If contrary to this state of affairs, they try to determine good on the basis of unethical realities as is done in hedonism, naturalism, and utilitarianism, then a naturalistic mistake is made. The question of the nature of duty is always open. [5, § 13]

Moore's decisive mistake was his attempt to develop a specific version of metaethics, starting from metaphysical ethics. A logical analysis of the language of metaphysical ethics did not lead to its translation on a scientific footing. Metaethics did not leave the field of metaphysics. Modern proponents of metaethics replicate Moore's mistake many times. In my opinion, the correct method is first to determine the contours of scientific ethics, in particular, technical, medical and economic ethics. Then its content summarizes in philosophical ethics as a formal generalization of the similar content of special ethics. Genuine metaethics is equal to special ethics.

Further, all metaphysical ethical terms, if necessary, to preserve them, including the good, receive a new interpretation. Good acts as a steady observance of the principle of maximizing the prosperity of all stakeholders. Prosperity itself is understood in the context of basic axiological discipline. For example, in the economy, prosperity is, first of all, maximization of the norm of profit on the advanced capital and wages of workers and employees. The question of the nature of good is not open. An open question is the ways of further development of economic theory, and with it economic ethics.

Of course, the development of ethics, as well as any other axiological theory, meets with certain difficulties. [3; 2] Considering many of them, Richmond Campbell concluded that moral knowledge is possible. [2] Unfortunately, this, in my opinion, the correct conclusion is not accompanied by any detailed description of ethical scientific theories. The same goes for Chris Gowans' review. [3] Both authors do not consider the main issue of the modern philosophy of ethics, namely, specific ways of transferring metaphysical ethics on a scientific footing.

References

1. Ayer, A.J. (1952) [1936] Language, Truth and Logic. New York: Dover Publications.
2. Campbell, R. (2019) Moral epistemology. The Stanford Encyclopedia of Philosophy. Available at: https://plato.stanford.edu/archives/win2019/entries/moral-epistemology/
3. Gowans, C. (2019) Moral relativism. The Stanford Encyclopedia of Philosophy. Available at: https://plato.stanford.edu/archives/sum2019/entries/moral-relativism/
4. Hume, D. (1965) [1739] A Treatise of Human Nature. Ed. by P.H. Nidditch. London: Oxford University Press, 1965.
5. Moore, G. E. (1903) Principia Ethica. Cambridge: Cambridge University Press.
6. Shafer-Landau, R. (Ed.). (2012) Ethical theory: an anthology. Second ed. Oxford: Wiley-Blackwell.
7. Stevenson, C. L. (1944) Ethics and Language. New Haven: Yale University Press.
8. Wittgenstein, L. (1922) Tractatus Logico-Philosophicus. London: Kegan, P., Trench, T. & CO., LTD; New York: Harcourt, B. & Company, Inc.

22.2. The construction of scientific ethical theory

As you know, any scientific theory has a certain content and dynamics, which is realized through cycles of conceptual transduction. Metaphysical ethical theories do not fulfill these conditions. This circumstance confronts researchers with the need to construct consistently scientific theories in full accordance with scientific criteria. Let us turn in this connection, first, to the principles of ethical theory. In my opinion, this is, firstly, the principle of maximizing the prosperity of all stakeholders; secondly, the principle of responsibility. The need for the principle of maximizing prosperity was justified in the previous section. The necessity of the principle of responsibility was discussed in section 6.9.

Is it advisable to put into operation, in addition to those already mentioned, any other principles of ethical theories? It is difficult to find a clear answer to this question, first, insofar as there is no proper experience in constructing ethical theories. For many centuries, people have difficulty determining the most relevant ethical points. With this in mind, I believe that numerous examples of moral codes set a definite guideline for their search. Some of them were discussed earlier; see, for example, section 14.6. Authors of various moral codes urge people to achieve happiness, freedom, and justice, to be honest, loyal to customers and in solidarity with colleagues, to realize the moral integrity of the person, her integrity.

The content of the most popular ethical trends, namely, the aretological, deontological and utilitarian ethics, is also indicative. Aristotle, the founder of aretological ethics, among many virtues designed to control people's passions, preferred practical wisdom (prudence), moderation, courage, and justice. Aristotle says that the "virtuous activity in accordance with reason" is the eudaimonia (happiness or well-being). [1,

1097b22-1098a20]. The most authoritative representative of deontological ethics, Immanuel Kant, insisting on the observance of moral duty, believed that this is how a person realizes his freedom. Act in accordance with universal maxims. [3, 30] The one who does not kill, does not lie, does not steal, does not use another as a means is free.

John Stuart Mill, as one of the founders of classical utilitarianism, paid special attention to supplementing the first principle of ethics, namely the principle of maximizing happiness for the greatest number of people, with secondary principles.

> It is a strange notion that the acknowledgement of a first principle is inconsistent with the admission of secondary ones. ...Whatever we adopt as the fundamental principle of morality, we require subordinate principles to apply it by: the impossibility of doing without them, being common to all systems, can afford no argument against any one in particular: but gravely to argue as if no such secondary principles could be had, and as if mankind had remained till now, and always must remain, without drawing any general conclusions from the experience of human life, is as high a pitch, I think, as absurdity has ever reached in philosophical controversy. [5, 70]

Mill was most interested in the possibility of generalizing various ethical theories. Expressed in modern language, he represented a variant of formal ethics, in which the values of people are called utilities that shape happiness in accordance with their nature. He was well aware that justice and freedom are extremely relevant values. But he considered these principles secondary to the principle of maximizing happiness. Mill's mistake was the distortion of the combination of the special and the formal. The formal does not precede special factors but merely expresses their similarity. Mill also did not take into account that the formal cannot be likened to the special. The principle of maximizing happiness for him, in fact, is not only a formal but also a special principle. The identification of the formal with the special is untenable.

When I argue that axiological theories should deductively begin with the principles of maximizing prosperity and the principle of responsibility, both of these principles, when included in special theories, for example, in technology or economics, lose all their formal features. Prosperity is understood in accordance with specific guidelines.

Using the example of deontic and utilitarian ethics, it is reasonable to emphasize the extremely one-sided expression in the metaphysical ethical systems of the achievements of the philosophy of science. In virtue ethics, the emphasis is placed on the characteristics of people as the essences of ethical theory. The essences of any axiological theory are people who, in accordance with this theory, have certain characteristics that are commonly called values. The virtues of people are nothing but the values of people. The confusion begins when virtues are considered outside their connection with laws and principles. This is precisely the main drawback of virtue ethics. The virtues of people can be realized only in the cycles of conceptual transduction.

Deontological ethics with its concept of duty expresses the desire to give holistic description of ethics. How should this be understood? Apparently, as the need for comprehensive development of ethics, because otherwise, it is impossible to avoid the extremely unfavorable evolution of people. The trouble with proponents of deontological ethics is that they do not provide a detailed description of ethical theories.

The topic of integrity in ethics leads to the concept of integrity, which often appears in ethical codes. For ethics, this topic is far from random. Ethics involves an organic combination of all ethical theories. The exclusion from the ethical whole of at least one axiological science is a direct path to catastrophe.

Integrity is a confident possession of not only one developed ethical theory in its entirety [4], but also all theories. It acts as an integral whole with its variety of interdisciplinary connections. Integrity is the equivalent of the harmonious ethical development of personality. In my opinion, integrity is another candidate for the high title of ethical principles. In accordance with its content, the triumph of ethical affairs should be ensured by the system of interdisciplinary connections of this ethical theory with all other ethical theories relevant to the situation in question.

Turning once again to classical utilitarianism, I note that a method for calculating the utilities or values has been proposed. Ethics culminates in maximizing integral utility. The main disadvantage of this approach is that the calculation of values is understood as manipulating them directly. The vast majority of authors, describing ways to maximize integral utility, completely forget about the cycles of conceptual transduction. The way people live is that they are steadily improving their theories, including the implementation of their practical projects. At the same time, they achieve the maximization of utility values and the minimization of disability values. Desired is achieved through conceptual transduction. Thus, we should talk about maximizing the utilities and, accordingly, minimizing the disutility through conceptual transduction.

The utilitarian concept of happiness deserves special mention. As repeatedly emphasized earlier, there are various forms of manifestation of the theory, including emotional ones. Happiness appears as the dominant emotion if the theory is successfully implemented. Understanding of its content is achieved only when the content of theories is taken into account, including the history of their evolution in the intratheoretical and intertheoretical cycles of their implementation. Classical utilitarianism, of course, is associated with the absolutizing of the emotional life of people. There is no reason to forget other aspects of human life.

Thus, in my opinion, the construction of a scientific ethical theory involves a scientific interpretation of all those concepts that are used with some success in metaphysical ethics. There is a huge range of opinions regarding these concepts. Their consideration goes far beyond the tasks that I am trying to solve. Let me limit myself to one illustrative example.

As a result of careful research, The International Ethics Standard identified 10 ethical principles: 1) accountability, 2) confidentiality, 3) conflict of interest, 4) financial responsibility, 5) integrity, 6) lawfulness, 7) reflection, 8) standard of service, 9) transparency, 10) trust. [2, 4] Of course, not all of these values are genuine principles. As explained above, the first contenders for the role of ethical principles are to maximize prosperity, responsibility, and integrity. As for other values, their meaning can be clarified in the light of these principles. The key to explaining accountability is the principle of responsibility. Accountability is the responsibility of some individuals to others. Genuine accountability assumes that subjects of responsibility are guided by advanced theories. Financial responsibility is nothing more than a concretization of the principle of responsibility in relation to the financial sphere. Lawfulness is, obviously, a concretization of the principle of integrity. The requirement of reflection acts as an indispensable improvement of the theory. Four values, namely trust, transparency, confidentiality and conflict of interest, are aimed at achieving discursive harmony, including individual and group theories. In accordance with the principles and values of ethical theory, a standard of service is implemented.

The above example shows that it is quite possible to transform metaphysical ethics into a scientific conception. Unfortunately, the vast majority of authors are satisfied with metaphysical theories. In the age of science, ethics, expressing perhaps the highest aspirations of people, is isolated from it. This situation seems to be extremely scandalous, testifying to an extremely superficial understanding of the relevance of the philosophy of science.

References

1. Aristotle's Nicomachean Ethics. (2012) Bartlett, R.C. and Collins, S.D. (Eds. and trans.). Chicago: The University of Chicago Press.
2. International Ethics Standards. (2016)An Ethical Framework for the global property market. London: International Ethics Standards Coalition.
3. Kant, I. (1993) [1785] Grounding for the Metaphysics of Morals. Transl. by J.W. Ellington. Third ed. Indianapolis, Cambridge: Hackett Publishing company, INC.

4. Killinger, B. (2010) Integrity: Doing the Right Thing for the Right Reason. Montreal: McGill-Queen's University Press.
5. Mill, J.S. (2001) Utilitarianism. Oxford: Oxford University Press.

22.3. Conceptual transduction versus reflective equilibrium

The existence of ethics in the metaphysical shell makes it extremely difficult to understand its conceptual and methodological structure. In this regard, the method of reflective equilibrium was perceived as a significant innovation, especially after its use by John Rawls in relation to ethics and political philosophy. [2; 1] By definition, reflective equilibrium implies consistency, moreover, a balance between some general principles and specific judgments. [6, 139-141] In the specified context, the use of the terms 'balance' and 'equilibrium' in the field of social science seems more acceptable than in the field of natural science. The fact is that the authors of fundamental documents in the field of social science, for example, of texts of constitutions, are forced to seek agreement with each other by comparing the values (norms) that are preferable to them. In contrast to them, representatives of the natural sciences do not seem to need such coordination of individual positions, because they proceed from descriptive facts.

Assessing the status of the reflective equilibrium method, I will proceed from the theory of conceptual transduction, the relevance of which was substantiated earlier throughout the book. In accordance with this theory, the ethical content of axiological theories in methodological terms does not differ from the methods of these conceptions themselves. Methods of ethics are methods of conceptual transduction. This is not difficult to understand insofar as a particular ethical theory is part of the corresponding basic theory. Thus, economic ethics is part of economic theories; technical ethics is part of technical theories. Etc. Methods of economic ethics are methods of economic theories. Methods of technical ethics are methods of technical theories.

Of course, special ethical theories should be distinguished from formal ethical theories. Ethics considered by philosophers is a formal theory. In this connection, a reasonable question arises about the status of ethics methods. Is it acceptable to consider methods of conceptual transduction as methods of ethics? There seems to be a negative answer to this question. These methods are not found in ethical texts. However, the negative answer is untenable. The fact is that formal ethics in itself, irrespective of special ethics, is untenable. Its original content is rooted in special ethics. Given this circumstance, it turns out that it is unlawful to contrast the methods of formal ethics with the methods of special ethics. Formal ethics reveals the similarity of the methods of special sciences, i.e. methods of conceptual transduction. Its formal nature does not give rise to question the methods of conceptual transduction. Thus, the conclusion that the methods of ethics are methods of conceptual transduction remains valid in relation to both special and formal ethics.

Above, I examined ethical methods in light of the theory of conceptual transduction. Unfortunately, most ethicists do not own this theory. It is clear that their theories appear in the form of some alternative to the theory of conceptual transduction, including its methodology. It is precisely in this connection that many ethicists turn to the reflective equilibrium method. The consistency of its conceptual units indicates the organic connection of this method with the concepts of scientific explanation. In this regard, the reflective equilibrium method is regarded as quite reasonably as a concretization of a scientific explanation. The development of knowledge from explication to reflective equilibrium is considered as conceptual re-engineering. [1] This line of knowledge development is especially clearly seen in the pioneering work of Rudolf Carnap, Nelson Goodman, and John Rawls. [1] Carnap presented a popular version of understanding scientific explanation as the transition from explicandum to explicatum [2, 3], Goodman developed a criterion of extensional isomorphism of principles and concrete judgments [4, 13-22], Rawls clarified the ethical orientation of conceptual re-engineering [5].

At this point, I do not consider in detail the concepts of Carnap and Goodman. They sought to clarify the nature of scientific explanation, linking its content, primarily with the methods of deduction and induction. From the standpoint of the theory of conceptual transduction, this approach seems to be very limited. A scientific explanation is conceptual transduction in all the richness of not only of deduction and induction but also adduction and abduction and all methods of intertheoretical transduction. Both Carnap and Goodman did not consider in unity all methods of conceptual transduction.

Goodman's development of the criterion of extensional isomorphism of the components of the theory allows him to be considered the founder of the reflective equilibrium method. The term 'reflective equilibrium' is widely known thanks to Rawls. What is the content of extensional isomorphism from the standpoint of the theory of conceptual transduction? Is there a need for this concept? Of course, between the concepts of individual theories, as well as between theories, there is a certain consistency. It is realized in the processes of conceptual transitions using methods of conceptual transduction. Through deduction, principles are passed on to hypothetical variables; as a result, there is consistency between principles and variables. The relationship between them is deductive and not isomorphic. Thanks to adduction, a transition is made from hypothetical variables to facts; the relation between them is adductive and not isomorphic. Thanks to abduction, a transition is made from inductive principles to deductive ones. The relationship between these principles is abductive. Thanks to the interpretation, they are moving from an obsolete theory to its updated version; the relationship between theories is interpretative, not isomorphic. Thus, whenever there is a transition from one concept to another, there is a certain consistency between the beginning of these transitions and their end. In my opinion, for its characterization, the term 'isomorphism', as well as the term 'existential isomorphism' is inappropriate. It is imperative to understand that the coherence of concepts is determined by the content of the respective methods. Among them, there is no isomorphism method.

The time has come to directly appeal to the reflective equilibrium method. He acts as the ideal that the researcher should strive for, achieving harmony between principles and specific judgments and overcoming the conflict of interests. Let me once again turn to the theory of conceptual transduction. In accordance with its content, a conflict of interest does not arise on its own, but in the content of theories. Initial principles are also part of theories. The urgent two-fold task is, firstly, to harmonize the theories of various subjects and organizations, and secondly, to do this in the best way. The second problem is solved by the sequential implementation of cycles of conceptual transduction. Coordination of positions occurs through the development of intertheoretical relations. It seems that it is in this case that the achievement of reflective equilibrium occurs. Of course, it is reasonable for representatives of various league-theories to consider carefully the arguments of their opponents, avoiding a harmful confrontation. However, it must be taken into account that the theory of conceptual transduction is constantly oriented towards achieving not reflective equilibrium, but scientific progress. This fact highlights the main disadvantages of the reflective equilibrium method.

Proponents of this method, firstly, have little to say about the mechanisms for achieving reflective equilibrium. Secondly, they lack a pronounced tendency to achieve ethical progress. Thus, the reflective equilibrium method is not a worthy alternative to conceptual transduction. T.M. Scanlon notes, «[I]t seems to me that this method, properly understood, is in fact the best way of making up one's mind about moral matters and about many other subjects. Indeed, it is the only defensible method: apparent alternatives to it are illusory. » [6, 149] My opinion is fundamentally different. I argue that the reflective equilibrium method itself has a largely obscure content. It becomes clearer when viewed from the perspective of conceptual transduction. In this case, the need for the reflective equilibrium method disappears.

Unfortunately, as I have already noted, in the ethical studies, the relevance of the scientific approach is underestimated. This circumstance, as a rule, is expressed in oblivion of the methods of conceptual transduction. Perhaps the most striking example in this regard is the widespread belief that in ethics, and not only in it, but also in all axiological theories, the calculation of values is fundamental and decisive, which ultimately helps maximize positive values. This calculation is relevant, but we must not forget that the values themselves are not something given; they are constituted in cycles of conceptual transduction. If researchers do not taken the latter into account, then the calculation turns into a very superficial conceptual act. Unfortunately, this circumstance takes place in the vast majority of decision-making theories. As a rule, ethicists do not taken into account that these theories are of a formal nature. Their content can be clarified only when researchers refer to those basic axiological theories that are the basis of formal theories. In the absence of such treatment, researchers will certainly fall into the field of metaphysics.

References

1. Brun, G. (2017) Conceptual re-engineering: from explication to reflective equilibrium. Synthese Springer Science+Business Media.
2. Carnap, R. (1950) Logical Foundations of Probability. Chicago: The University of Chicago Press.
3. Daniels, N. (2018) Reflective equilibrium. The Stanford Encyclopedia of Philosophy. Available at: https://plato.stanford.edu/archives/fall2018/entries/reflect ive-equilibrium/
4. Goodman, N. 1966 [1951] The Structure of Appearance. Indianapolis, New York,Kansas City: Bobbs-Merrill.
5. Rawls, J. (1999) [1971] A Theory of Justice. Second ed. Cambridge, MA: Harvard University Press.

6. Scanlon, T.M. (2003) Rawls on justification. In Freeman, S. (Ed.). The Cambridge Companion to Rawls. New York: Cambridge University Press, 139–167.

22.4. Ethical pluralism

A characteristic feature of modern ethics is rampant pluralism, the awareness of which meets with significant difficulties. [16; 17] This pluralism is largely a consequence of the dominance in the ethics of metaphysics, in the framework of which new ethical theories are sometimes completely unproven. However, ethical pluralism is not an idle fiction. In determining the status and future ethics, it is extremely important. In this regard, I will consider two main trends in the development of ethical pluralism. This is, firstly, ethical pluralism, which is a consequence of the development of axiological sciences. Secondly, ethical pluralism as characteristic of the main philosophical trends, in particular, phenomenology, hermeneutics, and poststructuralism.

The first trend, in fact, is an innovation, unfortunately, little known following from my interpretation of the nature of ethics. Let me remind the reader that, in accordance with this interpretation, this or that special ethics is without fail included in well-defined axiological theories. There are no two pluralisms, on the one hand, the pluralism of axiological theories and, on the other hand, the pluralism of ethical concepts. These pluralisms do not differ from each other. In this case, ethical pluralism fully functions within the framework of science and, therefore, is scientific. It is substantiated through scientific methods, i.e. methods of conceptual transduction, and therefore not arbitrary. The situation with metaphysical ethical pluralism, implemented by the main philosophical trends, is fundamentally different.

Philosophical trends, as a rule, largely develop regardless of scientific theories. As a result, the evidence base of ethics is sharply weakening; its pluralism is largely acquiring an eclectic character. I believe that overcoming this form of eclecticism can greatly contribute to the development of scientific ethics. In this regard, I will consider a number of ethical theories that function as part of the main philosophical trends, noting their strengths and weaknesses.

Phenomenological ethics

As is known, the phenomenology of Edmund Husserl has a pronounced ethical orientation. «In our philosophizing, then-how can we avoid it? - we are *functionaries of mankind*. The quite personal responsibility of our own true being as philosophers, our inner personal vocation, bears within itself at the same time the responsibility for the true being of mankind; the latter is, necessarily, being toward a *telos* and can only come to realization, *if at all*, through philosophy-through us, *if we* are philosophers in all seriousness. » [11, 17] In this regard, ethics comes to the fore. «It must be, or at least be postulated an art theory that stands above all human art doctrines with a rule that encompasses them as a whole, but that is ethics. » [12, 4] The piquancy of the situation is that Husserl, trying to develop the phenomenological method in detail, did not succeed in writing an ethical work generalizing his efforts. Nevertheless, he clearly demonstrated his approach to assessing the state of ethics and the possibilities for its improvement in lectures delivered to students during the summer semesters of 1920 and 1924. [12] Husserl used his method of synthesis of the impression to criticize various ethical theories, especially Kant's ethics. He accused Kant of underestimating emotionally and financially motivated volitional acts.

At this point, another feature of the phenomenological approach to ethics should be emphasized. All phenomenologists attach importance to the emotional sphere. In my opinion, it is in this connection that they attach paramount importance to the feeling of love and hatred. In this regard, perhaps the most striking was the performance of Max Scheler. He writes, «Love and hate are acts in which the value-realm accessible to the feelings of a being...is either *extended* or *narrowed*». [18, 261]

Phenomenological ethics, of course, gives ethics a very vital, specifically sensual character. [2; 13] However, it is not without significant flaws. The most important of them is that phenomenologists, even those who really wanted this, were not able to put either philosophy or ethics on a scientific footing.

Hermeneutic ethics

The hermeneutical project in its modern form acts as a theory of mutual understanding of people. [14; 19] The very presence of this understanding indicates the establishment of cooperation of people for the benefit of not individual entities, but their communities. This fact indicates the unity of hermeneutic and ethical projects. In this regard, hermeneutical ethics stands at the forefront. Jürgen Habermas represents it in the most famous form. [9]

The scientific approach involves testing ethics as an independent theory. Since it does not pass this test, ethics is defined as a superstructure (formal) theory. Such a course of argumentation is completely alien to Habermas. He fears an instrumental reason with its reliance on factuality and, therefore, on science. Ethics is counterfactual. Habermas does not deny the connection between ethics and science. However, he interpreted it in favor of ethics, the conclusions of which are strongly recommendatory in nature for all sciences. The ethical mind transcends the instrumental one.

Habermas uses the adjectives deontological, universalistic, cognitive, and formal to describe the most general features of discourse ethics. [9, 196] The formal moment exempts from the need for direct reference to the content of the non-philosophical axiological sciences. The cognitive approach allows you to adhere to the positions of communicative rationalism, denying ethical intuitionism. The universalistic approach allows us not to be limited to issues of solidarity in individual social communities. In this regard, deontological morality with its emphasis on the values of justice is a necessity. Morality - ethics – pragmatics, such is the philosophically oriented value hierarchy of Habermas. Habermas's philosophical credo clearly expresses his following conclusion.

> I think that the task of philosophy is to clarify the conditions under which moral and ethical questions alike can be decided rationally by the participants themselves. The moral point of view enables us to grasp generalizable interests in common; an ethical decision to adopt a conscious plan of life first puts a person or group in the proper frame of mind to appropriate critically their own life history, or identity-constituting traditions, in the light of an authentic life project. But philosophy cannot arrogate to itself the task of

finding answers to substantive questions of justice or of an authentic, unfailed life, for it properly belongs to the participants. It can help prevent confusions; for example, it can insist that moral and ethical questions not be confused with one another and thereby be addressed from an inappropriate perspective. But when it offers material contributions to the theory of justice – as Rawls does in some sections of his book or if it becomes engaged in drawing up normative blueprints for an emancipated society – as do Ernst Bloch and Agnes Heller the philosophical author steps back into the role of an expert who makes proposals from the perspective of a citizen participating in the political process. [10, 175-176]

Habermas seeks to substantiate all his conclusions by referring to the arguments of the discourse participants. If they are sincere, democratic, comply with the rules of logic, and then there are no barriers to the recognition of common values for them. As a result, discourse participants constitute ethics and morality. Values for all, not just individual groups of people, comprise morality with its principle of solidarity. As for the ethical and moral methods of argumentation, Habermas is extremely concise on this score. They are essentially absent. Such is the payment for breaking the connection between ethics and informal axiological theories. Habermas mainly discusses the possibility of constructing ethics and morality. Nevertheless, he does not present both of them in a distinct form.

Poststructuralist ethics

Among the main philosophical trends, poststructuralist philosophy occupies a special place due to its radicalism. The rejection of rationality and realism, the prevalence of multiplicity, uncertainty and randomness, the concentration of attention mainly not on social phenomena, but on the bizarre stories of individuals, casts doubt on the possibility of a successful development of ethics. Unexpectedly for many researchers, poststructuralist philosophy proclaimed not so much 'the end of ethics' as the possibility of a radically new understanding of the ethical. [1; 4; 5; 7] Beginning in the 1980s, many prominent poststructuralists, abandoning their former lack of attention to ethics, began to make stubborn attempts at its regular development. [15; 8, 117-148]

Michel Foucault introduced the concept of the care of the self as a practice of freedom. [6, 281-302] His main idea is that ethics is a relation of self to itself in terms of its moral activity. Contrary to popular belief, ethics is not a collection of normative theories of human communities. Such theories suppress the freedom and originality of individuals, and therefore must be rejected. Foucault comes to the ethics of the care of the self, criticizing and problematizing the history of traditional ethics.

A discerning researcher can hardly be satisfied with the method of criticism and problematization of Foucault, not spelled out in any detail. Against this background, Jacques Derrida's research on the construction of ethics based on the method of deconstruction attracted wide attention. First, he reveals the very possibility of justice. [3] Justice is an ideal to which one aspires, but it is not attainable. Derrida's decisive thought is that effectively moving towards justice is possible only through deconstruction, aporetic transgression. Ethics as such a movement acquires an aporetic character. This policy addresses responsibility, gift, hospitality, forgiveness, and mourning. All these ethical phenomena are contradictory.

The works of Foucault and Derrida shows that like phenomenologists and hermeneutists poststructuralists either consciously or ignorantly abandon scientific methods. Derrida replaces them with the technique of multiplying aporias. They are arbitrary; Derrida does not prove their legitimacy in any way. All this leads to uncontrolled permissiveness.

Both phenomenologists, hermeneutists, and poststructuralists did not notice that all the dominant dominants of their philosophizing were productively mastered by the sciences. I mean the interest of phenomenologists in the mentality of people, and the desire of hermeneutists to explain the consensus of people about certain values, and the desire of poststructuralists to affirm the ideals of pluralism. If ethics is isolated from the successes of science, then it becomes weak, unconvincing and ineffective. Today, philosophy, isolated from science, is nonsense. No less nonsense is also the isolation of ethics from scientific ethics.

References

1. Bauman, Z. (1993) Postmodern Ethics. Oxford: Blackwell.
2. De Warren, N. (2017) Husserl and Phenomenological Ethics. In The History of Moral Philosophy. Cambridge: Cambridge University Press, 562-576.
3. Derrida, J. (1992) Deconstruction and the Possibility of Justice. Ed. by D. Cornell, M. Rosenfeld, and D.G. Carlson. New York: Routledge, 1992
4. Evink, E. (2009) (In)finite responsibility. How to avoid the contrary effects of Derrida's ethics. Philosophy and Social Criticism 35(4), 467–481.

5. Fagan, M. (2013) Ethics and Politics after Post-structuralism: Levinas, Derrida, Nancy. Edinburgh: Edinburgh University Press.

6. Foucault, M. (1997) The Essential Works of Michel Foucault. Vol. 1: Ethics: Subjectivity and Truth. Ed. by P. Rabinow. New York: The New Press.

7. Fuh, S-j. (2003) Derrida and the Problem of Ethics. Concentric: Studies in English Literature and Linguistics 29(1), 1-22.

8. Gutting, G. (2011) Thinking the Impossible: French Philosophy since 1960. Oxford: Oxford University Press.

9. Habermas, J. (1990) [1983] Moral Consciousness and Communicative Action. Trans. By C. Lenhardt, and S.W. Nicholsen. Cambridge, MA: MIT Press.

10. Habermas, J. (1993) [1991] Justification and Application. Trans. by C.P.Cronin, Cambridge, MA: MIT Press.

11. Husserl, E. (1970) [1936] The Crisis of European Sciences and Transcendental Phenomenology. Translated, with an Introduction by D. Carr. Evanston: Northwestern University Press.

12. Husserl, E. (2004) [1920, 1924] Einleitung in die Ethik: Vorlesungen Sommersemester 1920/1924 [Introduction to Ethics: Lectures Summer Semester 1920/1924]. Peucker, H. (Ergs.) Dordrecht/Boston/London: Kluver Akademic Publishers. [In German].

13. Kazanjian, M.M. (2020) Ethics and phenomenology. Internet encyclopedia of philosophy. Available at: https://www.iep.utm.edu/eth-phen/#SH2d/

14. Kettner, M. (2006) Discourse ethics Apel, Habermas, and Beyond. In C. Rehmann-Sutter et al. (Eds.). Bioethics in Cultural Contexts. Dordrecht: Springer, 299–318.

15. Lawler, P. (2008) The ethics of postmodernism. In The Oxford Handbook of International Relations. Ed. by C. Reus-Smit and D. Snidal, 378-390.

16. Mason, E. (2018) Value pluralism. The Stanford Encyclopedia of Philosophy. Available at: https://plato.stanford.edu/archives/spr2018/entries/value-pluralism/

17. Schaber, P. (2005) Ethical pluralism. In: Nitta, T. Studies into the Foundations of an Integral Theory of Practice and Cognition. Sapporo: Hokkaido University Press, 139-156.

18. Scheler, M. (1973) [1916] Formalism in Ethics and Non-Formal Ethics of Values. Trans. by M. Frings and R. Funk. Evanston: Northwestern University Press.

19. Van Tongeren, P. (1966) Ethics, tradition and hermeneutics. Ethical Perspectives 3(3), 175-183.

22.5. Truth in ethics?

Numerous attempts to clarify the status of ethics are often associated with a consideration of its relationship with the concept of truth. Moreover, various interpretations use the adjective 'moral'. They say, for example, moral, and not ethical, realism and cognitivism. Ethics is understood as a theory of morality. In my opinion, in this case, we have to deal with the case of forgetting the principle of theoretical representation. In accordance with it, the nature of any phenomena is theoretical. There is no morality beyond ethics. Ethics is not a theory of morality. It is right to talk about ethical, not moral.

The existing alienation of ethics from axiological sciences makes it extremely difficult to determine its true status. It is not surprising that a heap of interpretations of the correlation of ethics with the concept of truth appears. Such, in particular: moral realism and anti-realism, naturalism and non-naturalism, generalism and particularism, relativism and absolutism. Below I give popular formulations of various interpretations of the place of truth in ethics.

> Moral realists are those who think that, in these respects, things should be taken at face value— moral claims do purport to report facts and are true if they get the facts right. Moreover, they hold, at least some moral claims actually are true. That much is the common and more or less defining ground of moral realism (although some accounts of moral realism see it as involving additional commitments, say to the independence of the moral facts from human thought and practice, or to those facts being objective in some specified way). [9, 1]

> [M]oral anti-realism is the denial of the thesis that moral properties – or facts, objects, relations, events, etc. (whatever categories one is willing to countenance) – exist mind-independently. [2, 2.1]

> Quasi-realism is best thought of not as a philosophical position but as a philosophical *program*. The quasi-realist is someone who endorses an anti-realist metaphysical stance but who seeks, through philosophical maneuvering, to *earn the right* for moral discourse to enjoy all the trappings of realist talk. [2, Supplement. Projectivism and Quasi-realism]

While the term 'moral naturalism' has a number of different meanings, it is most frequently used to describe naturalistic versions of moral realism. Moral realists hold that there are objective, mind-independent facts and properties; moral naturalists hold that these objective, mind-independent moral facts are natural facts. [3, 1]

Very roughly, non-naturalism in meta-ethics is the idea that moral philosophy is fundamentally autonomous from the natural sciences. [6, 1]

Roughly put, non-cognitivists think that moral statements have no substantial truth conditions. Furthermore, according to non-cognitivists, when people utter moral sentences they are not typically expressing states of mind which are beliefs or which are cognitive in the way that beliefs are. Rather they are expressing non-cognitive attitudes more similar to desires, approval or disapproval

Cognitivism is the denial of non-cognitivism. Thus it holds that moral statements do express beliefs and that they are apt for truth and falsity. [11, 1]

Moral generalists think morality is best understood in terms of moral principles; moral particularists deny this. [7, 1]

The term 'moral relativism' is understood in a variety of ways. Most often it is associated with an empirical thesis that there are deep and widespread moral disagreements and a metaethical thesis that the truth or justification of moral judgments is not absolute, but relative to the moral standard of some person or group of persons. [1, 1]

Somewhat unexpectedly, it turns out that all the above interpretations of the nature of truth in ethics are contradictory. Calling for help traditional concepts of truth does not lead to decisive success. The correspondent concept of truth leads to realism, coherent to relativism. [4] Projectivism is combined with quasi-realism. [5] A pragmatic approach leads to a duty ethics option. [10] Disagreement in idealized conditions leads to relativism. [8]

I do not consider the above sources. Their authors are undoubted experts on current ethical issues. However, my approach is fundamentally different from theirs. Considering the truth in ethics, I deliberately proceed from the theory of conceptual transduction, believing that only in this case ethics is not isolated from science. It turns out that it is not at all necessary to fall into the clutches of conflicting definitions, or realism - or anti-realism, or cognitivism - or non-cognitivism, or generalism - or particularism, etc.

Let me remind readers that according to the theory of conceptual transduction, the most developed theories are true, respectively, all their contents, including people, objects, principles, laws, and variables, is also true. As for the correspondent and coherent conception of truth, they do not take into account the cycles of conceptual transduction. That is why their content does not stand up to criticism.

Naturalism or anti-naturalism? Of course, naturalism!

Naturalism is a requirement of science. Is ethics scientific? Sure, yes. Ethical content is directly inherent in axiological theories. They are scientific, and ethics is scientific along with them. Authors of anti-naturalism liken ethics to metaphysical theories. They do not translate common sense theories onto the scientific footing. In this case, the requirements of naturalism, of course, cannot be fulfilled.

Realism or anti-realism? Of course, realism!

Strictly speaking, realism boils down to one requirement, namely, principles, laws, and variables, including facts, must be representations of individuals and organizations. This takes place in every axiological scientific theory, including with respect to its ethical content. As for the facts, they are inherent in any axiological scientific theory. There are, for example, economic, medical, family and marriage facts. Suppose that in accordance with ethical requirements, businessperson undertakes to increase the wages of workers and employees. Wage growth, expressed in monetary units, is an economic, including and ethical factor. As for quasi-realism, it does not have clear content.

Cognitivism or non-cognitivism? Of course, cognitivism!

Cognitivism involves the use of the concept of truth in theory. The processes of conceptual transduction lead to the rejection of false knowledge and the strengthening of true knowledge. This takes place in any scientific axiological theory, including its ethical part.

Generalism or particulzrism? Of course, generalism!

The requirement of generalism is to use principles. Principles, including ethical principles, are inherent in all axiological scientific theories. Only undeveloped theories do without principles. If they are given a more developed form, then principles are used.

Relativism or absolutism? Of course, Relativism!

All modern axiological sciences are characterized by pluralism. This means that in relation to them relativism triumphs, and not absolutism. Undoubtedly, it should be borne in mind that scientific relativism is not identical to arbitrariness. The pluralism of theories fits perfectly with the concept of truth. The triumph of truth is that theories are improved, including their pluralism.

Thus, numerous paired contradictory constructs in relation to understanding the phenomenon of truth in ethics are the result of not so much scientific insights as uncritical assimilation of ethics to theories of common sense. Truth in ethics has no less clear content than truth in relation to any scientific axiological theory.

References

1. Gowans, C. (2019) Moral relativism. The Stanford Encyclopedia of Philosophy. Available at: https://plato.stanford.edu/archives/sum2019/entries/moral-relativism/
2. Joyce, R. (2016) Moral anti-realism. The Stanford Encyclopedia of Philosophy. Available at: https://plato.stanford.edu/archives/win2016/entries/moral-anti-realism/
3. Lutz, M. and Lenman, J. (2018) Moral naturalism. The Stanford Encyclopedia of Philosophy. Available at: https://plato.stanford.edu/archives/fall2018/entries/naturalism-moral/
4. Lynch, M.P. (2013) Truth in ethics. In LaFollette, H. (Ed.). The International Encyclopedia of Ethics. Malden, MA: Wiley-Blackwell, 5220-5228.

5. McDowell, J. (1988) Projection and Truth in Ethics. Lindley Lecture. Kansas: Department of Philosophy, University of Kansas.
6. Ridge, M. (2019) Moral non-naturalism. The Stanford Encyclopedia of Philosophy. Available at: https://plato.stanford.edu/archives/fall2019/entries/moral-non-naturalism/
7. Ridge, M. and McKeever, S. (2016) Moral particularism and moral generalism. The Stanford Encyclopedia of Philosophy. Available at: https://plato.stanford.edu/archives/win2016/entries/moral-particularism-generalism/
8. Rowland, R. (2017) The Significance of significant fundamental moral disagreement. Noûs 51(4), 802-831.
9. Sayre-McCord, G. (2017) Moral realism. The Stanford Encyclopedia of Philosophy. Available at: https://plato.stanford.edu/archives/fall2017/entries/moral-realism/
10. Smith, M. (2020) Function and truth in ethics. Oxford Scholarship Online. DOI:10.1093/acprof:oso/9780199381357.003.0011
11. van Roojen, M. (2018) Moral cognitivism vs. non-cognitivism. The Stanford Encyclopedia of Philosophy. Available at: https://plato.stanford.edu/archives/fall2018/entries/moral-cognitivism/

Conclusion. Philosophy of science facing new challenges

At the end of work on this book, I came to the firm belief that the modern intellectual must certainly be an encyclopedist. Maximizing the completeness of knowledge and its detail is the only antidote against the growth of catastrophic phenomena.

With modern rhythms of development, which are inevitably accompanied by a variety of, including paradoxical and catastrophic effects, the phenomenon of science needs a thorough and updated understanding. All branches of science have become extremely refined areas of human culture. In this regard, the need for a philosophy of science has not decreased, but, on the contrary, increased many times over. This was shown above when analyzing the many problematic issues of all modern branches of science, in particular, in determining ways to comprehend scientific pluralism.

Unfortunately, it must be noted that the development of the philosophy of science often does not keep pace with the tread of individual sciences. The philosophical and scientific community is not without difficulty mastering the higher floors of science, represented by metascience and the philosophy of science. In this regard, there is a widespread lack of will for refined knowledge. Modern science has a complex dynamic network structure, which is designed to ensure all-round progress. In this regard, the dynamics of integration and differentiation are constantly changing. In modern science, it has a multistage character. Researchers, changing it, intently study and the smallest, and the largest, and the numerous steps between them.

Another feature of modern science is the sharp intensification of interdisciplinary research. Everywhere the fullness of knowledge is in demand. And it is achieved only through interdisciplinary transduction. The independence of individual disciplines is not denied, scientific isolationism is rejected. Never before have the links between the natural, formal, and axiological branches of science been as close as they are today. Despite the specifics of various branches of science, their unity is constantly growing.

As the contents of this book show, pluralism is a characteristic feature of modern science. Truth does not belong to one, but it is not arbitrary. This circumstance brought to life a special kind of scientific synthesis, namely, pluralistic synthesis. It provides a multidimensional truth.

Modern science has a vector character, it does not back away, but provides a line of progressive development. Unconditional priority is given to the most developed theories. They are called upon to ensure scientific progress.

In the modern world, small can be no less significant than large. This means that the price of errors rises sharply. That is why in science they are guided by the most developed theories. In this regard, the scientific community does not have the right to ignore underdeveloped, in particular, the ordinary knowledge. The scientific community is forced to take responsibility for ensuring the viability of any kind of knowledge. To the extent possible, it should be drawn into the orbit of the most developed knowledge. In this regard, the enlightening activity of scientists is of great importance.

Science culminates in ethics. Ethics should not remain on the periphery of science. Its true place is the pinnacle of scientific knowledge. Without transferring it there, the collisions of modern science cannot be resolved. But it is also necessary to consider that it is the scientific ethics that sets the most relevant guidelines for the development of mankind. With every turn of history, the need for scientific ethics increases.

Without the philosophy of science and ethics, mankind is hardly capable of confronting the formidable challenges to which it is forced to find relevant answers in the struggle for its favorable future. It is in this connection that the validity of science, metascience and the philosophy of science is once again being checked.

Subject index

Abduction 5, 21, 22, 26, 33, 34, 37, 41, 54, 74, 75, 82, 88, 90, 94, 106, 107, 109, 113, 174, 187, 189, 220, 223 - 227, 244, 305, 315, 318, 342, 357-361, 386, 402, 403, 411-413, 422, 423, 451, 452, 459, 461, 476, 480, 494-496, 515, 529, 538, 550, 552, 561, 570, 574, 590, 605, 609, 632, 639, 641, 643, 644, 701, 715, 727, 795, 804, 820, 845 - 849, 897, 937, 949, 1002, 1030, 1041, 1093

abstractions 35-37, 77, 89, 92, 98, 107, 121, 156, 162, 195, 201, 248, 252, 254, 268, 281, 302, 311, 315, 319, 327, 336, 461, 499, 509, 510, 714, 808, 854, 856, 877, 944, 968, 996, 1002, 1049, 1056, 1074-1076

adduction 21, 23,24, 33, 37, 41, 54, 75, 94, 113, 144, 174, 186, 189, 220, 225, 244, 305, 315, 318, 342, 357, 358, 403, 411- 415, 428, 430, 452, 459, 461, 476, 480, 496, 513, 515, 526, 529, 530, 538, 550-552, 561, 570, 590, 605, 632, 639, 644, 664, 715, 727, 795, 804, 807, 820, 848, 897, 937, 949, 1002, 1029, 1030, 1041, 1093, 1094

aesthetic experience 1033-1051, 1051

aesthetic relativity of chemistry 440-444

agricultural ethics 605-608

agricultural theories 614-617

agrology, philosophy of 602-607

analytic and synthetic sentences 34, 113,1014

archeology of Foucault 141, 142, 176, 592, 978

art as a set of offset theories 1036, 1062, 1071-1074

art, philosophy of 1026-1077

ascent from the abstract to the concrete 93, 325

asymptotic freedom in quantum field theory 387

axioms of logic and mathematics 21.87, 89,249, 259, 260

beauty 442, 443, 1030-1032

Name index

Capurro, R. 340

Carlson, D.G. 1203

Carnap, R. 33, 35, 38, 59, 101-104, 110, 114, 116, 146, 147, 212, 217, 224, 231, 235, 239, 390, 514, 805, 1093, 1096

Carr, D. 133

Carrara-Augustenborg, C. 765

Carroll, N. 1027, 1032, 1050, 1052. 1069

Carruthers, P. 764, 765

Carter, A. 914, 916

Carter, J.A. 765

Cartwright, N. 652

Casadio, C. 809

Cavell, S. 1047, 1-48, 1052

Cellucci, C. 803, 809

Cerar, Dr. Miro. 967, 970

Chalmers, D.J. 327

Chamizo, J.A. 427, 428, 435

Chang, H. 809

Chang, R. 818, 823

Charmaz, K. 717, 718

Charon, R. 689

Chen, M. 1067, 1069

Cheng, P.W. 644

Childress, J.F. 653-657, 689

Chomsky, N. 152, 153, 164, 181-184

Chong, D. 894, 895

Chris, J.J. 452

Eilenberg, S. 267, 271

Einstein, A. 40, 47, 49, 53, 79, 344, 350, 352, 360, 361, 366, 378, 389, 520, 575, 989

Eisenstein, S.J. 1044-1048, 1052

Eldridge R. 1069, 1070

Ellerman, D. 272

Ellington, J.W. 1090

Engels, F. 96, 469, 522, 566, 1017. 1019, 1056

Engler, G. 441, 444

Englert, F. 388

Epple, A. 1025

Epstein, B. 801, 802

Ernest, P. 291, 292, 294, 298

Erwin, D. 482

Esslin, M. 1056, 1060

Estlund, D. 928, 929

Estrela, M.T. 737

Etxabe, J. 967, 971

Eusepi, G. 887

Evans, N. 191

Evans, J.S. 659, 660, 662

Evans, V. 197

Everett, H. 366, 371, 722

Evink, E. 1103

Fagan, M. 1104

Falcon, A. 644

Falzon, C. 1053

Freyenhagen, F. 918, 922

Friedman, M. 854, 857, 868, 874, 875, 880, 881, 886, 887

Frigge, R. 302

Friis, J. 580

Frings, M. 1105

Froeyman, A. 995, 999

Frolov, I.T. 245

Frost, N.A. 786

Frynas, J.G. 836

Fuh, S-j. 1104

Fullbrook, E. 871

Funk, R. 1105

Fursova, P.V. 485, 487

Gabbay, D.M. 824

Gabriel, M. 826, 831

Gadamer, H.-G. 120, 128-132, 143, 590, 593, 740, 977, 980

Galenson, D.W. 1076

Gallagher, S. 790

Galligan, D.J. 937, 938, 942

Garber, D. 90

Gardner, J. 946

Gardner, P. 730

Garriga, E. 836

Gasser-Wingate, M. 85

Gendler, T.S. 899, 943

Gensler, H.J. 206

Ilyenkov, E. 96

Infeld, L. 344

Inkpen, R. 448, 997, 999

Innis, R.E. 568, 562

Introna, L. 340

Irrgang, B. 591, 594

Isaacson, J.H. 672

Jablonka, E. 490, 492, 493

Jackson, J. 950

Jacquette, D. 207

Jahr, F. 685, 689

Jakobson, R. 191

James, F. 714, 717, 718

James, W. 71, 75, 117, 405, 406

Jansen, N. 954-956

Janssen T. 198

Janssen-Lauret, F. 767, 771

Jaśkowski, S. 237, 246, 247

Jeffrey, I. S. 440

Jenkins, E. 697, 698, 704

Jenkins, I. 1076

Jenkins, K. 1022, 1024, 1025

Jennings, B. 536

Jensen, A.K. 983, 985

Johannsen, W. 486, 487, 507, 511

Johnson, C.R. 332, 337

Turing, A. 255, 317-320, 328, 330, 332

Turner, D. 997, 999

Turner, J.H. 803, 810, 815

Turner, R. 317-321

Tylor, E.B. 553, 560

Tymoczko, T. 290

Tyuryukanov, A.N. 487

Ubel, P.A. 651

Uebel, T. 797

Uemov, A.I. 236

Ulman, Y. I. 834, 836

Väänänen, J. 245

Vahabi, M. 839, 842

Valdés, P. 549

Van Brakel, J. 393, 400

Van Dijk, T.A. 171, 176

Van Fraassen, B. C. 367, 371

Van Franzosi, R. 998, 999

Van Huyssteen, J.W.V. 621

Van Roojen, M. 1111

Van Tongeren, P. 1105

Van Valin, R.D.J. 188, 191

Van Wyk, M.M. 721, 731

Vanderveken, D. 672

Vann, R.T. 1021, 1025

Vasiliev, N.A. 236, 241

Vasyukov, V.L. 227